Second Edition

Pearson Edexcel GCSE (9–1)
Mathematics
Higher
Student Book

Series editors: Dr Naomi Norman and Katherine Pate

1

ed for
earson Edexcel
Qualifications

Pearson

Published by Pearson Education Limited, 80 Strand, London, WC2R 0RL.

www.pearsonschoolsandfecolleges.co.uk

Text © Pearson Education Limited 2020
Project managed and edited by Just Content Ltd
Typeset by PDQ Digital Media Solutions Ltd
Original illustrations © Pearson Education Limited 2020
Cover photo/illustration by © David S. Rose/Shutterstock, © Julias/Shutterstock, © Attitude/Shutterstock, © Abstractor/Shutterstock, © Ozz Design/Shutterstock, © Lazartivan/Getty Images

The rights of Jack Barraclough, Chris Baston, Ian Bettison, Sharon Bolger, Ian Boote, Judith Chadwick, Ian Jacques, Catherine Murphy, Su Nicholson, Naomi Norman, Diane Oliver, Katherine Pate, Glyn Payne, Jenny Roach, Peter Sherran and Robert Ward-Penny to be identified as authors of this work have been asserted by them in accordance with the Copyright, Designs and Patents Act 1988.

First published 2020

23 22 21 20
10 9 8 7 6 5 4 3 2 1

British Library Cataloguing in Publication Data

A catalogue record for this book is available from the British Library.

ISBN 978 1 292 34613 7

Printed in Slovakia by Neografia

A note from the publisher

In order to ensure that this resource offers high-quality support for the associated Pearson qualification, it has been through a review process by the awarding body. This process confirms that this resource fully covers the teaching and learning content of the specification or part of a specification at which it is aimed. It also confirms that it demonstrates an appropriate balance between the development of subject skills, knowledge and understanding, in addition to preparation for assessment.

Endorsement does not cover any guidance on assessment activities or processes (e.g. practice questions or advice on how to answer assessment questions), included in the resource nor does it prescribe any particular approach to the teaching or delivery of a related course.

While the publishers have made every attempt to ensure that advice on the qualification and its assessment is accurate, the official specification and associated assessment guidance materials are the only authoritative source of information and should always be referred to for definitive guidance.

Pearson examiners have not contributed to any sections in this resource relevant to examination papers for which they have responsibility.

Examiners will not use endorsed resources as a source of material for any assessment set by Pearson. Endorsement of a resource does not mean that the resource is required to achieve this Pearson qualification, nor does it mean that it is the only suitable material available to support the qualification, and any resource lists produced by the awarding body shall include this and other appropriate resources.

Pearson has robust editorial processes, including answer and fact checks, to ensure the accuracy of the content in this publication, and every effort is made to ensure this publication is free of errors. We are, however, only human, and occasionally errors do occur. Pearson is not liable for any misunderstandings that arise as a result of errors in this publication, but it is our priority to ensure that the content is accurate. If you spot an error, please do contact us at resourcescorrections@pearson.com so we can make sure it is corrected.

Contents

1	**Number**	1
	Prior knowledge check	
1.1	Number problems and reasoning	1
1.2	Place value and estimating	3
1.3	HCF and LCM	5
1.4	Calculating with powers (indices)	8
1.5	Zero, negative and fractional indices	11
1.6	Powers of 10 and standard form	14
1.7	Surds	17
	Check up	20
	Strengthen	22
	Extend	26
	Test ready	28
	Unit test	30

2	**Algebra**	32
	Prior knowledge check	
2.1	Algebraic indices	32
2.2	Expanding and factorising	35
2.3	Equations	37
2.4	Formulae	39
2.5	Linear sequences	42
2.6	Non-linear sequences	45
2.7	More expanding and factorising	49
	Check up	52
	Strengthen	54
	Extend	58
	Test ready	60
	Unit test	62

3	**Interpreting and representing data**	64
	Prior knowledge check	
3.1	Statistical diagrams 1	64
3.2	Time series	68
3.3	Scatter graphs	71
3.4	Line of best fit	74

3.5	Averages and range	78
3.6	Statistical diagrams 2	82
	Check up	85
	Strengthen	87
	Extend	91
	Test ready	94
	Unit test	96

4	**Fractions, ratio and percentages**	98
	Prior knowledge check	
4.1	Fractions	98
4.2	Ratios	100
4.3	Ratio and proportion	103
4.4	Percentages	105
4.5	Fractions, decimals and percentages	108
	Check up	110
	Strengthen	111
	Extend	115
	Test ready	117
	Unit test	119

	Mixed exercise 1	121

5	**Angles and trigonometry**	125
	Prior knowledge check	
5.1	Angle properties of triangles and quadrilaterals	125
5.2	Interior angles of a polygon	129
5.3	Exterior angles of a polygon	133
5.4	Pythagoras' theorem 1	136
5.5	Pythagoras' theorem 2	139
5.6	Trigonometry 1	142
5.7	Trigonometry 2	145
	Check up	148
	Strengthen	150
	Extend	156
	Test ready	158
	Unit test	160

6	**Graphs**	**162**
	Prior knowledge check	
6.1	Linear graphs	162
6.2	More linear graphs	165
6.3	Graphing rates of change	168
6.4	Real-life graphs	172
6.5	Line segments	176
6.6	Quadratic graphs	178
6.7	Cubic and reciprocal graphs	181
6.8	More graphs	183
	Check up	186
	Strengthen	189
	Extend	194
	Test ready	196
	Unit test	198

7	**Area and volume**	**200**
	Prior knowledge check	
7.1	Perimeter and area	200
7.2	Units and accuracy	203
7.3	Prisms	207
7.4	Circles	210
7.5	Sectors of circles	214
7.6	Cylinders and spheres	218
7.7	Pyramids and cones	221
	Check up	224
	Strengthen	226
	Extend	230
	Test ready	232
	Unit test	234

	Mixed exercise 2	**236**

8	**Transformations and constructions**	**240**
	Prior knowledge check	
8.1	3D solids	240
8.2	Reflection and rotation	243
8.3	Enlargement	246
8.4	Translations and combinations of different transformations	250
8.5	Scale drawings and bearings	254
8.6	Constructions 1	258
8.7	Constructions 2	261
8.8	Loci	264
	Check up	267
	Strengthen	270
	Extend	276
	Test ready	278
	Unit test	280

9	**Equations and inequalities**	**283**
	Prior knowledge check	
9.1	Solving linear inequalities	283
9.2	Solving quadratic equations 1	286
9.3	Solving quadratic equations 2	288
9.4	Completing the square	291
9.5	Solving simple simultaneous equations	294
9.6	More simultaneous equations	297
9.7	Solving linear and quadratic simultaneous equations	299
	Check up	302
	Strengthen	303
	Extend	306
	Test ready	308
	Unit test	310

10	**Probability**	**312**
	Prior knowledge check	
10.1	Combined events	312
10.2	Mutually exclusive events	315
10.3	Experimental probability	318
10.4	Independent events and tree diagrams	320
10.5	Conditional probability	324
10.6	Venn diagrams and set notation	327
	Check up	331
	Strengthen	333
	Extend	336
	Test ready	338
	Unit test	340

	Mixed exercise 3	**342**
	Answers	**346**
	Index	**404**

Pearson Edexcel GCSE (9–1)
Mathematics
Second Edition

Pearson Edexcel GCSE (9–1) Mathematics Second Edition is built around a unique pedagogy that has been created by leading educational researchers and teachers in the UK. This edition has been updated to reflect six sets of live GCSE (9–1) papers, as well as feedback from thousands of teachers and students and a two-year study into the effectiveness of the course.

The new series features a full range of print and digital resources designed to work seamlessly together so that schools can create the course that works best for their students and teachers.

*Active*Learn service

The *Active*Learn service brings together the full range of planning, teaching, learning and assessment resources.

What's in *Active*Learn for GCSE (9–1) Mathematics?

- ☑ **Front-of-class Student Books** with accompanying PowerPoints, worksheets, videos, animations and homework activities

- ☑ **254 editable and printable homework worksheets**, linked to each Master lesson

- ☑ **Online, auto-marked homework activities** with integrated videos and worked examples

- ☑ **76 assessments and online markbooks**, including end-of-unit, end-of-term, end-of-year and baseline tests

- ☑ **Interactive Scheme of Work** brings everything together, connecting your personalised scheme of work, teaching resources and assessments

- ☑ **Individual student access to videos, homework and online textbooks**

Student Books

The Student Books use a mastery approach based around a well-paced and well-sequenced curriculum. They are designed to develop mathematical fluency, while building confidence in problem-solving and reasoning.

The unique unit structure enables every student to acquire a deep and solid understanding of the subject, leaving them well-prepared for their GCSE exams, and future education or employment.

Together with the accompanying online prior knowledge sections, the Student Books cover the entire **Pearson Edexcel GCSE (9–1) Mathematics course**.

The new four-book model means that the Second Edition Student Books now contain even more meaningful practice, while still being a manageable size for use in and outside the classroom.

Foundation tier

Higher tier

Pearson Edexcel GCSE (9–1)
Mathematics Second Edition
Higher Student Book

1

Building confidence

Pearson's unique unit structure has been shown to build confidence.
The **front-of-class** versions of the Student Books include lots of extra
features and resources for use on a whiteboard.

Master

Learn fundamental knowledge and skills over a series of lessons.

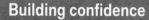

*Active*Learn **homework**

Links to online homework
worksheets and exercises for
every lesson.

Students can make sure they are ready
for each unit by downloading the relevant
Prior knowledge check. This can be
accessed using the QR code in the
Contents or via *Active*Learn.

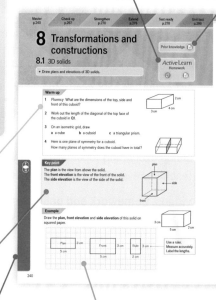

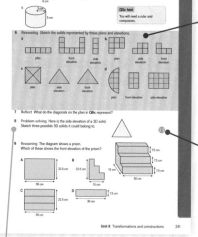

Warm up

Accessible questions
designed to develop
mathematical fluency.

Key points

Explains key concepts
and definitions.

Crossover content between
Foundation and Higher tiers
is indicated in side bars.

Worked example

Step-by-step worked
examples focus on
the key concepts.

Problem-solving and **Reasoning**
questions are clearly labelled.
Future skills questions help
prepare for life after GCSE.
Reflect questions encourage
reflection on mathematical
thinking and understanding.

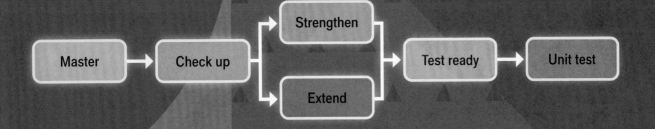

Master → Check up → Strengthen / Extend → Test ready → Unit test

Check up

After the Master lessons, a Check up test helps students decide whether to move on to the Strengthen or Extend section.

Strengthen

Students can choose the topics they need more practice on. There are lots of hints and supporting questions to help.

Extend

Applies and develops maths from the unit in different situations.

Working towards A level

These questions take familiar ideas and extend them with styles of question that are typical of AS and A level papers. Students who enjoy tackling these questions might want to consider taking A level Mathematics.

Test ready

The **Summary of key points** is used to identify areas that need more practice and **Sample student answers** familiarise students with good exam technique.

Unit test

The exam-style Unit test helps check progress.

Mixed exercises

These sections bring topics together to help practise applying different techniques to a range of questions types, which is required in GCSE exams.

Teaching and learning materials can be downloaded from the blue hotspots.

Click on any question to view it full-size, and then click 'Show' to reveal the answer.

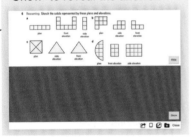

Helpful videos walk you step-by-step through answers to similar questions.

Exam-style questions are included throughout the books to help students prepare for GCSE exams.

Exam tips point out common errors and help with good exam technique.

Interactive Scheme of work

The Interactive Scheme of Work makes reordering the course easy. You can view your plan for your year, term or lesson, and access all the related teaching, learning and assessment materials.

*Active*Learn Progress & Assess

The Progress & Assess service is part of the full *Active*Learn service, or can be bought as a separate subscription. It includes assessments that have been designed to ensure all students have the opportunity to show what they have learned through:

- a 2-tier assessment model
- separate calculator and non-calculator sections
- online markbooks for tracking and reporting
- mapping to indicative 9–1 grades

Assessment Builder

Create your own classroom assessments from the bank of GCSE (9–1) Mathematics assessment questions by selecting questions on the skills and topics you have covered. Map the results of your custom assessments to indicative 9–1 grades using the custom online markbooks. Assessment Builder is available to purchase as an add-on to the *Active*Learn service or Progress & Assess subscriptions.

Purposeful Practice Books

A new kind of practice book based on cutting-edge approaches to help students make the most of practice.

With more than 4500 questions, our Pearson Edexcel GCSE (9–1) Mathematics Purposeful Practice Books are designed to be used alongside the Student Books and online resources. They:

- use minimal variation to build in small steps, consolidating knowledge and boosting confidence
- focus on strengthening problem-solving skills and strategies
- feature targeted exam practice with questions modified from real GCSE (9–1) papers, and exam guidance from examiner reports and grade indicators informed by **ResultsPlus**.

1 Number

Prior knowledge

1.1 Number problems and reasoning

*Active*Learn
Homework

- Use pictures or lists to help you to solve problems.
- Work out the total number of ways of performing a series of tasks.

Warm up

1 **Fluency** How many possible outcomes are there when a dice is rolled and a coin is flipped at the same time?

2 a Copy and complete this list of all possible outcomes for spinner A and spinner B.

 2, 1   4, 1   6, 1

 2, 3   4, 3   ...

 b How many outcomes are there altogether?

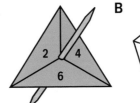

3 How many possible outcomes are there when

 a rolling a dice   b flipping a coin   c spinning A in **Q2**   d spinning B in **Q2**?

 e **Reflect** Write a sentence explaining what you notice about your answers to

 i **Q1** and **Q3a** and **b** above   ii **Q2b** and **Q3c** and **d** above

4 **Problem-solving** There are 12 chairs in a library.
 The librarian puts 2, 3 or 4 chairs at each study table.

 a Describe the different ways the study tables can be arranged so that all the chairs are used.

 b **Reflect** Write a sentence explaining how you made sure you listed all the combinations without missing any.

 c What is the maximum number of study tables in the library?

> **Q4a hint**
>
> Drawing a picture or writing a list are useful problem-solving strategies.

5 A restaurant offers a set menu for birthday parties.
 Write down all possible combinations of starters and mains.
 Use letters for combinations, for example VP for vegetable soup and pizza.

6 The restaurant in **Q5** decides to offer fish (F) as a main course.

 a How many possible combinations are there now?

 b Copy and complete.

 3 starters and 4 mains: ☐ combinations

 3 starters and 5 mains: ☐ combinations

 a starters and *b* mains: ☐ combinations

> **Starters**
> Vegetable Soup (V)
> Salad (S)
> Melon (M)
>
> **Mains**
> Pizza (P)
> Spaghetti Bolognaise (B)
> Curry (C)
> Lasagne (L)

7 A different restaurant offers 2 starters, 4 mains and 3 desserts.

   a How many possible combinations are there?

   b **Reasoning** Phil is going to order one of the following combinations: (1) a starter and a main, (2) a main and a dessert, (3) all three courses.
Show that there are 44 different options for Phil's meal.

> **Exam-style question**
>
> **8** Antony is choosing a toothbrush and a sponge.
> There are 16 different toothbrushes and some sponges.
> Antony says, 'There are 196 different ways to choose a toothbrush and a sponge.'
> Could Antony be correct?
> Show how you get your answer. **(2 marks)**

> **Exam-style question**
>
> **9** Jess has a 4-digit password for her mobile phone.
> Each digit can be between 0 and 9 **inclusive**.
>
>   **a** How many choices are possible for each digit of the code? **(1 mark)**
>
>   **b** What is the total number of 4-digit passwords that Jess can create? **(1 mark)**
>
> Jess would like to choose an even number.
> The code can start with a zero.
>
>   **c** How many different ways are possible now? **(2 marks)**

---

10 Three people, A, B and C, enter a race.

   a Write down the different orders in which they can finish first, second and third.

   b **Reasoning** Harry says that there are 3 possible winners, but then only 2 possibilities for second place and only one person left for third place.
Is Harry correct? Explain your answer.

   c How many different ways can people finish in

     i a 4-person race

     ii a 6-person race

     iii a 10-person race?

---

11 **Problem-solving** Eddie needs to choose a 6-digit code for his computer password.

   a How many codes can Eddie create using

     i 6 numbers   **ii** 4 numbers followed by 2 letters   **iii** 1 number followed by 5 letters?

Eddie decides that he does not want to repeat a digit or a letter.

   b How many ways are possible in parts **i** to **iii** now?

1.2 Place value and estimating

Active Learn
Homework

- Estimate an answer.
- Use place value to answer questions.

Warm up

1 **Fluency** $3.5 \times 2.9 = 10.15$
Write two related division facts.

2 Write each number to
  i 1 significant figure
  ii 2 significant figures
  iii 3 significant figures
  a 873 209   **b** 2019   **c** 0.007 059

3 Use the priority of operations to work out
  a $7 \times 5 - 4 \times 2$ **b** $5^2 + 3 \times 8$ **c** $\sqrt{29 - 4}$

4 Work out the mean of 3, 6, 7, 9, 15 and 20.

5 $3.7 \times 9.86 = 36.482$
Use this fact to work out these calculations.
  a 37×9.86 **b** 3.7×0.0986
  c 0.0037×98.6
  d **Reflect** Count the number of digits after the decimal point in each calculation and the number of digits after the decimal point in each answer. Write a sentence explaining what you notice.

> **Q5a hint**
>
> Compare with the given calculation.
>
> $$\times \square \left(\begin{array}{l} 3.7 \times 9.86 = 36.482 \\ 37 \times 9.86 = \boxed{} \end{array} \right) \times \square$$

6 Use the fact given in **Q5** to work out these calculations.
  a $36.482 \div 9.86$ **b** $3648.2 \div 98.6$ **c** $364.82 \div 370$

7 **Reasoning** $54.8 \times 7.29 = 399.492$
  a Write three more calculations that have the same answer.
  b Write a division that has an answer of 54.8.
  c Write a division that has an answer of 0.729.
  d Charlie says that $54.8 \times 72.9 = 3989.44$.
     Explain why Charlie must be wrong.

Exam-style question

8 $(3.7)^5 = 693$ correct to 3 significant figures.
Write the value of $(0.37)^5$ correct to
3 significant figures.   **(2 marks)**

> **Exam tip**
>
> When working with decimals, always think carefully about the position of the decimal point. How many digits would you expect after the decimal point for $(3.7)^5$?

9   Use a number line to estimate the value of
    a $\sqrt{5}$ b $\sqrt{6}$
    c $\sqrt{7}$ d $\sqrt{8}$
    Round each estimate to 1 decimal place.

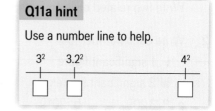

10 Estimate each value to the nearest tenth.
    Write your answers using ≈, meaning 'is approximately equal to'.
    a $\sqrt{47} \approx \square$ b $\sqrt{22}$ c $\sqrt{84}$
    d $\sqrt{127}$ e $\sqrt{10}$ f $\sqrt{40}$

11 Estimate to the nearest whole number:
    a 3.2^2 b 4.7^2 c 1.7^2
    d 7.1^2 e 6.3^2 f 9.8^2

Q11a hint

Use a number line to help.

3^2 3.2^2 4^2

12 Estimate answers to these calculations.
    a $(11.2 - \sqrt{50.3}) \times 4.08$
    b $(1.98 \times 3.14)^2 \div 8.85$

Key point

For $\dfrac{\text{calculation 1}}{\text{calculation 2}}$ work out (calculation 1) ÷ (calculation 2) using the priority of operations.

13 Estimate answers to these calculations.

    a $\dfrac{\sqrt{15 + 9^2}}{4.8^2}$ b $\dfrac{88.72 - 21.9}{\sqrt{35.5}}$ c $\sqrt{\dfrac{27.3 - 1.85}{3.93 \times 5.42}}$

Q13c hint

The whole of the expression is being square rooted. So estimate the numerator and denominator before square rooting.

    d Use your calculator to work out each answer.
      Give your answers correct to 1 decimal place.

    e Write a sentence explaining how you decided what to round each number to.

    f **Reflect** Does it matter if you round the numerator or the denominator first?

14 **Problem-solving** A large dice has a side length of 9.2 cm.
    Estimate the surface area of the dice.

15 **Problem-solving** The area of a square is 80 cm².
    Estimate the perimeter of the square.

16 **Problem-solving** A mosaic uses 150 square tiles. The total area is 3000 cm².
    a Estimate the side length of a tile.
    b Use a calculator to check your answer.

17 **Problem-solving** Pieces of turf are 1 m long by 0.5 m wide. Each piece costs £3.79.
    a Estimate the cost of turf required to cover these spaces.
      i 9.6 m by 2.4 m   ii 6.2 m by 1.9 m   iii 4.4 m by 2.1 m
    b Use a calculator to work out each answer.
      How good were your estimates?
    c **Reflect** Is it better to overestimate or underestimate a cost? Explain your choice.

1.3 HCF and LCM

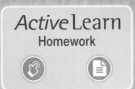
Active Learn
Homework

- Write a number as the product of its prime factors.
- Find the HCF and LCM of two numbers.

Warm up

1 Fluency a List all the factors of 20.

b Which of these factors are prime numbers?

2 a Write down all the prime numbers between 1 and 20.

b Write down all the factors of 24.

c Copy and complete this Venn diagram.

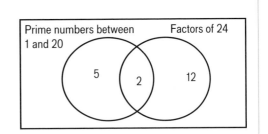

Prime numbers between 1 and 20 — Factors of 24

5   2   12

3 Find the HCF of 30 and 48.

4 Write these products using index notation (with an index or power).

a $5 \times 5 \times 5 = 5^{\square}$

b $2 \times 2 \times 2 \times 2 \times 2 = 2^{\square}$

c $2 \times 3 \times 5 \times 5 = 2 \times 3 \times 5^{\square}$

d $2 \times 2 \times 2 \times 3 \times 3 = \square^{\square} \times \square^{\square}$

e Work out the answers to parts **a** to **d**.

5 a Copy this factor tree for 40.
Complete the pairs of factors below each number.

b Circle the prime factors in your factor tree.

c Write 40 as a product of its prime factors.
$40 = \square \times \square \times \square \times \square$

d Write 40 as a product of its prime factors using index notation.
$40 = \square^{\square} \times \square$

6 Draw a factor tree for 75.
Then write 75 as a product of its prime factors using index notation.

7 Steve and Ian are asked to find 60 as a product of its prime factors.
Steve begins by writing $60 = 5 \times 12$.
Ian begins by writing $60 = 6 \times 10$.

a Work out a final answer for Steve.

b Work out a final answer for Ian.

8 Reflect Write a sentence explaining what you notice about your two answers to **Q7**.

9 a Start the **prime factor decomposition** of 48 in three different ways.

b Reflect Does it matter which two factors you choose first?

10 Reflect a Write your own short mathematical definition of these words.

    i prime   **ii** factor   **iii** decomposition

    b Use your definition to write (in your own words) the meaning of prime factor decomposition.

11 Express each number as a product of its prime factors in **index** form (also called index notation).

    a 18   **b** 42   **c** 25

    d 36   **e** 24   **f** 80

12 120 can be written as a product of its prime factors in the form $2^m \times n \times p$.
Work out m, n and p.

13 a Write 80 as a product of its prime factors.

    b Explain how you can use the prime factor decomposition of 80 to quickly work out the prime factor decomposition of

    i 160   **ii** 40

14 Problem-solving The prime factor decomposition of 2100 is $2^2 \times 3 \times 5^2 \times 7$.

    a Harry says the prime factors of 75 appear in the prime factor decomposition of 2100, so 2100 is divisible by 75.
    Is 2100 divisible by 24, 12 or 30?

    b Use prime factors to show that 792 is divisible by 12.

    c Is 792 divisible by 132? Explain your answer.

    d Is 792 divisible by 27? Explain your answer.

Example

Find the highest common factor and lowest common multiple of 24 and 60.

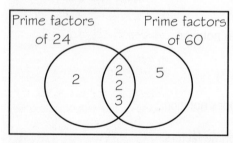

$24 = 2 \times 2 \times 2 \times 3$
$60 = 2 \times 2 \times 3 \times 5$

Write each number as a product of prime factors.

The highest common factor (HCF) of 24 and 60 is $2 \times 2 \times 3 = 12$

Multiply the common prime factors.

The lowest common multiple (LCM) of 24 and 60 is $2 \times 2 \times 2 \times 3 \times 5 = 120$

Multiply all the prime factors.

15 Express these numbers as products of their prime factors.
Draw Venn diagrams to find the HCF and LCM.

    a 24 and 30   **b** 20 and 42   **c** 8 and 18

    d 15 and 45   **e** 27 and 36   **f** 33 and 66

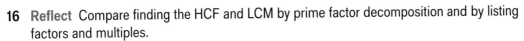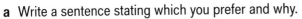

16 **Reflect** Compare finding the HCF and LCM by prime factor decomposition and by listing factors and multiples.

    a Write a sentence stating which you prefer and why.

    b Do you think one method is easier for large numbers? Explain your answer.

17 $48 = 2^4 \times 3$ and $36 = 2^2 \times 3^2$

    Write, as a product of its prime factors,

    a the HCF of 48 and 36

    b the LCM of 48 and 36.

> **Q17 hint**
>
> You could draw a Venn diagram.

Exam-style question

18 $A = 2^3 \times 3^4 \times 5^2$ and $B = 2^2 \times 3^6 \times 5$

    Write, as a product of its prime factors,

    a the HCF of A and B

    b the LCM of A and B **(2 marks)**

> **Exam tip**
>
> Sometimes it can be useful to draw a picture (e.g. a Venn diagram) to answer exam questions.

---

19 In prime factor form, $700 = 2^2 \times 5^2 \times 7$ and $1960 = 2^3 \times 5 \times 7^2$

    a What is the HCF of 700 and 1960? Give your answer in prime factor form.

    b What is the LCM of 700 and 1960? Give your answer in prime factor form.

    c Which of these are factors of 350 and 1960?

       i $2 \times 5 \times 7$

       ii 49

       iii 20

       iv $2^2 \times 5 \times 7^2$

    d Which of these are multiples of 350 and 1960?

       i $2^3 \times 5 \times 7^3$

       ii $2^6 \times 5^2 \times 7^2$

       iii $2^2 \times 5 \times 7$

> **Q19c hint**
>
> What factors do 700 and 1960 have in common? Any factor of this number will be a factor of 350 and 1960.

> **Q19d hint**
>
> What multiples do 700 and 1960 have in common? Any multiple of this number will be a multiple of 350 and 1960.

Exam-style question

20 One bus leaves the bus station every 10 minutes.
    Another bus leaves every 8 minutes.
    At 2.30 pm both buses leave the bus station.

    a At what time will this next happen?   **(2 marks)**

    b How many times in the next 3 hours will both buses be at the bus station?   **(1 mark)**

> **Exam tip**
>
> It is not enough to only show working. You must answer the questions, giving a time for part **a** and a number for part **b**.

---

21 **Future skills** Amber wants to tile her bathroom. It measures 1.2 m by 2.16 m.
    She finds square tiles with a side length of 10 cm, 12 cm or 18 cm.
    Which of these tiles will fit the wall exactly?

22 **Reflect** Explain how you knew whether to find the HCF or LCM for **Q20a** and **Q21**.

23 **Problem-solving** The LCM of two numbers is 18. One of the numbers is 18.

    a Write down all the possibilities for the other number.

    b Describe the set of numbers you have created.

1.4 Calculating with powers (indices)

- Use powers and roots in calculations.
- Multiply and divide using index laws.
- Work out a power raised to a power.

*Active*Learn
Homework

Warm up

1 **Fluency** $\square^2 = 121$ so $\sqrt{121} = \square$
Give possible positive and negative answers.

2 Work out

  a 3^3 **b** $(-4)^2$ **c** $(-1)^3$ **d** 4×4^2

  e $4^2 + 3^2$ **f** 0.2^3 **g** $3 \times \sqrt{16}$ **h** $\sqrt{81} \times \sqrt{64}$

3 Work out   **a** $\dfrac{4 \times 4 \times 4 \times 4}{4 \times 4}$ **b** $\dfrac{3 \times 3 \times 3 \times 3 \times 3 \times 3}{3 \times 3 \times 3}$

4 Copy and complete.

  a $5^{\square} = 25$ **b** $\square^3 = 27$ **c** $2^{\square} = 16$ **d** $10^{\square} = 10$

> **Q4c hint**
> $2 \times 2 \times \ldots = 16$

Key point

The inverse of a cube is the **cube root**.
$2^3 = 8$, so the cube root of 8 is $\sqrt[3]{8} = 2$

5 Work out

  a $\sqrt[3]{27}$ **b** $\sqrt[3]{-1}$ **c** $\sqrt[3]{1000}$ **d** $\sqrt[3]{-125}$

  e **Reflect** Write a sentence explaining why it is possible to find the cube root of a negative number, but not the square root.

6 Use the priority of operations to work out these. Use a calculator to check your answers.

  a $43 + \sqrt[3]{-27}$ **b** $33 - \sqrt[3]{-8} - (-4)^2$ **c** $\sqrt{4^2 + 3^2}$

  d $\sqrt{5^2 + 3 \times \sqrt[3]{-27}}$ **e** $\sqrt[3]{10^2 + 5^2}$ **f** $\dfrac{5^2 \times \sqrt[3]{-27}}{\sqrt[3]{-8} - \sqrt{9}}$

  g $\dfrac{-3^3}{\sqrt{9}} \times \dfrac{-\sqrt{64}}{\sqrt[3]{-1}}$ **h** $\dfrac{0.2^2 \times \sqrt[3]{-125}}{\sqrt[3]{8}}$

> **Q6c and d hint**
> The square root applies to the whole calculation.

7 Work out

  a $[(3^3 - 5^2) \times 2]^3$ **b** $20 - [3 \times 4^2 - (2^2 \times 3^2)]$

  c $[72 \div (7 - 5)^3 - 3] \div \sqrt{9}$

> **Q7 hint**
> Square brackets make the inner and outer brackets easier to see. Work out inner brackets first.

8 Work out

  a $\sqrt[4]{16}$ **b** $\sqrt[4]{81}$ **c** $\sqrt[5]{100\,000}$

> **Q8a hint**
> $\square^4 = 16$ $\sqrt[4]{16} = \square$

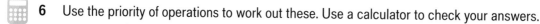

9 Work out

    a i $10^3 \times 10^2$ **ii** 10^5 **iii** $10^6 \times 10^2$ **iv** 10^8

    b How can you work out the answers to part **a** by using the indices of the powers you are multiplying?

    c Check your rule works for   **i** $10^3 \times 10^4$ **ii** $10^5 \times 10$ **iii** $10^{-2} \times 10^{-3}$

10 Write each product as a single power.

    a $3^2 \times 3^4 = 3^{\square}$ **b** $4^2 \times 4^8$ **c** $9^3 \times 9^4$ **d** $5^6 \times 5^3$

Key point

To multiply powers, add the indices. $x^m \times x^n = x^{m+n}$

11 Find the value of a.

    a $8^4 \times 8^a = 8^7$ **b** $6^5 \times 6^a = 6^7$ **c** $2^3 \times 2^a = 2^{10}$

Key point

You can only add the indices when multiplying powers of the same number.

12 Write these calculations as a single power. Give your answers in index form.

    a $27 \times 3^5 = 3^{\square} \times 3^5 = 3^{\square}$ **b** $4^3 \times 64$ **c** 5×125

    d 32×4 **e** $8 \times 8 \times 8$ **f** $9 \times 27 \times 3$

13 **Reasoning**

    a i Work out $\dfrac{5 \times 5 \times 5 \times 5 \times 5}{5 \times 5}$ by cancelling. Write your answer as a power of 5.

      ii Copy and complete. $5^5 \div 5^2 = 5^{\square}$

    b Copy and complete. $4^6 \div 4^2 = \dfrac{4 \times 4 \times 4 \times 4 \times 4 \times 4}{4 \times 4} = 4^{\square}$

    c Work out $6^5 \div 6^4$

    d **Reflect** Explain how you can quickly find $7^9 \div 7^3$ without writing all the 7s.

14 Work out   **a** $7^6 \div 7^2$ **b** $4^5 \div 4^3$ **c** $3^6 \div 3^5$

Key point

To divide powers, subtract the indices. $x^m \div x^n = x^{m-n}$

15 Find the value of a.

    a $9^6 \div 9^a = 9^4$ **b** $4^5 \div 4^a = 4$ **c** $7^6 \div 7^a = 7^9$

16 **Problem-solving**

    a Rokey multiplies three powers of 9 together: $9^{\square} \times 9^{\square} \times 9^{\square} = 9^{12}$

    What could the three powers be when

      i all three powers are different   **ii** all three powers are the same?

    b Harvey divides two powers of 5: $5^{\square} \div 5^{\square} = 5^6$

    What could the two powers be when

      i both numbers are greater than 5^{20}

      ii the power of one number is double the power of the other number?

17 Work out these. Write each answer as a single power.

a $5^3 \times 5^7 \div 5^4$ **b** $6^3 \div 6^2 \times 6^7$ **c** $\dfrac{5^4 \times 5^3}{5^5}$ **d** $\dfrac{8^2 \times 8^6}{8^7}$

18 **Problem-solving / Future skills** The hard drive of Tom's computer holds 2^{38} bytes of data. He buys a USB memory stick that holds 2^{34} bytes of data.

a How many memory sticks does he need to back up his computer?

He buys an external hard drive that holds 2^{39} bytes of data.

b What fraction of the external hard drive does he use when backing up his computer?

19 Copy and complete.

a $(2^3)^5 = 2^3 \times \square^\square \times \square^\square \times \square^\square \times \square^\square = 2^\square$

b $(6^4)^3 = \square^\square \times \square^\square \times \square^\square = 6^\square$

c $(8^7)^2 = \square^\square \times \square^\square = 8^\square$

d **Reflect** Write a sentence explaining what you notice about the powers in the question and the powers in the final answer.

> **Key point**
>
> To work out a power to another power, multiply the indices together. $(x^m)^n = x^{mn}$

20 Write as a single power.

a $(2^3)^4$ **b** $(6^2)^5$ **c** $(4^2)^{-3}$ **d** $(5^{-2})^{-6}$

21 **Reasoning** Alison writes $(3^4)^5$ as 3^9.

a Write a sentence explaining what Alison has done wrong.

b Write a calculation using powers of 3 and no brackets that gives the answer 3^9.

22 **a** Write as single powers of 10. The first one is started for you.

i $100^4 = (10^2)^4 = 10^\square$

ii 100^6 **iii** 100^{10} **iv** 1000^2 **v** 1000^4 **vi** 1000^8

b Write a sentence explaining what you notice about

i the powers of 10 in your answers to parts **i**, **ii** and **iii** and the powers of 100 in each question

ii the powers of 10 in your answers to parts **iv**, **v** and **vi** and the powers of 1000 in each question

---

Exam-style question

23 $\dfrac{(7^3)^x}{7^4} = 7^5$

Find the value of x. **(2 marks)**

Exam tip

Make sure you know when to add, subtract or multiply indices when working with single powers of the same number.

---

24 Write each calculation as a single power.

a $8 \times 32 \times 8$ **b** $\dfrac{5^8}{125}$ **c** $\dfrac{16 \times 64 \times 16}{4^4}$

1.5 Zero, negative and fractional indices

Active Learn
Homework

- Use negative indices.
- Use fractional indices.

Warm up

1 **Fluency** What are **a** 6^2 **b** 2^3 **c** $\sqrt[3]{27}$ **d** $\sqrt[4]{16}$?

2 Work out **a** $1 \div \frac{3}{5}$ **b** $3 \times \frac{2}{5}$ **c** $\frac{2}{5} \div \frac{3}{5}$ **d** $\frac{2}{5} - \frac{3}{4}$

3 Write each calculation as a single power.

a $3^4 \times 3^6$ **b** $2^5 \div 2^3$ **c** 16×8 **d** 9×27 **e** $3^6 \div 3^3$

4 Work out

a $(5^2)^4$ **b** $\left(\frac{1}{2}\right)^2$ **c** $\left(\frac{2}{3}\right)^2$ **d** $\sqrt{\frac{1}{25}}$ **e** $\sqrt[3]{-\frac{8}{27}}$

---

5 Work out the value of n.

a $40 = 5 \times 2^n$ **b** $3^n \times 3^n = 3^8$

c $5^{2n} \div 5^n = 5^6$ **d** $\frac{1}{2} \times 4^n = 32$

> **Q5a hint**
>
> $40 = 5 \times \square$
>
> How do you write this number as $2^\square$?

6 **a** Use a calculator to work out

i 2^{-1} **ii** 4^{-1} **iii** 5^{-1} **iv** 10^{-1}

b Write your answers to part **a** as fractions.

c Use a calculator to work out

i 2^{-2} **ii** 4^{-2} **iii** 5^{-2} **iv** 10^{-2}

d Write your answers to part **c** as fractions.

e Work out **i** $\left(\frac{1}{2}\right)^{-1}$ **ii** $\left(\frac{3}{4}\right)^{-2}$

f **Reflect** Write down the rule for writing negative indices as fractions.

7 **a** Match the equivalent cards.

b Write matching cards for the two cards that are left over.

c Copy and complete:

$$\left(\frac{2}{3}\right)^{-1} = \square, \text{ so } \left(\frac{a}{b}\right)^{-1} = \frac{\square}{\square}$$

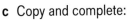

Key point

$x^{-n} = \dfrac{1}{x^n}$ for any number n, $x \neq 0$

---

8 Work out these. Write each answer as a single power.

a $6^2 \div 6^{-3} \times 6^7$ **b** $\dfrac{5^4 \times 5^{-3}}{5^5}$ **c** $\dfrac{8^{-2} \times 8^{-6}}{8^{-7}}$

9 Problem-solving

   a Copy and complete. $2^3 \div 2^3 = 2^\square$

   b Write down 2^3 as a whole number.

   c Copy and complete. $2^3 \div 2^3 = 8 \div \square = \square$

   d Copy and complete using parts **a** and **c**. $2^3 \div 2^3 = 2^\square = \square$

   e Repeat parts **a** and **b** for $7^5 \div 7^5$.

   f Write down a rule for a^0, where a is any number.

> **Key point**
>
> $x^0 = 1$, where x is any non-zero number.

10 Work out

   a 3^{-1} **b** 2^{-4} **c** 10^{-5} **d** $\left(\frac{3}{4}\right)^{-1}$

   e $\left(\frac{7}{10}\right)^{-2}$ **f** $\left(\frac{4}{5}\right)^{-3}$ **g** $\left(5^{-1}\right)^0$ **h** $\left(7^{-1}\right)^{-1}$

11 Work out these by first converting mixed numbers to improper fractions.

   a $\left(1\frac{1}{4}\right)^{-1}$ **b** $\left(2\frac{3}{4}\right)^{-2}$ **c** $\left(2\frac{2}{5}\right)^{-2}$ **d** $\left(3\frac{1}{3}\right)^{-3}$

12 Work out these by first converting decimals to fractions.

   a $(0.7)^{-1}$ **b** $(0.1)^{-5}$ **c** $(0.4)^{-3}$ **d** $(1.2)^{-2}$

13 a Use a calculator to work out

     i $49^{\frac{1}{2}}$ **ii** $16^{\frac{1}{2}}$ **iii** $121^{\frac{1}{2}}$ **iv** $\left(\frac{4}{25}\right)^{\frac{1}{2}}$

   b Copy and complete. $a^{\frac{1}{2}}$ is the same as the _____ _____ of a.

   c Use a calculator to work out

     i $27^{\frac{1}{3}}$ **ii** $1000^{\frac{1}{3}}$ **iii** $-1^{\frac{1}{3}}$ **iv** $\left(\frac{1}{1000}\right)^{\frac{1}{3}}$

   d Copy and complete. $a^{\frac{1}{3}}$ is the same as the _____ _____ of a.

   e Copy and complete.

     i $625 = 5^\square$ so $625^{\frac{1}{4}} = \square$ **ii** $32 = \square^5$ so $32^{\frac{1}{5}} = \square$

> **Key point**
>
> $x^{\frac{1}{n}} = \sqrt[n]{x}$ so $x^{\frac{1}{2}} = \sqrt{x}$ (square root) $x^{\frac{1}{3}} = \sqrt[3]{x}$ (cube root)
> $x^{\frac{1}{4}} = \sqrt[4]{x}$ (fourth root) $x^{\frac{1}{5}} = \sqrt[5]{x}$ (fifth root)

14 Evaluate

   a $36^{\frac{1}{2}}$ **b** $81^{\frac{1}{2}}$ **c** $\left(\frac{1}{9}\right)^{\frac{1}{2}}$

   d $\left(\frac{49}{100}\right)^{\frac{1}{2}}$ **e** $\left(\frac{16}{25}\right)^{\frac{1}{2}}$ **f** $\left(\frac{64}{49}\right)^{\frac{1}{2}}$

   g $-8^{\frac{1}{3}}$ **h** $\left(\frac{1}{27}\right)^{\frac{1}{3}}$ **i** $\left(\frac{-64}{125}\right)^{\frac{1}{3}}$

> **Q14 hint**
>
> Evaluate means 'work out the value of'.

15 Miguel says '$\frac{1}{4}$ of 64 is 16 so $64^{-\frac{1}{4}} = -16$.'
Explain what is wrong with what Miguel says. **(2 marks)**

It is not enough to state the answer to $\frac{1}{4}$ of 64 and the correct answer to $64^{-\frac{1}{4}}$. You must explain what a power of $\frac{1}{4}$ means, and what a negative power means.

16 Work out these. The first one is started for you.

a $25^{-\frac{1}{2}} = \dfrac{1}{25^{\frac{1}{2}}} = \dfrac{1}{\square}$

b $64^{-\frac{1}{3}}$ **c** $\left(\frac{9}{25}\right)^{-\frac{1}{2}}$ **d** $\left(\frac{8}{27}\right)^{-\frac{1}{3}}$

Example

Work out the value of   **a** $27^{\frac{2}{3}}$ **b** $16^{-\frac{3}{4}}$

a $27^{\frac{2}{3}} = \left(27^{\frac{1}{3}}\right)^2 = 3^2 = 9$

Use the rule $(x^m)^n = x^{mn}$. Work out the cube root of 27 first. Then square your answer.

b $16^{-\frac{3}{4}} = \dfrac{1}{16^{\frac{3}{4}}} = \dfrac{1}{\left(16^{\frac{1}{4}}\right)^3} = \dfrac{1}{2^3} = \dfrac{1}{8}$

Use $x^{-n} = \dfrac{1}{x^n}$

17 Work out these. The first one is started for you.

a $64^{\frac{2}{3}} = \left(64^{\frac{1}{3}}\right)^2 = \left(\sqrt[3]{64}\right)^2 = \square^2 = \square$ **b** $10\,000^{\frac{3}{4}}$ **c** $16^{\frac{3}{2}}$

d $8^{\frac{4}{3}}$ **e** $\left(\frac{4}{9}\right)^{\frac{3}{2}}$ **f** $27^{-\frac{2}{3}}$ **g** $-81^{-\frac{3}{4}}$ **h** $\left(\frac{81}{16}\right)^{-\frac{1}{2}}$

Key point

$x^{\frac{m}{n}} = \left(\sqrt[n]{x}\right)^m$

18 Work out

a $27^{-\frac{1}{3}} \times 9^{\frac{3}{2}}$ **b** $\left(\frac{4}{25}\right)^{-\frac{3}{2}} \times \left(\frac{8}{27}\right)^{\frac{1}{3}}$ **c** $\left(\frac{81}{16}\right)^{\frac{3}{4}} \times \left(\frac{9}{25}\right)^{-\frac{3}{2}}$

First work out $27^{-\frac{1}{3}}$. Then work out $9^{\frac{3}{2}}$. Then multiply these numbers together.

19 Find the value of n.

a $16 = 2^n$ **b** $\sqrt[3]{27} = 27^n$ **c** $\frac{1}{100} = 10^n$

d $\sqrt{\frac{4}{9}} = \left(\frac{9}{4}\right)^n$ **e** $\left(\sqrt{3}\right)^7 = 3^n$ **f** $\left(\sqrt[4]{8}\right)^7 = 8^n$

20 **Problem-solving / Reasoning** Will says that $25^{-\frac{1}{2}} \times 64^{\frac{2}{3}} = 80$.

a Show that Will is wrong.   **b** What mistake did he make?

21 Write these as single powers of 2.
The first one is started for you.

a $8^{\frac{1}{4}} = \left(2^{\square}\right)^{\frac{1}{4}} = 2^{\square}$ **b** $8^{\frac{2}{5}}$ **c** $16^{-\frac{1}{5}}$ **d** $(32)^{\frac{3}{4}}$

When a calculation involves bases that are multiples of a single number (e.g. 3, 9, 27 are all multiples of 3) always consider writing as powers of the lowest base (i.e. $3^{\square}$).

22 $9^{\frac{3}{4}} \times 3^p = 27^{\frac{1}{5}}$
Work out the exact value of p. **(3 marks)**

1.6 Powers of 10 and standard form

- Write a number in standard form.
- Calculate with numbers in standard form.

Warm up

1 **Fluency** Which of these are the same as $\div 10$?

A $\times \frac{1}{10}$ **B** $\times 0.01$ **C** $\times 10^{-1}$

2 Work out

a 4.5×1000 **b** 0.0063×100 **c** 69.4×0.1 **d** 845.3×0.001

3 Copy and complete. If your answer is a fraction, write it as a decimal too.

a $10^4 = \square$ **b** $10^{\square} = 1000$ **c** $10^0 = \square$ **d** $10^{-1} = \square$

e $10^{-2} = \square$ **f** $10^{-3} = \square$ **g** $10^{-4} = \square$ **h** $10^{\square} = 0.000001$

4 Copy and complete.

a $5\,670\,000 = \square$ million   **b** $4\,908\,340\,000 = \square$ billion

Key point

Some powers of 10 have a name called a **prefix**. Each prefix is represented by a letter. For example, kilo means 10^3 and is represented by the letter k, as in kg for kilogram.

5 Copy and complete the table of **prefixes**.

Prefix	Letter	Power	Number
tera	T	10^{12}	1 000 000 000 000
giga	G	10^9	
mega	M		1 000 000
kilo	k	10^3	
deci	d		0.1
centi	c	10^{-2}	
milli	m		0.001
micro	μ	10^{-6}	
nano	n		0.000 000 001
pico	p	10^{-12}	

Q5 hint
Prefix is the beginning part of a word.

Q5 hint
μ, the letter for the prefix micro, is the Greek letter mu.

6 Convert

a 15 mg into grams   **b** 7 nm into metres

c 1.7 g into kg   **d** 7.3 ps into seconds.

Q6a hint
Use a number line
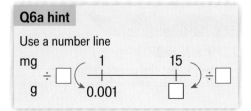

7   Write these measurements in metres.

   a The size of the influenza virus is about $1.2\,\mu m$.

   b The radius of a hydrogen atom is $25\,pm$.

   c A fingernail grows about $0.9\,nm$ every second.

8   Copy and complete.

   a $45\,000 = 4.5 \times \square$ **b** $10\,000 = 10^{\square}$ **c** $45\,000 = 4.5 \times 10^{\square}$

   d $0.0045 = 4.5 \times \square$ **e** $0.001 = 10^{\square}$ **f** $0.0045 = 4.5 \times 10^{\square}$

> ### Key point
>
> A number is in **standard form** when it is in the form $A \times 10^{n}$, where $1 \leqslant A < 10$ and n is an integer.
> For example, 6.3×10^{4} is in standard form because 6.3 is between 1 and 10.
> 63×10^{4} is *not* in standard form because 63 does not lie between 1 and 10.
> Standard form is sometimes also called **scientific notation**.

9   Which of these numbers are in standard form?

   A 4.5×10^{7} **B** 13×10^{4} **C** 0.9×10^{-2}

   D 9.99×10^{-3} **E** 4.5 billion   **F** 2.5×10

10 Write these numbers in standard form.

   a $87\,000$ **b** $1\,042\,000$

   c $1\,394\,000\,000$ **d** 0.007

   e $0.000\,002\,84$ **f** $0.000\,100\,3$

> **Q10 hint**
>
> Write the number between 1 and 10 first.
> Then multiply by a power of 10.

11 Write these as **ordinary numbers**.

   a 4×10^{5} **b** 3.5×10^{2} **c** 6.78×10^{3}

   d 6.2×10^{-2} **e** 8.93×10^{-5} **f** 4.04×10^{-3}

12 Write these numbers in order, starting with the smallest.

   A 3.62×10^{16} **B** 2.197×10^{15} **C** 2.8×10^{16} **D** 3.96×10^{14}

> ### Key point
>
> The symbol $\neq$ means 'not equal to'.

13 Copy and complete. Write $=$ or $\neq$ between each pair of numbers.

   a $7.2 \times 10^{6} \;\square\; 72\,000$ **b** $0.0061 \;\square\; 6.1 \times 10^{-4}$

   c $0.000\,029 \;\square\; 2.9 \times 10^{-5}$ **d** $6.87 \times 10^{4} \;\square\; 6870$

   e $1.999 \times 10^{4} \;\square\; 1.9 \times 10^{5}$ **f** $0.000\,000\,012\,4 \;\square\; 1.24 \times 10^{-8}$

   g **Reasoning** Alex says that all the pairs of numbers could have the symbol $\geqslant$ between them.
   Is Alex correct? Explain.

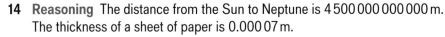

14 **Reasoning** The distance from the Sun to Neptune is $4\,500\,000\,000\,000\,m$.
   The thickness of a sheet of paper is $0.000\,07\,m$.

   a Write each of these numbers in standard form.

   b Enter each number from part **a** in your calculator and press the [=] key. Compare your
   calculator number with the standard form number.

   c **Reflect** Explain why scientists use standard form for very large and very small numbers.

Example

Work out $(5 \times 10^3) \times (7 \times 10^6)$.

$5 \times 7 \times 10^3 \times 10^6$

$= 35 \times 10^9$

$35 = 3.5 \times 10^1$

$35 \times 10^9 = 3.5 \times 10^1 \times 10^9 = 3.5 \times 10^{10}$

> Rewrite the multiplication grouping the numbers and the powers.

> Simplify using multiplication and the index law $x^m \times x^n = x^{m+n}$
> This is not in standard form because 35 is not between 1 and 10.

> Write 35 in standard form.

> Work out the final answer.

15 Work out these. Give your answers in standard form and as ordinary numbers. Use a calculator to check your answers.

   a $(3 \times 10^2) \times (2 \times 10^5)$ **b** $(5 \times 10^3) \times (4 \times 10^7)$

   c $(8 \times 10^{-2}) \times (6 \times 10^7)$ **d** $(8 \times 10^6) \div (4 \times 10^3)$

   e $\dfrac{9 \times 10^{-2}}{3 \times 10^6}$ **f** $\dfrac{2 \times 10^3}{8 \times 10^7}$

   g $(5 \times 10^3)^2$ **h** $(4 \times 10^{-2})^3$

16 **Problem-solving** A water molecule has a mass of 3×10^{-26} kg.
A bottle contains 1.7×10^{25} molecules of water.
Calculate the mass of water in the bottle.

Exam-style question

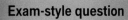

17 The Sun is a distance of 1.5×10^8 km from Earth.
Saturn is a distance of 1.28×10^9 km from Earth.
Ethel says, 'Saturn is more than ten times the distance
from Earth than the Sun is.'
Is Ethel right? You must show how you get your answer.

(2 marks)

Exam tip

It is not enough only to compare powers of 10. You must include working that shows you have considered the decimals multiplying the powers of 10 too.

18 **a** Write these numbers as ordinary numbers.

     i 8×10^4 **ii** 3×10^2

   b Use your answer to part **a** to work out $(8 \times 10^4) + (3 \times 10^2)$ as an ordinary number.
     Then give your answer in standard form.

19 Work out these. Give your answers in standard form.

   a $3.4 \times 10^5 + 6.7 \times 10^4$ **b** $9.8 \times 10^4 - 2.2 \times 10^2$

   c $7.21 \times 10^2 + 6.2 \times 10^{-1}$ **d** $8.326 \times 10^5 - 7 \times 10^{-1}$

Exam-style question

20 $(7 \times 10^x) + (7 \times 10^y) + (7 \times 10^z) = 700\,070.07$
Write down a possible set of values for x, y and z.

(3 marks)

Exam tip

Don't just write down the possible values – show how you worked out the values.

1.7 Surds

- Understand the difference between rational and irrational numbers.
- Simplify a surd.
- Rationalise a denominator.

Active Learn
Homework

Warm up

1 **Fluency** Which of these are integers?

-3 -3.5 $\frac{3}{5}$ 5 $0.\dot{5}$

2 What does the dot above the 5 mean in $0.\dot{5}$?

3 Work out

a $\sqrt{4} \times \sqrt{4}$ **b** $\sqrt{25} \times \sqrt{25}$ **c** $\sqrt{8} \times \sqrt{8}$ **d** $\sqrt{10} \times \sqrt{10}$

4 Solve these equations, giving positive and negative answers, $x = \pm\sqrt{\square}$

a $x^2 = 9$ **b** $x^2 - 16 = 0$ **c** $2x^2 = 32$ **d** $\frac{1}{2}x^2 = 18$ **e** $2x^2 - 1 = 49$

Key point

A **surd** is a number written exactly using square or cube roots.
For example $\sqrt{3}$ and $\sqrt{5}$ are surds. $\sqrt{4}$ and $\sqrt[3]{27}$ are not surds, because $\sqrt{4} = 2$ and $\sqrt[3]{27} = 3$

5 Write to 2 decimal places.

a $\sqrt{5}$ **b** $\sqrt{7}$

c $\sqrt{19}$ **d** $\sqrt{53}$

e **Reflect** Write a sentence explaining which is more exact, the square root or the decimal.

Q5 hint

Use the S⇔D button on your calculator to switch between decimal form and surd or fraction form.

6 **a** Work out

i $\sqrt{2} \times \sqrt{3}$ **ii** $\sqrt{6}$

b Work out

i $\sqrt{3}\sqrt{5}$ **ii** $\sqrt{15}$

c What do you notice about your answers to parts **a** and **b**?

d Find the missing numbers.

i $\sqrt{2} \times \sqrt{6} = \sqrt{\square}$ **ii** $\sqrt{2} \times \sqrt{\square} = \sqrt{10}$ **iii** $\sqrt{\square}\sqrt{7} = \sqrt{35}$

Key point

$\sqrt{mn} = \sqrt{m}\sqrt{n}$

7 Find the value of the integer k to simplify these surds.

a $\sqrt{40} = \sqrt{\square}\sqrt{10} = k\sqrt{10}$ **b** $\sqrt{150} = \sqrt{\square}\sqrt{6} = k\sqrt{6}$

c $\sqrt{128} = k\sqrt{2}$ **d** $\sqrt{108} = k\sqrt{3}$

8 For each of these surds, find a factor that is also a square number. Then simplify. The first one is started for you.

a $\sqrt{20} = \sqrt{\square}\sqrt{5} = \square\sqrt{\square}$ **b** $\sqrt{300}$ **c** $\sqrt{44}$

d $\sqrt{250}$ **e** $4\sqrt{50}$ **f** $6\sqrt{56}$

9 Use a calculator to work out $\sqrt{75}$

a as a simplified surd

b as a decimal

Q9 hint

Make sure you know how to switch between surd form and decimals on your calculator.

10 a **Reasoning** A surd simplifies to $4\sqrt{5}$. What could the original surd be?

b **Reflect** Write a sentence explaining how you found the surd.

Key point

$$\sqrt{\frac{m}{n}} = \frac{\sqrt{m}}{\sqrt{n}}$$

---

11 Simplify

a $\sqrt{\frac{7}{4}} = \frac{\sqrt{7}}{\sqrt{4}} =$ **b** $\sqrt{\frac{5}{9}}$ **c** $\sqrt{\frac{20}{49}}$

d $\sqrt{\frac{18}{25}}$ **e** $\left(\sqrt{\frac{3}{8}}\right)^2$

Q11e hint

$$\left(\sqrt{\frac{3}{8}}\right)^2 = \frac{\sqrt{\square}}{\sqrt{\square}} \times \frac{\sqrt{\square}}{\sqrt{\square}}$$

Key point

A **rational** number can be written as a fraction in the form $\frac{a}{b}$, where a and b are integers and $b \neq 0$.

2 is rational as it can be written as $\frac{2}{1}$. $0.\dot{2}$ is rational as it can be written as $\frac{2}{9}$. $\sqrt{2}$ is irrational.

---

12 Which of these are irrational?

$\sqrt[3]{6}$ $\quad \frac{3}{8} \quad$ $\sqrt{6.25} - 4$ $\quad -\sqrt{8} \quad$ $\sqrt{17}$ $\quad 1.\dot{4} \quad$ $\sqrt{\frac{4}{49}}$ $\quad 0.3$

13 a Solve the equation $x^2 - 90 = 0$, giving your answer as a surd in its simplest form.

b **Reflect** Write a sentence explaining whether you can solve the equation $x^2 + 90 = 0$ in the same way.

Q13a hint

$x^2 = \square$

$x = \pm\sqrt{\square}$

$x = \pm\square\sqrt{\square}$

14 Solve these equations, giving each answer as a surd in its simplest form.

a $4x^2 = 200$ **b** $\frac{1}{2}x^2 = 80$ **c** $3x^2 = 36$ **d** $2x^2 - 14 = 42$

15 a Multiply the integers, then the surds, to work out

i $5\sqrt{2} \times 4\sqrt{27}$ **ii** $4\sqrt{5} \times 6\sqrt{12}$

iii $9\sqrt{10} \times 4\sqrt{5}$ **iv** $8\sqrt{12} \times 3\sqrt{3}$

v $\left(11\sqrt{5}\right)^2$ **vi** $\left(2\sqrt{3}\right)^3$

Give each answer as a surd in its simplest form.

Q15a vi hint

$\left(2\sqrt{3}\right)^3 = 2\sqrt{3} \times 2\sqrt{3} \times 2\sqrt{3}$

b Use a calculator to check your answers to parts **i** to **vi**.

Example

Rationalise the denominator. **a** $\dfrac{1}{\sqrt{2}}$ **b** $\dfrac{5}{\sqrt{75}}$

a $\dfrac{1}{\sqrt{2}} = \dfrac{1}{\sqrt{2}} \times \dfrac{\sqrt{2}}{\sqrt{2}}$

$= \dfrac{\sqrt{2}}{\sqrt{4}} = \dfrac{\sqrt{2}}{2}$

> Multiplying by $\dfrac{\sqrt{2}}{\sqrt{2}}$ is the same as multiplying by 1, so this does not change the value.

b $\sqrt{75} = \sqrt{25}\sqrt{3} = 5\sqrt{3}$

> First simplify $\sqrt{75}$.

$\dfrac{5}{\sqrt{75}} = \dfrac{5}{5\sqrt{3}} = \dfrac{1}{\sqrt{3}} \times \dfrac{\sqrt{3}}{\sqrt{3}} = \dfrac{\sqrt{3}}{\sqrt{9}} = \dfrac{\sqrt{3}}{3}$

> Simplify the fraction before rationalising.

16 Rationalise the denominators. Simplify your answers if possible.

a $\dfrac{1}{\sqrt{7}}$ **b** $\dfrac{1}{\sqrt{5}}$ **c** $\dfrac{1}{\sqrt{20}}$ **d** $\dfrac{2}{\sqrt{8}}$

e $\dfrac{3}{\sqrt{15}}$ **f** $\dfrac{32}{\sqrt{40}}$ **g** $\dfrac{11}{\sqrt{11}}$

17 **Reasoning** Show that $\left(\dfrac{2}{\sqrt{10}}\right)^3 = \dfrac{2\sqrt{10}}{25}$

> **Q17 hint**
>
> 'Show that' means show your working.

> **Exam tip**
>
> Questions will not always state that you need to rationalise.
>
> $\dfrac{\sqrt{\square}}{\square}$ shows rationalised form.

19 The area of a rectangle is $20\,\text{cm}^2$.
   The length of one side is $\sqrt{5}\,\text{cm}$.
   Work out the length of the other side. Give your answer as a surd in its simplest form.

20 Work out the areas of these shapes.
   Give each answer in its simplest form.

a

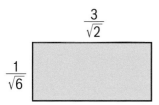

b

c

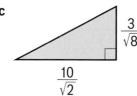

1 Check up

Active Learn
Homework

Calculations, factors and multiples

1 Alice is ordering a bicycle.
The bicycle is offered with two different choices of tyres, five different types of saddle, and in six different colours.
How many different combinations must Alice choose from?

2 $16.7 \times 9.2 = 153.64$
Use this fact to work out the calculations below.
Check your answers using an approximate calculation.

  a 167×9.2

  b $1.5364 \div 1.67$

3 Estimate the value of $\sqrt{54}$ to the nearest tenth.

4 **a** Estimate

    i $(\sqrt{65.1} - 6.17) \times 1.98$

    ii $\dfrac{\sqrt{8.19 \times 6.43}}{6.84 \times \sqrt{3.97}}$

  b Use your calculator to work out each answer.
    Give your answers correct to 1 decimal place.

5 Write 90 as a product of its prime factors in index form.

6 Find the highest common factor (HCF) and lowest common multiple (LCM) of 14 and 18.

7 In prime factor form, $2450 = 2 \times 5^2 \times 7^2$ and $68\,600 = 2^3 \times 5^2 \times 7^3$.

  a What is the HCF of 2450 and 68 600? Give your answer in prime factor form.

  b What is the LCM of 2450 and 68 600? Give your answer in prime factor form.

Indices and surds

8 Copy and complete.

  a $10^{\square} = 1000$ **b** $2^{\square} = 16$

  c $\sqrt[3]{-27} = \square$ **d** $5^{\square} = 1$

9 Work out

  a $\sqrt[3]{\dfrac{9^2 - 1^2}{10}}$

  b $[(6^2 - 2^5) \times 3]^2$

  c $\sqrt{\sqrt{81} + (-2)^3}$

10 Write each product as a single power.

   a $9^{-3} \times 9^{7}$ **b** $27 \times 9 \times 27$

   c $5^{7} \div 5^{2}$ **d** $\dfrac{2^{8} \times 16}{2^{5}}$

   e $(2^{4})^{3}$ **f** $(4^{2})^{-1}$

11 Work out

   a 2^{-4} **b** $25^{\frac{3}{2}}$ **c** $\left(\dfrac{16}{81}\right)^{\frac{3}{4}}$

   d $16^{-\frac{1}{2}}$ **e** $32^{-\frac{2}{5}}$

12 Simplify

   a $\sqrt{63}$

   b $5\sqrt{1000}$

13 Rationalise the denominators. Simplify your answers if possible.

   a $\dfrac{1}{\sqrt{10}}$ **b** $\dfrac{2}{\sqrt{6}}$ **c** $\dfrac{1}{\sqrt{24}}$

   d $\dfrac{4}{\sqrt{8}}$ **e** $\left(\dfrac{1}{\sqrt{6}}\right)^{3}$

Standard form

14 Write these numbers in standard form.

   a 32 040 000

   b 0.0007

15 Write these as ordinary numbers.

   a 5.6×10^{4}

   b 1.09×10^{-3}

16 Work out these. Give your answers in standard form.

   a $(5 \times 10^{4}) \times (9 \times 10^{7})$

   b $(3 \times 10^{8}) \div (6 \times 10^{5})$

   c $8 \times 10^{3} + 6 \times 10^{2}$

17 **Reflect** How sure are you of your answers? Were you mostly

   Just guessing 🙁   Feeling doubtful 😐   Confident 🙂

   What next? Use your results to decide whether to strengthen or extend your learning.

Challenge

18 There are 6 chess players in a tournament.
   Each player plays two games against each other player.
   Work out the number of games played.

1 Strengthen

*Active*Learn
Homework

Calculations, factors and multiples

1 A game uses tokens that are two different shapes:

Each token can be numbered 1 or 2.
Each token can be one of these colours: red, black or white.

a Draw all the different tokens for the game.

b Write a sentence explaining the method you used to make sure you didn't miss any tokens.

2 Copy and complete these number patterns.

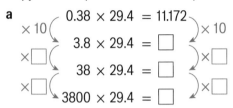

a
$0.38 \times 29.4 = 11.172$
$\times 10$ ( ) $\times 10$
$3.8 \times 29.4 = \square$
$\times \square$ ( ) $\times \square$
$38 \times 29.4 = \square$
$\times \square$ ( ) $\times \square$
$3800 \times 29.4 = \square$) $\times \square$

b
$6011.545 \div 94.67 = 63.5$
$\times 10$ ( ) $\times 10$
$60115.45 \div 94.67 = \square$
$\times \square$ ( ) $\times \square$
$601154.5 \div 94.67 = \square$
$\times \square$ ( ) $\times \square$
$60115450 \div 94.67 = \square$) $\times \square$

3 $8.9 \times 7.21 = 64.169$

Use this fact to work out the calculations below.
Check your answers using an approximate calculation.

a 8.9×72.1 **b** 8.9×7210 **c** 0.89×0.721

> **Q3 hint**
>
> Write out a number pattern to help you.

4 a Use the fact given in **Q3** to complete this related division fact.

$\square \div 7.21 = \square$

b Use your division fact to work out

  i $641.69 \div 7.21$ **ii** $641.69 \div 72.1$ **iii** $64.169 \div 72.1$

5 a Copy and complete this square root number line.

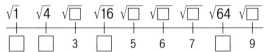

$\sqrt{1}$ $\sqrt{4}$ $\sqrt{\square}$ $\sqrt{16}$ $\sqrt{\square}$ $\sqrt{\square}$ $\sqrt{\square}$ $\sqrt{64}$ $\sqrt{\square}$

$\square$ $\square$ 3 $\square$ 5   6   7 $\square$ 9

b Use the number line to estimate each value to the nearest tenth.

  i $\sqrt{50}$ **ii** $\sqrt{60}$ **iii** $\sqrt{75}$

6 a Estimate

  i $\sqrt{4.09 \times 8.96}$ **ii** $25.76 - \sqrt{4.09 \times 8.96}$

  iii $\sqrt[3]{26.64} + \sqrt{80.7}$ **iv** $\dfrac{\sqrt{6.91 \times 9.23}}{3.95^2 \div 2.03^2}$

> **Q6a i hint**
>
> Round each number to the nearest whole number. Which square root is it closest to on your square root number line?

b Use a calculator to work out each answer.
Give your answer correct to 1 decimal place.

7 Copy and complete these calculations in index form.

  a $2 \times 2 \times 2 \times 3 \times 3 = 2^3 \times 3^\square$ **b** $2 \times 2 \times 3 \times 5 = 2^\square \times \square \times \square$

  c $3 \times 3 \times 3 \times 3 \times 7 \times 7 =$

8 **a** Copy and complete this factor tree for 60 until you end up with just prime factors.

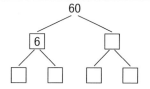

b Write 60 as a product of its prime factors.

c Write your answer to part **b** in index form.

9 Draw a factor tree for each of these numbers.

    a 24   **b** 80   **c** 30   **d** 16   **e** 72

10 Write each number in **Q9** as a product of its prime factors in index form.

11 **a** Write 18 as a product of its prime factors. $18 = \square \times \square \times \square$

    b Write 45 as a product of its prime factors. $45 = \square \times \square \times \square$

    c Copy and complete this diagram.

       i Put any prime factors of both numbers where circles overlap.

      ii Put the remaining prime factors of 18 in the left-hand part of the left circle.

     iii Put the remaining prime factors of 45 in the right-hand part of the right circle.

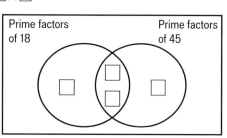

    d Use the Venn diagram to work out

       i the highest common factor (HCF)   **ii** the lowest common multiple (LCM).

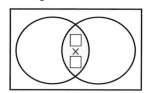   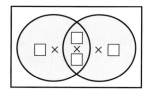

12 Use the method in **Q11** to find the HCF and LCM of

    a 20 and 30   **b** 21 and 28   **c** 15 and 25   **d** 44 and 36

Indices and surds

1 Copy and complete.

    a $2 \times 2 \times 2 = 2^{\square} = \square$ **b** $5 \times 5 = 5^{\square} = \square$ **c** $-3 \times -3 \times -3 = (-3)^{\square} = \square$

2 Work out

    a $2^4 = \square$ **b** $5^3 = \square$ **c** $2^{\square} = 64$ **d** $10^{\square} = 1000$

3 Work out any powers or roots. Then multiply or divide to calculate the answer.

    a $3 \times \sqrt{49}$ **b** $2^3 \times \sqrt{16}$ **c** $\sqrt[3]{-27} \times \sqrt{64}$

    d $10^2 \div -\sqrt{25}$ **e** $(-3)^2 \times \sqrt{49}$ **f** $\sqrt{9} \times \sqrt[3]{-125} \times \sqrt[3]{-1000}$

4 Use the priority of operations to work out

    a $5 \times (4^2 - 3^2) - 2^3$ **b** $[(9^2 \div 3^2) + 2^2]^2$

    c $\sqrt{\sqrt{49} + \sqrt[3]{8}}$

5 Copy and complete.

  a $(3\times3\times3\times3\times3)\times(3\times3\times3)=3^{\square}\times3^{\square}=3^{\square}$

  b $(4\times4\times4\times4)\times(4\times4\times4\times4\times4\times4)=4^{\square}\times4^{\square}=4^{\square}$

  c $\dfrac{⑥\times⑥\times\;6\;\times\;6}{⑥\times⑥}=\dfrac{6^4}{2^2}=6^{\square}$ **d** $\dfrac{7\times7\times7\times7\times7\times7}{7\times7\times7}=\dfrac{7^{\square}}{7^{\square}}=7^{\square}$

  e To multiply powers of the same number, _____ the indices.
     To divide powers of the same number, _____ the indices.

6 Use the rules from **Q5** to work out

  a $5^6\times5^3$ **b** $7^2\times7^9$ **c** $5^8\div5^3$

  d $9^8\div9^2$ **e** $8^4\times8^{-6}$ **f** $7^3\div7^{-4}$

Q6c hint

$5^8\div5^3=\dfrac{5^8}{5^3}$

7 Write these products as a single power of a prime number.

  a $16\times8=2^{\square}\times2^{\square}=$ **b** $25\times125\times25$

  c $16\times64\times8$ **d** $27\times27\times9$

8 Copy and complete.

  a $(4^2)^3=4^2\times4^2\times4^2=4^{\square}$ **b** $(6^3)^4=6^3\times6^3\times6^3\times6^3=6^{\square}$

  c $(7^5)^2=$ **d** $(8^3)^7=$

  e To work out a power in a bracket raised to a power, _____ the indices.

9 **a** Work out using a calculator.

    i 5^0 **ii** 7^0 **iii** 192^0 **iv** $(-3)^0$

  b Use your answer to part **a** to work these out without a calculator.

    i 12^0 **ii** $(-6)^0$ **iii** 2456^0 **iv** 10^0

10 **a** Work out using a calculator.

    i $\sqrt{169}$ **ii** $169^{\frac12}$

  b Use your answer to part **a** to work these out without a calculator.

    i $64^{\frac12}$ **ii** $25^{\frac12}$ **iii** $81^{\frac12}$ **iv** $144^{\frac12}$

  c Work out using a calculator.

    i $\sqrt[3]{512}$ **ii** $512^{\frac13}$

  d Use your answer to part **c** to work these out without a calculator.

    i $125^{\frac13}$ **ii** $27^{\frac13}$ **iii** $1000^{\frac13}$ **iv** $8^{\frac13}$

  e Use what you have learned in parts **a** to **d** to copy and complete.
    $16^{\frac14}=\sqrt[\square]{16}=\square$

11 **a** Work out

    i $64^{\frac13}$ **ii** $64^{\frac23}$

  b Use your answers to **Q10d** to help you work out

    i $125^{\frac23}$ **ii** $27^{\frac23}$ **iii** $1000^{\frac23}$ **iv** $8^{\frac23}$

  c Use your answer to **Q10e** to help you work out $16^{\frac34}$.

Q11a ii hint

$64^{\frac23}=\left(64^{\frac13}\right)^2$
Work out $64^{\frac13}$ and square your answer.

12 a Copy and complete.

    i $4^{-3} = \dfrac{1}{4^{\square}}$ **ii** $\dfrac{1}{10^5} = 10^{\square}$ **iii** $\dfrac{1}{2} = 2^{\square}$ **iv** $3^{-\frac{1}{3}} = \dfrac{1}{3^{\square}}$ **v** $\left(\dfrac{7}{6}\right)^{\square} = \dfrac{36}{49}$

  b Work out

    i 4^{-1} **ii** 10^{-2} **iii** $36^{-\frac{1}{2}}$ **iv** $125^{-\frac{1}{3}}$

13 Copy and complete.

  a $50 = \square \times 2$, so $\sqrt{50} = \sqrt{\square} \times \sqrt{2} = \square\sqrt{2}$

  b $84 = \square \times 21$, so $\sqrt{84} = \sqrt{\square} \times \sqrt{\square} = \square\sqrt{\square}$

  c Simplify

    i $\sqrt{96}$ **ii** $\sqrt{175}$ **iii** $\sqrt{128}$

> **Q13c i hint**
>
> Write the square numbers up to 100. Find a square number that is a factor of 96.

14 Work out

  a $\sqrt{9} \times \sqrt{9}$ **b** $\sqrt{36} \times \sqrt{36}$ **c** $\sqrt{17} \times \sqrt{17}$ **d** $\sqrt{21} \times \sqrt{21}$

15 Copy and complete to rationalise the denominator. Simplify your answer if possible.

  a $\dfrac{1}{\sqrt{17}} = \dfrac{1}{\sqrt{17}} \times \dfrac{\sqrt{17}}{\sqrt{17}} =$ **b** $\dfrac{3}{\sqrt{21}} = \dfrac{3}{\sqrt{21}} \times \dfrac{\sqrt{21}}{\sqrt{21}} =$

  c $\dfrac{1}{\sqrt{8}} = \dfrac{1}{\sqrt{4}\sqrt{2}} = \dfrac{1}{\square\sqrt{2}} = \dfrac{1}{\square\sqrt{2}} \times \dfrac{\sqrt{2}}{\sqrt{2}} =$ **d** $\dfrac{6}{\sqrt{20}} = \dfrac{6}{\sqrt{\square}\sqrt{\square}} = \dfrac{6}{\square\sqrt{\square}} = \dfrac{6}{\square\sqrt{\square}} \times \dfrac{\sqrt{\square}}{\sqrt{\square}} =$

Standard form

1 Are these numbers in standard form? If not, give reasons why.

  a 9.004×10^{-3} **b** 32×10^5

  c 7.3 million   **d** 0.8×10^7

> **Q1 hint**
>
> A number written in standard form looks like this.
>
>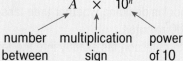
>
> $A \quad \times \quad 10^n$
>
> number between 1 and 10   multiplication sign   power of 10

2 Write each number using standard form.

  a $68\,000 = 6.8 \times 10^{\square}$

  b $94\,000\,000$

  c $801\,000$ **d** 0.000004

  e 0.0039 **f** $0.000\,000\,053$

> **Q2a hint**
>
> 6.8 lies between 1 and 10. How many times do you need to multiply by 10 to get $68\,000$?

> **Q2d hint**
>
> How many times do you need to divide by 10 to get 0.000004?

3 Work out these calculations.
The first one is started for you.

  a $(4 \times 10^2) \times (2 \times 10^7) = \underbrace{4 \times 2}_{\square} \times \underbrace{10^2 \times 10^7}_{10^{\square}} = \square \times 10^{\square}$ **b** $(3 \times 10^9) \times (2 \times 10^5)$

  c $(6 \times 10^4) \times (1 \times 10^{-2})$ **d** $(6 \times 10^8) \times (8 \times 10^4)$

  e $(7 \times 10^3) \times (8 \times 10^6)$ **f** $(8 \times 10^{-4}) \times (6 \times 10^{-2})$

> **Q3d hint**
>
> $48 = 4.8 \times 10^{\square}$

4 a Write 2.5×10^4 and 1.3×10^{-2} as ordinary numbers.

  b Use your answers to part **a** to help you work out $(2.5 \times 10^4) + (1.3 \times 10^{-2})$.

> **Q4a hint**
>
> $10^4 = 10\,000$ $10^{-2} = \frac{1}{100}$

1 Extend

1 **Problem-solving** Square A has a side length of 9.2 cm. Square B has a perimeter of 34.4 cm. Square C has an area of 80 cm^2.

   a Which square has the greatest perimeter?

   b Which square has the smallest area?

2 Show that $27^2 = 9^3 = 3^6$.

Exam-style question

3 Here are some properties of a number.
   • It is a common factor of 216 and 540.
   • It is a common multiple of 9 and 12.
   Write two numbers with these properties. **(6 marks)**

Exam tip

There are 6 marks so most of them are likely to be for showing your working.

---

4 **a** Write 48, 90 and 150 as products of their prime factors.

   b Use a Venn diagram to work out the HCF and LCM of 48, 90 and 150.

   c **Reflect** Write a sentence explaining how the diagram can be used to find the HCF and LCM of any two of the numbers.

Q4b hint

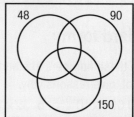

Put prime factors of all three in the very centre first.

5 A new school is deciding whether their lessons should be 30, 50 or 60 minutes.
   Each length of lesson fits exactly into the total teaching time of the school day.

   a How long is the teaching time of the school day?

   b Ryan says there is more than one answer to this question. Is Ryan correct? Explain your answer.

6 **Reasoning**

   a Use prime factors to explain why numbers ending in a zero must be divisible by 2 and 5.

   b How many zeros are there at the end of $2^4 \times 3^7 \times 5^6 \times 7^2$?

   c Use prime factors to work out $32 \times 9 \times 3125$. Write your answer as an ordinary number and in standard form.

7 Write each of these as a simplified product of powers.

   a $10^5 \times 2^3 \times 5^4 = (2 \times 5)^5 \times 2^3 \times 5^4 = 2^\square \times 5^\square \times 2^3 \times 5^4 = 2^\square \times 5^\square$

   b $6^3 \times 2^4 \times 3^3$ **c** $15^3 \times 10^4 \times 6^2$ **d** $30^4 \times 24^2 \times 15^3$

8 Every six months, new car licence plates are issued in the UK.
   A licence plate consists of two letters, then two numbers, then three letters.
   The numbers are fixed, but the letters vary.

   a If all letters can be used, how many possible combinations are there?

   b If only 21 letters can be used, how many possible combinations are there?

9 Estimate the value of 5.1^4

Q9 hint

$5.1^4 = 5.1^2 \times 5.1^2$

10 Write each answer **i** as an ordinary number **ii** in standard form.

   a Saturn has a diameter of 116 460 000 m. Convert this to kilometres.

   b The distance from the Sun to Mars is 227 900 000 km. Convert this to metres.

   c The diameter of a grain of sand is 4 μm. Convert this to metres.

   d The wavelength of an X-ray is 0.1 nm. Convert this to metres.

11 **Problem-solving** A container ship carries 1.8×10^8 kg. An aeroplane can carry 3.8×10^5 kg. What is the difference in the mass they can carry? Write your answer in standard form.

12 Work out

   a $(2.5 \times 10^3) \div (0.5 \times 10^7) + 1.265 \times 10^{-4}$ **b** $(1.2 \times 10^3)^2 - 4.3 \times 10^8$

Exam-style question

13 Work out **a** $\dfrac{5}{\sqrt{2}} + \dfrac{8}{\sqrt{32}}$ **b** $\dfrac{7}{\sqrt{72}} - \dfrac{3}{\sqrt{8}}$ **(1 mark)**

   Write each answer in the form $a\sqrt{2}$.   **(2 marks)**

Exam tip

To add and subtract fractions you need to write them with a common denominator.

---

14 Write $3^{-\frac{1}{2}}$ as a surd and rationalise the denominator.

Exam-style question

15 A restaurant offers 5 starters, 7 mains and 3 desserts. A customer can choose

   • just one course

   • any combination of two courses

   • all three courses.

   Show that a customer has 191 options altogether.

                     (3 marks)

Exam tip

Show your working clearly.

---

16 Estimate the value of

   a $(3.1 \times 10^3)^2$ **b** $\sqrt{62 \times 10^4}$ **c** $(1.9 \times 10^{-2})^3$

17 Estimate to the nearest whole number.

   a 2.7^3 **b** 1.4^3 **c** 2.1^4

   d $\sqrt[3]{40}$ **e** $\sqrt[3]{12}$ **f** $\sqrt[5]{30}$

Q17d hint

Use a number line to help.

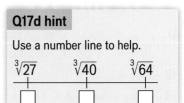

18 $(4 \times 10^x) \times (7.1 \times 10^y) \times 10^3 z = 568$

   a Work out the possible values of x, y and z.

   b Explain why there is no single solution for x, y and z.

19 **Problem-solving** $5^p = \dfrac{1}{625}$ $5^q = \dfrac{1}{\sqrt{5}}$ $5^r = 5\sqrt{5}$

   Work out the value of $p + q + r$.

20 A fraction with an integer numerator and a surd denominator rationalises to give $\dfrac{\sqrt{7}}{7}$.

   Write two different possibilities for the fraction.

1 Test ready

Summary of key points

To revise for the test:

- Read each key point, find a question on it in the mastery lesson, and check you can work out the answer.

- If you cannot, try some other questions from the mastery lesson or ask for help.

Key points

1 When there are m ways of doing one task and n ways of doing a second task, the total number of ways of doing the first task then the second task is $m \times n$. → **1.1**

2 For $\dfrac{\text{calculation 1}}{\text{calculation 2}}$ work out (calculation 1) ÷ (calculation 2) using the priority of operations. → **1.2**

3 You can round numbers to 1 or 2 significant figures to estimate the answers to calculations, including calculations with powers and roots. → **1.2**

4 You can use a **prime factor tree** to write a number as the product of its **prime factors**. → **1.3**

5 You can use a **Venn diagram** of prime factors to work out the **highest common factor** and **lowest common multiple** of two numbers. → **1.3**

6 The **prime factor decomposition** of a number is the number written as the product of its prime factors. It is usually written in index form. → **1.3**

7 The inverse of a cube is the **cube root**. → **1.4**

8 To multiply powers, add the indices: $x^m \times x^n = x^{m+n}$
To divide powers, subtract the indices: $x^m \div x^n = x^{m-n}$
To work out a power to another power, multiply the indices together: $(x^m)^n = x^{mn}$ → **1.4**

9 You can only add and subtract the indices when multiplying powers of the same number. → **1.4**

10 $x^{-n} = \dfrac{1}{x^n}$ for any number n, $x \neq 0$
$x^0 = 1$, where x is any non-zero number. → **1.5**

11 $x^{\frac{1}{n}} = \sqrt[n]{x}$ so $x^{\frac{1}{2}} = \sqrt{x}$ (square root) $x^{\frac{1}{3}} = \sqrt[3]{x}$ (cube root)
$x^{\frac{1}{4}} = \sqrt[4]{x}$ (fourth root) $x^{\frac{1}{5}} = \sqrt[5]{x}$ (fifth root) → **1.5**

12 $x^{\frac{m}{n}} = \left(\sqrt[n]{x}\right)^m$ → **1.5**

13 Some powers of 10 have a name called a prefix. Each **prefix** is represented by a letter. For example, kilo means 10^3 and is represented by the letter k, as in kg for kilogram. → **1.6**

14 A number in **standard form** is written in the form $A \times 10^n$, where A is a number between 1 and 10 and n is an integer. → **1.6**

15 To write a number in standard form:

- work out the value of A

- work out how many times A must be multiplied or divided by 10

- this is the value of n. → **1.6**

16 The symbol $\neq$ means 'not equal to'. → **1.6**

Sample student answers

Exam-style question

1 Work out $\dfrac{3.1 \times 10^{-4} + 6.2 \times 10^{3}}{4.6 \times 10^{-2}}$

Give your answer in standard form, correct to 3 significant figures. **(2 marks)**

$$\frac{0.000\,31 + 6200}{0.046} = \frac{6200.000\,31}{0.046}$$
$$= 135\,000$$

The student will probably only get 1 mark. Why?

Exam-style question

2 Work out $\dfrac{1}{\sqrt{3}} \div \dfrac{2}{\sqrt{6}}$

Give your answer in the form $\dfrac{\sqrt{a}}{b}$ where a and b are integers. **(3 marks)**

$$\frac{1}{\sqrt{3}} \div \frac{2}{\sqrt{6}} = \frac{1}{\sqrt{3}} \times \frac{2}{\sqrt{6}}$$
$$= \frac{2}{\sqrt{3}\,\sqrt{6}}$$
$$= \frac{2}{\sqrt{3} \times \sqrt{3} \times \sqrt{2}}$$
$$= \frac{2}{3\sqrt{2}}$$
$$= \frac{2}{3\sqrt{2}} \times \frac{\sqrt{2}}{\sqrt{2}}$$
$$= \frac{2\sqrt{2}}{3 \times 2}$$
$$= \frac{\sqrt{2}}{3}$$

What mistake has the student made?
Has the student given their answer in the correct form?

1 Unit test

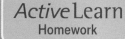

Active Learn
Homework

1 $6.23 \times 5.4 = 33.642$

   a Write down one more multiplication with an answer of 33.642. **(1 mark)**

   b Write down a division with an answer of 0.623. **(1 mark)**

2 List these numbers in order, starting with the smallest.
Show your working.

   3.4^2 $\sqrt[3]{27}$ $\sqrt{69}$ 13.74 **(3 marks)**

3 **a** Write 42 as a product of its prime factors. **(2 marks)**

   b Use your answer to write 84^3 as a product of its prime factors in index form. **(2 marks)**

4 Work out the HCF and LCM of 75 and 30. **(3 marks)**

5 Ben and Sadie are doing a sponsored walk around a circuit.
Ben takes 25 minutes to do one circuit and Sadie takes 45 minutes.
They start together at 9.30 am.
When will they next cross the start line together? **(2 marks)**

6 **a** Estimate $(17.9 - \sqrt{36.13}) \times 3.89$ **(1 mark)**

   b Use a calculator to work out the answer.
Give your answer correct to 1 decimal place. **(1 mark)**

7 Find the value of a.

   a $5^3 \times 5^a = 5^9$ **(1 mark)**

   b $6^a \div 6^{-5} = 6^8$ **(1 mark)**

   c $8^a \times 8^a = 8^4$ **(1 mark)**

8 Write $\dfrac{(3^8)^4}{3^2}$ as a single power. **(2 marks)**

9 Use prime factors to determine whether 2520 is divisible by 18. **(2 marks)**

10 Write each number in standard form.

   a 0.000 000 65 **(1 mark)**

   b 320×10^7 **(1 mark)**

   c 0.9 million **(1 mark)**

11 Write $\left(\frac{4}{3}\right)^{-2}$ as a fraction in its simplest form. **(2 marks)**

12 Let $x = 1.2 \times 10^5$ and $y = 6 \times 10^4$. Work out

   a $x + y$ **(1 mark)**

   b $x - y$ **(1 mark)**

   c xy **(1 mark)**

   d $\dfrac{y}{x}$ **(1 mark)**

   Write your answers in standard form.

13 Find the value of

   a $400^{\frac{1}{2}}$ **(1 mark)**

   b $100^{\frac{3}{2}}$ **(2 marks)**

14 Work out the value of x when

   a $9^{18} = 27^{x}$ **(2 marks)**

   b $8^{\frac{1}{2}} \times 2^{x} = 16^{\frac{2}{3}}$ **(2 marks)**

15 Work out the area of this shape.
Write your answer as a simplified surd.

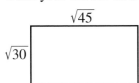

                                                         (3 marks)

16 How many different 4-digit odd numbers are there, where the first digit is not zero?

                                                         (3 marks)

17 Rationalise the denominator.

   $\dfrac{8}{\sqrt{6}}$ **(2 marks)**

18 One sheet of paper is 9×10^{-3} cm thick.
Mark wants to put 500 sheets of paper into the paper tray of his printer.
The paper tray is 4 cm deep.
Is the paper tray deep enough for 500 sheets of paper?
You must explain your answer.   **(3 marks)**

                                                      (TOTAL: 50 marks)

19 **Challenge** $(4 \times 10^{a}) \times (7.1 \times 10^{b}) \times 10^{3}c = 5.68 \times 10^{-3}$

   a Write down a possible set of values for a, b and c.

   b Which value(s) can change? Explain.

20 **Reflect** Look back at the work you did in this unit.
Which topic did you find most difficult?
Choose two or three questions you found difficult to answer in that topic.
Work with a classmate (and/or your teacher) to better understand how to answer
these questions.
(This is a good thing to do at the end of every unit.)

2 Algebra

Prior knowledge

2.1 Algebraic indices

- Use the rules of indices to simplify algebraic expressions.

*Active*Learn
Homework

Warm up

1 **Fluency** Evaluate

  a $16^{\frac{1}{2}}$ **b** $8^{\frac{1}{3}}$ **c** $16^{\frac{1}{4}}$ **d** $32^{\frac{1}{5}}$

2 Write as a power of 2.

  a $2^3 \times 2^4$ **b** $2^5 \div 2^2$ **c** $(2^3)^4$ **d** $\frac{1}{2}$

3 Write as a power of a single number.

  a $\dfrac{10^4 \times 10^3}{10^2}$ **b** $\dfrac{5^{-2}}{5^{-4}}$ **c** $(5^{-2})^3 \times 5^9$ **d** $\dfrac{(3^{10})^{\frac{1}{2}}}{3^2}$

Key point

$x^m \times x^n = x^{m+n}$

4 Simplify

  a $x^3 \times x^4 = \overbrace{x \times x \times x}^{3} \times \overbrace{x \times x \times x \times x}^{4} = x^{\square}$ **b** $x^2 \times x^5$

  c $a^7 \times a^4$ **d** $y^2 \times y^3 \times y^4$ **e** $t^3 \times t \times t^5$

5 Simplify

  a $2a^3 \times 3a^5 = 2 \times 3 \times a^3 \times a^5 =$ **b** $4c \times 2c^5$ **c** $4n^2 \times 10n^5$

  d $v^3 \times 7v^2$ **e** $5s^2t \times 3s^3t^5$ **f** $2pq^2 \times 5p^2q^3 \times 3p^3q$

Key point

$x^m \div x^n = x^{m-n}$

6 Simplify

  a $x^5 \div x^3 = \dfrac{x^5}{x^3} = \dfrac{\cancel{x} \times \cancel{x} \times \cancel{x} \times x \times x}{\cancel{x} \times \cancel{x} \times \cancel{x}} = x^{\square}$ **b** $x^7 \div x^4$ **c** $\dfrac{p^8}{p^5}$

  d $y^7 \div y$ **e** $\dfrac{r^{10}}{r^9}$ **f** $\dfrac{t^3 \times t^5}{t^6}$ **g** $\dfrac{n^3 \times n \times n^2}{n^4}$

7 Simplify

  a $\dfrac{14g^{10}}{7g^8}$ **b** $\dfrac{6f^5}{2f}$ **c** $6x^4 \div 2x^2$ **d** $12w^7 \div 4w^5$

  e $\dfrac{16a^2b}{8ab}$ **f** $\dfrac{20a^2b^2}{4ab}$ **g** $\dfrac{20m^3t^5}{5m^2t^2}$ **h** $\dfrac{15r^5s^3}{5r^3s}$

8 Simplify

  a $(x^3)^2 = x^3 \times x^3 = \square$ **b** $(x^6)^3$

  c $(t^3)^3$ **d** $(j^2)^9$

9 **Reasoning** Which of these expressions are equivalent?

    $9x^2 \times x^3$ $(3x^2)^3$ $(3x^3)^2$ $27x^6$ $(-3x^3)^2$ $3x^3 \times 9x^2$

10 Simplify

  a $(2r^2)^3$ **b** $(3f^4)^2$ **c** $\left(\dfrac{b^2}{2}\right)^3$ **d** $(np)^2$

  e $(np)^3$ **f** $(n^2p)^3$ **g** $(2xy)^3$ **h** $(2xy^4)^3$

Exam-style question

11 **a** Simplify $t^3 \times t^5$ **(1 mark)**

    b Simplify $(4xy^2)^3$ **(2 marks)**

    c Simplify $\dfrac{18a^5 b^3}{6a^3 b}$ **(2 marks)**

Exam tip

In part **b**, everything inside the brackets is cubed.

12 **a** Multiply or divide each pair of expressions connected by a line in this diagram. Divide in the direction of the arrow.

    b **Reflect** Explain which pair of expressions was easiest to multiply/divide. Why?

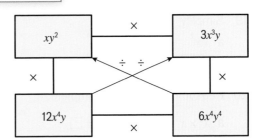

13 Simplify

  a $(2x^2y^3)^3$ **b** $(6x^5y^2)^2$ **c** $(3x^2y)^4$ **d** $\left(\dfrac{2x^4y^5}{3xy^3}\right)^2$

14 **Reasoning** Copy and complete.

  a $x^3 \div x^3 = x^{\square - \square} = x^{\square}$

    $x^3 \div x^3 = \dfrac{x^3}{x^3} = \square$

    Therefore $x^{\square} = \square$

  b $x^3 \div x^4 = \dfrac{x \times x \times x}{x \times x \times x \times x} = \dfrac{\square}{\square}$

    $x^3 \div x^4 = x^{\square - \square} = x^{\square}$

    Therefore $x^{\square} = \dfrac{\square}{\square}$

  c $x^3 \div x^5 = \dfrac{x \times x \times x}{x \times x \times x \times x \times x} = \dfrac{\square}{\square}$

    $x^3 \div x^5 = x^{\square - \square} = x^{\square}$

    Therefore $x^{\square} = \dfrac{\square}{\square}$

15 Simplify

a b^{-1} **b** h^{-2} **c** y^{-3} **d** p^0

e $a^3 \times a^{-1}$ **f** $\dfrac{a^3}{a^{-1}}$ **g** $\dfrac{4x^3y}{2xy^{-1}}$ **h** $4x^3y \times 2x^{-2}y^{-1}$

Exam-style question

16 a Simplify $3c^2d^3 \times 4cd^{-2}$ **(2 marks)**

    b $x^4 \times x^n = x^7$

    Find the value of n.   **(1 mark)**

    c $\dfrac{a^5 \times a^m}{a^2} = a^{-1}$

    Find the value of m.   **(2 marks)**

---

17 Simplify

a $\left(t^2\right)^{-3}$ **b** $\left(x^{-1}\right)^{-2}$ **c** $\left(q^2\right)^0$ **d** $\left(w^{-1}\right)^{-1}$

18 Simplify

a $\left(x^7y^2\right)^0$ **b** $\left(e^2f^3\right)^{-1}$ **c** $\left(2p^5q\right)^{-2}$ **d** $\left(\dfrac{2u^4}{5v^3}\right)^{-1}$

e $\left(a^{-2}b\right)^{-1}$ **f** $\left(3pq^{-4}\right)^{-2}$ **g** $\left(2s^{-3}t\right)^{-2}$ **h** $\left(5s^{-3}t^2\right)^{-2}$

19 Simplify

a $\sqrt{x^2}$ **b** $\sqrt{x^4}$ **c** $\sqrt{9x^2}$ **d** $\sqrt{9x^4}$

e $\sqrt{4x^6}$ **f** $\sqrt{4x^8}$ **g** $\sqrt{36x^2y^4}$ **h** $\sqrt{16x^4y^6}$

20 Reasoning Copy and complete.

a $x^{\frac{1}{2}} \times x^{\frac{1}{2}} = x^{\square + \square} = x^{\square} = \square$

    $\sqrt{x} \times \sqrt{x} = \square$

    Therefore $x^{\frac{1}{2}} = \square$

b $x^{\frac{1}{3}} \times x^{\frac{1}{3}} \times x^{\frac{1}{3}} = x^{\square + \square + \square} = x^{\square} = \square$

    $\sqrt[3]{x} \times \sqrt[3]{x} \times \sqrt[3]{x} = \square$

    Therefore $x^{\frac{1}{3}} = \square$

Key point

$x^{\frac{1}{n}} = \sqrt[n]{x}$ and $x^{\frac{m}{n}} = \left(\sqrt[n]{x}\right)^m$

---

21 Simplify

a $x^{\frac{1}{2}} \times x$ **b** $x^{\frac{1}{2}} \times x^{\frac{3}{2}}$ **c** $y^{\frac{1}{3}} \times y^{\frac{2}{3}}$ **d** $y^{\frac{1}{3}} \times y^{\frac{4}{3}}$

22 Simplify

a $\left(16b^2\right)^{\frac{1}{2}}$ **b** $\left(8c^3\right)^{\frac{1}{3}}$ **c** $\left(16c^6\right)^{\frac{1}{2}}$ **d** $\left(16c^6d^4\right)^{-\frac{1}{2}}$

e $\left(4x^{-2}y^8\right)^{-\frac{1}{2}}$ **f** $\left(16d^4\right)^{-\frac{1}{4}}$ **g** $\left(32x^{10}y^{-5}\right)^{-\frac{1}{5}}$

23 Simplify

a $\dfrac{x^{\frac{1}{2}}}{x^{\frac{1}{2}}}$ **b** $\dfrac{x^{\frac{3}{2}}}{x^{\frac{1}{2}}}$ **c** $\dfrac{r^{\frac{5}{2}}}{r}$ **d** $\dfrac{r^{\frac{5}{2}}}{r^2}$

e $\dfrac{6p^{\frac{1}{2}}}{2p^{\frac{3}{2}}}$ **f** $\dfrac{10p^{\frac{3}{2}}}{5p^{\frac{1}{2}}}$ **g** $\left(4a^2\right)^{\frac{3}{2}}$ **h** $\left(9a^2b^4\right)^{\frac{3}{2}}$

2.2 Expanding and factorising

*Active*Learn
Homework

- Expand brackets.
- Factorise algebraic expressions.

Warm up

1 Fluency Expand

a $4(x+2)$ **b** $3(q-5)$ **c** $7(2m+1)$ **d** $-2(y+6)$

2 Simplify   **a** $4a+2+5a+3$ **b** $3x+5-2x-1$ **c** $4r+2s-4r+3s$

3 Factorise

a $5x+15$ **b** $10y+25$ **c** x^2-x **d** $3y^2+y$

4 Reasoning a Write down an expression containing brackets for the area of the rectangle.

   b Copy and complete the diagram to show the areas of the two small rectangles.

   c What do you notice about your answers to parts **a** and **b** ?

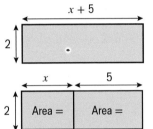

Key point

The $\equiv$ symbol shows an identity. In an **identity** the two expressions are equal for *all* values of the variables. $2(x+5) \equiv 2x+10$ is an identity.

An **equation**, such as $2x=6$, is only true for certain values of x (in this case $x=3$).

5 Reasoning State whether each relation is an equation or an identity. Rewrite the identities using $\equiv$

a $x \times x = x^2$ **b** $3x+4x-x = 6x$ **c** $3x-1 = 2x+1$ **d** $\dfrac{6x}{3} = 2x$

6 Reasoning By drawing rectangles show that

a $3x(x+4) \equiv 3x^2+12x$ **b** $x(2y+z) \equiv 2xy+xz$ **c** $x(y+z) \equiv xy+xz$

7 Expand

a $x(x+7)$ **b** $y(y^2-3)$ **c** $2y(y^2-3)$ **d** $t(2t-4)$

e $t(2t-w)$ **f** $st(1+w)$ **g** $3st(tw+3)$ **h** $3st(st+5)$

8 Expand and simplify, by collecting like terms.

a $6(e+3)+2e$ **b** $6y+2(y+7)$ **c** $4x-2(x+5)$

d $6(m+2)+3(m+5)$ **e** $3(2x+7)-5(x+4)$ **f** $2(5x+y)+3(x+2y)$

9 Expand and simplify

a $4y(y-3)+7y$ **b** $7t^2+3t(t-2)$ **c** $8t^2-(3t+2)$

d $2p(p+q)-q(p-q)$ **e** $2w-w(1-3w)$ **f** $5e(e+f)-2f(e-f)$

Exam-style question

10 Expand and simplify $3(1+4x)-2(x-5)$ **(2 marks)**

11 Find the HCF, by finding the HCF of the numbers, then the letters.

  a $4x$ and $6xy$ **b** $3xy$ and $5x$ **c** $8xy$ and $12y$ **d** $5x^2y$ and $10xy^2$

12 Factorise completely. Then expand again to check your answer.

  a $2x+12$ **b** $4x+6y$ **c** $4x+6xy$ **d** $3ab-5b$

  e $7xy+7xz$ **f** $ab-abc$ **g** t^3+2t^2 **h** $6p^2q-9pq$

  i $3x^2z+12xz$ **j** $20jk^2-15j^2k$ **k** $12pqr-10pqs$ **l** $8d^2ef+10def^2$

Exam-style question

13 **a** Expand $4x(2x-5y)$ **(1 mark)**

  b Factorise completely $4cp-6cp^2$ **(1 mark)**

  c Simplify $\sqrt{9m^4n^6}$ **(2 marks)**

14 **a** What is the HCF of $4(s+2t)^2$ and $8(s+2t)$?

  b Copy and complete.

$$4(s+2t)^2-8(s+2t) = \square(s+2t)[(s+2t)-\square]$$
$$= \square(s+2t)(s+2t-\square)$$

15 Factorise completely

  a $14(p+1)^2+21(p+1)$ **b** $5(c+1)^2-10(c+1)$ **c** $12(y+4)^2-8(y+4)$

  d $(a+3b)^2-2(a+3b)$ **e** $5(f+5)+10f(f+5)$ **f** $5(a+b)^2-10(a+b)$

Key point

Consecutive integers are one after the other.
Any even integer is in the 2 times table and can be written as $2n$ for some value of n.

Example

Show algebraically that the product of any two consecutive integers is divisible by 2.

> One of these two numbers must be even,
> so it can be written as $2m$ for some whole number, m.
> If the other number is n then their product is
> $2m \times n = 2mn$
> $2mn$ has a factor of 2 so it is divisible by 2.

Numbers 1, 2, 3, 4, 5, ... are odd, even, odd, even, odd, etc. so a pair of consecutive numbers must contain one odd and one even.

16 **Reasoning**

  a In three consecutive numbers, at least one is even and one is a multiple of 3. Choose two different sets of three consecutive integers and show that this is true.

  b Show algebraically that the product of three consecutive integers is divisible by 6.

  c What happens for four consecutive integers? Can you use algebra to show it?

17 **a** Explain why two consecutive integers can be written as $2m$ and $2m+1$ or $2n-1$ and $2n$.

  b Show algebraically that the sum of two consecutive integers is always odd.

2.3 Equations

Active Learn
Homework

- Solve equations involving brackets and numerical fractions.
- Use equations to solve problems.

Warm up

1 Fluency Write down the lowest common multiple (LCM) of
  a 2 and 3   **b** 6 and 8   **c** 2, 3 and 12

2 Expand and simplify
  a $2(4x+3)$ **b** $2(3x+1)+3(5x-2)$ **c** $2(2x+1)-3(4x-5)$

3 Solve these equations.
  a $4x-5=23$ **b** $3(7x+4)=33$ **c** $\dfrac{2x}{7}=6$

4 **a** Copy and complete to begin to solve the equation.
    b Solve the equation.

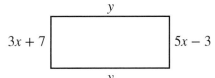

5 Solve
  a $2x+4=x+9$ **b** $5x+3=7x-5$ **c** $x-5=3x-25$ **d** $11x-7=9x-11$

Exam-style question

6 Here is a rectangle.
All measurements are in centimetres.
The area of the rectangle is $84\,\text{cm}^2$.
Show that $y=4$ **(4 marks)**

                                  y

$3x+7$ $5x-3$

                                      y

7 **a** Expand
    i $4(3x-4)$ **ii** $7(x-3)$
  b Use your answers to part **a** to solve $4(3x-4)=7(x-3)$.

8 **a** Expand and simplify $2(3x+5)-3(x-2)$
  b Use your answer to part **a** to solve $2(3x+5)-3(x-2)=25$.

9 Solve these equations.
  a $2(3x-1)+5(x+3)=24$ **b** $2(x-1)-(3x-4)=3$

Exam-style question

10 Solve $4x+3=2(x-5)$.   **(3 marks)**

Exam tip

Unless a question asks for a decimal answer, give non-integer solutions to an equation as exact fractions.

11 Solve

a $2(4x-1)+3(x+2)=1$ **b** $4(2x+3)=5(3x-2)$ **c** $3(2x+9)=2(4x-1)$

d $9x-2(3x-5)=6$ **e** $5(4x-3)-(6-5x)=0$ **f** $7(3-5x)=2(x-6)$

g Explain why the fraction solution for part **a** is more accurate than the decimal.

12 Copy and complete to begin to solve the equation. Then solve the equation.

$$\times 4\left(\frac{7x-1}{4}=5\right)\times 4$$
$$7x-1=\square$$

13 Solve

a $\dfrac{5x-3}{2}=11$ **b** $9=\dfrac{4x+5}{3}$ **c** $\dfrac{4-x}{7}=3$ **d** $\dfrac{6-5x}{2}=14$

e $\dfrac{9x-2}{5}=3x$ **f** $\dfrac{3-2x}{4}=1+x$ **g** $\dfrac{7x+11}{2}=3x+1$ **h** $\dfrac{5-3x}{6}=2x-7$

14 Copy and complete to begin to solve the equation. Then solve the equation.

$$\times (x-4)\left(\frac{10}{x-4}=3\right)\times (x-4)$$
$$\square=\square(x-4)$$

15 Solve

a $\dfrac{8}{x-3}=2$ **b** $3=\dfrac{12}{x+6}$ **c** $\dfrac{5}{x+2}=7$ **d** $\dfrac{11}{2x-1}=4$

16 Copy and complete to begin to solve the equation. Then solve the equation.

$$\times 9\left(\frac{2x+1}{3}=\frac{x-5}{9}\right)\times 9$$
$$\frac{9(2x+1)}{3}=\square-\square$$
$$\square(2x+1)=x-5$$

17 a Reasoning By multiplying both sides of the equation $\dfrac{x}{2}-\dfrac{x}{3}=\dfrac{7}{12}$ by 12, and cancelling, show that $6x-4x=7$. Then solve the equation.

b In **Q16** and **Q17a**, how could you choose the number to multiply by?

> **Key point**
>
> To solve an equation involving fractions, multiply each term on both sides by the LCM of the denominators.

18 Solve these equations.

a $\dfrac{b-4}{2}=\dfrac{b+1}{4}$ **b** $\dfrac{n}{2}-\dfrac{n}{5}=\dfrac{3}{10}$ **c** $\dfrac{c-1}{4}+\dfrac{c+1}{8}=\dfrac{3}{2}$

d $\dfrac{2}{3x+1}=5$ **e** $\dfrac{x-1}{3}+\dfrac{x+1}{2}+\dfrac{x}{6}=7$

19 Problem-solving Find the size of the smallest angle in the triangle.

2.4 Formulae

- Substitute numbers into formulae.
- Rearrange formulae.
- Distinguish between expressions, equations, formulae and identities.

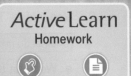

Active Learn
Homework

Warm up

1 **Fluency** Use the formula $A = lw$ to calculate the area of a rectangle of length $3\,m$ and width $2\,m$.

2 **a** Write 75 million in standard form. **b** Write 3×10^8 as an ordinary number.

3 Use a calculator to work out 1.05^4. Round your answer to 2 decimal places.

Key point

An **expression** contains letter and/or number terms but no equals sign,
e.g. $2ab$, $2ab + 3a^2b$, $2ab - 7$
An **equation** has an equals sign, letter terms and numbers.
You can solve it to find the value of the letter, e.g. $2x - 4 = 9x + 1$

An **identity** is true for all values of the letters, e.g. $\dfrac{4x}{2} \equiv 2x$, $x(x+y) \equiv x^2 + xy$

A **formula** has an equals sign and letters to represent different quantities, e.g. $A = \pi r^2$
The letters are **variables** as their values can vary.

4 Write whether each of these is an expression, an equation, an identity or a formula.

    a $E = mc^2$ **b** $4x + 7 = 2x$ **c** $2v$ **d** $2(x + y) = 2x + 2y$

    e $2p^2q^3$ **f** $C = 2\pi r$ **g** πd **h** $2\pi r = 7$

    i $(uv^2)^4 = u^4v^8$ **j** $\dfrac{2x}{5} = 9$

    k **Reflect** Write your own examples of an expression, an equation, an identity and a formula. Beside each one, write how you know what it is.

5 **Problem-solving** x office workers send an email to each other.

    a Starting with smaller numbers, look for a pattern.

             2 workers   3 workers   4 workers

             A   B   A   B   C

    emails

             B   A   B C A C A B

    number of emails 2×1 3×2

    b Write an expression for the number of emails sent by x workers.

6 Use the formula $Q = 2P^3$ to work out the value of Q when

    a $P = 10$ **b** $P = -1$

7 Use the formula $D = 2X^2 + Y$ to work out the value of D when

  a $X = 10$ and $Y = 150$ **b** $X = -2$ and $Y = 0$

8 **Reasoning** The instructions describe how to cook a joint of beef.

> Cook for 30 minutes at 220°C, followed by 40 minutes per kilogram at 160°C

  a Work out the total time taken to cook a 2.5 kg joint of beef.

  b Write a formula for the total time, T (minutes) to cook m kg of beef.

9 **Problem-solving**

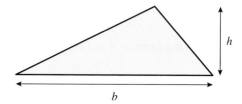

  a Write a formula, in terms of b and h, for the area, A, of the triangle.

  b Use the formula to work out the value of

    i A when $b = 6$ and $h = 3$

    ii b when $A = 20$ and $h = 4$

10 **Future skills** An amount £P is put into a bank account paying r% interest. After n years the value of the savings, S, is given by the formula

$$S = P\left(1 + \frac{r}{100}\right)^n$$

Joe invests £10 000 in this account in January 2020. The interest rate is 4.6%. How much will his investment be worth in January 2025? Give your answer to the nearest penny.

11 **Problem-solving** A car, initially travelling at a speed of u m/s, accelerates at a constant rate of a m/s². The distance, s, travelled in t seconds is given by the formula

$$s = ut + \frac{1}{2}at^2$$

  a A car joins a motorway travelling at 10 m/s and has a constant acceleration of 0.6 m/s². Work out the distance travelled by the car in 20 s.

  b Work out the acceleration of a Formula 1 car which starts from rest $(u = 0)$ and travels 70 m in 2.5 s.

Key point

The **subject** of a formula is the letter on its own, on one side of the equals sign.

Example

a Make s the subject of the formula $v^2 = u^2 + 2as$

b Make x the subject of the formula $y = \dfrac{ax + b}{c}$

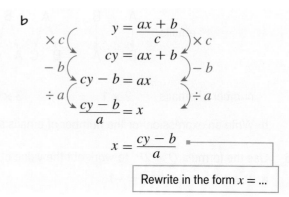

12 Change the subject of each formula to the letter(s) given in the brackets.

a $v = u + at$ [a]

b $E = m - 2n$ [n]

c $W = \dfrac{3G}{H}$ [G]

d $R = \dfrac{Q}{7} + C$ [Q]

e $T = \dfrac{V - W}{3}$ [V, then W]

f $s = ut + \frac{1}{2}at^2$ [a, then u]

Exam-style question

13 $v^2 = u^2 + 2as$

$u = 7$, $a = -2$, $s = 12$

a Work out a value of v.   **(2 marks)**

b Make a the subject of $v^2 = u^2 + 2as$ **(2 marks)**

---

 14 The formula $F = \dfrac{9C}{5} + 32$ is used to convert temperatures from degrees Celsius to degrees Fahrenheit.

    a Convert 28 °C into degrees Fahrenheit.

    b Make C the subject of the formula.

    c Convert 104 °F into degrees Celsius.

15 **a** Make T the subject of the formula $S = \dfrac{D}{T}$

    b Sometimes the distance between Earth and Mars is about 57.6 million kilometres.
The speed of light is approximately 3×10^8 m/s.
Estimate the time taken for light to travel from Mars to Earth.

 16 **Reasoning** The formula $d = \sqrt{2Rh}$, where $R \approx 6.7 \times 10^6$ metres is the radius of the Earth, gives the approximate distance to the horizon of someone whose eyes are h metres above sea level. Use this formula to estimate the distance (to the nearest metre) to the horizon of someone who is 1.7 m tall who stands

    a at sea level

    b on the summit of Mount Taranaki, New Zealand, which is 2518 m above sea level

---

Exam-style question

17 $P = \sqrt{\dfrac{x}{l^3}}$

$x = 3.8 \times 10^{-5}$

$l = 5.1 \times 10^{-2}$

    a Work out the value of P.
Give your answer in standard form correct to 3 significant figures.   **(2 marks)**

    b x is increased by 5%.
l is increased by 10%.
Tanya says, 'The value of P will increase because both x and l are increased.'
Tanya is wrong. Explain why.   **(2 marks)**

2.5 Linear sequences

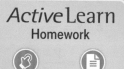

*Active*Learn
Homework

- Find the general term or nth term of an arithmetic sequence.
- Determine whether a particular number is a term of a given arithmetic sequence.

Warm up

1 Fluency What is the next term in the sequence 3.7, 4.1, 4.5, 4.9, 5.3, ...?

2 Work out the outputs when each of these numbers is used as an input to this function machine.

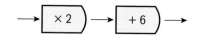

a 0 **b** 5 **c** 10

3 Write down the previous term and the next term in this sequence.

$\square$, 7, 10, 13, 16, 19, 22, $\square$, ...

Key point

The **nth term** of a sequence tells you how to work out the term at position n (any position). It is also called the **general term** of the sequence.

4 Write down the first five terms of the sequence with nth term

a $2n$ **b** $3n+1$ **c** $-4n$ **d** $-2n+3$

Key point

u_n denotes the nth term of a sequence. u_1 is the first term, u_2 is the second term, and so on.

5 Work out the 1st, 2nd, 3rd, 10th and 100th terms of the sequence with nth term

a $u_n = 5n - 3$ **b** $u_n = 7 + 3n$ **c** $u_n = 100 - 2n$ **d** $u_n = \frac{1}{2}n + 2$

Key point

In an **arithmetic sequence**, the terms increase (or decrease) by a fixed number called the **common difference**.

6 For each arithmetic sequence, work out the common difference and hence find the 3rd term.

> **Q6 hint**
>
> 'Hence' means 'use what you have just found to help you'.

a 0.63, 0.65, ... **b** $\frac{1}{4}, \frac{3}{4}, \ldots$

c 2, −3, ... **d** 0.569, 1.569, ...

7 Reasoning

a Find the common difference for each sequence in **Q4** and **Q5**.

b Where does the common difference appear in the nth term?

c Predict the common difference for each sequence.

  i nth term $5n - 2$ **ii** $u_n = -3n + 4$

d Work out the first three terms of each sequence to check your predictions.

Example

a Work out the nth term of the sequence 3, 7, 11, 15, ...

b Is 45 a term of the sequence?

a

$$+4 \quad +4$$
$$3, \quad 7, \quad 11, \quad 15, \quad ...$$
$$4n \quad 4, \quad 8, \quad 12, \quad 16, \quad ... \Big) -1$$

> The common difference is 4. Write out the first five terms of the sequence for $4n$, the multiples of 4. Work out how to get from each term in $4n$ to the term in the sequence.

The nth term is $4n - 1$

b $\quad 45 = 4n - 1$

> Write an equation using the nth term and solve it.

$\quad 46 = 4n$

$\quad 11.5 = n$

45 cannot be in the sequence because 11.5 is not an integer.

> There is an 11th term and a 12th term but not an 11.5th term.

8 Write down, in terms of n, expressions for the nth term of these arithmetic sequences.

　a 3, 5, 7, 9, 11, ...　　**b** 14, 18, 22, 26, 30, ...　　**c** 2, 12, 22, 32, 42, ...

　d 13, 10, 7, 4, 1, ...　　**e** 56, 53, 50, 47, ...　　**f** 3.2, 4.5, 5.8, 7.1, ...

9 **Reasoning**

　a Show that 596 is a term of the arithmetic sequence 5, 8, 11, 14, ...

　b Show that 139 cannot be a term of the arithmetic sequence 4, 11, 18, 25, ...

　c **Reflect** Explain how the worked example helped you to answer this question.

10 Here are the first five terms of an arithmetic sequence.

　　3, 9, 15, 21, 27

　a Find an expression, in terms of n, for the nth term of this sequence.

　b Ben says that 150 is in the sequence.
　　Is Ben right? Explain your answer.

11 **Problem-solving** Find the 100th term of this sequence.
　　0.05, 0.09, 0.13, 0.17, ...

12 **Reasoning** The nth term of the sequence 5, 13, 21, 29, 37, ... is $8n - 3$.

　a Solve $8n - 3 = 1000$

　b Use your answer to part **a** to find the first term in the sequence that is greater than 1000.

13 **Reasoning**

　a Find the first term in the arithmetic sequence 2, 11, 20, 29, 38, ... that is greater than 4000.

　b Find the first term in the arithmetic sequence 400, 387, 374, 361, ... that is less than 51.

14 **Problem-solving** Frank weighs 100 kg. He goes on a diet and loses 0.4 kg a week.
　After how many weeks will Frank weigh less than 89 kg?

15 **Problem-solving** Martina trains for a marathon. In her first week of training she runs 5 miles.
　Each week after that she increases her run by 0.8 miles.
　How many weeks of training will it take before she runs more than 26 miles?

Unit 2 Algebra　　43

16 **Reasoning** The nth term of an arithmetic sequence is $u_n = 7n + 3$.

    a Write down the values of the first four terms, u_1, u_2, u_3, u_4.

    b Write down the value of the common difference, d.

    c By substituting $n = 0$, work out the value of the zero term, u_0.

    d What do you notice about your answers to parts **b** and **c**, and the numbers that appear in the formula, $u_n = 7n + 3$?

    e Find the zero term of each sequence in **Q5**.

> **Key point**
>
> The nth term of an arithmetic sequence = common difference $\times n$ + zero term

17 **a** Work out the zero term in this sequence. $\square$,   1,   5,   9,   13,   ...

                                         u_0 u_1 u_2 u_3 u_4

    b Find u_n.

18 Here are the first four terms in a sequence.

    $\frac{1}{2}, \frac{3}{4}, \frac{5}{6}, \frac{7}{8}$

    a Find the nth term of the numerators.   **b** Find the nth term of the denominators.

    c Hence find the nth term of the sequence.

19 Find the nth term, u_n, of each sequence.

    a $\frac{7}{4}, \frac{12}{8}, \frac{17}{12}, \frac{22}{16}, \cdots$ **b** $\frac{2}{5}, \frac{5}{7}, \frac{8}{9}, \frac{11}{11}, \cdots$

20 **Reasoning**

    a Find the outputs when the terms in each of these arithmetic sequences are used as inputs to the function machine.

      i 2, 5, 8, 11, 14, ...   **ii** 10, 20, 30, 40, 50, ...

    b Compare the common differences for each input sequence with the common difference for the output sequence. How are these related to the operations used in the function machine?

> **Key point**
>
> When an arithmetic sequence with common difference d is input into this function machine, the output sequence has common difference $p \times d$.

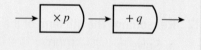

21 **Reasoning** In this function machine, the input sequence is 3, 7, 11. The output sequence is 10, 18, 26.

    a Work out the common difference for the input sequence.

    b Work out the common difference for the output sequence.

    c Use your answers to parts **a** and **b** to find the value of p in the function machine.

    d Work out the value of q.

22 **Reasoning** Find the values of p and q in this function machine.

2.6 Non-linear sequences

- Solve problems using geometric sequences.
- Work out terms in Fibonacci sequences.
- Find the nth term of a quadratic sequence.

*Active*Learn
Homework

Warm up

1 Fluency Find the next term of each sequence.

a 1, 2, 4, 7, 11, 16, 22, ...   b 0.25, 1, 4, 16, ...

2 Find the term-to-term rule and work out the missing numbers in these geometric sequences.

a 3, 6, 12, 24, ☐, ☐, ...   b 81, ☐, 9, 3, 1, ☐, ...

c 2, −6, ☐, −54, 162, −486 , ...

3 a Increase £1200 by 4%.

b Decrease £180 by 15%.

Key point

In a **Fibonacci sequence** the term-to-term rule is 'add the two previous terms to get the next one'.

4 a Find the next three terms in each of these Fibonacci sequences.

i 2, 3, ☐, ☐, ☐, ...   ii 1, 4, ☐, ☐, ☐, ...   iii −2, 1, ☐, ☐, ☐, ...

b Is a Fibonacci sequence an arithmetic sequence? Explain.

Key point

In a **geometric sequence** the terms increase (or decrease) by a **constant multiplier**.

5 a Write down the first four terms of each sequence.

i $u_n = \dfrac{1}{n}$ ii $u_n = 2^n$ iii $u_n = 0.3^n$

b Which of these are geometric sequences?

6 Write down the first five terms of these geometric sequences.

a First term $= \sqrt{2}$; term-to-term rule is 'multiply by $\sqrt{2}$'

b First term $= 3$; term-to-term rule is 'multiply by $2\sqrt{3}$'

7 Here are the first four terms of a geometric sequence.

1, 3, 9, 27

$u_1 = 1$

$u_2 = 1 \times 3$

$u_3 = 1 \times 3^2$

Continue the pattern to show that the 10th term of the geometric sequence is $u_{10} = 3^9$.

8 Write an expression for the 10th term of each geometric sequence.

    a 1, 2, 4, 8, ...

    b 10, 100, 1000, 10 000, ...

    c 5000, 2500, 1250, 625, ...

    d $5, 5\sqrt{5}, 25, 25\sqrt{5}, ...$

9 **Reasoning** Ian is a millionaire. He promises to donate £10 to charity one month, £20 the next month, £40 the next month and so on.

    a Write the amounts as a sequence.

    b Predict the number of months until Ian donates over £1000.

Q9b hint

'Predict' means make a good guess about what might happen. Check your guess and improve it if you need to.

10 **Reasoning** The nth term of a sequence is $u_n = 10^n$. Show that the product of u_5 and u_8 is u_{13}.

Exam-style question

11 **a** Write down the first four terms in the sequence with nth term $u_n = 2^n$ **(2 marks)**

      b Use algebra to show that the product of any two terms in the sequence is also a term in the sequence.

                                       (2 marks)

Exam tip

The question refers to *any* two terms so no credit is given for just checking it out for particular numbers.

Key point

A **quadratic sequence** has n^2 and no higher power of n in its nth term.

12 **Reasoning** **a** Write down the first six terms of the sequence $u_n = n^2$.

    b Compare each sequence with the sequence for n^2 to work out a formula for the nth term.

      i 2, 5, 10, 17, 26, 37, ...

      ii 0, 3, 8, 15, 24, 35, ...

      iii 4, 9, 16, 25, 36, 49, ...

13 Copy and complete this diagram to work out the next term in the sequence 0, 1, 8, 21, ...

    sequence   0   1   8   21   ☐

    1st differences   +1   +7   +13   ☐

    2nd differences   +6   +6   ☐

Q13 hint

Begin with the second difference box, then the first difference box and finally the sequence box.

14 Work out the next term of each sequence.

    a 6, 21, 46, 81, ...

    b 2, 7, 16, 29, ...

    c 0, 1, 3, 6, ...

Q14 hint

Work out the first and second differences.

15 a Copy and complete to work out first and second differences for the sequence
$u_n = n^2 + 7$

sequence   8   11   16   23   32

1st differences   +3   +5   +7   ☐

2nd differences   +2   ☐   ☐

b Copy and complete for the sequence
$u_n = 3n^2 - n - 2$

sequence   0   8   22   42   68

1st differences   +8   +14   ☐   ☐

2nd differences   +6   ☐   ☐

c Are the second differences increasing, decreasing or constant?
What is the connection between the formula for the nth term and the second differences?

> **Key point**
>
> The second differences of a quadratic sequence, $u_n = an^2 + bn + c$, are constant and equal to $2a$.

Example

Find a formula for the nth term of the sequence 8, 23, 48, 83, 128, ...

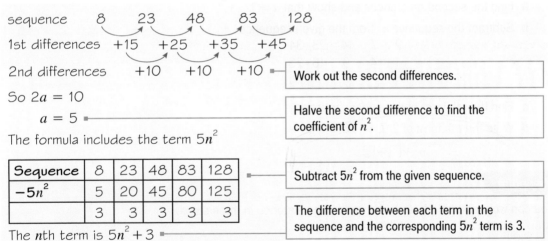

sequence   8   23   48   83   128

1st differences   +15   +25   +35   +45

2nd differences   +10   +10   +10 — Work out the second differences.

So $2a = 10$

$a = 5$ — Halve the second difference to find the coefficient of n^2.

The formula includes the term $5n^2$

Sequence	8	23	48	83	128
$-5n^2$	5	20	45	80	125
	3	3	3	3	3

Subtract $5n^2$ from the given sequence.

The difference between each term in the sequence and the corresponding $5n^2$ term is 3.

The nth term is $5n^2 + 3$

16 Reasoning Find a formula for the nth term of each of these quadratic sequences.

  a 3, 9, 19, 33, 51, ...

  b −2, 7, 22, 43, 70, ...

  c 4, 7, 12, 19, 28, ...

  d 1, 19, 49, 91, 145, ...

  e 9, 6, 1, −6, −15, ...

  f 4.5, 6, 8.5, 12, 16.5, ...

17 **Reasoning** Each number in Pascal's triangle is found by adding the pair of numbers immediately above it.

Row 0   1

Row 1   1   1

Row 2   1   2   1

Row 3   1   3   3   1

Row 4   1   4   6   4   1

a Work out the numbers in Row 5.

b Copy and complete the table for the sum of the numbers in each row.

c Work out a formula for the sum of the numbers in row n.

Row, n	0	1	2	3	4	5
Sum	1	2				

Exam-style question

18 Here are the first six terms of a quadratic sequence.
$-3, 3, 13, 27, 45, 67$
Find an expression, in terms of n, for the nth term of this sequence.   **(3 marks)**

Exam tip

Check your answer by substituting $n = 1, 2, 3, ...$

19 The sequence 2, 7, 14, 23, 34, ... has nth term in the form $u_n = an^2 + bn + c$

a Find the second differences and show that $a = 1$.

b Subtract the sequence n^2 from the given sequence.

$$
\begin{array}{ccccc}
2 & 7 & 14 & 23 & 34 \\
-\quad 1 & 4 & 9 & 16 & 25 \\
\hline
1 & \square & \square & \square & 9
\end{array}
$$

c Find the nth term of this linear sequence.

d Write the nth term of 2, 7, 14, 23, 34, ...

$$n^2 + \square - \square$$

Key point

You can work out the nth term of a quadratic sequence in three steps.
Step 1 Work out the second differences.
Step 2 Halve the second difference to get the coefficient, a, of the n^2 term.
Step 3 Subtract the sequence an^2 from the given sequence. You may need to add a constant, or find the nth term of the remaining linear sequence.

20 Use the method in **Q19** to find the nth term of each sequence.

a 4, 10, 18, 28, 40, ...

b 0, 1, 4, 9, 16, ...

c 5, 12, 23, 38, 57, ...

d 3, 11, 25, 45, 71, ...

2.7 More expanding and factorising

- Expand the product of two brackets.
- Use the difference of two squares.
- Factorise quadratic expressions of the form $x^2 + bx + c$

Warm up

1 Fluency a What is the square root of 64?

    b What are the factor pairs of   **i** 12   **ii** −6?

2 Simplify

    a $(2x)^2$ **b** $(5y)^2$ **c** $\sqrt{16t^2}$ **d** $\sqrt{100n^2}$

3 a Copy and complete this expression for the area of the whole rectangle. $(x + \square)(\square + 1)$

    b Write an expression for the sum of the areas of the smaller rectangles.
Collect like terms and simplify.

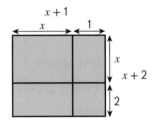

Key point

To expand **double brackets**, multiply each term in one bracket by each term in the other bracket.

Example

Expand and simplify $(x + 3)(x + 5)$.

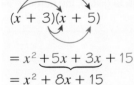

$$= x^2 \underbrace{+ 5x + 3x}_{} + 15$$
$$= x^2 + 8x + 15$$

Multiply each term in the 2nd bracket by each term in the 1st bracket.
FOIL: Firsts, Outers, Inners, Lasts

4 Expand and simplify

    a $(x+6)(x+10)$ **b** $(x+6)(x-3)$ **c** $(x-4)(x+10)$ **d** $(x-3)(x-4)$

Key point

To **square** a single bracket, multiply it by itself, then expand and simplify.
$(x+1)^2 = (x+1)(x+1) = x^2 + 2x + 1$

5 Expand and simplify

    a $(x+2)^2$ **b** $(x-3)^2$ **c** $(x+5)^2$ **d** $(x-4)^2$

6 Expand and simplify

  a $(2x+3)(x+5)$ **b** $(3x+2)(2x+1)$ **c** $(3x+1)^2$ **d** $(2x-1)^2$

7 **a** Copy and complete to evaluate $51^2 - 49^2$ without a calculator.

  $(51+49)(51-49) = 2 \times \square = \square$

  b Without using a calculator work out

  i $101^2 - 99^2$ **ii** $1.03^2 - 0.97^2$

8 Expand and simplify

  a $(x-4)(x+4)$ **b** $(x-2)(x+2)$ **c** $(m-8)(m+8)$

  d **Reflect** Explain why your answers can be called 'difference of two squares'.

9 Complete these factorisations.

  a $x^2 - 25 = (x-\square)(x+\square)$ **b** $y^2 - 49 = (y+\square)(y-\square)$
  c $t^2 - 81$ **d** $100 - n^2$

Key point

A **quadratic expression** contains a term in x^2 but no higher power of x.

---

10 **Problem-solving** Find the missing terms in these quadratic expressions.

  a $(x+2)(x+\square) = x^2 + \square x + 6$ **b** $(x-\square)(x+8) = x^2 + 5x - \square$

Example

Factorise $x^2 + 5x + 6$

$x^2 + 5x + 6$

| | Write a pair of brackets with x in each one. $x \times x$ gives the x^2 term. |

$(x \qquad)(x \qquad)$

| | Work out all the factor pairs of 6, the number term. |

$1 \times 6 \qquad\qquad 2 \times 3$

| | Work out which factor pair will **add** to give 5, the number in the x term. |

$1 + 6 = 7 \qquad\qquad 2 + 3 = \circledast 5$

$(x + 2)(x + 3)$

| | Write each number in a bracket. |

Check: $(x + 2)(x + 3) = x^2 + 5x + 6$

| | Expand the brackets to check the factorisation is correct. |

---

11 Factorise

  a $x^2 + 8x + 7$ **b** $x^2 + 7x + 12$ **c** $x^2 + 8x + 15$ **d** $x^2 + 2x + 1$

12 Factorise

  a $x^2 + 2x - 3$ **b** $x^2 - 2x - 3$

  c $x^2 - 6x - 7$ **d** $x^2 - 6x - 16$

Q12a hint

For a product of -3, one number must be positive and one number must be negative.

---

13 Factorise

    a $x^2 - 6x + 8$ **b** $x^2 - 7x + 12$

    c $x^2 - 4x + 4$ **d** $x^2 - 14x + 24$

Q13 hint

For a positive product but a negative sum, both numbers must be negative.

14 **Problem-solving** A rectangular piece of paper has length $(x + 5)$ cm and width $(x + 2)$ cm. A square with sides of length x cm is removed.

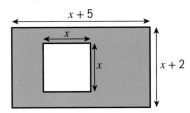

    a Write an expression for the area of the rectangle before the square is cut out.
Expand the brackets.

    b Write an expression for the shaded area.

    c The shaded area is $31\,\text{cm}^2$. Find the value of x.

15 **Problem-solving / Reasoning**
The two rectangles shown have the same area.
Find the value of x.

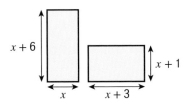

16 Copy and complete these factorisations.

    a $4x^2 - 9 = (2x)^2 - \square^2 = (2x + \square)(2x - \square)$

    b $16y^2 - 1 = (\square y)^2 - \square^2 = (\square y + \square)(\square y - \square)$

17 Factorise

    a $9m^2 - 25$ **b** $81 - 25c^2$ **c** $x^2 - 49y^2$

18 Copy and complete to factorise $3x^2 - 12$

$$3x^2 - 12 = 3(x^2 - \square)$$
$$= 3(x + \square)(x - \square)$$

Exam-style question

19 Factorise fully $4x^2 - 16$ **(2 marks)**

Exam tip

Check you cannot factorise your answer any further.

2 Check up

Active Learn
Homework

Simplifying, expanding and factorising

1 Simplify

   a $4p \times 5p^3$

   b $15x^4 \div 3x^2$

   c $(4d^2)^3$

   d $\dfrac{n^5 \times n^2}{n^6}$

2 Expand and simplify

   a $3(2p+q) - 2(3p-q)$

   b $x(2x-3) + 5x$

3 Factorise

   a $2xy - 6y$

   b $3ab - 6a^2$

4 Expand and simplify

   a $(x+4)(x-6)$

   b $(x+5)^2$

5 Simplify

   a $2x^{-2}$ **b** $4x^0$

   c $(b^2)^{-3}$ **d** $(y^4)^{\frac{1}{2}}$

   e $(9c^2)^{\frac{1}{2}}$ **f** $\dfrac{16p^{-2}}{4p^3}$

6 Expand and simplify

   a $(x+3)(x-5)$ **b** $(x+3)^2$

7 Factorise

   a $x^2 - 81$

   b $x^2 - 9x + 14$

Equations and formulae

8 Write whether each of these is an expression, an equation, an identity or a formula.

   a $v = u + at$

   b $a^2 - b^2 = (a-b)(a+b)$

   c mv

   d $4a = 5$

9 Solve
$$4x - 3 = 2x + 6$$

10 Solve
$$2(3x + 1) = 5(x - 3)$$

11 Use the formula $z = f^2 - 2g$ to work out the value of z when $f = 10$ and $g = 3$.

12 An electrician charges a £25 call-out fee, plus £36 per hour.
Write a formula for his total charge £C for n hours' work.

13 **a** Make y the subject of the formula $x + 3y = 4$
   b Make b the subject of the formula $S = 6ab + 4a^2$

14 Solve
$$\frac{x}{3} - \frac{x}{4} = \frac{5}{6}$$

Sequences

15 Write down the next two terms in the Fibonacci sequence
   3, 4, 7, 11, ...

16 Work out the first four terms and the 20th term of the sequence with nth term $u_n = 4n + 7$.

17 **a** Find the nth term of the arithmetic sequence
   2, 11, 20, 29, ...
   b Show that 167 cannot be a term in this sequence.
   c Find the first number in the sequence that is greater than 167.

18 Find the nth term of the sequence
   10, 19, 34, 55, ...

19 **Reflect** How sure are you of your answers? Were you mostly

Just guessing   Feeling doubtful   Confident 🙂

What next? Use your results to decide whether to strengthen or extend your learning.

Challenge

20 **a** Multiply together the four pairs of connected terms and expand your answers.

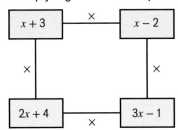

   b Add together your answers and simplify the result
   Would the result have been the same if you had expanded in a different order?
   c Factorise your simplified expression.

2 Strengthen

Active Learn
Homework

Simplifying, expanding and factorising

1 Simplify

a $t^3 \times t^2 = \overbrace{t \times t \times t}^{3} \times \overbrace{t \times t}^{2} = \overbrace{t \times t \times t \times t \times t}^{5} = t^{\square}$

b $t^4 \times t^3$

c $t \times t^3$

2 Simplify, by adding the indices.

a $t^{-2} \times t^4$ **b** $t^{-6} \times t^{-1}$ **c** $t^{\frac{1}{2}} \times t^{\frac{3}{2}}$ **d** $t^{\frac{1}{2}} \times t^{-\frac{3}{2}}$

3 Simplify, by multiplying numbers first, then letters.

a
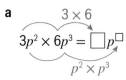
$3p^2 \times 6p^3 = \square p^{\square}$

b $8z \times 9z^4$ **c** $7b^3 \times 2b^5$

d $2r^5 \times 4r^{-2}$ **e** $5s^{-2} \times 2s^{-4}$ **f** $2x^{\frac{1}{3}} \times 3x^{\frac{2}{3}}$ **g** $2m^{\frac{1}{3}} \times 3m^{\frac{1}{3}}$

4 Copy and complete.

a $t^6 \div t^2 = t^{6-2} = t^{\square}$ **b** $t^5 \div t^2 = t^{\square - \square} = t^{\square}$ **c** $t^3 \div t^3 = t^{\square} = \square$

d $\dfrac{x^5}{x^3} = x^{5-\square} = x^{\square}$ **e** $\dfrac{x^{-1}}{x^2} = x^{-1-\square} = x^{-\square}$ **f** $\dfrac{y}{y^{-2}} = y^{1--2} = y^{\square}$

5 Simplify, by dividing the numbers first, then the letters.

a $20p^6 \div 4p^2 = \square p^{\square}$

b $\dfrac{12a^7}{4a^2}$ **c** $\dfrac{9y^{-1}}{3y^2}$ **d** $\dfrac{6p}{3p^{-2}}$

6 Copy and complete.

a $(x^2)^2 = \square^{\square} \times \square^{\square} = \square^{\square}$ **b** $(x^2)^3 = \square^{\square} \times \square^{\square} \times \square^{\square} = \square^{\square}$

c $(x^2)^4 = \square^{\square} \times \square^{\square} \times \square^{\square} \times \square^{\square} = \square^{\square}$

d What do you notice about powers and brackets? What is the rule?

7 Simplify, using your rule from **Q6**.

a $(x^3)^4$ **b** $(a^4)^{\frac{1}{2}}$ **c** $(r^2)^{-1}$ **d** $(g^{\frac{1}{3}})^3$

8 **a** Expand $3(2x + y)$ using a multiplication grid.

    b Expand $2(3x - 4y)$

    c Expand and simplify $3(2x + y) + 2(3x - 4y)$

×	2x	y
3		

9 Expand and simplify

    a $2(4c + 5d) + 3(c - 3d)$ **b** $6(3m + n) - 4(m - n)$

10 Copy and complete the factorisations.

a $3ab^2 - 2ab = ab(\square \, ... \, \square)$

b $5p^2q - 2pq = \square(5p \, ... \, \square)$

c $8xy + 6x = 2\square(\square \, ... \, \square)$

d $4rp + 6p = \square(\square \, ... \, \square)$

e $3st^2 - 6st = \square(\square \, ... \, \square)$

f $14ab^2 + 21b = \square(\square \, ... \, \square)$

11 **a** Copy and complete the multiplication grid.

b Use your answer to part **a** to expand

$$(x+4)(x+5) = x^2 + 5x + \square + 20$$
$$= x^2 + \square x + 20$$

×	x	+5
x	x^2	$5x$
+4		+20

12 Use this grid to expand $(x-6)^2$

×	x	−6
x	x^2	
−6		

13 Expand and simplify

a $(x-4)(x+4)$ **b** $(x+1)(x-3)$ **c** $(x-7)(x-4)$

14 **a** There are three pairs of positive integers whose product is 12. One pair is 1 and 12. Write down the other two pairs.

b Which pair of numbers in part **a** add up to 8?

c Use your answer to part **b** to factorise $x^2 + 8x + 12$

$$\square \times \square = 12$$
$$(x + \square)(x + \square) = x^2 + 8x + 12$$
$$\square + \square = 8$$

15 Factorise **a** $x^2 + 13x + 12$ **b** $x^2 + 7x + 12$

16 **a** There are four pairs of integers whose product is −10. One pair is −2 and +5. Write down the other three pairs.

b Use your answers to part **a** to factorise

i $x^2 - 9x - 10$ **ii** $x^2 + 9x - 10$ **iii** $x^2 + 3x - 10$ **iv** $x^2 - 3x - 10$

Equations and formulae

1 Use words from this box

an identity   a formula   an expression   an equation

to complete these sentences.

a When there is no = sign it is _____

b When the two sides are always equal it is _____

c When you can solve it to find the value of the letter it is _____

2 Write whether each of these is an identity, a formula, an expression or an equation.

a $2x$ **b** $x + 2x = 3x$ **c** $M = 2x$ **d** $2x = 1$

3 When $U = 5$ and $V = 3$, work out

a V^2 **b** $4V^2$ **c** $4V^2 + U$ **d** $4V^2 - U$

4 Use the formula $t = r^2 - 3s$ to work out t when $r = 5$ and $s = 2$.

5 Make x the subject of the formula $y = 2x - 4$.

$y = 2x - 4$

$+4 \left(\begin{array}{c} y = 2x - 4 \\ y + \square = \square \\ \dfrac{\square + \square}{\square} = x \end{array} \right) +4$

$\div 2 \left(\qquad \right) \div 2$

$x \rightarrow \boxed{\times 2} \rightarrow \boxed{- \square} \rightarrow y = 2x - 4$

$x \leftarrow \boxed{\div \square} \leftarrow \boxed{+ \square} \leftarrow y$

6 Make x the subject of $y + 3x = 5$.

7 **a** Make Q the subject of the formula $P = \dfrac{Q}{a} + b$.

b Make b the subject of $c = \dfrac{3b}{4}$.

c Make s the subject of $x = y + 2s$.

8 Copy and complete to solve the equations.

a

$3x + 6 = 5x$

$-3x \left(\qquad \right) -3x$

$\square = 2x$

$\div 2 \left(\qquad \right) \div 2$

$\square = x$

b

$7x - 4 = 5x + 2$

$-5x \left(\qquad \right) -5x$

$\square - 4 = \square$

$+4 \left(\qquad \right) +4$

$\square = \square$

$\div \square \left(\qquad \right) \div \square$

$x = \square$

9 Solve the equation $5x - 1 = 3x + 7$.

10 **a** Expand the brackets. **i** $7(2x - 4)$ **ii** $2(3x + 5)$

b Rewrite the equation $7(2x - 4) = 2(3x + 5)$ using your expressions from part **a**.

c Solve the equation.

11 **a** Expand and simplify $7(2x + 1) - 3(4x + 3)$.

b Solve $7(2x + 1) - 3(4x + 3) = 5$.

12 Solve these equations. Start by multiplying both sides of the equation by 5.

a $\dfrac{x}{5} = 4$ **b** $\dfrac{3x}{5} = 1$ **c** $\dfrac{x - 1}{5} = 2$ **d** $3 = \dfrac{2x + 1}{5}$

13 Solve these equations.

a $\dfrac{x}{6} = 3$ **b** $\dfrac{4x}{7} = 1$ **c** $\dfrac{x + 4}{3} = 5$ **d** $\dfrac{3x - 1}{2} = 10$

e Explain how you decide what to multiply by.

14 **a** Find the LCM of 4 and 5.

b Multiply both sides of $\dfrac{x}{4} - \dfrac{x}{5} = 3$ by the LCM of 4 and 5.

c Show that simplifying your equation from part **b** gives $5x - 4x = 60$.

d Find x.

Sequences

1 In a Fibonacci sequence, the rule is 'add two terms to get the next'.
Write down the next two terms in each of these Fibonacci sequences.

a 1, 1, 2, 3, 5, 8, ... **b** 5, 7, 12, 19, 31, ... **c** 2, 4, 6, 10, 16, 26, ...

2 Substitute $n = 1$, $n = 2$, $n = 3$ into each formula to work out the first three terms of the sequence with nth term

   a $u_n = 2n + 3$ **b** $u_n = 50 - 2n$ **c** $u_n = n^2 + 1$ **d** $u_n = 10n^2$

3 The first five terms of an arithmetic sequence are 3, 6, 9, 12, 15.

   a These are multiples of ☐.

   b What is the 12th term?

   c Copy and complete this statement.
     The general term is ☐n

4 Work out a formula for the nth term of each of these arithmetic sequences.

   a 10, 20, 30, 40, 50, ...   **b** 7, 14, 21, 28, 35, ...   **c** 12, 24, 36, 48, 60, ...

5 These two sequences have the same common difference.
     Sequence A: 4, 8, 12, 16, 20, ...
     Sequence B: 7, 11, 15, 19, 23, ...

   a Work out the nth term of sequence A.

   b What do you add to each term in sequence A to get the terms in sequence B?

   c Write the nth term of sequence B.

6 **a** Write down the next two terms in each of these arithmetic sequences.

     i 6, 12, 18, 24, ...   **ii** 1, 3, 5, 7, ...   **iii** 4, 7, 10, 13, ...   **iv** 25, 20, 15, 10, ...

   b Find the nth term of each sequence in part **a**.

7 **a** Write down the first five terms of the sequence with nth term $u_n = 10 + 4n$

   b Explain why 351 cannot be a term of this sequence.

   c Will there be any odd numbers in this sequence?

   d Solve $10 + 4n = 102$.
     Which term of the sequence is 102?

8 **a** Copy and complete the first and second differences for this sequence and work out the next term.

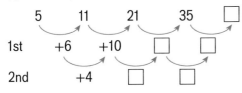

   b The nth term is $an^2 + b$ where a is half the second difference.
     Work out the value of a.

   c For the first term, $n = 1$ and the term is 5.
     Substitute $n = 1$ and your value of a into $an^2 + b = 5$ to find b.

   d Write down the nth term.

9 Find the nth term of each of these quadratic sequences.

   a 9, 21, 41, 69, ... **b** −9, −6, −1, 6, ...

> **Q9 hint**
>
> Use the method from **Q8**.

2 Extend

1 **Reasoning** **a** Write down the next three terms in each sequence.

 i $u_1 = 5, \dots u_{n+1} = u_n + 1$ **ii** $u_1 = 40, \dots u_{n+1} = \frac{1}{2}u_n$

 iii $u_1 = 7, \dots u_{n+1} = u_n - 4$ **iv** $u_1 = 1, \dots u_{n+1} = -3u_n$

 b Which of these sequences are arithmetic and which are geometric?

Q1a i hint

$u_2 = u_1 + 1$

2 **Reasoning**

 a The 1st term of an arithmetic sequence is 0.341 and the 2nd term is 0.407.
 Work out the 3rd term.

 b The 1st term of an arithmetic sequence is 9 and the 3rd term is 14. Work out the 2nd term.

3 **Problem-solving** The first four terms of a sequence are
 $-127, -124, -121, -118$
 How many terms in this sequence are negative?

4 **a** Find the next four terms in each Fibonacci sequence.

 i $n, n, \square, \square, \square, \square, \dots$ **ii** $0, m, \square, \square, \square, \square, \dots$

 b **Reasoning** Write two different Fibonacci sequences with 5th term 30.

Exam-style question

5 $100^x \times 10000^y = 10^t$
 Show that $2x + 4y = t$. **(2 marks)**

---

 6 **Future skills** A clothing store monitors sales in-store and online.
 Sales for the 2014 to 2017 are shown in the table.

Year	2014	2015	2016	2017	2018	2019
In-store	31 250	25 000	20 000	16 000		
Online	640	960	1440	2160		

 Assuming both types of sales form a geometric sequence

 a work out the sales of each type for 2018 and 2019

 b work out the year when online sales are predicted to exceed in-store sales

7 **Problem-solving** The area of this rectangle is $x^2 - 3x - 10$.
 Find the length of the rectangle.

8 **Future skills** The formula gives the monthly repayments, £M, needed to pay off a mortgage
 over n years when the amount borrowed is £P and the interest rate is $r\%$.

$$M = \frac{Pr\left(1 + \frac{1}{100}r\right)^n}{1200\left[\left(1 + \frac{1}{100}r\right)^n - 1\right]}$$

 Calculate the monthly repayments when the amount borrowed is £250 000 over 25 years and
 the interest rate is 5%.

9 **Problem-solving** Raj attempts a multiple choice test with 20 questions.
He scores 5 marks for a correct answer but loses 2 marks if it is incorrect.
Raj attempts all 20 questions and gets a total score of 51.
Let x be the number of correct answers. How many answers were correct?

10 **Problem-solving / Reasoning** Show that the difference in the
areas of these two squares is $4x + 4$

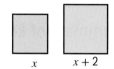

x $x + 2$

11 Change the subject to the letter given in the brackets.

a $A = \dfrac{(a+b)h}{2}$ $[a]$
b $V = \frac{1}{3}\pi r^2 h$ $[h]$

c $S = \dfrac{a(r^n - 1)}{r - 1}$ $[a]$
d $a^2 x - b^2 y = c$ $[y]$

12 Simplify

a $4x^{\frac{1}{2}} y^{-2} \times 3x^{\frac{3}{2}} y^3$
b $\left(2m^{-\frac{1}{4}} n^{\frac{3}{4}}\right)^4$
c $\sqrt[3]{8 p^{-3} q^{12}}$
d $\left(9x^6 y^5\right)^{\frac{1}{2}}$

Exam-style question

13 The formula $C = \dfrac{5(F - 32)}{9}$ converts temperatures from °F to °C.

F is the temperature in °F. C is the temperature in °C.
The minimum temperature in a classroom should be 20 °C.
The temperature in a classroom is 77 °F.

a Decide whether or not the temperature in the classroom is lower than the minimum
temperature should be.   **(3 marks)**

b Make F the subject of the formula $C = \dfrac{5(F - 32)}{9}$ **(3 marks)**

---

14 **Reasoning a** Explain why $2n + 1$ is an odd number for any integer n.
b Show that the product of two odd numbers is always odd.

15 Factorise completely

a $x^2 - 12x + 32$ **b** $x^2 - 12x + 36$ **c** $x^2 - x - 2$ **d** $\dfrac{x^2}{25} - \dfrac{y^2}{49}$

16 Solve

a $3(2x - 1) - 4(3x - 2) = 10$
b $\frac{2}{3}(x + 4) = \frac{4}{5}(x - 1)$

c $\dfrac{x}{6} - \dfrac{3x}{8} = 1$
d $\dfrac{5x + 7}{14} = \dfrac{1 - 2x}{21}$

17 **Reasoning** Show that the difference between consecutive square numbers is always an
odd number.

18 Find the nth term of each sequence.

a $1, -5, -15, -29, -47, \ldots$
b $0, -1, -4, -9, -16, \ldots$

Q18 hint

The second differences are
negative so $-\square n^2 + bn + c$

2 Test ready

Summary of key points

To revise for the test:

- Read each key point, find a question on it in the mastery lesson, and check you can work out the answer.

- If you cannot, try some other questions from the mastery lesson or ask for help.

Key points

1 $x^m \times x^n = x^{m+n}$ → **2.1**

2 $x^m \div x^n = x^{m-n}$ → **2.1**

3 $(x^m)^n = x^{mn}$ → **2.1**

4 $x^0 = 1$ → **2.1**

5 $x^{-m} = \dfrac{1}{x^m}$ → **2.1**

6 $x^{\frac{1}{n}} = \sqrt[n]{x}$ → **2.1**

7 $x^{\frac{m}{n}} = (\sqrt[n]{x})^m$ → **2.1**

8 The $\equiv$ symbol shows an identity.
   In an **identity** the two expressions are equal for *all* values of the variables.
   $2(x+5) \equiv 2x+10$ is an identity. → **2.2, 2.4**

9 An **equation**, such as $2x = 6$, is only true for certain values of x (in this case $x = 3$).
   An equation has an equals sign, letter terms and numbers.
   You can solve it to find the value of the letter, e.g. $2x - 4 = 9x + 1$ → **2.2, 2.4**

10 **Consecutive integers** are one after the other.
    Any even integer is in the 2 times table and can be written as $2n$ for some value of n. → **2.2**

11 Unless a question asks for a decimal answer, give non-integer solutions to an
    equation as exact fractions. → **2.3**

12 To solve an equation involving fractions, multiply each term on both sides by the
    LCM of the denominators. → **2.3**

13 An **expression** contains letter and/or number terms but no equals sign,
    e.g. $2ab$, $2ab + 3a^2b$, $2ab - 7$ → **2.4**

14 A **formula** has an equals sign and letters to represent different quantities, e.g. $A = \pi r^2$
    The letters are **variables** as their values can vary. → **2.4**

15 The **subject** of a formula is the letter on its own, on one side of the equals sign. → **2.4**

16 The n**th term** of a sequence tells you how to work out the term at position n (any position).
    It is also called the **general term** of the sequence. → **2.5**

17 u_n denotes the nth term of a sequence. u_1 is the first term, u_2 is the second term,
    and so on. → **2.5**

18 In an **arithmetic sequence**, the terms increase (or decrease) by a fixed number
    called the **common difference**. → **2.5**

19 The nth term of an arithmetic sequence $=$ common difference $\times n +$ zero term → **2.5**

20 When an arithmetic sequence with common difference d is input into a 2-step function machine where the first step is $\times p$ and the second step is $+q$, the output sequence has common difference $p \times d$. → **2.5**

21 In a **Fibonacci sequence** the term-to-term rule is 'add the two previous terms to get the next one'. → **2.6**

22 In a **geometric sequence** the terms increase (or decrease) by a **constant multiplier**. → **2.6**

23 A **quadratic sequence** has n^2 and no higher power of n in its nth term. → **2.6**

24 The second differences of a quadratic sequence, $u_n = an^2 + bn + c$, are constant and equal to $2a$. → **2.6**

25 You can work out the nth term of a quadratic sequence in three steps.
Step 1 Work out the second differences.
Step 2 Halve the second difference to get the coefficient, a, of the n^2 term.
Step 3 Subtract the sequence an^2 from the given sequence. You may need to add a constant, or find the nth term of the remaining linear sequence. → **2.6**

26 To expand **double brackets**, multiply each term in one bracket by each term in the other bracket. → **2.7**

27 To **square** a single bracket, multiply it by itself, then expand and simplify.
$(x+1)^2 = (x+1)(x+1) = x^2 + 2x + 1$ → **2.7**

28 A **quadratic expression** contains a term in x^2 but no higher power of x. → **2.7**

Sample student answers

Exam-style question

1 Factorise fully $5x^2 - 45$ **(2 marks)**

$5(x^2 - 9)$

The student is likely to get only 1 mark for this answer. Why?
Complete the answer for the full 2 marks.

Exam-style question

2 Make b the subject of $y^2 = 3ab - x^2$ **(2 marks)**

$y^2 = 3ab - x^2$

$\dfrac{y^2}{3a} = b - x^2$

$b = \dfrac{y^2}{3a} + x^2$

The student is likely to get 0 marks for this answer. Why?
Write the correct answer for the full 2 marks.

2 Unit test

1 Work out the next two terms of the Fibonacci sequence, 4, 7, 11, 18, 29, ... **(2 marks)**

2 Write whether each of these is an expression, a formula, an equation or an identity.

    a $4(3x+1) = 5x-6$ **(1 mark)**

    b $4(3x+1)$ **(1 mark)**

    c $4(3x+1) = 12x+4$ **(1 mark)**

    d $F = 4(3c+1)$ **(1 mark)**

3 Solve $7x+3 = 2x-12$. **(2 marks)**

4 Solve $\dfrac{11-m}{3} = 5m+1$. **(3 marks)**

5 Solve $7(x+5)-6(2x+1) = 0$. **(2 marks)**

6 Simplify

    a $7q^2 \times 9q^3$ **(2 marks)**

    b $\dfrac{25y^4}{5y}$ **(2 marks)**

    c $(c^4)^2$ **(1 mark)**

    d $(25d^6)^{\frac{1}{2}}$ **(1 mark)**

7 Expand and simplify $4(x+6)-3(1-2x)$. **(2 marks)**

8 Expand

    a $3x(4x+y)$ **(2 marks)**

    b $(x+4)(x-3)$ **(2 marks)**

    c $(x-7)^2$ **(2 marks)**

    d $(2x+7)(x-1)$ **(2 marks)**

9 Find the first three terms of the sequence with nth term $u_n = 81 \times \left(\frac{1}{3}\right)^n$ **(3 marks)**

10 **a** Find the nth term of the arithmetic sequence 4, 10, 16, 22, 28, ... **(2 marks)**

    b Show that 231 is not in the sequence. **(1 mark)**

    c Find the smallest number in this sequence which is greater than 234. **(2 marks)**

11 Simplify

    a $(3x^4)^0$ **(1 mark)**

    b $(16x^4)^{\frac{1}{2}}$ **(1 mark)**

    c $\dfrac{8x^2y^{-1}}{4x^3y}$ **(2 marks)**

12 Find the nth term of the sequence

    $\dfrac{25}{7}, \dfrac{21}{10}, \dfrac{17}{13}, \dfrac{13}{16}, \cdots$ **(3 marks)**

13 Work out a simplified expression for the area of this shape. All the angles are right angles.

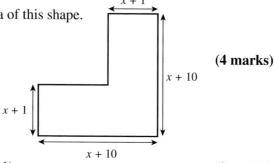

(4 marks)

14 Make x the subject of the formula $y = 5(xt - 1)$. **(2 marks)**

15 Show algebraically that the difference between any two odd numbers is always even. **(2 marks)**

16 Here are the first five terms of a sequence.

2, 11, 26, 47, 78

Find an expression, in terms of n, for the nth term of this sequence. **(3 marks)**

17 The diagram shows an isosceles triangle. All lengths are in centimetres.

a Write down an equation for x. **(1 mark)**

b Solve the equation. **(2 marks)**

c Work out the length of BC. **(2 marks)**

18 $E = \frac{1}{2}mv^2$

a Find E when $m = 6 \times 10^{-3}$ and $v = 3 \times 10^3$. **(1 mark)**

b Make m the subject of the formula. **(2 marks)**

19 Factorise completely

a $x^2 - 16$ **(1 mark)**

b $6y^2 - 9xy$ **(2 marks)**

c $x^2 + 3x - 10$ **(2 marks)**

d $4x^2 - 100$ **(2 marks)**

(TOTAL: 70 marks)

20 **Challenge**

a Work out

   i $1 + 2$ ii $1 + 2 + 3$ iii $1 + 2 + 3 + 4$ iv $1 + 2 + 3 + 4 + 5$

b By substituting $n = 2, 3, 4$ and 5 into the formula $\frac{1}{2}n(n + 1)$, verify that this formula produces the sum of the first n positive whole numbers.

c Use the formula in part **b** to work out the sum of the first 100 whole numbers.

d Work out

   i $1^3 + 2^3$ ii $1^3 + 2^3 + 3^3$ iii $1^3 + 2^3 + 3^3 + 4^3$ iv $1^3 + 2^3 + 3^3 + 4^3 + 5^3$

e Compare your answers with those for part **a**, and write a formula for the first n cube numbers.

21 **Reflect** Look back at the work you did in this unit. Which topic did you find most difficult?

Choose two or three questions you found difficult to answer in that topic. Work with a classmate (and/or your teacher) to better understand how to answer these questions. (This is a good thing to do at the end of every unit.)

3 Interpreting and representing data

3.1 Statistical diagrams 1

Prior knowledge

- Construct and use back-to-back stem and leaf diagrams.
- Construct and use frequency polygons and pie charts.

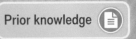
*Active*Learn
Homework

Warm up

1 Fluency What are the mode, median and range of 2, 2, 4, 7?

2 The stem and leaf diagram shows the masses of a group of people in a lift.

   a How many people are in the lift?

   b What is the mass of the heaviest person in the lift?

   c A safety notice in the lift reads, 'Maximum 12 persons, total weight 800 kg'.
   Explain whether this group of people can travel in the lift safely.

```
5 | 4
6 | 3 4 7
7 | 0 2 6 8
8 | 3 9
```

Key: 5 | 4 means 54 kg

Key point

A **pie chart** represents a set of data. Each sector represents a category within that set of data.

3 Reasoning The pie charts show the ages of people attending an open air theatre and a music festival.
1500 attended the theatre and 20 000 attended the festival.

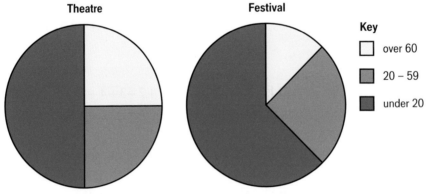

Theatre   **Festival**

Key
- over 60
- 20 – 59
- under 20

   a How many people under 20 attended the theatre?

   b Which pie chart has the larger sector for over-60s?

   c Show that there are more over-60s at the festival than at the theatre.

Key point

When n data values are written in order, the **median** is the $\frac{n+1}{2}$th value.

4 The stem and leaf diagram shows some children's heights in cm.

9	4 7
10	3 8 8 9
11	0 2 3 6
12	1 5 9

Key: 9 | 4 represents 94 cm

a Work out the range.

b Find the mode.

c Count the number of values, n.

d Work out $\dfrac{n+1}{2}$ to find which is the middle value.

e Find the median.

5 The stem and leaf diagram shows the times taken, in seconds, to complete a puzzle.

30	8 8 9
31	1 2 3 4 4 8 9
32	0 3 5 5 7 7 7
33	2 2 3 3 6 6 8 8
34	1 2 3 3 5

Key: 30 | 8 represents 30.8 seconds

a Work out the range.

b Work out the median.

c **Reasoning** Max says, 'The mode is 3, because 3 occurs most often in the diagram.' Is Max correct? You must explain your answer.

Key point

To compare two sets of data, compare an average (mean, median or mode) and the range of each set. A small range shows the data values are all similar, or consistent.

---

6 The table shows the median and range of scores obtained by Sophie and Celia after playing many rounds of golf. In golf, a lower score is better. Write two sentences comparing Sophie and Celia's scores.

	Median	Range
Sophie	71	13
Celia	93	25

Key point

A **back-to-back stem and leaf diagram** compares two sets of data.

Example

The back-to-back stem and leaf diagram shows the annual salaries of employees working in an ICT company.

Male		Female
8	1	9 9
9 5 2 0	2	1 2 6 7
8 7 3 0	3	0 4 4
	4	5 6
	5	4

Key: (Male) 8 | 1 represents £18 000
(Female) 1 | 9 represents £19 000

a Find the median and range for males and for females.

b Compare the distribution of salaries of the male and female employees.

a Male range: $38\,000 - 18\,000 = £20\,000$
Female range: $54\,000 - 19\,000 = £35\,000$

9 males, so median male salary is the $\dfrac{9+1}{2}$ = 5th value = £29 000

12 females so median female salary is the $\dfrac{12+1}{2}$ = 6.5th value, halfway between £27 000 and £30 000 = £28 500

b Female employees' salaries have a larger range so they are less consistent. The median salaries for males and females are similar.

Write a sentence comparing ranges and medians.

7 **Problem-solving** A group of students take maths and English exams.
The back-to-back stem and leaf diagram shows their results.

Maths		English
5 4	3	
	4	1 5
9 4 0	5	3 4 8 8
3 1	6	0 2 9
6 6	7	8
8	8	

Key: (Maths) 4 | 3 represents 34 marks
on the Maths exam
(English) 4 | 1 represents 41 marks
on the English exam

a Find the median and range of scores for each of the exams.

b Compare the distribution of marks in the two exams.

c What does the shape of this back-to-back stem and leaf diagram show you about the ranges for maths and English?

8 **Reasoning** The heights (in cm, measured to the nearest cm) of two types of tulip are recorded.
Type A: 24, 37, 52, 26, 29, 46, 47, 29, 30, 36, 48, 55, 59
Type B: 16, 23, 34, 37, 31, 13, 64, 52, 53, 37, 43, 39, 38, 42, 42, 37

a Draw a back-to-back stem and leaf diagram for this data.

b Use the shape of your diagram to compare the distribution of heights of the two types of tulip.

Key point

To draw a **frequency polygon** you can join the midpoints of the tops of the bars in a frequency diagram with straight lines.

---

9 The table shows the heights of 100 students.

a Copy and complete the frequency diagram.
The data is continuous so there are no gaps between bars.

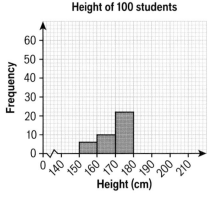

Height of 100 students

Height, h (cm)	Frequency
$140 \leqslant h < 150$	0
$150 \leqslant h < 160$	6
$160 \leqslant h < 170$	10
$170 \leqslant h < 180$	22
$180 \leqslant h < 190$	52
$190 \leqslant h < 200$	10
$200 \leqslant h < 210$	0

b Draw a frequency polygon on the same diagram, by drawing straight lines to connect the midpoints of the tops of the bars.

c **Reflect** Describe how to draw a frequency polygon without drawing a frequency diagram first.

10 The frequency table shows people's times to complete a charity fun run.

Time, t (min)	Frequency
$20 \leqslant t < 40$	4
$40 \leqslant t < 60$	5
$60 \leqslant t < 80$	12
$80 \leqslant t < 100$	9
$100 \leqslant t < 120$	7
$120 \leqslant t < 140$	3

a Copy and complete the frequency polygon.

b From the table, what is the shortest possible time taken?

c Work out an estimate for the range.

d Explain why your answer to part **c** is only an estimate.

Time to complete a fun run

11 The table gives information about the weights of 40 dogs.

Weight, w (kg)	Frequency
$0 \leqslant w < 10$	4
$10 \leqslant w < 20$	11
$20 \leqslant w < 30$	20
$30 \leqslant w < 40$	3

Draw a frequency polygon for this information.

(2 marks)

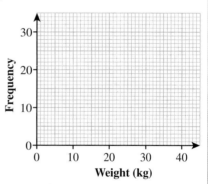

12 **Reasoning** A group of Year 10 students are each asked to guess the price of a can of cola and a small bunch of bananas.
The results are displayed on the frequency polygons.

a Which data set has the greater range?

b Would you expect the median of data set A to be greater than, less than or about the same as the median of data set B?

c Which data set do you think gives the prices for cola?

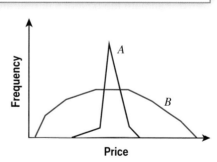

3.2 Time series

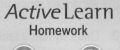

ActiveLearn
Homework

- Plot and interpret time series graphs.
- Use trends to predict what might happen in the future.

Warm up

1 **Fluency** How many months are there in **a** a year **b** one quarter of a year?

2 Match each sequence with the correct description.

a 3, 5, 7, 9, 11, 13, 15, 17, 19, 21	**A** The values are constant.
b 0, 26, 46, 60, 69, 76, 81, 84, 85, 85	**B** The values increase at a constant rate.
c 4, 4, 4, 4, 4, 4, 4, 4, 4, 4	**C** The values decrease at a constant rate.
d 12, 11, 10, 9, 8, 7, 6, 5, 4, 3	**D** The values increase at a decreasing rate.
e 1, 3, 7, 2, 0, 4, 8, 6, 2, 5	**E** The values fluctuate up and down.

Key point

A **time series** graph is a line graph with time plotted on the horizontal axis.

3 **Reasoning** The table shows the temperature of a hospital patient recorded on the hour every 2 hours during a 24-hour period.

Time	00:00	02:00	04:00	06:00	08:00	10:00	12:00	14:00	16:00	18:00	20:00	22:00
Temperature (°C)	36.7	36.8	37.1	37.4	37.8	38.3	38.0	38.2	37.4	37.3	37.2	37.1

a What is the patient's temperature at 6 pm?

b What is the patient's maximum temperature during this period? At what time did it occur?

c Represent this time series on a line graph. Use a vertical axis from 36 to 39.

d Estimate the patient's temperature at 7 am. Explain why this is an estimate.

e Describe how the temperature varies.

4 Each week of the autumn term, a teacher records the number of pieces of late homework.

Week	1	2	3	4	5	6	7	8	9	10	11	12
Number of late homeworks	38	34	26	14	8	7	18	10	7	15	25	40

a Draw a time series graph for this data.

b Describe how late homework varies during the course of the term.

5 The table shows the depth of sea water in a harbour between midnight and noon.

Time	Midnight	1 am	2 am	3 am	4 am	5 am	6 am	7 am	8 am	9 am	10 am	11 am	Noon
Depth (m)	10	12.5	14.3	15	14.3	12.5	10	7.5	5.7	5	5.7	7.5	10

a Draw a time series graph for the data.

b What time is the maximum water depth?

c Describe how the water depth changes over time.

d It is only safe for a ship to enter the harbour when the water depth exceeds 7.5 m. During which times is it not safe for ships to enter the harbour?

6 **Reasoning** The time series graph shows the prices of two magazines over the last 6 years.

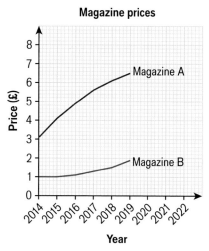

Magazine prices

a What was the price of magazine A in 2016?

b Suzy says the price of magazine A has risen more than the price of magazine B during this period. Is she correct? Give a reason for your answer.

c Suzy also says that the rate of increase in the price of magazine A is slowing down. Is she correct? Give a reason for your answer.

d Predict the prices of each magazine in 2022. Explain why these predictions could be inaccurate.

Key point

A time series graph is useful for identifying trends. The **trend** is the general direction of change.

Example

The table shows the quarterly price of a tonne of wheat (in dollars) during the last three years.

2017				2018				2019			
Q1	Q2	Q3	Q4	Q1	Q2	Q3	Q4	Q1	Q2	Q3	Q4
250	279	101	157	348	371	230	264	451	477	322	347

Prices are recorded every 3 months so the first quarter covers January, February and March.

a What is the price in the third quarter (Q3) of 2018?

b Draw a time series graph of the data.

c In which quarter is the price the lowest?

d Describe the variation in prices during this period and comment on the overall trend.

a $230

b **Wheat prices**

c Q3 of 2017

d The price of wheat fluctuates up and down during the course of each year. The overall trend shows a general increase in prices. ⟵ Describe any patterns.

7 **Problem-solving** The table shows the quarterly sales (in thousands) of umbrellas during the last three years.

2017				2018				2019			
Q1	Q2	Q3	Q4	Q1	Q2	Q3	Q4	Q1	Q2	Q3	Q4
89	75	24	85	80	66	19	76	75	62	17	73

  a What are the sales in the second quarter of 2018?

  b Draw a time series graph for this data.

  c In which quarter are sales the highest?

  d Describe the variation in umbrella sales during this period and comment on the overall trend.

  e Calculate the mean quarterly sales for each year.

8 **Reasoning** The table shows the profit (in millions of pounds) of an ICT company over the past 10 years. The profit for 2015 is not known.

Year	2010	2011	2012	2013	2014	2015	2016	2017	2018	2019
Profit (£m)	0.5	0.7	0.8	1.1	1.4	?	2.4	3.1	4.1	5.3

  a Draw a horizontal axis from 2010 to 2020 and a vertical axis from 0 to 7.
    Draw a line graph for this time series.

  b Describe the overall trend.

  c Estimate what the profit might have been in 2015.

  d Predict what the profit might be in 2020.

  e How reliable are your values in parts **c** and **d**?

Exam-style question

9 Rosie has drawn a time series graph to show the numbers, in thousands, of hits on a website.

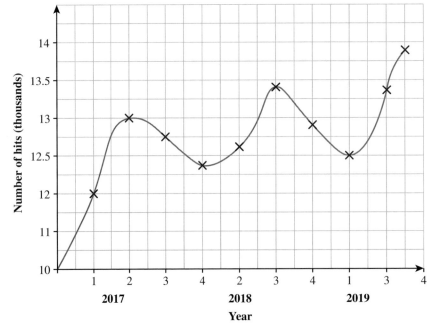

Write down two things that are wrong or could be misleading with this graph. **(2 marks)**

3.3 Scatter graphs

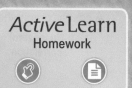
Active Learn
Homework

- Plot and interpret scatter graphs.
- Determine whether or not there is a linear relationship between two variables.

Warm up

1 Fluency State whether each line has a positive, negative or zero gradient.

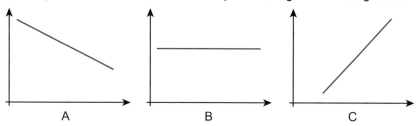

       A   B   C

2 Draw x- and y-axes on graph paper from 0 to 8. Plot five points with coordinates
$A(2, 4.75)$, $B(5, 3.5)$, $C(4, 3.75)$, $D(7, 3)$ and $E(3, 4)$.
Four of the points lie on a line. Which point does not lie on the line?

Key point

Bivariate data has two variables. Plotting these on a **scatter graph** can show whether there is a relationship between them.

3 Eight students took a maths test and a science test. Their marks are displayed in the table.

Student	A	B	C	D	E	F	G	H
Maths mark	3	9	7	3	6	10	5	1
Science mark	4	8	4	2	5	7	3	1

  a Copy and complete the scatter graph.
Student A scored 3 in maths and 4 in science so draw a cross at (3, 4).

  b Copy and complete the sentence.
In general, students with higher maths scores got _____ science scores and students with lower maths scores got _____ science scores.

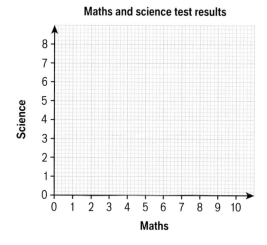

Maths and science test results

Key point

A scatter graph shows a relationship or **correlation** between variables.

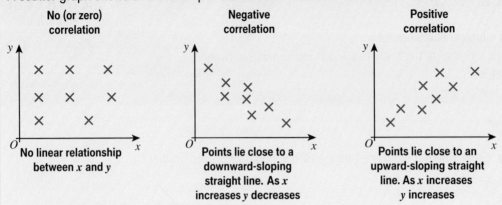

No (or zero) correlation

No linear relationship between x and y

Negative correlation

Points lie close to a downward-sloping straight line. As x increases y decreases

Positive correlation

Points lie close to an upward-sloping straight line. As x increases y increases

4 The daily sales and price of ice cream are recorded, together with the maximum outside temperature. Three scatter graphs are plotted from the data.

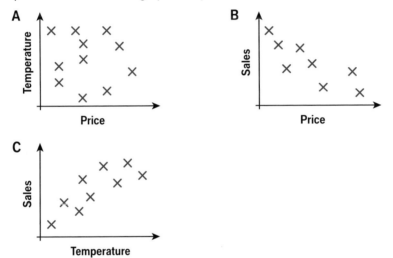

A — Temperature / Price

B — Sales / Price

C — Sales / Temperature

a For each graph state whether there is positive, negative or no correlation.

b For graph B, copy and complete the sentence.
As price increases, sales _____

c For graph C, copy and complete the sentence.
As temperature increases, _____

5 **Reasoning** A car dealer notes the engine size of seven models of car and the distance they travel on a litre of petrol.

Engine size (litres)	1	1.4	1.6	2	3	3.5	4
Distance (km)	16	14.2	13.5	11.7	9.2	8.4	7.1

a Draw a scatter graph for this data.
Put engine size on the horizontal axis and distance on the vertical axis.

b Write down the type of correlation.

c Describe the relationship between the two variables.

6 Reasoning An auction house asks an art dealer to award six paintings marks out of 10, without disclosing the names of the artists.
The market value (in £100 000s) and dealer's score for each painting are in the table.

Score	2	7	5	3	8	4
Market value	3.5	1.8	5.6	4.3	8.4	2.5

a Draw a scatter graph.

b Describe any correlation between the score and the value of the paintings.

7 Reasoning A survey of seven British towns records the number of serious road accidents in a week, together with the number of takeaway restaurants.

Number of restaurants	85	15	10	52	71	25	90
Number of accidents	27	9	4	19	17	12	19

a Draw a scatter graph and comment on any relationship between the two variables.

b A local councillor notices that there has been a sharp increase in the number of road accidents in recent years. She puts the blame on an increase in the number of takeaway restaurants. Does the scatter graph provide statistical evidence to support the councillor's view?

8 What sort of correlation would you expect to find between

a height above sea level and air temperature

b adults' weekly calorie intake and their weight

c a student's shoe size and their marks on a French exam?

9 Future skills In a chemistry experiment, the mass of chemical produced, y, and temperature, x, are recorded.

x (°C)	100	110	120	130	140	150	160	170	180	190	200
y (mg)	34	39	41	45	48	47	41	35	26	15	3

a Plot these points on a scatter graph.

b State the type of correlation between mass and temperature.

c Describe in words what happens to the mass of chemical produced as the temperature increases from 100 to 200 °C.

10 A manufacturer of mp3 players monitors the cost of quality control (in £10 000s) and the percentages of faulty items.
The results are shown on the scatter graph.

a State the type of correlation between these variables.

b Describe the relationship between cost of quality control and percentage of faulty items.

c What was the highest percentage of faulty items in the data set?

d Find the range of the cost of quality control.

Quality control of mp3 players

Cost of quality control (£10 000s)

3.4 Line of best fit

- Draw a line of best fit on a scatter graph.
- Use the line of best fit to predict values.

Active Learn
Homework

Warm up

1 **Fluency** Complete this sentence.
When the correlation between x and y is negative, as values of x increase, values of y _____

2 What is the value of
a y when $x = 6$
b x when $y = 2.5$?

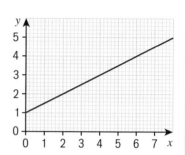

Key point

A **line of best fit** is the line that passes as close as possible to the points on a scatter graph. It represents the trend in the data.

3 **Reasoning** Which line, A, B or C, is the best line of best fit for the data points on the scatter graph?

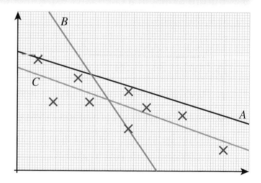

Example

The scatter graph shows the GDP per capita (in $1000s) and life expectancy (in years) for eight countries.

GDP per capita and life expectancy

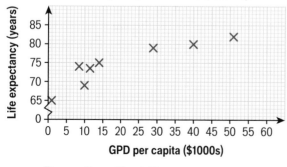

Hint

The gross domestic product (GDP) measures the value of goods and services produced by a country. The GDP per capita is the GDP divided by the number of people in that country.

a Draw a line of best fit.

b The GDP per capita in the UK is $36 000. Estimate the life expectancy of a baby born in the UK.

a

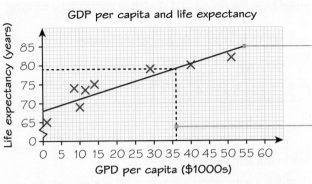

GDP per capita and life expectancy

Life expectancy (years) / GPD per capita ($1000s)

> Position a transparent ruler over the scatter graph so it follows the overall trend. Move it slightly so you have roughly the same number of points above and below the line.

> Start at $36 000 on the horizontal axis, go up to the line of best fit and read off the answer on the vertical axis.

b Estimated life expectancy in the UK is 79 years.

4 The table shows the height and weight of eight athletes.

Height (cm)	155	166	170	175	178	192	193	198
Weight (kg)	50	65	64	77	67	85	115	95

Q4 hint

Scatter graphs are also called scatter diagrams.

a Draw a scatter graph for this data.

b Draw a line of best fit on your graph.

c Use your line of best fit to estimate the weight of an athlete who is 185 cm tall.

d Estimate the height of an athlete who weighs 60 kg.

Key point

Individual points which are outside the overall pattern of a scatter graph are called **outliers**.
If they are likely to be from incorrect readings you can ignore them.

Exam-style question

5 The scatter graph shows the age and price of 10 cars.

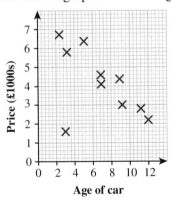

Price (£1000s) / Age of car

One of the points is an outlier.

a Write down the coordinates of this point. **(1 mark)**

b For all the other points, write down the type of correlation. **(1 mark)**

The price of another car is £6000.

c Estimate the age of this car. **(2 marks)**

A car salesperson says, 'Older cars cost less.'

d Does the scatter graph support what the car salesperson says?
Give a reason for your answer. **(1 mark)**

6 **Reasoning** An elastic rope is suspended from the ceiling and stretched vertically by hanging weights on the end.
The table shows the weight, W (in newtons), and length, L (in cm), of the elastic.

W (N)	1	2	4	4.5	5	6.5	8.5	9	10
L (cm)	12.4	14.8	18.6	20.4	21.2	24.5	29.4	30.4	40

  a Draw a scatter graph for this data.

  b Which point is an outlier?

  c Draw a line of best fit passing close to the remaining eight points.

  d Use the line to estimate the length of the elastic when a mass of 7 N is suspended.

7 **Reasoning** The table shows the height and shoe size of a group of male college students.

Height (cm)	158	168	164	167	174	178	173	185
Shoe size	4	5	6	8.5	8.5	10	10.5	12

  a Draw a scatter graph for the data.

  b Draw a line of best fit and use it to estimate

    i the shoe size of someone who is 175 cm tall

    ii the height of someone with shoe size 7

    iii the height of someone with shoe size 13.5.

  c Which of the estimates in part **b** do you think is the least reliable? Give a reason for your answer.

> **Key point**
>
> Using a line of best fit to predict data values within the range of the given data is called **interpolation** and is usually reasonably accurate.
> Using a line of best fit to predict data values outside the range of the given data is called **extrapolation** and may not be accurate.

8 **Problem-solving** A chemical engineer heats gas inside a sealed tank.
She measures the temperature (in kelvins, K) and pressure (in atmospheres, atm).

Temperature (K)	300	303	304	312	325	339	343	351
Pressure (atm)	1.4	1.5	1.7	2.0	2.2	2.3	2.5	3.0

Draw a scatter graph and

  a estimate the temperature required to create a pressure of 2.8 atm

  b estimate the pressure when the temperature is 308 K.

9 **Reasoning** Jack and Joe perform an identical experiment in a science lesson. The scatter graphs show their results.

  a Use the given lines of best fit to work out two estimates for the value of y at $x = 3$.

  b Which of the estimates is likely to be more reliable? Give a reason for your answer.

Jack's results

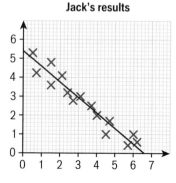

Joe's results

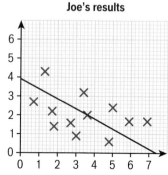

10 The scatter graph shows the distance, *d*, of ten flats from a city centre and the monthly rent, *M*, for each.

Distance from city centre and rent

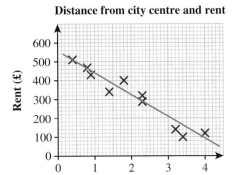

Distance (km)

> **Exam tip**
>
> Always draw lines on your diagram for any readings from your graph. If you get the answer wrong, you may still get marks for using the correct method.

a Write down the type of correlation. **(1 mark)**

b Dan's flat is 2.5 km from the city centre.
The monthly rent is £750.
The point representing this information would be an outlier on the scatter graph.
Explain why. **(1 mark)**

c Estimate the monthly rent of a flat that is 2.7 km from the city centre. **(1 mark)**

11 The table shows the age, *x*, and mass, *y*, of a sample of 11 boys.

x (years)	2	4	6	8	10	12	14	16	18	20	22
y (kg)	13	16	21	25	33	40	51	60	67	71	72

a Draw a scatter graph of this data.

b Use a line of best fit to estimate the mass of

  i a 15-year-old

  ii a 24-year-old.

c Which of the answers in part **b** is likely to be the more reliable?

d By drawing a smooth curve close to the data points, make new estimates of the masses in part **b**.

e Which of the two models is the more accurate? Give a reason for your answer.

12 **Reflect** A lot of the questions in this lesson ask you to estimate.
Write a definition of the word 'estimate' in your own words.

3.5 Averages and range

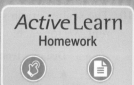
*Active*Learn
Homework

- Decide which average is best for a set of data.
- Estimate the mean and range from a grouped frequency table.
- Find the modal class and the class containing the median.

Warm up

1 **Fluency a** Write down the number which is halfway between 11 and 20.

   b What is the middle value in the interval $20 \leqslant x < 40$?

2 The table shows the scores when a dice is rolled.

   a How many times is the dice rolled in total?

   b What is the modal score?

Score	1	2	3	4	5	6
Frequency	4	1	3	3	2	1

Key point

The **mean** is the total of the set of values divided by the number of values.

3 Jo has 4 cards. There is a number on each card.
The mean of the 4 numbers on Jo's cards is 12.
Work out the number on the 4th card.

4 There are 14 boys and 11 girls in a class.
The class has a test.
The mean mark for all the boys is 9. The mean mark for all the girls is 6.
Work out the mean mark for the class. Give your answer to the nearest whole number.

5 **Reasoning** The annual salaries of staff who work in a cake shop are
£12 000, £12 000, £15 000, £18 000, £40 000.

   a Work out the mean, median and mode of staff salaries.

   b The company wishes to quote one of the averages in an advertisement for new staff.
The number quoted in the advert must represent a typical salary that you could reasonably expect to earn.
Which of the averages would be the most appropriate? Give reasons for your answer.

6 **Reasoning** The sizes of shoes sold in a shop during a morning are
5, 5.5, 5.5, 6, 7, 7, 7, 7, 8.5, 9, 9, 10, 11, 11.5, 12, 13

   a Work out the mean, median and mode of these shoe sizes.

   b The shop manager wishes to buy more stock but is only allowed to buy shoes of one size.
Which one of these averages would be the most appropriate to use?
Give reasons for your answer.

7 **Reasoning** State whether it is better to use the mean, median or mode for these data sets.
Give reasons for your answers.

   a Times taken for five people to perform a task (in seconds): 6, 25, 26, 30, 30.

   b Car colour: red, red, grey, black, black, black, blue.

8 **Future skills** The monthly costs of heating a shop in the winter months are shown in the table.

Month	Heating cost
Nov	£180
Dec	£190
Jan	£270
Feb	£240
Mar	£180

   a Work out the mean, median and mode of heating costs.

   b The shop must provide a report of expenses and overheads to its accountant.
   Which of the averages is the most appropriate to provide in the report? Give reasons for your answer.

9 **Reflect** In your own words, write notes on the differences between mean, median and mode. Include an example of when each would be appropriate to use.

10 Identify the outliers in the data sets.
Find the range of each data set.

> **Q10 hint**
> Think about whether the outlier is likely to be a correct value, and whether to include it in your calculation.

   a The masses of six members of a local wrestling team:
   7 kg, 76 kg, 82 kg, 89 kg, 96 kg, 101 kg

   b The salaries of the six people who work in a restaurant:
   £14 000, £15 000, £15 000, £17 500, £19 000, £38 000

11 Identify the outliers in the data sets. Calculate a sensible value of the range.
Give a reason why you included or excluded the outlier in your calculation.

   a Nine temperature readings (in °C) recorded during a science experiment:
   34, 44, 30, 27, 500, 30, 40, 45, 2.9

   b The profit or loss made by a firm during the last six years (the negative numbers indicate a loss):
   £100 000, −£250 000, £50 000, £75 000, £150 000, −£25 000

> **Key point**
> When data is grouped, you can calculate an estimate for the mean.

> **Example**
> The table shows the times, T, taken for 100 people to queue for a rollercoaster at a theme park.
>
>   **a** Estimate the mean waiting time.
>   **b** Explain why the mean is only an estimate.
>   **c** Estimate the range.
>
> The third column gives an estimate of the waiting time in each class.
>
> The fourth column gives an estimate of the total waiting time in each class.
>
> **a**
>
> | Time, T (min) | Frequency, f | Class midpoint, x | xf |
> |---|---|---|---|
> | $0 \leqslant T < 20$ | 14 | 10 | $10 \times 14 = 140$ |
> | $20 \leqslant T < 40$ | 55 | 30 | $30 \times 55 = 1650$ |
> | $40 \leqslant T < 60$ | 31 | 50 | $50 \times 31 = 1550$ |
> | **Total** | 100 | | 3340 |
>
> $$\text{Mean} = \frac{\text{sum of waiting times}}{\text{total number of people}} = \frac{3340}{100}$$
>
> $$= 33.4 \text{ minutes}$$
>
> **b** The mean is an estimate because we don't know the exact times taken.
>
> **c** Range = $60 - 0 = 60$

12 Reasoning The grouped frequency table shows the lengths of Kate's phone calls during the last month.

Time, T (min)	Frequency, f	Midpoint, x	xf
$0 \leqslant T < 4$	27	2	$2 \times 27 = 54$
$4 \leqslant T < 10$	34		
$10 \leqslant T < 20$	15		
$20 \leqslant T < 60$	4		
Total			

a Copy and complete the table to estimate the mean length of phone calls.

b Estimate the range. Explain why this value is an estimate.

> **Key point**
>
> If the total frequency in a grouped frequency table is n, then the median lies in the class containing the $\dfrac{n+1}{2}$ th item of data.
>
> The **modal class** has the highest frequency.

13 Reasoning The times taken for students to do their maths homework are shown in the table.

t (min)	Frequency
$0 \leqslant t < 10$	3
$10 \leqslant t < 20$	5
$20 \leqslant t < 30$	8
$30 \leqslant t < 40$	5

a How many students took less than 10 minutes to do their homework?

b How many students altogether took less than 20 minutes to do their homework?

c How many students altogether took less than 30 minutes to do their homework?

d State the modal class.

e Explain why the median is the 11th data value.

f Use your answers to parts **a** to **d** to work out which class interval contains the median.

14 Problem-solving The table shows the distances jumped by two athletes training for a long jump event.

Distance, d(m)	Ben's frequency	Jamie's frequency
$6.5 \leqslant d < 7.0$	3	8
$7.0 \leqslant d < 7.5$	7	18
$7.5 \leqslant d < 8.0$	25	21
$8.0 \leqslant d < 8.5$	1	3
$8.5 \leqslant d < 9.0$	0	1

a How many jumps did Ben do in training?

b In which class interval is Ben's median?

c Work out which class interval contains Jamie's median distance.

d Calculate the mean distance jumped by each athlete.

e State the modal class and estimate the range for Ben and for Jamie.

f At the long jump event, both athletes must compete against the current champion, who jumped 8.31 m.
Who stands the better chance of beating the champion? Justify your answer.

15 **Problem-solving** Particulates are very small particles.
For example, dust and soot are both particulates.
The legal air pollution limits for particulates are a yearly mean of

- 40 mg in every cubic metre of air for coarse particles

- 25 mg in every cubic metre of air for fine particles.

The frequency polygons show the amounts of particulates a factory produced one year.

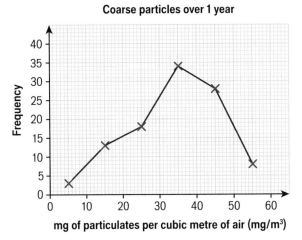

Coarse particles over 1 year

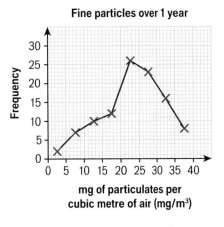

Fine particles over 1 year

Are the means above or below the legal limits for particulates?

Exam-style question

16 A rail company monitors delays on its peak time weekday service.
The results for the last month are shown in the frequency polygon.

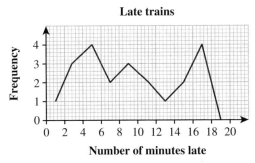

Late trains

Exam tip

Make sure you understand what the diagram represents before you begin.

a How many trains were more than 14 minutes late last month? **(1 mark)**

b The company offers compensation to its monthly season ticket holders if the mean delay on its peak weekday trains exceeds 10 minutes.
Should the company offer compensation for last month? **(3 marks)**

3.6 Statistical diagrams 2

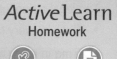
Active Learn
Homework

- Construct and use two-way tables.
- Choose appropriate diagrams to display data.
- Recognise misleading graphs.

Warm up

1 Fluency There are 670 boys in a school of 1200. How many girls are there?

2 The table shows the drink choices of a group of 40 people.

Drink	Tea	Coffee	Cola	Water
Frequency	8	20	5	7

   a Draw a pie chart to represent this data.

   b Draw a bar chart to represent this data.

Key point

A **two-way table** divides data into groups in rows across the table and in columns down the table.

3 Problem-solving A group of 180 students are asked whether they did their maths homework last night. The table shows some information about their responses. Copy and complete the table.

	Yes	No	Total
Boys		30	
Girls	25		100
Total			180

4 Reasoning A clinical trial is carried out to compare the effect of two drugs for the treatment of hay fever.

One hundred hay fever sufferers were given either drug A or drug B. After a week, the patients were asked to choose one of three responses: no change, improved or much improved.

	No change	Improved	Much improved	Total
Drug A	10			60
Drug B			13	
Total	17	65		100

   a Copy and complete the table.

   b What fraction of these patients were given drug B?

   c Which drug performed better in this trial?
     Give reasons for your answer.

5 Reasoning Students were asked whether they wanted more lockers in the school changing rooms. In Year 10, 110 of the 180 students wanted more lockers. In Year 11, 100 of the 210 students did not want more lockers.

   a Display this information in a two-way table.

   b The school will only buy new lockers if at least 60% of Year 10 and 11 students want them.
     Explain whether the school will buy the lockers.

6 The bar chart shows people's answers to the question,
'Do we need a high speed rail link?'

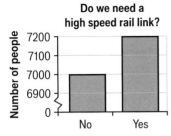

**Do we need a
high speed rail link?**

The government claims that this provides convincing evidence that people want the rail link.

a Look carefully at the vertical scale.
Explain why this bar chart is misleading.

b Write a sentence to explain what the bar chart really shows.

7 A supplier of 'Nutty Oats Muesli' claims that it provides more fibre than three rival brands.
It uses the bar chart to support this claim.

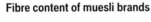

Fibre content of muesli brands

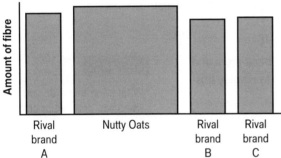

Give *two* reasons why this diagram is misleading.

8 **Reasoning** The line graph shows the share price of an ICT company on the first day of each month.

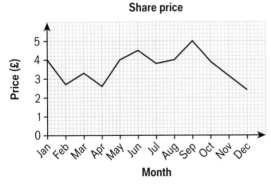

Share price

a Find the share price on 1 May.

b Amelia bought 250 shares on 1 February. She sold them on 1 October.
How much profit did she make?

c In which months should Amelia have bought and then sold her shares to make the
highest profit?

9 **Reasoning** A shop sells four types of crisps: ready salted (RS), cheese and onion (CO), salt and vinegar (SV), and smoky bacon (SB).
On one day, the shop sells these flavours to boys and girls:
Boys: CO, RS, CO, SV, SV, RS, RS, SB, CO, CO, RS, SB, RS, RS, CO, CO, RS, SV, SV, RS
Girls: RS, SB, SV, SV, CO, CO, RS, RS, RS, SV, RS, CO, SB, SV, SB, SV, SB, CO, SB, CO

   a Explain why it is not possible to display this data on a frequency polygon.

   b The shop manager decides to display the data on either a pie chart or a bar chart.
   Which should he use if he is most interested in

   i the proportion of each flavour bought by the boys or girls combined

   ii comparing the number of each flavour bought by boys and girls?

   c The shop manager orders 720 packets of crisps from a supplier.
   How many packets of cheese and onion crisps should he order?

10 A teacher records the marks awarded to boys and girls on a test:
   Boys: 23, 7, 10, 34, 10, 5, 3, 39, 31, 6, 7, 15, 21
   Girls: 1, 15, 25, 39, 17, 24, 11, 28, 6, 39, 20, 16

   a State one advantage of using a back-to-back stem and leaf diagram instead of a dual bar chart to display this information.

   Q10a hint
   What information do you lose when you draw a bar chart?

   b Draw a back-to-back stem and leaf diagram for this data.

   c Compare the performance of boys and girls on this test.

Exam-style question

11 A researcher wants to compare the waiting times at several hospital accident and emergency departments.
The table shows the waiting times at one of the hospitals over a morning.

Waiting time, T (min)	Frequency
$0 \leqslant T < 30$	20
$30 \leqslant T < 60$	35
$60 \leqslant T < 90$	30
$90 \leqslant T < 120$	24
$120 \leqslant T < 150$	15
$150 \leqslant T < 180$	12

Exam tip
Imagine trying to draw each diagram. You should also think about what the diagram is going to be used for.

Which *one* of these statistical diagrams would be the best diagram to use to display this data?
stem and leaf   pie chart   frequency polygon   scatter graph

Give reasons for your choice.   **(4 marks)**

3 Check up

Active Learn
Homework

Statistical diagrams

1 Copy and complete the two-way table, which shows the voting intentions of a group of men and women.

	Party A	Party B	Total
Men	120		200
Women			
Total		130	380

a How many women are in the group?

b How many women intend to vote for Party A?

2 A group of 48 adults are asked what their favourite subject was at school. They can choose from maths, English and science.
A group of 32 school children are asked the same question.
The pie charts show the choices for the adults and children separately.

a How many adults chose English?

b Reeshma says that an equal number of adults and children chose maths.
Is she correct? Give a reason for your answer.

Favourite mode of transport

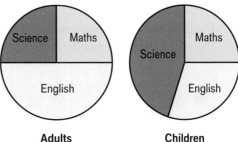

Adults   Children

3 The back-to-back stem and leaf diagram shows the lengths of cod and plaice caught by a fishing trawler.

a How many cod did the trawler catch?

b Find the ranges.

c Find the median length of plaice caught.

d Compare the distributions of the lengths of cod and plaice.

Cod		Plaice
7 4 1 0	1	7 8 8 9 9
9 7 4 1	2	7
8 7 3 0	3	0
9 4 3	4	2 5 5 5 5

Key: (Cod) 0 | 1 represents 10 cm
(Plaice) 1 | 7 represents 17 cm

4 Draw a frequency polygon for this data.

Time	$0 \leqslant t < 20$	$20 \leqslant t < 40$	$40 \leqslant t < 60$	$60 \leqslant t < 80$	$80 \leqslant t < 100$
Frequency	6	5	1	2	5

Averages and range

5 Identify the outliers in the data sets. Work out the range of each, including the outliers.

a Prices of TVs: £450, £450, £640, £690, £4800

b Heights of plants in cm: 42, 47, 39, 51, 22, 24

6 For the grouped frequency table

a estimate the mean

b find the class that contains the median

c estimate the range

d state the modal class.

Class	Frequency
$0 \leqslant x < 5$	7
$5 \leqslant x < 10$	15
$10 \leqslant x < 15$	13
$15 \leqslant x < 20$	4
$20 \leqslant x < 25$	1

Scatter graphs and time series

7 The time series graph shows the sales (in 1000s) of bottles of sun cream during the last three years.

a How many bottles were sold in the third quarter (Q3) of 2017?

b Give a possible reason why the sales fluctuate up and down.

c Describe the overall trend in sales over this three-year period.

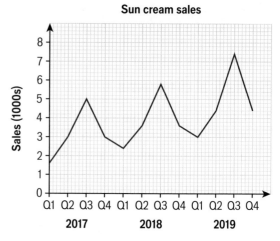

Sun cream sales

8 The table shows the marks awarded to seven candidates taking two maths exams. The information is displayed in the scatter graph together with a line of best fit.

Candidate	A	B	C	D	E	F	G
Marks for Paper 1	57	68	42	24	28	71	34
Marks for Paper 2	45	61	28	14	22	64	24

a Write down the type of correlation.

b Use the line of best fit to estimate the mark that someone might get on

  i Paper 2 if they get 50 on Paper 1

  ii Paper 1 if they get 90 on Paper 2.

c Which of your answers to part b would you expect to be more reliable?
Give reasons for your answer.

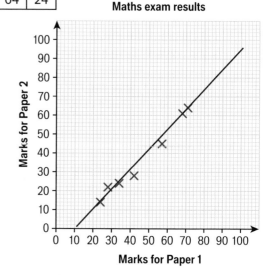

Maths exam results

9 **Reflect** How sure are you of your answers? Were you mostly

Just guessing 🙁   Feeling doubtful 😐   Confident 🙂

What next? Use your results to decide whether to strengthen or extend your learning.

Challenge

10 a Write down any four numbers and calculate the mean.

b Add 3 to each number in your list and calculate the new mean.

c What do you notice about your answers to parts a and b?

d Let the four numbers be w, x, y and z.
Use algebra to show that this works for any set of four numbers.

e What happens to the mean when each number is multiplied by c?
Use algebra to show you are correct.

3 Strengthen

Active Learn
Homework

Statistical diagrams

1 A group of 40 boys and 72 girls are asked to choose their favourite Olympic sport from archery, badminton, cycling and diving.
The pie charts show the choices for the boys and girls separately.

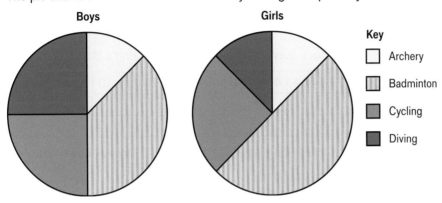

Boys **Girls**

Key
- ☐ Archery
- ▨ Badminton
- ▨ Cycling
- ▨ Diving

a What fraction of the girls' pie chart represents badminton?

b How many girls chose badminton?

c How many boys chose cycling?

d Work out the numbers for archery in each pie chart.
Sam says that equal numbers of boys and girls chose archery.
Is he correct? Give a reason for your answer.

2 A group of 20 children are asked if they have a pet. The information is shown in the two-way table.

a Work out the number of boys who have a pet.

b Work out the total number of boys.

c Work out the total number of girls.

d Fill in the remaining numbers in the table.

	Yes	No	Total
Boys		4	
Girls	3		
Total	5		20

3 The back-to-back stem and leaf diagram shows the times taken (in minutes) to complete a task by a group of boys and girls.

a How many boys are there in the group?

b Is the shortest time for the boys: 14 minutes or 41 minutes?

c Where would you record a time of 40 minutes in the girls' chart?

d How many girls took longer than 40 minutes to complete the task?

Boys		Girls
4	1	5 9 9
9 8 0 0	2	0 2 7 7
8 7 3 0	3	0 2 4
3	4	5 6

Key: (Boys) 4 | 1 represents 14 min
(Girls) 1 | 5 represents 15 min

4 a Copy and complete the back-to-back stem and
leaf diagram for these data sets.
A: 20, 27, 30, 30, 32, 38, 49
B: 26, 28, 28, 32, 33, 40

Set A		Set B
7 0	2	6 8 8
	3	
	4	

Key: (Set A) 7 | 2 represents 27
(Set B) 2 | 6 represents 26

b The median is the middle value.
If there are two middle values, the median is halfway
between them.
Find the median of each data set.

c The range is the difference between the largest and smallest values.
Find the range of each data set.

d Compare the data sets, by comparing the ranges and the medians.

5 Twenty people record the time, t hours, they spend on the internet during a day.

Time, t (hours)	$0 \leqslant t < 2$	$2 \leqslant t < 4$	$4 \leqslant t < 6$	$6 \leqslant t < 8$	$8 \leqslant t < 10$
Frequency	1	3	9	5	2
Time midpoint	1	3			

a Copy and complete the table to show the midpoints.

b Copy and complete the frequency polygon.
Plot the midpoints on the horizontal axis and
frequency on the vertical axis.

Time spent on internet

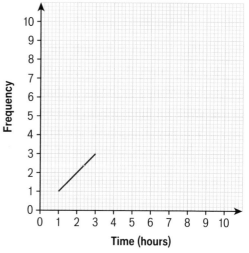

6 The frequency polygon shows the length
(in minutes) of 15 songs.

Length of songs

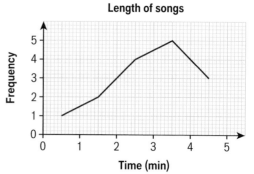

a Copy and complete the table.

Midpoint	0.5	1.5			
Interval	$0 \leqslant t < 1$	$1 \leqslant t < 2$			
Frequency	1	2			

b Check that the frequencies add up to 15.

Averages and range

1 Jason records the following lengths during a physics experiment.
3.4 cm, 5.8 cm, 2.9 cm, 4.8 cm, 46 cm, 5.8 cm

  a Which one of these values is an outlier?

  b Outliers can be removed if you think they are clear errors.
What do you think Jason might have done here?

  c Calculate the range.
Do not include the outlier value in your calculation.

2 A zoologist measures the lengths of 50 snakes (to the nearest cm).

Length, L (cm)	Frequency	Midpoint	Frequency × midpoint
$0 \leqslant L < 10$	7	5	$7 \times 5 = 35$
$10 \leqslant L < 20$	12	15	$12 \times 15 = 180$
$20 \leqslant L < 30$	20		
$30 \leqslant L < 40$	8		
$40 \leqslant L < 50$	3		
Total	50		

On a copy of the table

  a complete the third column to show the midpoints of each class

  b complete the fourth column to find the total length of all the snakes.

  c Divide the total length by the total number of snakes to work out the mean length.

  d The modal class is the one with the highest frequency.
Write down the modal class, $\square \leqslant L < \square$

  e There are 50 numbers in the grouped frequency table.

The median is the $\dfrac{50+1}{2} = 25.5$th number, so is halfway between the 25th and 26th numbers.

There are 7 numbers in the first group, 12 in the second (making 19 so far) and 20 in the third (making 39). The 25th and 26th numbers must be in the _____ group.
Write down the class that contains the median, $\square \leqslant L < \square$

Scatter graphs and time series

1 State whether each scatter graph shows positive, negative or no correlation.

  a

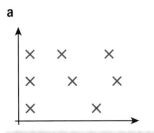

  b

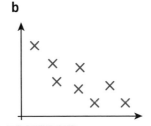

  c

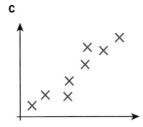

> **Q1 hint**
>
> Do the points lie close to a line? If not, there is no correlation. An uphill line shows positive correlation and a downhill line shows negative correlation.

2 In a science experiment a ball is dropped onto the ground five times to see if there is a connection between the height of the drop and the height of the bounce.

Drop (cm)	50	75	100	150	200
Bounce (cm)	24	38	42	80	92

a Copy and complete the scatter graph.

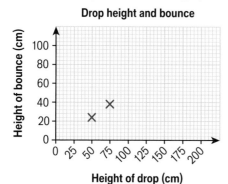

Drop height and bounce

b Copy and complete the sentence.
As the height of the drop increases, the height of the bounce _____ .

c Does the scatter graph show positive, negative or no correlation?

d Use a transparent ruler to draw a line so you have two or three points above the line and a similar number below.

e To predict the height of bounce when the ball is dropped from a height of 125 cm:

- Start at 125 cm on the horizontal axis.

- Draw a vertical line up until you hit the line of best fit.

- Now draw a horizontal line from that point across to the vertical axis and read off the answer.

3 The time series graph shows the numbers of ice creams sold by one shop in an English town.

a Describe how the sales varied in 2018.
Use these words in your description:

    increased   decreased   maximum

b Copy and complete this table of values from the graph.

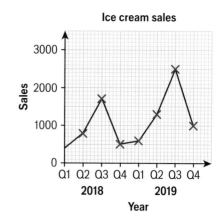

Ice cream sales

Year	Q1	Q2	Q3	Q4
2018	400		1700	
2019		1300		1000

c For every quarter in 2019, were sales lower or higher than in 2018?

d Was the overall trend in sales in 2018 and 2019 increasing or decreasing?

3 Extend

1 **Reasoning** Each point on the scatter graph shows the mass of a bag of fertiliser and its price.

   a Which two bags are the same price?

   b Which of B and D gives the better value for money?

   c Which two bags give the same value for money?

   d Which bag gives the worst value for money?

   e Describe the correlation.

   Give reasons for your answers.

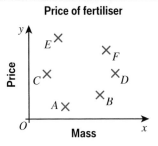

Price of fertiliser

2 **Reasoning** There is positive correlation between variables x and y, negative correlation between y and z, and negative correlation between z and w.
   State what type of correlation you would expect between

   a x and z b y and w c x and w

3 **Problem-solving/Reasoning**

   a Find a set of five positive whole numbers with

   • range 10

   • mode 4

   • median 6

   • mean 7

   Is there more than one possible set?

   b Repeat for a set of six numbers.
   Find as many possible answers as you can.

4 **Problem-solving** Two dozen tomato plants are grown in a greenhouse and the total weight of fruit produced by each plant is recorded.
   The same number of tomato plants of this variety are grown outdoors.
   The information is displayed in the frequency polygons.

   a Estimate the greatest mass of tomatoes produced by a plant grown outdoors.

   b How many plants grown in the greenhouse produce between 4 kg and 6 kg of fruit?

   c The grower claims that the average amount of fruit from plants grown in the greenhouse exceeds the average amount from outdoor plants by more than 3 kg.
   Does the data support this claim?

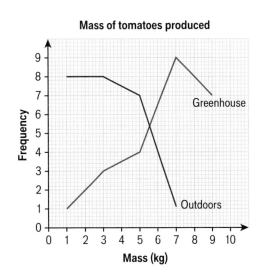

Mass of tomatoes produced

5 Reasoning A group of 50 students take a maths test.
Their marks out of 40 are shown in the table.

Marks	20–22	23–25	26–30	31–40
Frequency	1	15	22	12

a Estimate the mean mark and explain why this is only an estimate.

b Explain which class contains the median.

c Estimate the range.

d The student whose mark was between 20 and 22 has her paper re-marked.
She is awarded a new mark between 23 and 25.
Without doing any calculations, state whether the following will increase,
decrease or stay the same.

   i Range   **ii** Mean

6 Reasoning Every student in Year 10 completes a questionnaire
in which they are asked to choose their favourite takeaway food
from pizza, burger and curry.
The results are shown on the pie chart.

a 132 students chose pizza. How many chose burger?

b On a similar pie chart for Year 11, the angle of the sector for
pizza is 200°.
Explain why this does not necessarily mean that fewer
students in Year 11 chose pizza as their favourite.

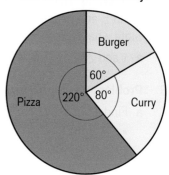

7 Reasoning The stem and leaf diagram shows the ages in
complete years of a sample of 24 men in a tennis club.

a Find the median age.

b The ages, in complete years, of a sample of 14 women from
the club are:
82, 58, 53, 9, 23, 81, 45, 48, 31, 77, 16, 23, 64, 62
Draw a back-to-back stem and leaf diagram for the men's and
women's ages.

c Without doing any further calculations, write one comparison
between the ages of men and women at the club.

```
0 | 8
1 | 2 8
2 | 1 6 7
3 | 1 4 7 9
4 | 0 0 0 2 5
5 | 0 7 7 8
6 | 2 3 4
7 | 0
8 | 3
```

Key: 1 | 2 means 12 years

8 The table shows the age and mass of a group of 10 people.

Age	5	8	12	13	15	30	40	45	52	55
Mass (kg)	18	30	45	49	57	76	79	81	83	84

a Plot these points on a scatter graph.

b Draw a line of best fit on the diagram.

c Use your line to estimate the mass of someone who is 23 years old.

d A better model is to use two different straight lines, one up to 20 years old and the other for
over 20.
Draw these on your diagram and use them to obtain a more reliable answer to part **c**.

9   **Problem-solving** The table shows the age distribution of male and female teachers in a school.

a Draw frequency polygons for these two sets of data on the same diagram.

b Compare the age distributions of male and female teachers.

c What feature of your diagram confirms that your comparison is correct?

Age, x (years)	Male	Female
$20 \leqslant x < 25$	1	0
$25 \leqslant x < 30$	2	9
$30 \leqslant x < 35$	3	10
$35 \leqslant x < 40$	7	12
$40 \leqslant x < 45$	10	8
$45 \leqslant x < 50$	10	7
$50 \leqslant x < 55$	12	4
$55 \leqslant x < 60$	4	0
$60 \leqslant x < 65$	1	0

10 The table shows the annual salaries of 200 employees of a company.

a Copy and complete the table.

b What percentage of employees are women?

c What percentage of men earn under £30 000?

	Under £30 000	At least £30 000	Total
Men	60		90
Women		50	
Total			200

d What percentage of employees earning at least £30 000 are women?

11 A biologist measures the lengths of 40 fish and records the results in a grouped frequency table. The mean length is 15.75 cm. Find x.

Length, L (cm)	$0 \leqslant L < 10$	$10 \leqslant L < x$	$x \leqslant L < 3x$
Frequency	6	24	10

12 A set of data values, x, are shown below.

4720   5030   1800   2340   2590   1170   4600   3950

a Rewrite the data as a set of y values, where $y = \dfrac{x}{100}$

b Calculate the mean of the y values.

c Use your answer to part **b** to calculate the mean of the original data values, x.

At A level, the answer to one part of a question is often linked to a later part. Here, part **c** is directly related to the answer to part **b**.

13 The grouped frequency table shows the times taken by some students on their journey to school.

Time, t (minutes)	Frequency
$0 \leqslant t < 10$	11
$10 \leqslant t < 15$	y
$15 \leqslant t < 25$	26
$25 \leqslant t < 40$	x
$40 \leqslant t < 50$	5

The mean time for this group of students is 21 minutes, and x and y are in the ratio $x : y = 4 : 3$.
Work out the values of x and y.

The link between different areas of mathematics, as required in this question, is typical of work at A level. This statistics question needs the usual technique for finding the mean from a grouped frequency table, but you will also need to use algebra skills to write and solve two equations in x and y based on the given information.

3 Test ready

Summary of key points

To revise for the test:

- Read each key point, find a question on it in the mastery lesson, and check you can work out the answer.

- If you cannot, try some other questions from the mastery lesson or ask for help.

Key points

1 A **pie chart** represents a set of data. Each sector represents a category within that set of data. → 3.1

2 When n data values are written in order, the **median** is the $\frac{n+1}{2}$th value. → 3.1

3 To compare two sets of data, compare an average (mean, median or mode) and the range of each set. A small range shows the data values are all similar, or consistent. → 3.1

4 A **back-to-back stem and leaf diagram** compares two sets of data. On the left-hand side the numbers are read backwards. → 3.1

5 A **frequency polygon** is a graph made by joining the midpoints of the tops of the bars in a bar chart with straight lines. → 3.1

6 A quicker way of drawing a frequency polygon is to plot the frequency against midpoints for each group. → 3.1

7 A **time series** graph is a line graph with time plotted on the horizontal axis. → 3.2

8 A time series graph is useful for identifying trends. The **trend** is the general direction of change. ▸ 3.2

9 **Bivariate data** is data that has two variables. Points can be plotted on a **scatter graph** to see if there is a link between them. → 3.3

10 A scatter graph shows a relationship or **correlation** between variables. → 3.3

11 Data displays positive correlation if the points on a scatter graph lie close to an upward-sloping straight line. Data displays negative correlation if the points on a scatter graph lie close to a downward-sloping straight line. → 3.3

12 A **line of best fit** is the line that passes as close as possible to the points on a scatter graph. It represents the trend in the data. → 3.4

13 Individual points which are outside the overall pattern of a scatter graph are called **outliers**. They can be removed from a data set provided a reason for their removal is given. → 3.4

14 Using a line of best fit to predict data values within the range of the given data is called **interpolation** and is usually reasonably accurate. → 3.4

15 Using a line of best fit to predict data values outside the range of the given data is called **extrapolation** and may not be accurate. → 3.4

16 The **mean** is the total of the set of values divided by the number of values. → 3.5

17 To estimate a mean from a grouped frequency table, add together the products of class midpoints and their frequencies, and divide by the total frequency. → 3.5

Sample student answer

Exam-style question

The table gives information about the heights of 60 tomato plants.

Height, h (cm)	Frequency
$0 \leqslant h < 10$	12
$10 \leqslant h < 20$	17
$20 \leqslant h < 30$	23
$30 \leqslant h < 40$	8

Draw a frequency diagram for this information. **(2 marks)**

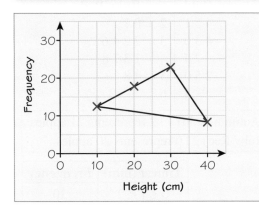

Write down two things that are wrong with the graph.

3 Unit test

*Active*Learn
Homework

1 To get a grade 9 in a GCSE exam, Bhavik must have a mean of at least 93%, averaged over three exam papers.
His mean score on the first two papers is 88%.
Is it still possible for him to achieve a grade 9 overall? Justify your answer. **(3 marks)**

2 The time series graph shows the rate of unemployment in a country over a 3-year period.

a What was the rate of unemployment in the second quarter of 2014?
Give your answer correct to 1 decimal place. **(1 mark)**

b Which quarter experienced the greatest fall in the rate of unemployment? **(1 mark)**

c Describe what this time series suggests about the trend in unemployment over the 3 years. **(1 mark)**

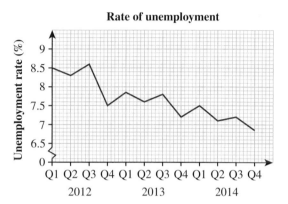

Rate of unemployment

3 The back-to-back stem and leaf diagram shows the number of apples growing on

a Find the range of the number of apples growing on 'Ruby Red' trees. **(1 mark)**

b Find the median number of apples growing on 'Autumn Gold' trees. **(2 marks)**

Autumn Gold		Ruby Red
4 5 1	2	0 7
4 3 0	3	2 2 4 6
7 4	4	1 3 7 8
2 5 0	5	4 8
4	6	

Key: (Autumn Gold) 1 | 2 represents 21 apples
(Ruby Red) 2 | 0 represents 20 apples

4 The table shows the time that 80 customers spent queuing in a bank.

a Work out an estimate for the mean queuing time. **(3 marks)**

b In which group is the median time? **(1 mark)**

c One of the customers whose time was recorded as 10 minutes actually only queued for 3 minutes.
Without doing any calculations, state whether your answers to parts **a** and **b** will increase, decrease or stay the same. **(2 marks)**

Time, t (min)	Frequency
$0 \leqslant t < 2$	20
$2 \leqslant t < 4$	25
$4 \leqslant t < 6$	18
$6 \leqslant t < 8$	2
$8 \leqslant t < 10$	6
$10 \leqslant t < 12$	9

5 The table shows the times taken to clean cars.

a Draw a frequency polygon to represent this data. **(2 marks)**

b State the modal class. **(1 mark)**

c Estimate the range. **(1 mark)**

Time, t (min)	Frequency
$0 \leqslant t < 10$	0
$10 \leqslant t < 20$	10
$20 \leqslant t < 30$	40
$30 \leqslant t < 40$	50
$40 \leqslant t < 50$	30

6 The table shows the number of hours six students spent revising for a maths test and their mark.

Time	5	2	8	1	6	4
Mark	80%	50%	90%	40%	75%	60%

   a Plot this data on a scatter graph. **(3 marks)**

   b Describe the correlation and explain what this means in this context. **(2 marks)**

   c Estimate the mark of someone who revises for 3 hours. **(1 mark)**

   d Jack says, 'The scatter graph shows that if I revise for 10 hours I should get 100%.'
     Comment on what Jack says. **(1 mark)**

7 An estate agent keeps a record of the types of property sold in the last month.

semi–detached	terraced	terraced	flat	detached	detached	flat
detached	flat	terraced	flat	flat	terraced	terraced
semi–detached	flat	detached	terraced	detached	flat	

   a Explain why it is not possible to draw a frequency polygon for this data. **(1 mark)**

   b Draw a pie chart for this data. **(3 marks)**

   c Next month's sales are also displayed on a pie chart.
     The angle for the sector representing flats is 140°.
     Explain whether this shows that the estate agent has sold more flats than last month.
     (1 mark)

8 100 people each bought an electronic tablet with a choice of 16 GB, 32 GB or 64 GB of memory.
   53 of the customers are women.
   12 of the women bought a 16 GB tablet.
   15 of the men bought a 32 GB tablet.
   20 of the 40 customers who bought a 64 GB tablet are men.

   a Draw a two-way table for this data. **(3 marks)**

   b What fraction of customers bought a 32 GB tablet? **(1 mark)**

                    (TOTAL: 35 marks)

9 **Challenge** A car manufacturer compares colour preferences of men and women.
   Potential customers are asked to pick their favourite colour from a list of four.
   The results are shown in the table.

Colour	creamy white	platinum grey	midnight blue	charcoal black
Men	2	13	25	20
Women	4	8	6	2

   Which one of these statistical diagrams could be used?
   scatter graph   frequency polygon   back-to-back stem and leaf diagram   pie chart
   Explain your choice.

10 **Reflect** Look back at the questions you answered in this test.

   a Which are you most confident that you have answered correctly?
     What makes you feel confident?

   b Which are you least confident that you have answered correctly?
     What makes you feel least confident?

   c Discuss the question you feel least confident about with a classmate.
     How does discussing it make you feel?

4 Fractions, ratio and percentages

4.1 Fractions

 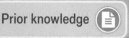
- Add, subtract, multiply and divide fractions and mixed numbers.
- Find the reciprocal of an integer, decimal or fraction.

Active Learn
Homework

Warm up

1 **Fluency** Write the mixed number $1\frac{1}{6}$ as an improper fraction.

2 Work out these. The first and last ones are started for you.

a $35 \times \frac{2}{7} = \frac{{}^{5}\cancel{35} \times 2}{{}_{1}\cancel{7}} = \square$ **b** $24 \times \frac{3}{8}$ **c** $8 \times \frac{5}{12}$ **d** $3 \div \frac{9}{11} = 3 \times \frac{11}{9} = \square$

3 Work out

a $21 \times 36 \div 14$ **b** $32 \times 45 \div 36$ **c** $9 \times 24 \div 8$

4 **Problem-solving** Tonia and Trinny are twins.
Their friends give them identical cakes for their birthday.
Tonia eats $\frac{1}{8}$ of her cake and Trinny eats $\frac{1}{6}$ of her cake.
How much cake is left ? Give your answer as a mixed number.

Key point

The **reciprocal** of the number n is $\frac{1}{n}$. You can also write this as n^{-1}.

5 Find the reciprocal of these.

a 8 **b** $\frac{2}{3}$ **c** $\frac{4}{3}$ **d** $\frac{1}{7}$

e **Reflect** Write a sentence explaining what happens when you multiply a number by its reciprocal.

6 Find the reciprocal of these decimals.

a 0.5 **b** 0.27 **c** 0.145 **d** 0.003

e **Reflect** What method did you use to work out the reciprocals of the decimal numbers?

7 Convert each number to an improper fraction.
Then find its reciprocal.

a $1\frac{1}{4}$ **b** $5\frac{2}{3}$ **c** 2.5 **d** 4.8

e Use a calculator to check your answers.

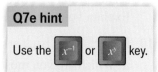

Q7e hint

Use the x^{-1} or x^{y} key.

8 Write a sentence explaining if it is possible to find the reciprocal of zero. Explain your answer.

Key point

It is often easier to write mixed numbers as improper fractions before doing a calculation.

9 Giving your answer as a mixed number in its simplest form where appropriate, work out

a $1\frac{1}{4} \times \frac{1}{6}$　　　b $1\frac{2}{5} \times \frac{2}{3}$　　　c $3\frac{3}{8} \times 1\frac{2}{9}$　　　d $2\frac{4}{5} \times 2\frac{1}{7}$

10 **Problem-solving** Work out the missing numbers.

a $2\frac{1}{2} \div \Box = \frac{1}{2}$　　b $2\frac{1}{2} \times \Box = \frac{1}{2}$

c Write inverse calculations to check your answers to parts **a** and **b**.

11 Giving your answer as a mixed number in its simplest form where appropriate, work out

a $1\frac{4}{7} \div \frac{2}{3}$　　　b $2\frac{7}{10} \div \frac{9}{25}$　　　c $2\frac{2}{3} \div 1\frac{7}{9}$　　　d $3\frac{1}{7} \div 2\frac{3}{4}$

12 **Reflect** Katherine says, 'Dividing by a fraction is the same as multiplying by the reciprocal of that fraction.'
Is she correct? Show working to explain your answer.

13 Work these out. The first one is started for you.

a $4\frac{7}{10} + 3\frac{1}{2} = \Box\frac{7}{10} + \frac{1}{2}$

　　$= \Box\frac{7}{10} + \frac{\Box}{10}$

　　$= \Box\frac{\Box}{10} = \Box\frac{\Box}{\Box}$

b $1\frac{9}{10} + 2\frac{3}{5}$

c $2\frac{7}{8} + 3\frac{1}{4}$

d $4\frac{4}{5} + 6\frac{5}{6}$

e $3\frac{4}{9} + 5\frac{3}{4}$

> **Q13d hint**
>
> Sometimes both denominators must be changed to add fractions.

14 Work these out. The first one is started for you.

a $4\frac{1}{2} - 1\frac{4}{5} = \frac{\Box}{2} - \frac{\Box}{5}$

　　$= \frac{\Box}{10} - \frac{\Box}{10}$

　　$= \frac{\Box}{10} = \Box\frac{\Box}{\Box}$

b $4\frac{1}{4} - 5\frac{3}{8}$

c $5\frac{3}{5} - 1\frac{7}{8}$

d $3\frac{1}{6} - 4\frac{1}{9}$

15 **Reflect**

a Do you always need to change mixed numbers to improper fractions to subtract? Explain.

b Does this method work when adding mixed numbers? Show working to explain.

Exam-style question

16 A part has broken on a machine and needs to be replaced.
The replacement must be between $7\frac{1}{18}$ cm and $7\frac{3}{18}$ cm long.
The diagram shows the replacement part.
Will this part fit the machine?
You must show your working.
(4 marks)

$4\frac{7}{9}$ cm　$2\frac{1}{3}$ cm

> **Exam tip**
>
> Explain your answer by showing your calculations. Write a sentence, 'The part will/will not fit the machine because ...'

17 **Problem-solving** Alice watched two films at the cinema.
The first film was $1\frac{5}{6}$ hours long and the second was $2\frac{1}{4}$ hours long.
How much longer was the second film than the first? Give your answer in minutes.

4.2 Ratios

- Write ratios in the form $1 : n$ or $n : 1$.
- Compare ratios.
- Find quantities using ratios.
- Solve problems involving ratios.
- Use bar models to help solve problems.

Active Learn
Homework

Warm up

1 **Fluency** Find the missing numbers.

a $\frac{1}{5} \times \square = 1$ **b** $\frac{2}{3} \times \square = 1$ **c** $\square \times \frac{5}{9} = 1$

2 Work out

a $\frac{2}{3}$ of 3 **b** $\frac{3}{4} \times \frac{10}{7}$ **c** $\frac{1}{2} \div 9$

3 Simplify these ratios.

a $3 : 6$ **b** $15 : 25$ **c** $24 : 42$

4 Convert the measures in each ratio to the same unit. Then simplify.

a $3\,cm : 15\,mm$ **b** $450\,g : 1.8\,kg$ **c** $1.8\,litres : 240\,ml$

5 Write each ratio in the form $1 : n$. The first one is started for you.

a
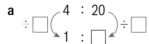

b $6 : 42$

c $28 : 14$ **d** $\frac{1}{3} : 2$ **e** $20 : 9$ **f** $\frac{3}{7} : \frac{2}{8}$

> **Q5c hint**
>
> The number on the right may not be a whole number.

Key point

You can compare ratios by writing them as **unit ratios**. In a unit ratio, one of the numbers is 1.

6 Write each ratio in the form $n : 1$. The first one is started for you.

a
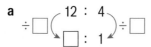

b $80 : 16$ **c** $30 : 45$

d $\frac{1}{2} : 7$ **e** $3 : \frac{1}{5}$ **f** $\frac{3}{4} : \frac{9}{10}$

7 Write these ratios in the form $1 : n$.

a £3 : 60p **b** $5\,kg : 80\,g$
c 2 hours : 45 minutes **d** $20\,cm : 7.3\,m$

> **Q7 hint**
>
> If the answer is not an integer, you can use fractions or decimals. Choose whichever is most accurate.

8 **Reasoning** In a school there are 52 teachers and 598 students.

a Write the student : teacher ratio in the form $n : 1$.

Another school has 85 teachers and 1020 students.

b Which school has the larger number of teachers per student?

9 **Problem-solving** Julie and Hammad each make a glass of orange squash.
Julie uses 42 ml of squash and 210 ml of water.
Hammad uses 30 ml of squash and 170 ml of water.
Who has made their drink stronger?

Q9 hint

Write the ratios in the form 1 : n

10 **Reasoning** Craig is painting his room orange.
He buys a tin of paint with red and yellow in the ratio 4 : 5.
Another tin of paint has yellow and red in the ratio 16 : 20.
Are the two tins of paint the same shade of orange? Explain your answer.

Key point

You can share amounts in a ratio.

---

11 **Reasoning** Archie and Ben share some money in the ratio 7 : 11.
Ben gets £132. How much money does Archie get?

Q11 hint

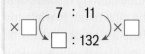

12 **Future skills** To make a tough adhesive,
Paul mixes 5 parts of resin with 2 parts of hardener.

   a Write down the ratio of resin to hardener.

   b To fix a birdbath, Paul uses 9 g of hardener. How many grams of resin does he use?

   c On another project, Paul used 12 g of resin. How much hardener did he use?

13 A scale model of Tower Bridge in London is 22 cm high. The real bridge is 66 m high.

   a Work out the scale of the model. Write it as the ratio of real height to model height.

   The bridge is 243 m long in real life.

   b How long is the model?

14 **Problem-solving** Sarah needs 150 g of butter to make 36 biscuits.
She also needs $1\frac{1}{6}$ as much flour as butter, and half as much sugar as flour.
Sarah is going to make 18 biscuits.
Work out how much sugar she needs to the nearest gram.

Q14 hint

Write the ratio
butter : flour : sugar : number of
                                biscuits

15 **Reasoning** On a farm, the number of chickens and the number of sheep are in the ratio 2 : 11.
The number of sheep and the number of cows are in the ratio 22 : 9.
There are 36 cows on the farm.
How many chickens are there?

Q15 hint

To work out the number of chickens, you need to know the number of sheep. You can work out the number of sheep using the ratio
sheep : cows
    22 : 9

Example

Share £126 between Lu and Katie in the ratio 2 : 5.

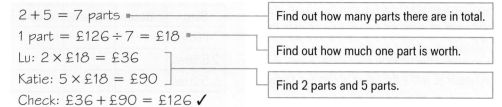

2 + 5 = 7 parts ◄—— Find out how many parts there are in total.
1 part = £126 ÷ 7 = £18 ◄—— Find out how much one part is worth.
Lu: 2 × £18 = £36
Katie: 5 × £18 = £90 ◄—— Find 2 parts and 5 parts.
Check: £36 + £90 = £126 ✓

16 Share 465 building blocks between Benji and Freddie in the ratio 7 : 8.
How many blocks does each person get?

17 James and Freya share a piece of fabric 20.4 m long in the ratio 3 : 2.
What length of fabric does Freya get?

18 **Problem-solving** The perimeter of a rectangle is 72 cm.
The ratio of its width to its length is 4 : 5.
Work out the area of the rectangle.

19 Share each quantity in the given ratio.

 a £374 in the ratio 2 : 4 : 5 **b** £46.80 in the ratio 1 : 3 : 4

 c 87 m in the ratio 3 : 1 : 6 **d** 774 kg in the ratio 2 : 7 : 2 : 1

 e **Reflect** How should you round your answer when working with money? What about with kg?

20 Some bunting is made of 99 triangles. There are red, white and blue triangles.
The ratio of red to white triangles is 5 : 2.
There are twice as many blue triangles as white triangles.

 a Copy and complete this bar model (rectangular bar) showing
the ratio of red to white to blue triangles.

 b How many triangles are blue?

Exam-style question

21 £242 is shared between Dan, Eva, Freddie and Gok.
The ratio of the amount Dan gets to the amount Eva gets
is 3 : 4.
Freddie and Gok each get half the amount Eva gets.
Work out the amount of money Dan gets. **(4 marks)**

Exam tip

You can draw bar models to help you answer exam questions.

22 In a bunch of flowers, there are some tulips and some roses.
The ratio of the number of tulips to the number of roses is 3 : 1.

 a Ali says, 'The number of flowers in the bunch must be a multiple of 4.' Explain how Ali knows.

 b The ratio of the number of red flowers to the number of yellow flowers in the bunch is 1 : 5.
Is Ali's statement in part **a** still correct? Explain.

 c Explain why the least possible number of flowers in the bunch is 12.

23 Write each ratio as a whole number
ratio in its simplest form.

 a 20 : 36.5

 b 71 : 120.5

 c 20.1 : 46.9

 d 90.3 : 6.02

Q23a hint

Multiply first by powers of
10 to make both sides of
the ratio whole numbers,
then simplify.

24 **Reasoning** Ben wants to make some turquoise paint.
He is going to mix blue, green and yellow paint in the
ratio 2.4 : 1.5 : 0.1
Copy and complete the table to show how much of each
colour Ben needs to make the paint quantities shown.

Size	Blue	Green	Yellow
1 litre			
2.5 litres			
5.5 litres			

4.3 Ratio and proportion

- Convert between currencies and measures.
- Recognise and use direct proportion.
- Solve problems involving ratios and proportion.

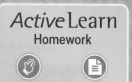

Active Learn
Homework

Warm up

1 Fluency A wildlife sanctuary has 7 adult tigers and 2 tiger cubs.
What proportion of the tigers are cubs?

2 Copy and complete these calculations. Find the missing fractions.

   a $\square \times 4 = 3$ **b** $\square \times 3 = 4$

3 Which of these ratios are equivalent?

   1 : 3   4 : 7   2 : 5   6 : 15   5 : 7.5

4 Future skills The exchange rate between British pounds (GBP) and Australian dollars (AUD) is 1 GPB : 1.80 AUD.

   a Convert 200 GBP to AUD.   **b** Convert 756 AUD to GBP.

5 Problem-solving / Future skills Kirsty buys a pair of jeans in the UK for £52.
On holiday in Hong Kong, she sees the same jeans on sale for HK$620.
The exchange rate is £1 = HK$12.40.
Where are the jeans cheaper?

6 Reasoning Ned and Adrian both go out for a bicycle ride one day.
Ned rides for 23.5 miles. Adrian rides for 41 km. 5 miles = 8 km.

   a Write the ratio of miles to kilometres in the form $1 : n$.

   b Work out who has ridden further and by how much.

7 A road is 7.6 m wide. Its width is divided for a bicycle lane and for cars in the ratio 1 : 3.

   a What proportion of the road width is taken up by the bicycle lane?

   b What is the width of the road that is left for cars?

Q7a hint

B	C	C	C

8 Reasoning In a theatre company, the ratio of musicians to actors is 3 : 5.
Jo says, '$\frac{3}{5}$ of the company are musicians.'
Alex says, 'No. The number of musicians is $\frac{3}{5}$ the number of actors.'
Is Jo correct or is Alex correct? Explain.

9 In a cake, the ratio of butter, b, to sugar, s, is 3 : 4.

   a Copy and complete the formulae.

      i $s = \square b$

      ii $b = \square s$

   b A recipe uses 117 g of butter. How much sugar does it use?

Q9a i hint

$b \; : \; s$

$3 \; : \; 4$

$\times \square$

$b \times \square = s$

10 **Reasoning** In a spicy beetroot recipe, for every 500 g of beetroot, there are 2 hot chillies.

    a Write a formula for c, the number of chillies used with n grams of beetroot.

    b Cara has 2.75 kg of beetroot. How many chillies does she need?

    Cara wants to make the recipe spicier. She doubles the number of chillies.

    c Write a formula for the new recipe.

Q10b hint

2.75 kg = ☐ g

> **Key point**
>
> When two quantities are in **direct proportion**, as one is multiplied by a number, n, so is the other.

11 **Future skills** In a science experiment, Kishan measures how far a spring extends when he adds different weights to it. The table shows his results.

Weight w, (N)	1	2	3	4	5
Extension, e (mm)	12	24	36	48	60

    a For each weight, write the ratio weight : extension in its simplest form.

    b **Reflect** What do you notice?

    c **Reasoning** Are the weight and extension in direct proportion? Explain.

12 **Future skills** The table gives readings P and Q in a science experiment.

P	5	10	14
Q	7.5	15	21

    a Write the ratio $P : Q$ in its simplest form.

    b Are P and Q in direct proportion? Explain.

    c Write a formula for Q in terms of P.

13 The values of A and B are in direct proportion. Work out the missing values P, Q, R and S.

Value of A	32	P	Q	20	72
Value of B	20	30	35	R	S

14 **Reasoning** 10 bread rolls cost £1.60. 15 bread rolls cost £2.24.
    Are the number of bread rolls and cost in direct proportion? Explain.

15 **Problem-solving** The length of the shadow of an object is directly proportional to the height of the object.
    A lamp post 4.8 m tall has a shadow 2.1 m long.
    Work out the height of a nearby bus stop with a shadow 1.05 m long.

16 **Future skills** Sophie can buy orange squash in two sizes: 2 litres for £4.75 or 600 ml for £1.80.
    Which size is better value for money?

> **Exam-style question**
>
> 17 Paolo is in Italy.
> The local deli sells packets of his favourite pasta.
> Each packet of pasta costs 4.20 euros. It weighs 240 g.
> In England, the same packet of pasta costs £12.75 per kg.
> The exchange rate is £1 = 1.16 euros.
> Work out whether the packet of pasta is better value for
> money in Italy or England.   **(4 marks)**

> **Exam tip**
>
> You only need to convert one of the prices into the other currency, not both, before you look at the weight.

4.4 Percentages

- Calculate using percentages and ratios.
- Work out percentage increases and decreases.
- Solve real-life problems involving percentages.

Active Learn
Homework

Warm up

1 Fluency What is
  a 10% of 250   **b** 30% of 250
  c 250 shared in the ratio 1 : 4   **d** 100 : 250 written in the form 1 : n?

2 Write down the single number you can multiply by to work out
  a an increase of 30%   **b** an increase of 5%
  c a decrease of 12%   **d** a decrease of 6%

3 Write the inverse calculations. Then work out the missing numbers.
  a $\square \times 1.2 = 60$ **b** $\square \times 0.8 = 96$

4 Problem-solving 270 bushes are planted to create a hedge. The bushes are bramble, hazel or holly. 30% of the bushes are bramble.
The ratio of the number of hazel bushes to the number of holly bushes is 5 : 4.
Work out the number of holly bushes planted.

> **Q4 hint**
>
> Read one sentence at a time and decide what calculation you need to do.

5 In a hospital there are 75 doctors and 240 nurses.
  a Write the ratio of doctors to nurses in the form 1 : n.
One year, 12% of the doctors leave but the number of nurses increases by 10%.
  b What is the ratio of doctors to nurses in the form 1 : n now?

6 Problem-solving Antony is 21 years old, Ross is 18 years old and Crista is 15 years old.
£540 is shared between them in the ratio of their ages.
Crista says, 'If the money is shared equally between all three of us, I get 20% more money.'
Is Crista correct? You must show your working.

Key point

In financial terms, 'appreciate' means to gain value and 'depreciate' means to lose value.

7 A gallery pays £6500 for an artwork by a famous artist.
The artwork appreciates by 3% each year.
Work out the value of the artwork after
  a 1 year   **b** 2 years

> **Q7b hint**
>
> The value at the end of year 1 appreciates another 3% in year 2.

8 Reasoning / Future skills Curtis buys a car for £9600.
The value of the car depreciates by 20% each year.
Work out the value of the car after 2 years.

9 **a** Work out the amount of simple interest earned in one year for each of these investments.

    i £1500 at 2% per year   **ii** £700 at 1.8% per year

 b Martina invests £14 500 for 3 years at 6.75% simple interest.
 How much is the investment worth at the end of the 3 years?

> **Q9b hint**
>
> Work out the amount of interest she earns each year and multiply by 3.

10 **Future skills** Income tax is paid on any money you earn over your personal tax allowance.
 The personal tax allowance is currently set at £12 500.
 Above this amount, tax is paid at different rates, depending on how much you earn.
 The table shows the rates for 2019/20.

Tax rate	Taxable income above your personal allowance
Basic rate 20%	£0 to £50 000
Higher rate 40%	£50 001 to £150 000

Work out the amount of income tax each of these people paid in the 2019/20 tax year.

 a Ella earns £26 500 per annum.

 b Sammy earns £28 760 p.a.

 c Antony earns £47 000 p.a.

 d Pippa earns £73 850 p.a.

> **Q10 hint**
>
> 'Per annum' (p.a.) means each year.
> Subtract the personal tax allowance before working out the tax owed.

11 **Future skills** Karen gets a gas bill. The cost of the gas before VAT was added was £361.20.
 VAT is charged at 5% on domestic fuel bills.
 What was the cost of the gas bill, including VAT?

12 **Future skills** Stuarts buys some stationery. 20% VAT is added to the price of the stationery.
 Stuart then has to pay a total of £52.56.
 What is the price of the stationery with no VAT added?

> **Q12 hint**
>
> ☐ × 1.2 = £52.56

13 In one year, the value of a computer depreciates by 6% to £846.
 How much was the computer worth at the start of the year?

14 The cost of living increased by 2% one year.
 The next year it increased by 3%.
 Copy and complete the calculation to work out the total percentage increase over these two years.

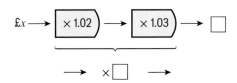

15 **Future skills** Manjit bought a house. The value of her house went up by 5% in the first year. In the second year, the value went down by 2%.
At the end of the two years, her house was worth £174 930.

   a What was the total percentage increase? Do not round your answer.

   b Work out the amount Manjit paid for her house.

Exam-style question

16 Ena invests £4000 in an account for one year.
At the end of the year interest is added to her account.
Ena pays tax on the interest at a rate of 20%.
She pays £15.20 tax.
Work out the percentage interest rate for the account.

                              (3 marks)

Exam tip

Read one sentence at a time. Write a calculation, even if some numbers are missing. Can you use inverse calculations to work out any missing numbers?

Key point

You can calculate a percentage change using the formula

$$\text{percentage change} = \frac{\text{actual change}}{\text{original amount}} \times 100$$

The percentage change may be a percentage loss or a percentage profit.

17 **Future skills** Inderjeet invests £3200. When her investment matures, she receives £3328.

   a What was the actual increase?

   b Work out the percentage increase in her investment.

18 Reena bought a jacket for £45. Six months later, she sold it for £34.65.
What was her percentage loss?

19 **Future skills** Guy spends £4.50 on flour, £8.25 on butter, £2.05 on eggs and £5.20 on jam.
He uses the ingredients to make 120 jam tarts.
He sells the jam tarts in packs of 4. Each pack is £1.30.
He sells all the packs.
Work out his percentage profit.

Q19 hint

Actual profit
= income from sales − costs

Exam-style question

20 Edwina makes 60 litres of pink paint by mixing red paint and white paint in the ratio 1 : 3.
Red paint is sold in 5-litre tins.
Each tin of red paint costs £22.
White paint is sold in 15-litre tins.
Each tin of white paint costs £30.
Edwina sells all the pink paint she makes in 5-litre tins.
She sells each tin of pink paint for £19.50.
Work out Edwina's percentage profit on each tin of pink paint she sells.   **(5 marks)**

Exam tip

There is a lot of information. Break it down and work out
1   costs
2   income from sales
3   actual profit
4   percentage profit.

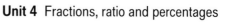

4.5 Fractions, decimals and percentages

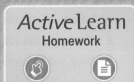
Active Learn
Homework

- Calculate using fractions, decimals and percentages.
- Convert a recurring decimal to a fraction.

Warm up

1 **Fluency** Which of these decimals **a** are recurring **b** is the largest?

A 0.125 **B** 0.1̇2̇5̇ **C** 0.12̇5̇ **D** 0.12̇5

2 Solve these equations.

a $9m = 3$ **b** $10n - n = 6$

3 Copy and complete this table.

Fraction		$\frac{1}{8}$		$\frac{2}{3}$		
Decimal	0.6		0.45			1.5
Percentage				80%		

4 Work out

a $\frac{3}{8}$ of 10 **b** 0.25 of 40 **c** $\frac{1}{6}$ of $\frac{3}{4}$

d 150% of £19 **e** $\frac{1}{7}$ to 3 decimal places.

5 Write

a 1.6 as a fraction of 6

b 1.5 as a percentage of 30

> **Q5a hint**
>
> Multiply the numerator and denominator by 10, then simplify.

6 **Reasoning** A restaurant manager buys a case of 12 bottles of sparkling water. He pays 90p per bottle. He sells $\frac{1}{4}$ of the bottles for £2.10 per bottle and the rest of the case for £2.40 per bottle.

a How much profit does he make?

b Express this profit as a percentage of the total cost price.

7 A researcher asks 180 Year 11 students what they want to do next year. $\frac{2}{3}$ of the students want to stay at school.
25% of the students want to go to college.
The rest of the students do not know.
Work out the number of students who do not know.

> **Q7 hint**
>
> You could draw a bar model.
>
>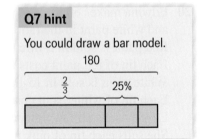

Exam-style question

8 A farmer uses 1.8 out of every 5 acres of land to grow crops.
She grows corn on $\frac{5}{6}$ of the land she uses for crops.
What percentage of the total area of her land does she use to grow corn? **(3 marks)**

---

9 Which is closer to 30%: $\frac{1}{3}$ or $\frac{2}{7}$? You must show your working.

10 **Problem-solving** The table shows the number of days of absence for Year 9 students in each school term over two years. Write three sentences comparing the absences in the two years. Use fractions, decimals, percentages, ratio or proportion.

Q10 hint

Choose calculations that will help you to compare.

	Term 1	Term 2	Term 3
Year 9 (2017/2018)	46	76	24
Year 9 (2018/2019)	28	64	36

11 **Problem-solving** Work out $\frac{1}{3}$ of 0.25 of 135% of £340. Show all your working out.

12 **Reasoning** Write the sum of the sequence $\frac{6}{10} + \frac{6}{100} + \frac{6}{1000} + \ldots$ (where ... indicates that the sequence goes on forever) as a fraction. Explain your answer.

Q12 hint

Write the fractions as decimals.

13 Show that if $99x = 37.5$, then $x = \frac{25}{66}$

Example

Write $0.\dot{3}$ as a fraction.

Call the recurring decimal n.

Multiply the recurring decimal by 10 to shift the sequence one place left.

$0.\dot{3} = 0.333\,333\,333\ldots = n$

so $10n = 3.333\,333\,333\ldots$

$10n - n = 3.333\,333\,333\ldots - 0.333\,333\,333\ldots$

$= 3.000\,000\,000\ldots$

Subtract the value of n from the value of $10n$. This makes all the numbers after the decimal point 0.

$9n = 3$

$n = \dfrac{3}{9}$

Solve the equation.

$n = \dfrac{1}{3}$

Simplify the fraction if possible.

Key point

All **recurring decimals** can be written as exact fractions.

14 Write these recurring decimals as exact fractions.

  a $0.\dot{6}$ **b** $0.\dot{1}$ **c** $0.\dot{5}\dot{2}$

  d $0.181\,818\ldots$ **e** $0.7\dot{4}\dot{3}$ **f** $0.\dot{2}6\dot{1}$

Q14 hint

Multiply by a power of 10. If 1 decimal place recurs, multiply by 10. If 2 decimal places recur, multiply by 100. If 3 decimal places recur, multiply by 1000.

15 $n = 0.1\dot{2}\dot{7}$

Show that $n = \frac{7}{55}$

Exam-style question

16 Using algebra, prove that

$0.3\dot{6} \times 0.5\dot{4}$

is equal in value to $\frac{1}{5}$ **(3 marks)**

Exam tip

Write down every step of your working, making sure each step leads logically to the next step.

4 Check up

Active Learn
Homework

Fractions

1 Work out
a $1\frac{3}{5}+2\frac{5}{8}$
b $3\frac{1}{6}-2\frac{7}{9}$
c $2\frac{1}{3}\times1\frac{1}{4}$
d $2\frac{4}{5}\div\frac{7}{10}$

Ratio and proportion

2 Write the ratio 350 ml : 2 litres as simply as possible, without units.

3 Write the ratio $\frac{5}{6}$: 3 in the form 1 : n.

4 The euro exchange rate is £1 = €1.27. Work out
a how many euros I would get for £45   **b** the price in pounds of a sofa priced at €488.95

5 Share £132 in the ratio 3 : 2 : 1.

6 Ellis makes some biscuits. For every 200 g of flour he uses, he needs 75 g of butter.
a Write a ratio for the amount of flour to the amount of butter.
b Write a formula for f, the amount of flour, in terms of the amount of butter, b.
c Ellis makes 24 biscuits using 300 g of flour. How many biscuits can he make with 375 g of butter?

Fractions, decimals and percentages

7 Work out the final amount when
a £450 is increased by 7%   **b** 877.2 kg is decreased by 3.2%

8 Simon scores 68 marks in his second maths test. In his first maths test he scored 85 marks. What is the percentage decrease in Simon's score?

9 The price of a laptop increases by 35%. The new price is £972. What was the original price?

10 Barbara invests £14 000.
In the first year, she earns 5.9% interest. In the second year, she earns 3.2% interest.
a What is the total percentage increase over the two years?
b How much money does she have after two years?

11 $x = 0.\dot{2}\dot{1}$ Prove that $x = \frac{7}{33}$

12 **Reflect** How sure are you of your answers? Were you mostly
Just guessing 😞   Feeling doubtful 😐   Confident 🙂
What next? Use your results to decide whether to strengthen or extend your learning.

Challenge

13 Find the cube root of the reciprocal of the square root of the reciprocal of 64.
Write a problem similar to this. Make sure you know the answer.

4 Strengthen

Active Learn
Homework

Fractions

1 Work out these. Each part **i** is started for you.

a i $\dfrac{1}{3} \times \dfrac{2}{5} = \dfrac{1 \times 2}{3 \times 5} = \dfrac{\square}{\square}$

ii $\dfrac{3}{7} \times \dfrac{1}{4}$

b i $1\dfrac{1}{3} \times \dfrac{2}{5} = \dfrac{4}{3} \times \dfrac{2}{5} =$

ii $1\dfrac{1}{3} \times \dfrac{2}{9}$

c i $2\dfrac{1}{2} \times 1\dfrac{1}{4} = \dfrac{\square}{2} \times \dfrac{\square}{\square} = \dfrac{\square}{\square} = 3\dfrac{\square}{\square}$

ii $2\dfrac{1}{4} \times 2\dfrac{1}{5}$

2 Work out these. Each part **i** is started for you.

a i $\dfrac{1}{5} \div \dfrac{1}{4} = \dfrac{1}{5} \times \dfrac{4}{1} =$

ii $\dfrac{1}{5} \div \dfrac{1}{6}$

reciprocal of $\dfrac{1}{4}$

b i $1\dfrac{1}{5} \div \dfrac{1}{4} = \dfrac{6}{5} \times \dfrac{\square}{\square} =$

ii $1\dfrac{1}{5} \div \dfrac{1}{6}$

reciprocal of $\dfrac{1}{4}$

c i $1\dfrac{1}{5} \div 1\dfrac{2}{3} = \dfrac{6}{5} \div \dfrac{5}{3} = \dfrac{6}{5} \times \dfrac{\square}{\square} =$

ii $1\dfrac{1}{5} \div 1\dfrac{3}{4}$

reciprocal of $\dfrac{5}{3}$

3 Change the mixed numbers to improper fractions to work out these. The first one is started for you.

a $2\dfrac{1}{3} + 3\dfrac{3}{4} = \dfrac{7}{3} + \dfrac{15}{4} = \dfrac{\square}{12} + \dfrac{\square}{12} = \dfrac{\square}{12} = \square\dfrac{\square}{\square}$

b $1\dfrac{2}{3} + 5\dfrac{1}{8}$

c $2\dfrac{4}{5} + 1\dfrac{2}{9}$

d $6\dfrac{1}{7} + 4\dfrac{7}{10}$

e $5\dfrac{1}{4} - 2\dfrac{3}{8}$

f $3\dfrac{2}{7} - 1\dfrac{3}{5}$

g $2\dfrac{1}{10} - 1\dfrac{7}{8}$

> **Q3 hint**
>
> To add or subtract fractions, write them with a common denominator.

Ratio and proportion

1 Share £72 in these ratios.

a $3:5$　　**b** $7:2$

c $1:2:9$　　**d** $3:2:1$

> **Q1a hint**
>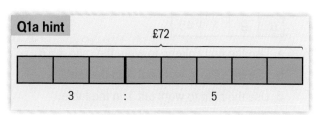

2 Which of these ratios are in the form

   a $1 : n$ **b** $n : 1$?

   A 3 : 1   **B** 5 : 2   **C** 2 : 1   **D** 1 : 7   **E** 8 : 9

3 Write each ratio in the form

   i $1 : n$ **ii** $n : 1$

   The first one is started for you.

   a $3 : 15$

   i   1 : n **ii** n : 1

       $\div 3 \left(\begin{array}{c} 3 : 15 \\ 1 : \square \end{array}\right) \div 3$ $\div 15 \left(\begin{array}{c} 3 : 15 \\ \square : 1 \end{array}\right) \div 15$

   b $8 : 2$ **c** $7 : 56$ **d** $42 : 24$

4 Convert the measures in each of these ratios to the same unit.
Choose the smaller unit.
The first one is started for you.

   a $150\,\text{ml} : 4\,\text{litres} = 150\,\text{ml} : \square\,\text{ml}$ **b** $100\,\text{g} : 2\,\text{kg}$

   c $30\,\text{m} : 80\,\text{cm}$

> **Q4a hint**
>
> ml are smaller than litres.
> 4 litres = $\square$ ml

5 Simplify each ratio answer you wrote in **Q4**.
Do not write the units.

> **Q5a hint**
>
> $\div 50 \left(\begin{array}{c} 150 : \square \\ \square : \square \end{array}\right) \div 50$

6 Simplify each of these ratios.

   a $6.5 : 4$

   b $5 : 8.5$

   c $2.8 : 4$

   d $5.6 : 8.8$

> **Q6a hint**
>
> Multiply by a number that gives
> a whole number on both sides of
> the ratio.
>
> $\times 2 \left(\begin{array}{c} 6.5 : 4 \\ 13 : 8 \end{array}\right) \times 2$

7 In 2007 the exchange rate from pounds to US dollars
was £1 = \$2.

   a How many dollars could you buy for

      i £4   **ii** £5?

   b How many pounds could you buy for

      i \$6   **ii** \$10?

> **Q7 hint**
>
> £ : \$
>
> $\times\square \left(\begin{array}{c} 1 : 2 \\ \square : \square \end{array}\right) \times\square$

8 A and B are in direct proportion.

A	4	8	Y
B	9	X	45

   a Use the first column to write the ratio $A : B$.

   b Use the ratio to work out X in the table.

   c Use the ratio to work out Y in the table.

9 a Copy and complete the bar model to show A, B and C in the ratio 1 : 2 : 4.

Q9b hint

The whole bar model is £280.
What is 1 part? What are 2 parts?

| A | B | B | |

b Share £280 in the ratio 1 : 2 : 4.

10 In a salad dressing recipe, for every 2 tablespoons of vinegar you use 6 tablespoons of oil.

a Write the ratio of vinegar to oil. Simplify the ratio.

b Use the ratio in part **a** to work out the amount of oil given the amount of vinegar.
oil = vinegar × ☐

c Use your answer to part **b** to write a formula for o, the amount of oil, in terms of v, the amount of vinegar.

Suzanne makes 300 ml of salad dressing with 5 tablespoons of vinegar.

d Use you formula in part **c** to work out how many tablespoons of oil Suzanne uses.

Q10e hint

Use your answer to part **d** to write the ratio
vinegar : oil : dressing.

e How much salad dressing can Suzanne make with 3 tablespoons of oil?

Fractions, decimals and percentages

1 Convert these percentages to decimals.

a 104%

b 126.5%

c 95%

d 88.3%

2 Use your answers to **Q1** to

a increase £400 by

   i 4%   **ii** 26.5%

b decrease £400 by

   i 5%   **ii** 11.7%

3 Betsy invests £3000.
When her investment matures, she receives £3135.

a Copy and complete the working to calculate the percentage increase of Betsy's investment.

   original amount = 3000

   actual change = 3135 − 3000 = 135

$$\text{percentage change} = \frac{\text{actual change}}{\text{original amount}} \times 100$$

$$= \frac{135}{3000} \times 100 = \square \%$$

Q3 hint

Draw this information as a bar model.

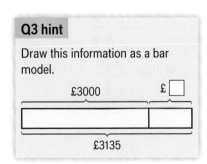

b Check your answer by increasing £3000 by the percentage you calculated.
Do you get £3135?

4 Work out the percentage loss made on each of these items.
For each part, copy and complete the following working. Check your answers.

    original amount = ☐

    actual change = ☐

$$\text{percentage change} = \frac{\text{actual change}}{\text{original amount}} \times 100 = \frac{\square}{\square} \times 100 = \square\%$$

  a Bought for £8, sold for £5.75

  b Bought for £145, sold for £120

  c Bought for £615, sold for £500

5 The price of a computer game after a 28% increase is £13.44.

  a What decimal number do you multiply by to increase the original price by 28%?

  b Copy and complete this function machine.

    Original price ⟶ (×☐) ⟶ £13.44

  c Work backwards through the function machine to find the original price.

6 Use the method in **Q5** to find the original price of

  a a sofa that costs £585 after a 25% discount

  b a house priced at £192 030 after its value rose by 3.8%.

7 Carol put £5000 in a savings account for 2 years.
The first year she earned 2.5% interest.
The second year she earned 3.1% interest.

  a Write a calculation to find the amount of money Carol has at the end of the first year.

  b Multiply your calculation from part **a** by 1.031 to find the amount in the account after two years.

8 Copy and complete.

  a $n = 0.\dot{6}\dot{3} = 0.63\square\square\square\square\dots$

  b $100n = 100 \times 0.\dot{6}\dot{3} = \square\square.\square\square\square\square\dots$

  c
$$\begin{array}{r} 1\,0\,0\,n \\ -\quad\quad n \\ \hline 9\,9\,n \end{array} \quad \begin{array}{r} \square\square.\square\square\square\square \dots \\ -\quad 0\,.\,6\,3\,\square\square \dots \\ \hline =\quad \square\square.\square\square\square\square \dots \end{array}$$

  d $99n = \square\square$

    $n = \dfrac{\square\square}{99} = \dfrac{\square}{11}$

4 Extend

1 **Reasoning**

    a Show that applying a 20% increase followed by a 20% decrease is the same as a 4% decrease overall.

    b Will the final amount be the same or different if you apply the decrease first, then the increase?

2 Work out $\dfrac{\frac{2}{5}+\frac{3}{8}}{1\frac{5}{9}}$

3 A photocopier increases the sides of a square in the ratio 2 : 3.
    What percentage increase is this?

4 **Problem-solving** The diagram shows three identical shapes, A, B and C.

    $\frac{4}{7}$ of shape A is shaded.

    $\frac{5}{6}$ of shape C is shaded.

    What fraction of shape B is shaded?

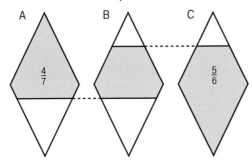

Exam-style question

5 *VWXY* is a rectangle with length 20 cm and width 12 cm.

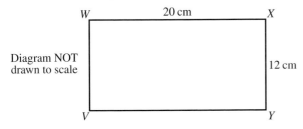

Diagram NOT drawn to scale

The length of the rectangle is increased by 30%.
The width of the rectangle is increased by 10%.
Find the percentage increase in the area of the rectangle. **(5 marks)**

---

6 **Reasoning** Gareth sells cupcakes.
    He adds 40% profit to the cost price.
    He sells the cupcakes for £1.68 each.
    He wants to increase his profit to 60% of the cost price.
    How much should he sell each cupcake for?

7   **Problem-solving** In a company, 65% of the workers are female.
    40% of the women drive to work.
    50% of the men drive to work.
    Write the ratio of employees who drive to work to those who do not drive to work.

8   Work out
    a $2^{-1} \div \frac{1}{2}$
    b $173^{-1} \div \frac{1}{173}$
    c $3^{-4} + 3^{-2}$

Exam-style question

9   A rectangular bar is split into 4 unequal sections, for example

    The sections are labelled A, B, C and D.
       A : C = 2 : 3
       B : C = 4 : 7
       B : D = 2 : 1
    Write the ratio A : B : C : D in its simplest form.   **(3 marks)**

    Q9 hint

    Draw the bar model. Begin by showing the ratio with the most parts, i.e. B : C = 4 : 7

10 Sam and Peter work for a company that sells bags of sweets.
    They want to have a special offer.
    Here's Sam's idea for a special offer:

    > Reduce the price by 20%
    > and do not change the number of sweets
    > in each bag

    Here is Peter's idea:

    > Put more sweets in each bag
    > and do not change the price

    Peter wants his idea to give the same value for money as Sam's idea.
    What percentage extra sweets does he need to add to each bag?

Exam-style question

11 A box of chocolates contains white chocolates and milk chocolates.
    Some of the chocolates have a nut inside them.
    Others have a fruit jelly inside them.
    The ratio of the number of white chocolates to milk chocolates is 7 : 3.
    The ratio of the number of white chocolates with a nut inside to the number of white chocolates with a fruit jelly inside is 5 : 2.
    The ratio of the number of milk chocolates with a nut inside to the number of milk chocolates with a fruit jelly inside is 2 : 1.
    Work out the fraction of all the chocolates that contain a fruit jelly.   **(4 marks)**

    Exam tip

    In an exam, you can work with fractions or percentages unless the question specifies.

4 Test ready

Summary of key points

To revise for the test:

- Read each key point, find a question on it in the mastery lesson, and check you can work out the answer.

- If you cannot, try some other questions from the mastery lesson or ask for help.

Key points

1 It is often easier to write mixed numbers as improper fractions before doing a calculation. → 4.1

2 To make the multiplication easier, you should divide by common factors before multiplying, if you can. → 4.1

3 The **reciprocal** of the number n is $\frac{1}{n}$. You can also write this as n^{-1}. → 4.1

4 To find the reciprocal of a fraction, swap the numerator and the denominator. For example, the reciprocal of $\frac{3}{4}$ is $\frac{4}{3}$. → 4.1

5 To find the reciprocal of a mixed number, first convert it into an improper fraction. → 4.1

6 To find the reciprocal of a decimal, write the decimal as a fraction. → 4.1

7 Sometimes both denominators must be changed to add fractions. → 4.1

8 You can compare ratios by writing them as **unit ratios**. In a unit ratio, one of the numbers is 1. The other number may or may not be a whole number. → 4.2

9 To share a quantity in a given ratio, you could work out what fraction of the total amount each person receives and then multiply each fraction by the total amount. Another method is to work out how much one part is worth and then multiply by the number of parts each person receives. → 4.2

10 When two quantities are in **direct proportion**, as one is multiplied by a number, n, so is the other. Their ratio also stays the same as they increase or decrease. → 4.3

11 **Simple interest** is the interest calculated only on the original amount invested. It is the same each year. → 4.4

12 **Value added tax (VAT)** is charged at 20% on most goods and services. Domestic fuel bills have a lower VAT rate of 5%. On some things no VAT is charged. → 4.4

13 In financial terms, 'appreciate' means to gain value and 'depreciate' means to lose value. → 4.4

14 Your income means the amount of money you earn or are paid, and 'per annum' (abbreviated to p.a.) means each year. → 4.4

15 You can calculate a percentage change using the formula
$$\text{percentage change} = \frac{\text{actual change}}{\text{original amount}} \times 100$$
→ 4.4

16 $$\text{Percentage loss (or profit)} = \frac{\text{actual loss (or profit)}}{\text{original amount}} \times 100$$
→ 4.4

17 When you are working out profits, remember to subtract any costs first. → 4.4

Sample student answers

Exam-style question

1 In 2018 a company reduced its workforce by 2.5% compared to 2017.
In 2019 the company merged with another company and the workforce increased by 20% compared to 2018.
What was the percentage increase in the workforce from 2017 to 2019? **(3 marks)**

$100\% - 2.5\% = 97.5\% = 0.975$
$100\% + 20\% = 1.2$
Percentage increase $= 0.975 \times 1.2 = 1.17\%$

Why is this student unlikely to get full marks for this answer?

Exam-style question

2 AD is a straight line. B and C are points on the straight line between A and D.
AC is 3.5 times the length of AB. C is the midpoint of BD.
What is the ratio of $AB : BC : CD$?
Give your answer as a whole number ratio in its simplest form. **(3 marks)**

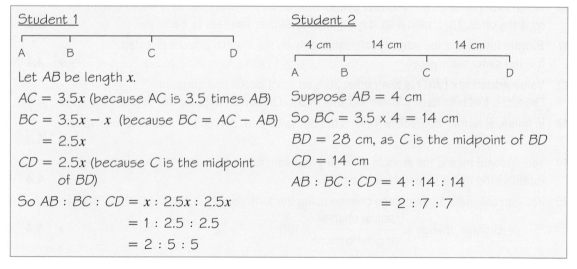

Student 1

Let AB be length x.
$AC = 3.5x$ (because AC is 3.5 times AB)
$BC = 3.5x - x$ (because $BC = AC - AB$)
$\quad = 2.5x$
$CD = 2.5x$ (because C is the midpoint of BD)
So $AB : BC : CD = x : 2.5x : 2.5x$
$\quad\quad = 1 : 2.5 : 2.5$
$\quad\quad = 2 : 5 : 5$

Student 2

Suppose $AB = 4$ cm
So $BC = 3.5 \times 4 = 14$ cm
$BD = 28$ cm, as C is the midpoint of BD
$CD = 14$ cm
$AB : BC : CD = 4 : 14 : 14$
$\quad\quad = 2 : 7 : 7$

a Student 1 and student 2 get different answers for the ratio $AB : BC : CD$.
Which student made a mistake? Explain the mistake the student made.

b For the student who made a mistake, rewrite the working to get the correct ratio.

4 Unit test

Active Learn
Homework

1 Find the reciprocal of

  a $2\frac{3}{4}$ **(1 mark)**

  b 1.275 **(1 mark)**

2 Work out

  a $2\frac{4}{5} \div 1\frac{3}{7}$ **(3 marks)**

  b $5\frac{2}{3} - 2\frac{7}{8}$ **(3 marks)**

3 Bernie buys pet insurance.
12% insurance premium tax is added to the price of the pet insurance.
Bernie has to pay a total of £180.88.
How much of this total is the insurance premium tax? **(2 marks)**

4 Alice has $8\frac{1}{4}$ acres of orchards.
Alice grows apple trees in $4\frac{5}{6}$ acres of the orchards.
She grows pear trees in the rest.
How many acres of pear trees does Alice have? **(3 marks)**

5 Selika gives her garden a makeover.
She spends money on plants, materials and labour in the ratio 1 : 5 : 12.
She spends £848.75 on materials.
Work out how much she spends in total. **(3 marks)**

6 In a nursing home, there are 16 nurses and 108 patients.

  a Write the nurse : patient ratio in the form of 1 : n. **(1 mark)**

  Another nursing home has 12.5% more nurses and 120 patients.

  b Which hospital has the better nurse : patient ratio?
    Explain your answer. **(3 marks)**

7 Cameron is going on holiday to Spain.
He needs to change some money into euros.
He can only change his money into €20 or €50 notes.
Cameron has up to £540 to change.
He wants to take as many euros as possible.
The exchange rate is £1 = €1.27.
How many euros will Cameron get? **(3 marks)**

8 J is directly proportional to K.

J	52	39	b
K	36	a	22.5

  a Work out the missing values, a and b, in the table. **(2 marks)**

  b Write a formula for J in terms of K. **(2 marks)**

9 Nathan makes fudge and sells it at a Christmas fayre.
He spends £2.14 on ingredients.
Nathan sells all the fudge and has £9.63 in the cash box at the end of the sale.
What percentage profit does Nathan make on the fudge? **(2 marks)**

10 £4500 is shared between 4 charities.
The donation to charity B is $\frac{5}{6}$ of the donation to charity D.
Charity D's donation is twice the donation to charity C.
The ratio of donations for charity C to charity A is 3 : 4.
Work out the donation to charity B. **(3 marks)**

11 A tourist attraction had a 3.75% fall in visitor numbers in June, compared to May.
There were 121 660 visitors in June.
In July there were 4.5% more visitors than in May.
What was the percentage increase in visitor numbers from June to July? **(5 marks)**

12 *EFGH* is a rectangle.
Length *EF* is 24 cm. Width *FG* is 3 cm.
The length of the rectangle decreases by 40% and the width increases by 30%.
What is the overall percentage change to the area of the rectangle?
State clearly if this is an increase or decrease. **(5 marks)**

13 Prove algebraically that $0.9\dot{6} \div 1.4\dot{5}$ is equal in value to $\frac{2}{3}$. **(3 marks)**

(TOTAL: 45 marks)

14 **Challenge** Boris, Carla and Dean share some money.
Boris gets $\frac{1}{10}$ of the money.
Carla and Dean share the rest of the money in the ratio 4 : 5.
What percentage of the money does Dean get?
Write your own money question, involving at least 3 people and a fraction,
a ratio and a percentage.
All your answers must be to 2 decimal places, 1 decimal place or integers,
so that they can be written in pounds and pence.

15 **Reflect** For this unit, copy and complete these sentences.
  • I showed I am good at _____
  • I found _____ hard.
  • I got better at _____ by _____
  • I was surprised by _____
  • I was happy that _____
  • I still need help with _____

Mixed exercise 1

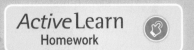

1 **Problem-solving** The frequency diagram shows some information about the heights of 50 saplings.

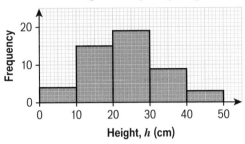

Estimate the mean height of the saplings.

2 **Reasoning**

a Write down the 137th odd number.

b Write an expression for the nth odd number.

3 **Reasoning** Here are the heights in centimetres of 20 students.

| 158 | 162 | 171 | 173 | 180 | 172 | 166 | 169 | 172 | 163 |
| 181 | 177 | 159 | 156 | 168 | 176 | 167 | 170 | 168 | 175 |

a Show this information in an ordered stem and leaf diagram.

b Work out the percentage of these students with a height greater than 170 cm.

Exam-style question

4 A tennis club has 80 members.
Half of the members are women.
The number of women in the tennis club is 4 times the number of men in the tennis club.
The rest of the members in the tennis club are children.
    the number of children in the tennis club : the number of men in the tennis club = n : 1
Work out the value of n.
You must show how you get your answer.   **(4 marks)**

---

5 **Problem-solving** How many times do two or more odd digits appear in a number when counting from 0 to 999?

Exam-style question

6 On Saturday, some adults and some children were in a football stadium.
The ratio of the number of adults to the number of children was 22 : 3.
Each person had a seat in a Home stand or had a seat in an Away stand.
$\frac{4}{5}$ of the children had seats in a Home stand.
318 children had seats in an Away stand.
There are exactly 15 800 seats in the football stadium.
On this Saturday, were more than 80% of the seats occupied?
You must show how you get your answer.   **(5 marks)**

Exam-style question

7 Jack is 6 years older than Tom.
   Seth is twice as old as Jack.
   The sum of their three ages is 90.
   Find the ratio of Tom's age to Jack's age to Seth's age.   **(4 marks)**

Exam-style question

8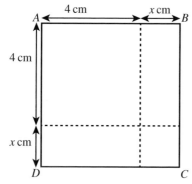

The area of square $ABCD$ is $30\,\text{cm}^2$.
Show that $x^2 + 8x = 14$.   **(3 marks)**

9 **Problem-solving** A number, n, is written as a product of its prime factors using index notation:
   $n = 2^3 \times 3^2 \times p^4$
   Work out $3n^2$ as a product of its prime factors using index notation.
   Give your answer in terms of p.

10 **Reasoning** The table shows information about the test results for a group of students for two different maths papers.

Student	A	B	C	D	E	F	G	H
Paper 1	43	25	18	36	33	38	28	45
Paper 2	45	21	22	35	30	43	31	48

Josh thinks that students who get high marks on Paper 1 also get high marks on Paper 2.

   a Draw a scatter graph to show the data.

   b Does the scatter graph support Josh's hypothesis?

   c Work out the mean test result for Paper 1.

   d Work out the mean test result for Paper 2.

   e Plot the mean test result for Paper 1 and 2 on your scatter graph.

   f Draw a line of best fit that passes through your means.

   g Clara achieved a mark of 37 on Paper 1.
      She was absent for Paper 2. Estimate Clara's mark for this paper.

11 **Problem-solving** Work out the positive values of p and q when

   a $\left(px^3\right)^2 = 25x^q$ b $\left(py^q\right)^6 = 64y^{24}$ c $\left(\dfrac{p}{64}\right)^{-\frac{2}{q}} = \dfrac{16}{9}$

12 **Problem-solving** Work out the values of p and q in the identity
$$3(2x+p) + 4(6x+7) \equiv qx+10$$

13 **Reasoning** The nth term of sequence S is $4n - 3$.
The nth term of sequence T is $15 - 7n$.
James says there is only one number that is in both sequence S and sequence T.
Is James correct? Explain your answer.

Exam-style question

14 The number of days, d, that it will take to plant 10 acres of woodland is given by $d = \dfrac{240}{n}$,
where n is the number of workers each day.
Harry's company will take 6 days to plant the woodland.
Georgie's company will take 5 days to plant the woodland.
Georgie's company will have to use more workers each day than Harry's company.
How many more? **(3 marks)**

---

15 The table shows the approximate diameter, in m,
of the planets in our solar system.

  a Work out the mean, median and mode of the diameters.

  b **Reasoning** State whether it is better to use the mean,
  median or mode for the diameter of the planets.
  Give reasons for your answer.

  c One planet has diameter approximately 10 times bigger
  than another planet.
  Which two planets are they?

Planet	Diameter (m)
Mercury	4.88×10^6
Venus	1.21×10^7
Earth	1.28×10^7
Mars	6.79×10^6
Jupiter	1.43×10^8
Saturn	1.21×10^8
Uranus	5.11×10^7
Neptune	4.95×10^7

Exam-style question

16 A company has to make a large number of boxes.
The company has 8 machines.
All the machines work at the same rate.
When all the machines are working, they can make all the boxes in 12 days.
The table gives the number of machines working each day.

	Day 1	Day 2	Day 3	All other days
Number of machines working	4	5	7	8

Work out the total number of days taken to make all the boxes. **(3 marks)**

---

17 **Problem-solving** Grace has five mixed number cards.
The mean of the five mixed numbers on Grace's cards is $2\frac{29}{60}$.
Grace turns over the first four cards.

 $2\frac{2}{3}$ $3\frac{3}{4}$ $1\frac{1}{2}$ $2\frac{4}{5}$

Work out the mixed number on the last card.

18 The number of animals in a population at the start of year y is P_y.

The number of animals at the start of year 1 is 300.

Given that $P_{y+1} = 1.05P_y$ work out the number of animals at the start of year 4.   **(2 marks)**

19 **Problem-solving** A is a cuboid with width 40 cm, length 50 cm and height a cm.

B is a cuboid with height b cm.

The width of B is 25% more than the width of A.

The length of B is 20% more than the length of A.

The volume of B is 10% more that the volume of A.

Work out the ratio $a:b$. Give your answer in its simplest form.

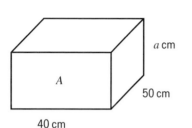

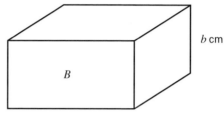

20 During one evening in a restaurant, each person chose 1 main course and 1 dessert.

Main course	Dessert
pasta	cheesecake
burger	ice cream

The number of people who chose pasta : the number of people who chose burger
$$= 5:3$$

Of those who chose pasta,
the number of people who chose cheesecake : the number of people who chose ice cream
$$= 3:7$$

Of those who chose burger,
the number of people who chose cheesecake : the number of people who chose ice cream
$$= 1:5$$

What fraction of the people chose cheesecake?

You must show how you get your answer.   **(4 marks)**

21 **Problem-solving** Mr Nelson is teaching his class about the planets.

Some students are to make a model of the Sun and a model of planet Earth.

Mr Nelson is going to hang the two models in the corridor.

He wants a distance of 24 m between the two models.

The actual average distance between Earth and the Sun is approximately 1.5×10^8 km.

Work out the scale that should be used. Give your answer in the form $1:n$.

22 Show that $\dfrac{\sqrt{5}}{3\sqrt{5} - 2}$ can be written in the form $\dfrac{a + b\sqrt{5}}{c}$ where a, b and c are integers.

   (3 marks)

5 Angles and trigonometry

Prior knowledge

5.1 Angle properties of triangles and quadrilaterals

* Derive and use the sum of angles in a triangle and in a quadrilateral.
* Derive and use the fact that the exterior angle of a triangle is equal to the sum of the two opposite interior angles.

Active Learn
Homework

Warm up

1 **Fluency a** Name these shapes.

i 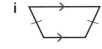   ii   iii

iv   v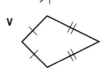

> **Q1b hint**
> Use arcs to show angles that are the same size, e.g.
> or

b Sketch each shape in part **a** and mark any angles that are the same size.

2 What are the sizes of all the angles in
   a an equilateral triangle
   b an isosceles triangle with one angle of $130°$
   c a kite with two angles of $60°$?

3 Work out the sizes of angles a, b and c.
   Choose the correct reasons for your answers from the box.

   > Corresponding angles are equal.
   > Alternate angles are equal.
   > Vertically opposite angles are equal.
   > Angles on a straight line add up to $180°$.

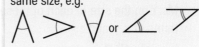

4 An angle of $74°$ is shown in the diagram.
   a Write down the letters of all other angles of size $74°$.
   Give reasons.
   b Explain why $o + p + q = 254°$.

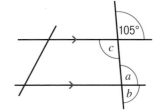

5 **Reasoning** Angles inside two parallel lines are called **co-interior** angles.
   Use this diagram to explain why co-interior angles add up to $180°$.

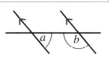

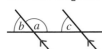

6 *ABC* and *CDE* are straight lines. *AE* is parallel to *BD*.
   Work out the size of angles

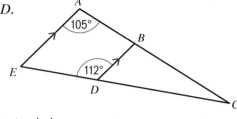

   a *ABD*   **b** *BDC*

   c *AEC*   **d** *ACE*

   Give reasons for your answers.

7 **Reasoning** *ABCD* is a parallelogram with its sides extended.

   a Which line is parallel to

   i *CD*   **ii** *CB*?

   b Work out the other angles in the parallelogram.
      Give reasons for your answers.

   c What do you notice about the opposite angles?

   d Repeat with different parallelograms.
      Is your observation in part **c** still true?

   e **Reflect** Write down the property of parallelograms that you have shown.

8 Triangle *ABC* is shown. *DE* is parallel to *AB*.

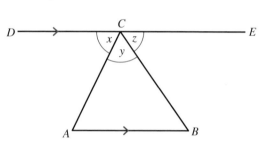

   a What is the value of $x + y + z$? Give a reason
      for your answer.

   b Copy the diagram.
      Mark on the size of each of these angles in
      terms of x, y and z

   i angle *CAB*

   ii angle *ABC*

   Give reasons for your answers.

   c Use your answer to part **a** to derive the sum of the angles
      in a triangle.

> **Q8c hint**
>
> $x + y + z = \square^\circ$
> The angle sum of
> a triangle is $\square^\circ$

Exam-style question

9 *ABC* and *DEF* are parallel lines.

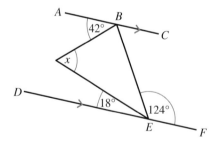

> **Exam tip**
>
> In an exam, you can write on the
> diagram any angles you work
> out to help find the angle asked
> for in the question. When a
> diagram includes parallel lines,
> look for alternate, corresponding
> and co-interior angles.

   Work out the size of angle x.
   Give a reason for each stage of your working.   **(4 marks)**

---

10 **Reasoning** In this diagram a diagonal
   divides the quadrilateral into two triangles.
   Use the diagram to prove that the angle
   sum of a quadrilateral is $360°$.

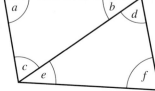

> **Q10 hint**
>
> Begin
> $a + b + c = \square^\circ$

Exam-style question

11 *ABCE* is a parallelogram.

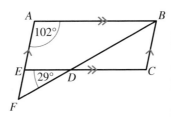

AEF is a straight line.
D is the point on *CE* so that
BDF is a straight line.
Angle *EDF* = 29°
Angle *BAE* = 102°

Show that angle *CBD* = 49°.
Give a reason for each stage of your working.

Exam tip

Do not assume *CBD* is 49°.
Instead, find angles in the
diagram (giving reasons) until
you can show working and give
a reason for *CBD* being 49°.

(4 marks)

Key point

When one side of a triangle is extended at a vertex
• the angle marked *x* is called the **interior angle**
• the angle marked *y* is called the **exterior angle**.

$x + y = 180°$ (angles on a straight line add up to 180°)

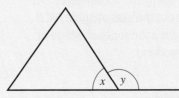

12 Work out the size of each angle marked with a letter.
Give reasons for your answers.

a

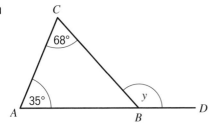

b

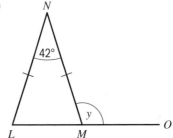

c

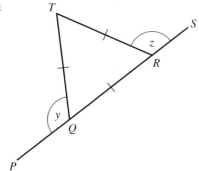

d Reflect Write a sentence explaining what you notice about the relationship between the
exterior angle of a triangle and the interior angles at the other two vertices.

Key point

The exterior angle of a triangle is equal to the sum of the
interior angles at the other two vertices.

angle *d* = angle *a* + angle *b*

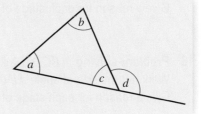

13 Reasoning *ABCD* is an isosceles trapezium.
BCE is an isosceles triangle.
DCEF is a straight line.
Angle *BEF* = 132°

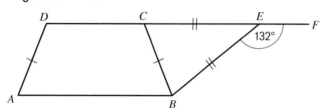

Q13 hint

Sketch the diagram. Mark on the diagram any angles you work out. When a diagram includes equal length sides, look for equal angles too.

Work out the size of angle *DAB*. Give a reason for each stage of your working.

14 Reasoning *BC* is parallel to *DE*.
Work out the size of angle *ACB*.
Give a reason for each stage of
your working.

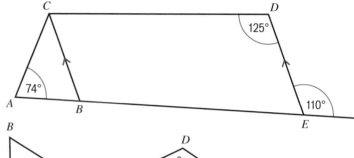

Example

Work out the size of angle *ABC*.
You must show all your working and
give reasons for your answers.

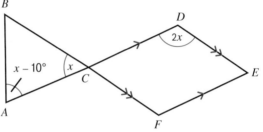

$\angle DCF = x$ (vertically opposite angles are equal) ◄———— Write a reason every time you write an angle.

$\angle CDE + \angle DCF = 180°$ (co-interior angles add
up to 180°)

$x + 2x = 180°$ ◄———— Form an equation using the angle property.

$3x = 180°$ ◄

$x = 60°$ ◄———— Collect like terms.

$\angle BCA = 60°$

$\angle BAC = x - 10 = 60 - 10 = 50°$ ◄———— Solve the equation to find x.

$\angle ABC = 180° - (60 + 50)°$ (angles in a
triangle add up to 180°)

———— Substitute the value of x to find angle *BAC*.

$= 180° - 110°$

$= 70°$

15 Problem-solving Work out the size of angle *ACB*.
Give a reason for each stage of your working.

16 Problem-solving *ABCD* is a kite.
Work out the size of angle *ADC*.
Give a reason for each stage of your working.

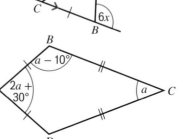

5.2 Interior angles of a polygon

- Calculate the sum of the interior angles of a polygon.
- Use the interior angles of polygons to solve problems.
- Use x for the unknown to help you solve problems.

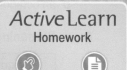

*Active*Learn
Homework

Warm up

1 **Fluency a** Name these polygons.

b What can you say about the sides and angles in a regular polygon?

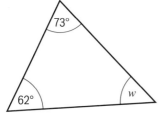

A   B   C   D

2 For each value of n, work out $(n - 2) \times 180$

a $n = 3$ **b** $n = 5$ **c** $n = 7$ **d** $n = 8$

3 Work out the size of each angle marked with a letter.
Copy and complete the correct reasons for your answers from the box.

a

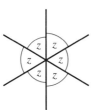

73°
62°
w

b

52°
x

c

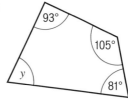

93°
105°
y
81°

d

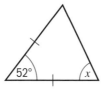

_____ triangles have two equal sides and two equal angles.
Angles in a triangle add up to ☐°.
Angles in a quadrilateral add up to ☐°.
Angles around a point add up to ☐°.

4 The angles in a triangle are in the ratio 1 : 2 : 3.
What are their sizes?

5 **a** Sketch this irregular pentagon.

b Draw in the diagonals from one vertex to all the other vertices.

c How many triangles make an irregular pentagon?

d Do the same number of triangles make a regular pentagon?

e Copy and complete.
Angles in a triangle add up to ☐°.
So angles in a pentagon add up to ☐ × ☐ = ☐°

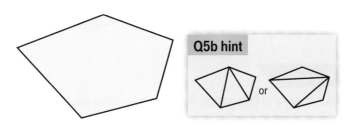

Q5b hint

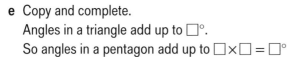

or

F
H

6 Use the same method as in **Q5** to work out the sum of the interior angles of

   a a hexagon

   b an octagon

7   **a** **Reasoning** Copy and complete the table.

Polygon	Number of sides (n)	Number of triangles formed	Sum of interior angles
triangle	3	1	180°
quadrilateral	4		
pentagon	5	3	540°
hexagon	6		
heptagon	7		

   b **Reflect** Write a sentence stating what you notice about the relationship between the number of sides (n) and the number of triangles formed.
Check your idea works for your answer to **Q6b**.

8 A regular polygon has 20 sides.

   a Use the formula sum $= (n-2) \times 180°$ to work out the sum of the interior angles of the polygon.

   b Work out the size of an interior angle.

   c **Reflect** Would you expect the answer to part **b** to be the same for an irregular polygon with 20 sides? Explain.

9 **Reasoning** Work out the size of each interior angle of a regular

   a pentagon

   b heptagon

   c polygon with 15 sides

10 The diagram shows a regular octagon and a regular hexagon.
Calculate the size of the angle a.
You must show all your working.

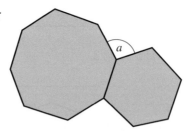

Q10 hint

Write any angle properties you use, for example
Angles in an octagon add up to ☐°.
Angles in a regular octagon are equal.

11 **Reasoning** A repeating pattern of identical regular hexagons and identical triangles tessellates like this.
Show that the triangles are equilateral.

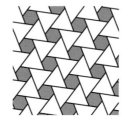

Q11 hint

Choose a vertex of the regular hexagon. What are the angles at that point?

12 Work out the size of each unknown interior angle in these irregular polygons.
Give reasons for your answers.

a

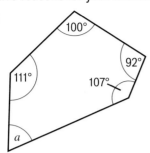

b

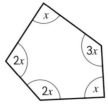

Q12b hint

To find x, solve
$x + 3x + x + 2x + 2x = \square°$

c

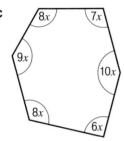

Exam-style question

13 XY and YZ are 2 sides of a regular decagon (10-sided polygon).
XZ is a diagonal of the decagon.

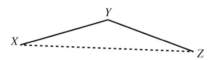

Work out the size of angle YXZ. **(3 marks)**

Exam tip

Sketch the diagram. Add anything you know about the shape. For example, can you mark any equal sides or angles? Can you work out and label the size of angle XYZ?

---

14 The sum of the interior angles of a polygon is $1620°$.
Copy and complete the working to find out the number of sides the polygon has.

$(n - 2) \times 180° = \square°$

$n - 2 = \dfrac{\square}{180}$

15 **Problem-solving** The sum of the interior angles of a polygon is $3060°$. Copy and complete.
The polygon has $\square$ sides.

16 **Problem-solving** A regular pentagon is divided into five isosceles triangles.
Work out the size of

a angle x **b** angle y **c** angle z

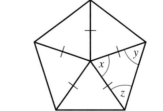

17 a **Reasoning** **Q16** shows a pentagon made from isosceles triangles.
What polygons can you make from equilateral triangles?

b **Reflect** Besides triangles, which other regular polygons can fit together like this to create a pattern without leaving any gaps? Explain.

18 In this pentagon, the internal angles are defined:

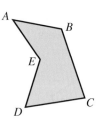

- angle *ABC* is 24° more than angle *BAE*
- angle *BAE* is half the size of angle *BCD*
- angle *AED* is 3 times the size of angle *BCD*
- angle *BCD* = angle *CDE*

a Sketch the diagram. Label angle *ABC* as *x*.

b Read the question again and label the other angles in terms of *x*.

c Write an equation in terms of *x*.

d What is the size of angle *AED*?

Exam-style question

19 The diagram shows a hexagon.
The hexagon has one line of symmetry.

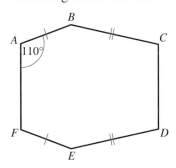

Exam tip

Sketch the diagram. Mark the angle you are trying to find as *x*. What other angles can you mark?

AB = *EF*
BC = *DE*
Angle *BAF* = 110°
Angle *CDE* = $\frac{2}{3}$ of angle *ABC*

Work out the size of angle *DEF*.
You must show your working.

(4 marks)

20 Problem-solving The diagram shows a heptagon.
The heptagon has one line of symmetry.

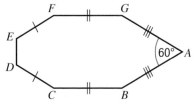

AB = *AG*
BC = *FG*
CD = *EF*
Angle *ABC* : angle *BCD* : angle *CDE* = 8 : 7 : 5
Work out the size of angle *DEF*.
You must show your working.

5.3 Exterior angles of a polygon

*Active*Learn
Homework

- Know the sum of the exterior angles of a polygon.
- Use the angles of polygons to solve problems.

Warm up

1 **Fluency** Work out the size of the unknown angles.

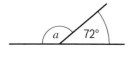

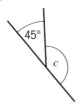
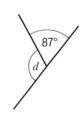

2 Work out the sum of the interior angles of

a a heptagon **b** a pentagon **c** a decagon **d** a hexagon

3 For each triangle work out

a the sizes of angles a, b and c

b the value of $a + b + c$

Give reasons for your answers.

i

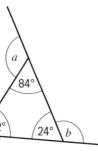

ii

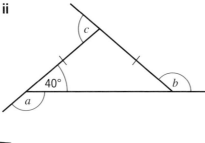

iii

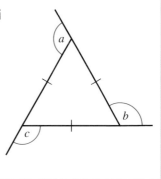

4 For each quadrilateral work out

a the sizes of angles a, b, c and d **b** the value of $a + b + c + d$

Give reasons for your answers.

i

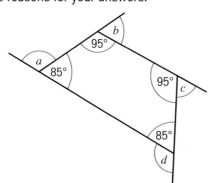

ii

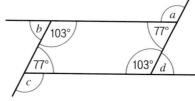

Key point

When one side of a polygon is extended at a vertex
• angle x is the interior angle
• angle y is the exterior angle

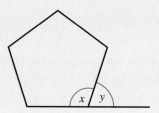

interior angle + exterior angle = 180°
(angles on a straight line add up to 180°)

5 Reasoning An irregular pentagon and an irregular hexagon are shown.

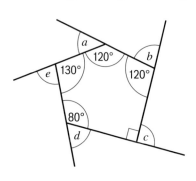 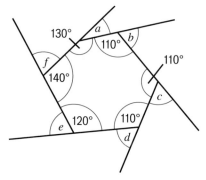

a Work out the sizes of the angles marked with letters.

b For each polygon, work out the sum of the exterior angles.

c Reasoning Show that the sum of the exterior angles is still 360° for a regular pentagon and for a regular hexagon.

Q5b hint

For the pentagon work out the value of $a+b+c+d+e$.

Q5c hint

Use what you know about interior angles.

Key point

The sum of the exterior angles of a polygon is always 360°.

In a regular polygon all the angles are the same size, so exterior angle $= \dfrac{360°}{\text{number of sides}}$

6 Work out the sizes of the unknown angles in each diagram. The first one is started for you.

a **b** **c**

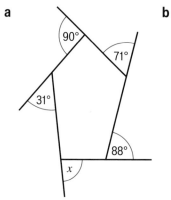 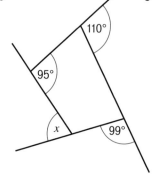 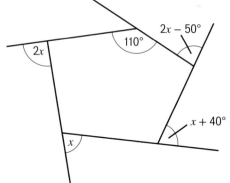

$x+31°+90°+71°+88°=360°$

Q6b and c hint

Sometimes you may have to find more angles before working out the sum of the exterior angles.

7 *ABCDEF* is a regular hexagon. *GAD* is a straight line.
Angle $GAB = x°$

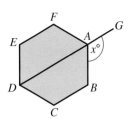

  a **Reflect** Write a sentence explaining why
    x is not an interior or an exterior angle.

  b **Problem-solving** Work out the value of *x*.
    Give a reason for each stage of your working.

Example

Each interior angle of a regular polygon is 140°.
How many sides does the polygon have?

Use interior angle + exterior angle = 180°
to work out the size of an exterior angle.

Exterior angle $= 180° - 140° = 40°$

Number of sides $= \dfrac{360°}{40°} = 9$

For a regular polygon, exterior angle $= \dfrac{360°}{\text{number of sides}}$

so number of sides $= \dfrac{360°}{\text{exterior angle}}$

---

8 How many sides does a regular polygon have if its exterior angle is
  a 10°   **b** 72°   **c** 20°?

9 How many sides does a regular polygon have if its interior
angle is

  a 120°   **b** 156°   **c** 162°?

> **Q9 hint**
>
> Work out the exterior angle first.

Exam-style question

10 The exterior angle of a regular polygon is half the size of
its interior angle.
How many sides does the polygon have? **(3 marks)**

> **Exam tip**
>
> Sometimes it can be helpful to
> draw a diagram to help answer
> an exam question.
>
>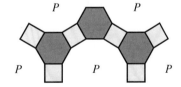
>
> Then write and solve an equation.

---

11 Identical squares and identical regular hexagons
tessellate with another regular polygon, *P*, like this.

  a Work out an interior angle of *P*.

  b How many sides does regular polygon *P* have?

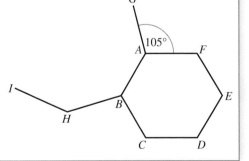

Exam-style question

12 One side of a regular hexagon
ABCDEF forms the side of a regular polygon
with *n* sides.
Angle $GAF = 105°$

Work out the value of *n*. **(4 marks)**

5.4 Pythagoras' theorem 1

- Calculate the length of the hypotenuse in a right-angled triangle.
- Solve problems using Pythagoras' theorem.

Active Learn
Homework

Warm up

1 Fluency Which of these are surds? Explain.

2    $\sqrt{4}$ $\sqrt{6}$ 4.6 $\sqrt{14}$ $\sqrt{16}$

2 Copy and complete to simplify these surds.

a $\sqrt{8} = \sqrt{\square} \times \sqrt{2} = \square\sqrt{2}$ **b** $\sqrt{45} = \sqrt{\square} \times \sqrt{\square} = 3\sqrt{\square}$

 3 $a = 4.5$ and $b = 6.2$. Work out

a $a^2 + b^2$ **b** $\sqrt{a^2 + b^2}$

Give your answers to 1 decimal place.

 4 Find the positive solution to the equation $x^2 = 12^2 + 8^2$
Give your answer correct to 3 significant figures.

  5 Reflect Dawn and Eleri are answering the same question.
Parts of their working are shown.

Dawn's working	Eleri's working
$x^2 = 33.846$	$x^2 = 33.846$
$x - \sqrt{33.8}$	$x - \sqrt{33.846}$
$x = \square$	$x = \square$

a Which working is more accurate? Write a sentence to explain.

b Will the accuracy of the working affect the answer?

Key point

In a right-angled triangle, the longest side is opposite the right angle.
It is called the **hypotenuse**.

hypotenuse

6 Reasoning Edward says, 'AC is the hypotenuse in this right-angled triangle.'
Is Edward correct? Write a sentence to explain.

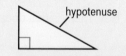

Key point

Pythagoras' theorem states that, in a right-angled triangle,
the square of the hypotenuse is equal to the sum of the squares
of the other two sides.

$$c^2 = a^2 + b^2$$

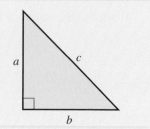

Example

Calculate the length of the hypotenuse.
Give your answer correct to 2 significant figures.

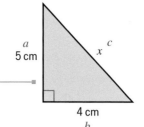

$a = 5, b = 4, c = x$ ◼━━━ | Sketch the triangle. Label the hypotenuse c and the other two sides a and b.

$c^2 = a^2 + b^2$
$x^2 = 5^2 + 4^2$
$\quad = 25 + 16$ ◼━━━ | Substitute the values of a, b and c into the formula for Pythagoras' theorem.
$\quad = 41$
$x = \sqrt{41}$ ━━━ | Use a calculator to find the square root.
$\quad = 6.4031...$ ◼
$x = 6.4\,\text{cm}$ (to 2 s.f.) ◼━━━ | Round your answer to 2 significant figures and put the units in your answer.

7 Look at the triangle in the example.
Does it matter which side is a and which side is b?
Show working with $a = 4$, $b = 5$, $c = x$ to support your answer.

8 Calculate the length of the hypotenuse in each triangle.
Give your answers correct to 3 significant figures.

Q8 hint

Do not round *before* taking the square root. Use all the figures on your calculator display.

a

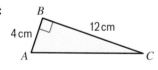

b

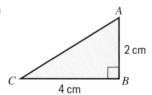

c

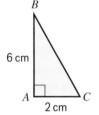

9 a For each right-angled triangle in **Q8**, work out the length of the hypotenuse as a simplified surd.
b **Reflect** Are your answers to **Q8** or **Q9a** more accurate? Write a sentence to explain.

10 a Calculate the length of the diagonal of a rectangle measuring 5 cm by 3.5 cm.
Give your answer to an appropriate degree of accuracy.
State the degree of accuracy after your answer,
e.g. 2 s.f. or 1 d.p.

Q10a hint

Sketch a right-angled triangle and label it.

b **Reflect** Write a sentence explaining how you chose the degree of accuracy.

11 **Problem-solving** A ship sails 5 miles north and then 8.1 miles east.
It then returns directly to its starting point.
What is the total distance the ship travels?

12 **Problem-solving** A roof truss is made of wood.
The vertical support bisects the horizontal span.
The wood costs £17.50 per metre.
Work out the total cost of wood for the roof truss.
Give your answer to an appropriate degree of accuracy.

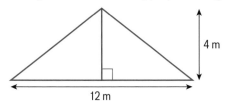

4 m

12 m

Q12 hint

'Bisect' means to divide in half.

Key point

A triangle with sides a, b and c, where c is the longest side, is right-angled only if $c^2 = a^2 + b^2$

13 **Reasoning** Can a right-angled triangle have sides of length
4 cm, 5 cm and 8 cm?
Explain your answers.

Q13 hint

If the triangle is right-angled, the longest side will be the hypotenuse.

Exam-style question

14 $ABCD$ is a trapezium.
$AB = 6$ cm
$BC = 8$ cm
$AD = 12$ cm

C ───8 cm─── B

6 cm

D ───12 cm─── A

Calculate the perimeter of $ABCD$.
Give your answer correct to 1 decimal place.   **(3 marks)**

Exam tip

Think about how shapes are made from other shapes.

Q14 hint

This trapezium divides into a rectangle and a right-angled triangle. What measurements do you know on the triangle?

Exam-style question

15 The diagram shows an irregular hexagon made of
4 right-angled triangles.
$AB = BC = CD = DE$

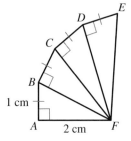

1 cm

A   2 cm   F

Show that $EF = 2\sqrt{2}$.   **(4 marks)**

Exam tip

You have to show an answer given as a simplified surd, so leave all your working in surd form.

5.5 Pythagoras' theorem 2

Active Learn
Homework
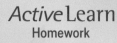

- Calculate the length of a shorter side in a right-angled triangle.
- Solve problems using Pythagoras' theorem.

Warm up

1 Fluency Which length marked on this circle is the diameter?

2 Calculate the length of the hypotenuse in this right-angled triangle.
Give your answer correct to 1 decimal place.

7 cm

4 cm

3 Solve these equations.
The first one is started for you.

a $5^2 = a^2 + 4^2$
$a^2 = 5^2 - 4^2$

b $10^2 = 6^2 + b^2$

c $5^2 + c^2 = 13^2$

d $d^2 + d^2 = 50$

Key point

You can use Pythagoras' theorem to work out the length of a shorter side in a right-angled triangle.

F
H

Example

Calculate the length m in this right-angled triangle.
Give your answer correct to 3 significant figures.

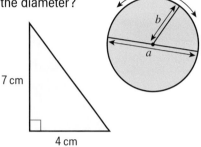

a m

b

4 cm

9 cm

c

$c^2 = a^2 + b^2$ — Sketch the triangle. Label the hypotenuse c and the other two sides a and b.

$9^2 = m^2 + 4^2$ — Substitute the values of a, b and c into Pythagoras' theorem.

$81 = m^2 + 16$

$m^2 = 81 - 16 = 65$ — Solve the equation.

$m = \sqrt{65}$

$\quad = 8.0622...$ — Use a calculator to find the square root.

$m = 8.06$ cm (to 3 s.f.) — Give your answer correct to 3 s.f. and include the units.

4 Work out the length of the side marked with a letter in each right-angled triangle.
Give your answers correct to 3 significant figures.

a
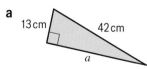
13 cm
42 cm
a

b
b
8.4 cm
5.6 cm

c
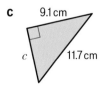
9.1 cm
c
11.7 cm

5 Work out the length of the unknown side in each right-angled triangle.
Give your answers in simplified surd form.

a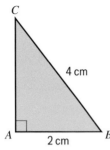

b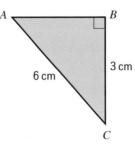

c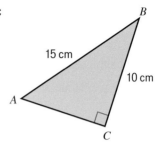

Exam-style question

6 *XYZ* is a right-angled triangle.

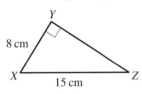

Here is Sam's method to find length *YZ*.

$$YZ^2 = XY^2 + XZ^2$$
$$= 8^2 + 15^2$$
$$= 64 + 225$$
$$= 289$$
$$YZ = \sqrt{289}$$
$$= 17\,\text{cm}$$

What mistake has Sam made? **(1 mark)**

Exam tip

When asked to identify a mistake, explain the mistake made. Do not simply write the correct working and answer.

7 A ladder of length 5 m leans against a vertical wall.
The foot of the ladder is 4.2 m from the base of the wall.
How far is the top of the ladder from the ground?

Q7 hint

Sketch the triangle and label it. State the degree of accuracy after your answer.

8 A ramp is to be used to go up one step.

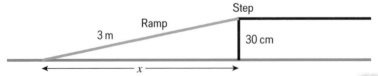

The ramp is 3 m long. The step is 30 cm high.
How far away from the step (*x*) does the ramp start?
Give your answer in metres, to the nearest centimetre.

Q8 hint

Convert lengths to the same units.

9 Calculate the vertical height of trapezium $ABCD$.
Give your answer in centimetres, to the nearest millimetre.

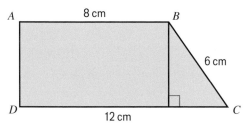

10 Problem-solving Work out the perimeter of triangle ACD.

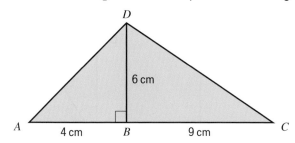

Give your answer correct to 3 significant figures.

11 Problem-solving ABC is an equilateral triangle with side length 2 cm.
D is the midpoint of the base of the triangle.
Work out the height of the triangle.
Give your answer in surd form.

12 Problem-solving Work out the side length of a square with a diagonal of 20 cm.
Give your answer in simplified surd form.

13 Problem-solving Calculate the length of the side of the largest square that *fits inside* a 12 cm
diameter circle.

Exam-style question

14 The diagram shows 4 identical equilateral triangles joined
together to make a parallelogram, $AEFB$.
$AB = BC = CD = DE = EF = 11$ cm

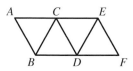

Work out the length of the diagonal of the parallelogram, AF.
Give your answer correct to 3 significant figures.

(3 marks)

Exam tip

Sometimes you must draw in
lines or extend sides on shapes
to work out a length. To find
a diagonal, draw in sides and
extend lengths to make a right-
angled triangle with the diagonal
as the hypotenuse.

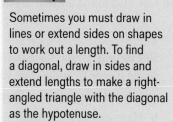

5.6 Trigonometry 1

- Use trigonometric ratios to find lengths in a right-angled triangle.
- Use trigonometric ratios to solve problems.
- Find angles of elevation and angles of depression.

*Active*Learn
Homework

Warm up

1 **Fluency** Name the hypotenuse in each triangle.

a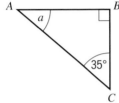

b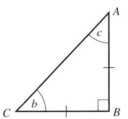

c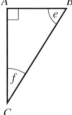

2 **a** Work out the size of each unknown angle in **Q1a** and **b**.

b In **Q1c**, size of angle d : size of angle $e = 2 : 3$. Work out the sizes of angles d and e.

3 Solve these equations.
Give your answers correct to 2 decimal places where necessary.

a $\dfrac{x}{5} = 4$ **b** $\dfrac{10}{x} = 5$ **c** $3.5 = \dfrac{x}{2.1}$ **d** $9.5 = \dfrac{10}{x}$

Key point

The side opposite the right angle is called the **hypotenuse**.
The side opposite the angle θ is called the **opposite**.
The side next to the angle θ is called the **adjacent**.

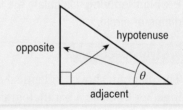

4 **Reasoning** Draw triangle ABC accurately using a ruler and protractor.
Angle $A = 90°$, angle $B = 30°$ and $AB = 5\,\text{cm}$

a Label the **hyp**otenuse (**hyp**), **opp**osite side (**opp**) and **adj**acent side (**adj**).

b Measure each unknown side, correct to the nearest millimetre.

c Write the fraction   **i** $\dfrac{\text{opposite}}{\text{hypotenuse}}$ **ii** $\dfrac{\text{adjacent}}{\text{hypotenuse}}$ **iii** $\dfrac{\text{opposite}}{\text{adjacent}}$

Convert each fraction to a decimal.
Give your answers correct to 1 decimal place.

d Repeat parts **a** to **c** for triangle ABC with

   i angle $A = 90°$, angle $B = 30°$ and $AB = 7\,\text{cm}$

   ii angle $A = 90°$, angle $B = 30°$ and $AB = 8\,\text{cm}$

e **Reflect** Write a description of what you notice about the ratios of sides in a triangle with angles $30°$, $60°$ and $90°$.

Key point

In a right-angled triangle:

- The **sine** of angle θ is the ratio of the opposite side to the hypotenuse, $\sin \theta = \dfrac{\text{opp}}{\text{hyp}}$

- The **cosine** of angle θ is the ratio of the adjacent side to the hypotenuse, $\cos \theta = \dfrac{\text{adj}}{\text{hyp}}$

- The **tangent** of angle θ is the ratio of the opposite side to the adjacent side, $\tan \theta = \dfrac{\text{opp}}{\text{adj}}$

You can find the sine, cosine and tangent of an angle using the [sin], [cos] and [tan] keys on your calculator.

5 Use your calculator to find these.
Give your answers correct to 1 decimal place where necessary.

a $\sin 35°$ **b** $\cos 17°$ **c** $\tan 82°$

Q5a hint

Press [sin] [3] [5] [=]
on your calculator.

Example

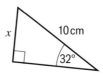

Calculate the length of the side marked x.
Give your answer correct to 3 significant figures.

$\text{angle} = 32°,\ \text{opp} = x,\ \text{hyp} = 10\,\text{cm}$	Identify the information given.
$\sin \theta = \dfrac{\text{opp}}{\text{hyp}}$	Write the relevant trigonometric ratio.
$\sin 32° = \dfrac{x}{10}$	Substitute into the trigonometric ratio.
$x = 10 \times \sin 32°$	Rearrange to make x the subject.
$= 5.2991...$	Use your calculator to work out x.
$x = 5.30\,\text{cm}$ (to 3 s.f.)	Round your answer, as required.

6 Sketch each triangle. Label its sides opp, adj and hyp.
Then use the correct trigonometric ratio to work out the unknown side, x.
Give your answers correct to 3 significant figures.

a

b

c

7 **Reflect** Mathematicians remember $\sin \theta = \dfrac{\text{opp}}{\text{hyp}}$, $\cos \theta = \dfrac{\text{adj}}{\text{hyp}}$ and $\tan \theta = \dfrac{\text{opp}}{\text{adj}}$ in different ways.

Some remember SOH CAH TOA (pronounced 'soak a toe – uh'!).
Others remember Some Old Horses Chew Apples Happily Throughout Old Age.
How will you remember them?

8 Calculate the length of the side marked x in each triangle.
Give your answers correct to 1 decimal place.

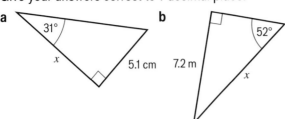

a 31° x 5.1 cm

b 52° 7.2 m x

c x 37° 4.5 cm

9 **Reflect** Write a sentence explaining what was different about working out x in **Q6** and **Q8**.

Exam-style question

10 PQR is a right-angled triangle.
$PQ = 14$ cm
Angle $Q = 90°$
Size of angle P : size of angle $R = 3 : 7$
Work out the length of PR.
Give your answer correct to 3 significant figures.

(4 marks)

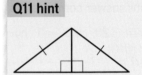

P 14 cm Q R

Exam tip

Use the ratio given in the question to work out the sizes of angles P and R. Now you can use either of two different trigonometric ratios to work out the length of PR. It doesn't matter which one you use, but you must show your working.

11 **Problem-solving / Reasoning**
A shed roof makes an angle of 41° with the horizontal.
The width of the shed is 6 m.
Calculate the height of the roof.
Give your answer correct to 2 significant figures.

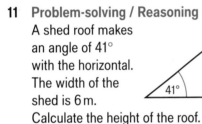

41° 41° 6 m

Q11 hint

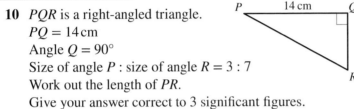

Key point

The **angle of depression** (d) is the angle measured downwards from the horizontal.
The **angle of elevation** (e) is the angle measured upwards from the horizontal.

d e

12 A cliff is 68 m high. The angle of depression from the top of the cliff to a raft on the sea is 29°.
How far is the raft from the bottom of the cliff?
Give your answer correct to the nearest metre.

Q12 hint

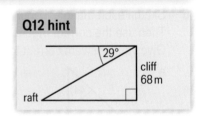

29° cliff 68 m raft

13 **Problem-solving** From a point 8 m away from the base of a flag pole, the angle of elevation to the bottom of a flag is 32°.
From the same point, the angle of elevation to the top of the flag is 41°.
Work out the depth of the flag.
Give your answer in metres, correct to the nearest centimetre.

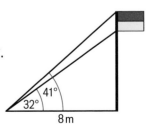

41° 32° 8 m

5.7 Trigonometry 2

- Use trigonometric ratios to calculate an angle in a right-angled triangle.
- Use trigonometric ratios to solve problems.
- Know the exact values of the sine, cosine and tangent of some angles.

*Active*Learn
Homework

Warm up

1 Fluency Name the opposite and adjacent sides in these triangles.

2 ABC is a right-angled triangle.
Calculate the length of AB, correct to 2 decimal places.

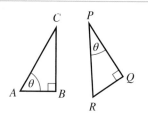

3 Copy and complete to rationalise the denominator of $\dfrac{1}{\sqrt{3}}$ $\qquad \dfrac{1}{\sqrt{3}} = \dfrac{1}{\sqrt{3}} \times \dfrac{\sqrt{\square}}{\sqrt{\square}} = \dfrac{\sqrt{\square}}{\square}$

Key point

If the lengths of two sides of a right-angled triangle are given, you can find a missing angle using the **inverse trigonometric functions**:
$$\sin^{-1} \qquad \cos^{-1} \qquad \tan^{-1}$$
Make sure you know how to use $\sin^{-1}$, $\cos^{-1}$ and $\tan^{-1}$ on your calculator.

4 Use the inverse function on your calculator to find the value of θ, correct to $0.1°$.

a $\sin\theta = 0.562$ **b** $\cos\theta = 0.805$

c $\tan\theta = 0.246$ **d** $\sin\theta = \frac{4}{5}$

e $\cos\theta = \frac{1}{14}$ **f** $\tan\theta = \frac{8.5}{11.5}$

> **Q4 hint**
> 'Correct to $0.1°$' means give your answer to 1 d.p.

> **Q4d hint**
> Enter $\frac{4}{5}$ as a fraction.

Example

Calculate the size of angle x.
Give your answer correct to 1 decimal place.

$\text{angle} = x, \text{opp} = 5\,\text{cm}, \text{hyp} = 9\,\text{cm}$ ──── Identify the information given.

$\sin\theta = \dfrac{\text{opp}}{\text{hyp}}$ ──── Write the relevant trigonometric ratio.

$\sin x = \dfrac{5}{9}$ ──── Substitute into the trigonometric ratio.

$x = \sin^{-1}\left(\dfrac{5}{9}\right)$ ──── Use $\sin^{-1}$ on your calculator to find the angle.

$\quad = 33.7489\ldots$

$x = 33.7°$ (to 1 d.p.) ──── Round your answer, as required.

Unit 5 Angles and trigonometry   145

5 Sketch each triangle. Label its sides opp, adj and hyp.
Then use the correct trigonometric ratio to work out the size of angle x.
Give your answers correct to 1 decimal place.

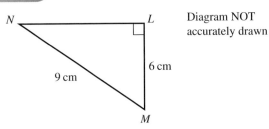

a 15 cm, 12 cm, x

b 7 cm, 3 cm, x

c 4.5 cm, 7.2 cm, x

Exam-style question

6

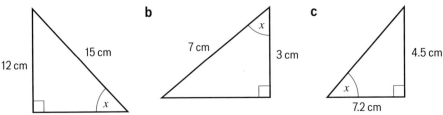

Diagram NOT accurately drawn

N, L, 6 cm, 9 cm, M

a Calculate the size of angle LMN.
Give your answer correct to 1 decimal place. **(2 marks)**

The length of the side MN is increased by 1 cm.
The length of the side LM is still 6 cm.
Angle MLN is still $90°$.

b Will the value of $\cos LMN$ increase or decrease?
You must give a reason for your answer. **(1 mark)**

Q6 hint

For part **b**, read the question carefully. It is asking about the value of $\cos LMN$, not the angle LMN. Therefore, you will be comparing fractions.

7 Problem-solving A tree 20 m in height stands on horizontal ground.

a Work out the angle of elevation of the top of the tree from point A.

b **Reflect** Write a sentence explaining how you can use your knowledge of angles in parallel lines to work out the angle of depression of point A from the top of the tree.

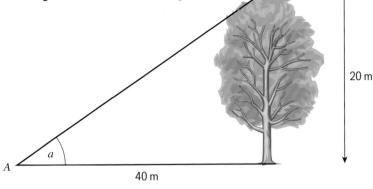

20 m

a

A

40 m

8 Problem-solving From P, a ship sails 3 km east and then 5 km north to its destination.
A helicopter flies from P directly to the ship.
On what angle (x) from north should the helicopter fly?
Give your answer correct to 1 decimal place.

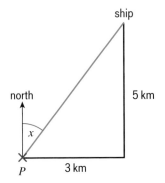

ship

north

5 km

x

P 3 km

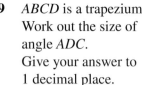

Exam-style question

9 *ABCD* is a trapezium.
Work out the size of
angle *ADC*.
Give your answer to
1 decimal place.

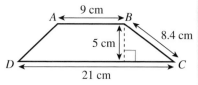

Exam tip

When a question involves right-
angled triangles, it is likely to
require use of trigonometry or
Pythagoras' theorem, or both.

(5 marks)

10 Problem-solving Calculate the size of angle θ in this diagram.

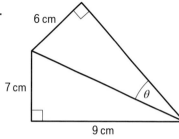

11 *ABC* is an isosceles triangle.

  a Use the diagram to write the value of $\tan 45°$.

  b Use Pythagoras' theorem to find the length
    of *BC*. Leave your answer in surd form.

  c Write these ratios as exact values
    using surds.

    i $\sin 45°$ **ii** $\cos 45°$

  d Rationalise the denominators in part **c** and give your answers as surds
    in their simplest form.

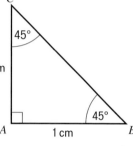

Q11c i hint

Your answer should
look like this:

$$\sin 45° = \frac{1}{\sqrt{\square}}$$

12 *ABC* is an equilateral triangle. *D* is the midpoint of *AC*.

  a Use the diagram to write these ratios as
    fractions.

    i $\cos 60°$ **ii** $\sin 30°$

  b Work out the length of *BD*.
    Leave your answer in surd form.

  c Write these ratios as exact values using surds.

    i $\sin 60°$ **ii** $\tan 60°$ **iii** $\cos 30°$ **iv** $\tan 30°$

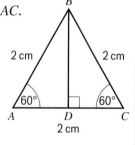

Q12c i hint

Your answer should
look like this:

$$\sin 60° = \frac{\sqrt{\square}}{\square}$$

13 a Copy and complete this table with exact values using surds.
    Use your answers to **Q11** and **Q12** to help you.

	0°	30°	45°	60°	90°
sin	0				1
cos	1				0
tan	0				

Q13 hint

For the exams you need to learn
the exact values of $\sin \theta$ and
$\cos \theta$ for $\theta = 0°, 30°, 45°, 60°$
and $90°$, and the exact values
of $\tan \theta$ for $\theta = 0°, 30°, 45°$
and $60°$.

  b Find the exact value of x in each of these triangles.

    i 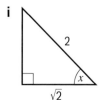   **ii** 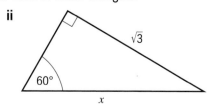   **iii**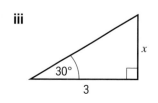

5 Check up

Angles and polygons

1 **a** What is the size of each interior angle of a regular decagon (10-sided polygon)?

   b What is the size of an exterior angle of a regular pentagon?

2 Part of a regular polygon is shown.
   How many sides does the polygon have?

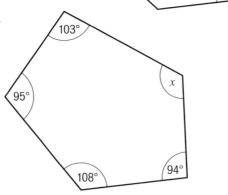

3 Work out the size of angle x.

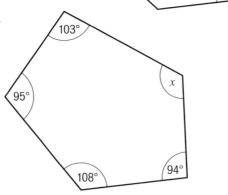

4 Work out the size of angle ABE.
   Give reasons for your working.

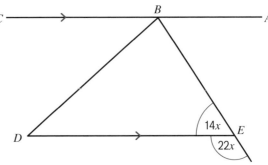

5 Show that for any quadrilateral
   $a + b + c + d = 360°$

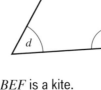

6 DEA is a straight line.
   BE and CD are parallel. $ABEF$ is a kite.
   Angle $ACD = 90°$
   Angle FAB is half the size of angle BEF.
   Work out the size of angle BEF.
   Give reasons for your working.

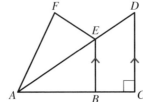

7 BCD is an isosceles triangle.
   AC is parallel to ED. AE is parallel to
   BD. Angle $BAE = 62°$
   Work out the size of the angle marked x.
   Give reasons for your working.

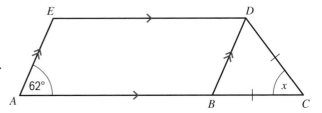

Pythagoras' theorem

8 Calculate the length of AC in each right-angled triangle.

a

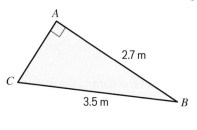

b

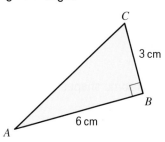

Give your answer to part **a** correct to 2 significant figures. Give your answer to part **b** in surd form.

9 A triangle has sides of length 3 cm, 6 cm and 7 cm. Is the triangle a right-angled triangle? Explain your answer.

10 A rectangle has a width of 13.4 cm and a diagonal of 21 cm.
Work out the area of the rectangle. Give your answer correct to 3 significant figures.

Trigonometry

11 Calculate the length of the side, or size of the angle, marked x in each triangle.
Give your answers correct to 3 significant figures.

a

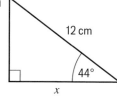

b

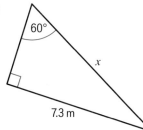

c

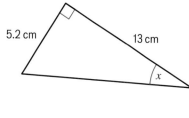

12 A kite is flying at a height of 11.7 m. The string of the kite is 14 m long.
What is the angle of elevation of the kite? Give your answer correct to 1 decimal place.

13 Write down the value of
a $\tan 45°$ **b** $\sin 30°$ **c** $\cos 60°$

14 **Reflect** How sure are you of your answers? Were you mostly

Just guessing   Feeling doubtful   Confident

What next? Use your results to decide whether to strengthen or extend your learning.

Challenge

15 a Work out the size of each angle in an isosceles triangle when one angle is twice the size of the other two angles.

b Work out the size of each angle when one angle is
i 3 times   **ii** 4 times   **iii** 10 times   **iv** 58 times
the size of the other two angles.

c **Reflect** Write a sentence describing what is happening to the shape as the unique angle increases in size.

5 Strengthen

Angles and polygons

1 **Reasoning** Mario divides some shapes into triangles to work out the sum of the interior angles.

a Copy and complete his table.

Polygon	Quadrilateral	Pentagon	Hexagon	Heptagon
	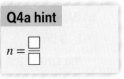			
Number of sides (n)	4			
Number of triangles	2			
Sum of interior angles	$2 \times 180° = 360°$			

b Copy and complete Mario's working to find an expression for the sum of the interior angles of *any* polygon.

> Number of sides $= n$
> Number of triangles $= n - \square$
> Sum of interior angles $= (n - \square) \times \square°$

c Use your answer to part **b** to work out the sum of the interior angles of a decagon (10-sided polygon).

2 Work out the size of each interior angle of these shapes. The first one has been started for you.

a a regular nonagon

Sum of interior angles $= (n - \square) \times \square°$
$= (9 - \square) \times \square°$
$= \square°$

Interior angle $= \square° \div 9$
$= \square°$

Q2 hint

In a **regular polygon** all the sides and all the angles are equal.

b a regular polygon with 12 sides   **c** a regular polygon with 20 sides

3 The sum of the exterior angles of any polygon is $360°$.
Divide $360°$ by the number of sides to work out the size of an exterior angle of

a a regular quadrilateral   **b** a regular decagon   **c** a regular polygon with 18 sides

4 **a** Rearrange the formula to make n (number of sides) the subject.

exterior angle $= \dfrac{360°}{n}$

b Use your answer to part **a** to work out how many sides a regular polygon has if the exterior angle is

i $90°$ **ii** $60°$ **iii** $30°$ **iv** $12°$

Q4a hint

$n = \dfrac{\square}{\square}$

5 Part of a regular polygon is shown.

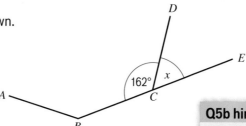

  a Which angle is

    i the interior angle

    ii the exterior angle?

  b Work out the size of x.

  c How many sides does the
    polygon have?

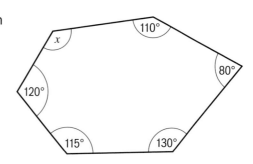

> **Q5b hint**
>
> Use the fact that angles on a
> straight line add up to 180°.

6 **a** Copy and complete the equation to show the sum
    of the interior angles of this hexagon.

    $x + 110° + 80° + 130° + \square° + 120° = \square°$

  b Solve the equation to work out the size of x.

7 Here is a kite.
Copy the kite.

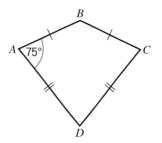

  a Label the other angle that is 75°.

  b Angle ABC is twice the size of angle ADC.
    Label angle ADC as x.
    Now label angle ABC in terms of x.

  c Write and solve an equation to work out the size of angle ABC.

8 Work out the size of angle ABC.
Give reasons for your working.
The working has been started
for you.

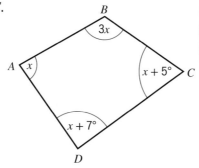

$x + 3x + x + 5 + x + 7 = \square°$
(angles in a quadrilateral
  add up to $\square°$)

$\qquad 6x + \square = \square°$

$\qquad\qquad 6x = \square°$

$\qquad\qquad\ x = \square°$

> **Q8 hint**
>
> Have you answered the
> question asked?

9 **Reasoning** Work out the values of x, y and z.
Give reasons for your working.

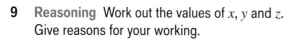
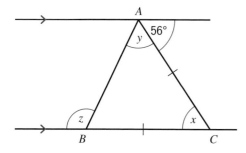

> **Q9 hint**
>
> Use these reasons:
> Alternate angles are equal.
> Angles in a triangle sum
> to 180°.
> Base angles of an isosceles
> triangle are equal.
> Angles on a straight line add
> up to 180°.

10 Reasoning Is each statement true or false?
Explain your answers.

a $m = x$ **b** $z = x + y$ **c** $m = y + z$
d $m = 180° - x$ **e** $x = 180° - (y + z)$

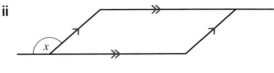

11 Reasoning Copy each diagram.

i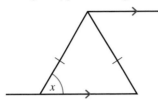

ii

a Write x in all the angles equal to x in each diagram.

b Write y in all the angles equal to $180 - x$ in each diagram.

c Look at your diagram for **ii**. What properties of parallelograms are shown?

Pythagoras' theorem

1 In a right-angled triangle, the hypotenuse is the longest side and is opposite the right angle.
Name the hypotenuse in each triangle.

a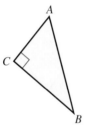

b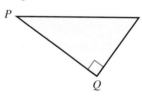

c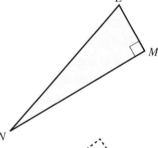

2 The hypotenuse of this right-angled triangle is labelled c.
Copy and complete these steps to find the
value of c.

$c^2 = 8^2 + \square^2$ (Pythagoras' theorem)
$c^2 = \square$
$c = \sqrt{\square}$
$c = \square$ cm

Q2 hint

In a right-angled triangle, the square of the
hypotenuse is equal to the sum of the squares of
the other two sides. This is Pythagoras' theorem.

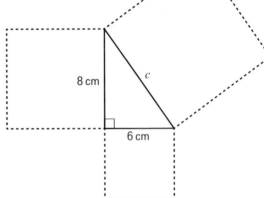

3 Use the same method as in **Q2** to calculate
the length c in these right-angled triangles.
Round your answer to 1 decimal place where necessary.

a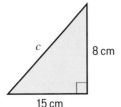

b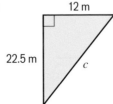

Q3b hint

Do not round before taking the
square root. You should find the
square root of 650.25.

4 One of the shorter sides of this right-angled triangle is labelled b.
Copy and complete these steps to find the value of b.

$c^2 = a^2 + b^2$ (Pythagoras' theorem)
$10^2 = \square^2 + b^2$
$100 = \square + b^2$
$b^2 = 100 - \square$
$b = \sqrt{\square}$
$b = \square$ cm

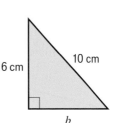

5 Use the same method as in **Q4** to calculate the length x in these right-angled triangles.
Round your answer to 1 decimal place where necessary.

a

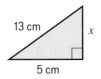

b

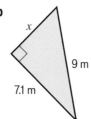

6 A rectangle has a width of 20 cm and a diagonal of 25 cm.

a Sketch the rectangle.
Label any sides you know and all the right angles.

b Work out the area of the rectangle.

Q6b hint

Area of a rectangle = width × $\square$

↑
First you must find this.

7 **Reasoning** Aaron says, 'Triangle ABC is right-angled'.
Is Aaron correct? Explain.

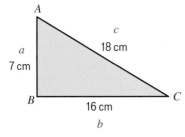

Q7 hint

A triangle is only right-angled if
$c^2 = a^2 + b^2$, where c is the longest
side.
Start:
$c^2 = 18^2 = \ldots$
$a^2 + b^2 = \ldots$

8 Work out the value of x in each right-angled triangle, giving your answers in simplified surd form.
The first two are started for you.

a

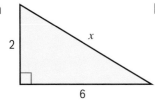

b

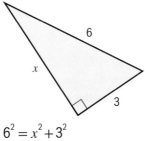

c

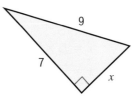

$x^2 = 2^2 + 6^2$
$\quad = \square + \square$
$\quad = \square$
$x = \sqrt{\square}$
$\quad = \sqrt{4} \times \sqrt{10}$
$\quad = \square\sqrt{10}$

$6^2 = x^2 + 3^2$
$x^2 = 6^2 - 3^2$

Trigonometry

1 Sketch these triangles and label the hypotenuse, opposite and adjacent sides.

a

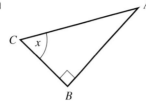

b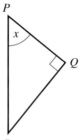

c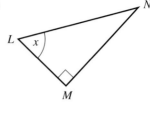

2 Write $\sin x$, $\cos x$ and $\tan x$ as fractions for this triangle.
The first one has been started for you.

$$\sin x = \frac{\text{opposite}}{\text{hypotenuse}} = \frac{\square}{\square}$$

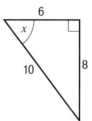

> **Q2 hint**
>
> Use SOH CAH TOA.

3 Use your calculator to find, correct to 2 decimal places

a $\sin 22°$ **b** $\tan 36°$ **c** $\cos 70°$ **d** $\tan 58°$

4 Copy and complete. Use your calculator to find each angle, correct to 1 decimal place.

a $\tan x = 0.345$ $x = \tan^{-1}(\square)$ **b** $\sin \theta = 0.806$ $\theta = \square^{-1}(0.806)$

c $\cos y = 0.7625$ $y = \cos^{-1}(\square)$ **d** $\sin a = \frac{2}{3}$ $a = \square^{-1}\left(\frac{2}{3}\right)$

e $\cos b = \frac{4.8}{5.1}$ $b = \cos^{-1}(\square)$

5 Sophie is calculating the length of the side marked x in this triangle.
Copy and complete her working.

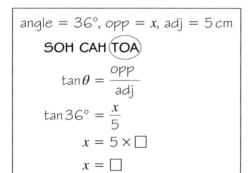

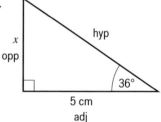

6 Use the same method as in **Q5** to calculate the length of the side marked x in each triangle.
Give your answers correct to 1 decimal place.

a

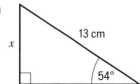

b

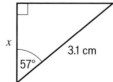

7 Calculate the size of angle x.
The working has been started for you.

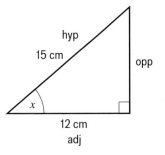

angle = x, adj = 12 cm, hyp = 15 cm

SOH (CAH) TOA

$\cos\theta = \dfrac{adj}{\Box}$

$\cos x = \dfrac{\Box}{\Box}$

$x = \cos^{-1}\left(\dfrac{\Box}{\Box}\right)$

$x = \Box°$

Q7 hint

Round your answer to 1 d.p.

8 Sketch the triangle ABC. Label angel ABC with an arc, $\triangle$.
Then use the same method as in **Q7** to calculate the size of angle ABC.
Give your answer correct to 0.1°.

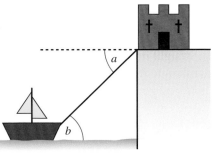

9 Which angle is an angle of elevation
and which is an angle of depression?

10 Problem-solving From the top of a vertical cliff, C, a boat, B, can be seen out at sea.
The cliff is 90 m high. The boat is 110 m from the base of the cliff.

a Copy and complete the diagram to show the information you are given.

b Choose the angle of elevation: ABC, BAC or BCA?

c Work out the angle of elevation of the cliff top from the boat.
Give your answer correct to 1 decimal place.

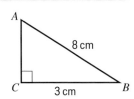

11 Use these diagrams to match the
sine, cosine and tangent
of 30°, 45° and 60° to the
correct value in the cloud.

a $\sin 30°$ **b** $\sin 45°$
c $\sin 60°$ **d** $\cos 30°$
e $\cos 45°$ **f** $\cos 60°$
g $\tan 30°$ **h** $\tan 45°$
i $\tan 60°$

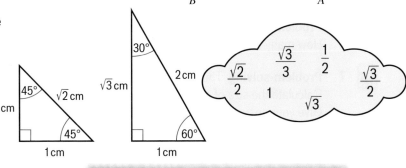

Q11 hint

$\dfrac{1}{\sqrt{2}} = \dfrac{1}{\sqrt{2}} \times \dfrac{\sqrt{2}}{\sqrt{2}} = \dfrac{\sqrt{2}}{2}$ $\dfrac{1}{\sqrt{3}} = \dfrac{1}{\sqrt{3}} \times \dfrac{\sqrt{3}}{\sqrt{3}} = \dfrac{\sqrt{3}}{3}$

12 Use your calculator to work out

a $\sin 0°$ **b** $\cos 0°$ **c** $\tan 0°$ **d** $\sin 90°$ **e** $\cos 90°$

5 Extend

1 **Reasoning** Sarah sees an aeroplane.
She estimates it is flying at a height of 56 000 feet.
The angle of elevation to the aeroplane is 49°.
What is the horizontal distance between Sarah and the plane?
Give your answer correct to 3 significant figures.

2 **Problem-solving** The length of the diagonal of a square is 10 cm.
Work out the length of a side of the square.
Give your answer correct to 1 decimal place.

3 Work out $\sqrt{\dfrac{4.5 \times \cos 38°}{9.7^2 - 4.88}}$
Give your answer correct to 3 significant figures.

Exam-style question

4 *BCDEF* is a regular pentagon.
ABC and *AFE* are straight lines.
Work out the size of angle *ABF*.
You must show how you got your answer.   (**3 marks**)

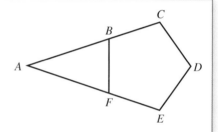

5 Angle $BCE = x°$
Write an expression for angle *ABE* in terms of x.

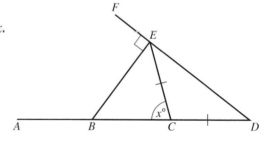

6 **Problem-solving** The exterior and interior angles of a regular polygon are in the ratio 1 : 4.
How many sides does the polygon have?

7 **Problem-solving** The area of triangle *ABC* is 42 cm².
Calculate the size of angle x.
Give your answer correct to 1 decimal place.

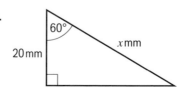

8 Here is a right-angled triangle.
Without using a calculator,
show that $x = 40$.

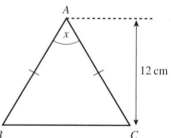

> **Q8 hint**
>
> You should know the exact value of cos 60°.

Exam-style question

9 Without using a calculator, work out the perimeter of the triangle.
Give your answer in simplified surd form.

(4 marks)

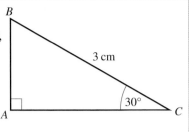

Exam tip

You should know the exact values of $\sin 30°$ and $\cos 30°$.

Exam-style question

10 X, Y and Z are points on the circumference of a circle, centre O.
XOZ is a diameter of the circle.
Prove that angle XYZ is $90°$.

(4 marks)

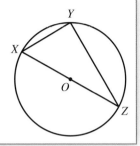

Q10 hint

Look for shapes that give you additional information. Join OY, and what type of triangles do you have? Label an angle that you know in one triangle as x and in the other triangle as y.

Exam-style question

11 The diagram shows three identical circles in a rectangle.
Each circle touches the other two circles and the sides of the rectangle as shown in the diagram.
The radius of each circle is 36 mm.
Work out the length of the diagonal of the rectangle.
Give your answer correct to 3 significant figures. **(4 marks)**

Q11 hint

To find the width of the rectangle, you will need to join the centres of the circles and work with the triangles that creates.

Working towards A level

12 The diagram shows that from the top of a vertical cliff, h metres high, two yachts can be seen.
The angles of depression of the two yachts are $36°$ and $54°$.
The distance between the two yachts is 28 metres.

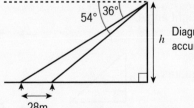

Diagram **NOT** accurately drawn

Work out the height of the cliff.
Give your answer correct to 3 significant figures.

Q12 hint

Let the distance between the base of the cliff and the nearer yacht be x. Use trigonometry to write two expressions for h in terms of x. Equate them and solve to find the value of x. Then use your answer in one of the two expressions to find the value of h.

At A level you often need to work out some other detail before you can find the answer required.

5 Test ready

Summary of key points

To revise for the test:

- Read each key point, find a question on it in the mastery lesson, and check you can work out the answer.

- If you cannot, try some other questions from the mastery lesson or ask for help.

Key points

1 Angles inside two parallel lines are called **co-interior** angles.

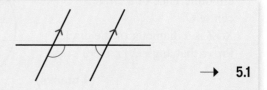

→ **5.1**

2 When one side of a polygon is extended at a vertex
- the angle marked x is called the **interior angle**
- the angle marked y is called the **exterior angle**.

$x + y = 180°$ (angles on a straight line add up to 180°)

→ **5.1, 5.3**

3 For any polygon, interior angle + exterior angle = 180° → **5.3**

4 The exterior angle of a triangle is equal to the sum of the interior angles at the other two vertices.
    angle d = angle a + angle b

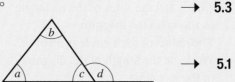

→ **5.1**

5 The sum of the interior angles of a polygon with n sides = $(n - 2) \times 180°$ → **5.2**

6 For shapes to fit together (**tessellate**), all the angles where the shapes meet *must* add up to 360°. → **5.2**

7 The sum of the exterior angles of a polygon is always 360°. → **5.3**

8 In a regular polygon all the angles are the same size,

so exterior angle = $\dfrac{360°}{\text{number of sides}}$ or number of sides = $\dfrac{360°}{\text{exterior angle}}$ → **5.3**

9 In a right-angled triangle, the longest side is opposite the right angle. It is called the **hypotenuse**. → **5.4**

10 **Pythagoras' theorem** states that, in a right-angled triangle, the square of the hypotenuse is equal to the sum of the squares of the other two sides.
    $c^2 = a^2 + b^2$

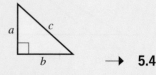

→ **5.4**

11 A triangle with sides a, b and c, where c is the longest side, is right-angled only if
$c^2 = a^2 + b^2$ → **5.4**

12 In a right-angled triangle, the side opposite the angle θ is called the **opposite**. The side next to the angle θ is called the **adjacent**.

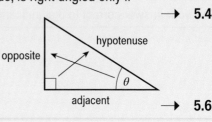

→ **5.6**

13 The **sine** of angle θ is the ratio of the opposite side to the hypotenuse, $\sin\theta = \dfrac{\text{opp}}{\text{hyp}}$ → **5.6**

14 The **cosine** of angle θ is the ratio of the adjacent side to the hypotenuse, $\cos\theta = \dfrac{\text{adj}}{\text{hyp}}$ → **5.6**

15 The **tangent** of angle θ is the ratio of the opposite side to the adjacent side,

$\tan\theta = \dfrac{\text{opp}}{\text{adj}}$ → **5.6**

16 The **angle of depression** (d) is the angle measured downwards from the horizontal.
The **angle of elevation** (e) is the angle measured upwards from the horizontal.

→ **5.6**

17 You can use $\sin^{-1}$, $\cos^{-1}$ or $\tan^{-1}$ on your calculator to find an angle when you know its sine, cosine or tangent. → **5.7**

18 You should know the exact values of the sine, cosine and tangent of these angles.

	0°	30°	45°	60°	90°
sin	0	$\dfrac{1}{2}$	$\dfrac{\sqrt{2}}{2}$	$\dfrac{\sqrt{3}}{2}$	1
cos	1	$\dfrac{\sqrt{3}}{2}$	$\dfrac{\sqrt{2}}{2}$	$\dfrac{1}{2}$	0
tan	0	$\dfrac{\sqrt{3}}{3}$	1	$\sqrt{3}$	

→ **5.7**

Sample student answer

Exam-style question

ABC and *DEF* are parallel lines.
BEG is a right-angled triangle.

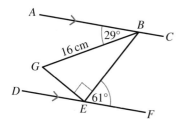

Work out the length of *BE*.
Give your answer correct to
3 significant figures. **(5 marks)**

$ABE = 61°$ (Z angles are equal)
$ABE = ABG + GBE$
so $61° = 29° + GBE$
$GBE = 61° - 29° = 32°$
angle = 32°, hyp = 16 cm, opp = BE
$\sin 32° = \dfrac{\text{opp}}{\text{hyp}}$
$= \dfrac{BE}{16}$
$BE = 16 \times \sin 32°$
$= 8.5\,\text{cm}$

a The student wrote, 'Z angles are equal.' How could this part of their answer be improved?

b Give two other ways that the answer could be improved.

5 Unit test

1 *ABCDEFGHI* is a regular nonagon.

   a What is the sum of the interior angles?

   b Work out the size of angle *HIJ*.

   (3 marks)

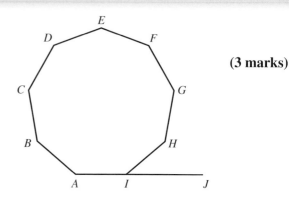

2 *ABC* and *DEF* are straight lines.
   AC is parallel to *DF*.
   BE = CE

   Work out the value of *x*.
   Give reasons for your answer.

   (3 marks)

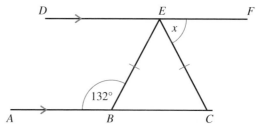

3 *ABC* and *DEFG* are straight lines.
   AC is parallel to *DG*.
   Prove that the angle sum of any
   triangle is 180°.

   (4 marks)

4 Write down the value of

   a tan 45°   **(1 mark)**

   b sin 90°   **(1 mark)**

   c cos 45°   **(1 mark)**

   d sin 60°   **(1 mark)**

5 Work out the length of side *BC* in each triangle.
   Give your answers correct to 3 significant figures.

   a   **b**   **(4 marks)**

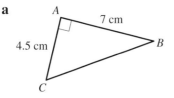

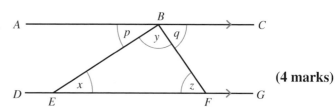

6 *PQS* and *QRS* are right-angled triangles.
   PS = 12.3 cm   *QS* = 7.2 cm   *RQ* = 6.4 cm
   Calculate the perimeter of the triangle *PRS*.
   Give your answer correct to 2 decimal places.

   (4 marks)

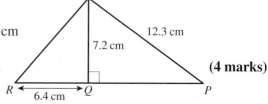

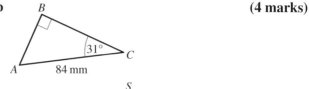

7 In this irregular pentagon, angle PQR = angle QRS = angle RST
Angle QPT is half the size of angle PQR.
Angle PTS is 36° more than angle QPT.
Work out the size of angle QPT.

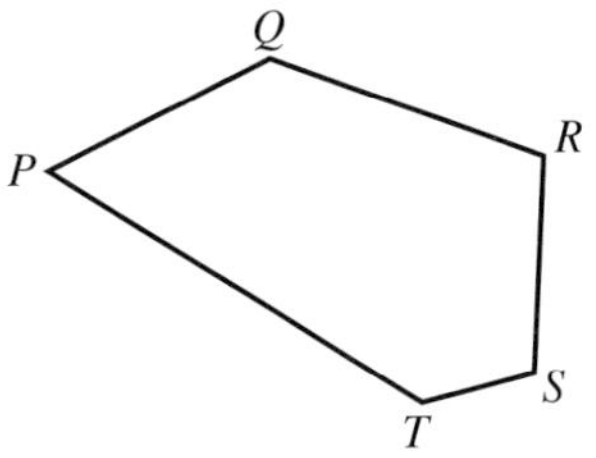

(3 marks)

8 XYZ is a right-angled triangle.
$YZ = 5.4$ m
$XZ = 7.6$ m

Calculate the size of the angle marked x.
Give your answer correct to 1 decimal place.

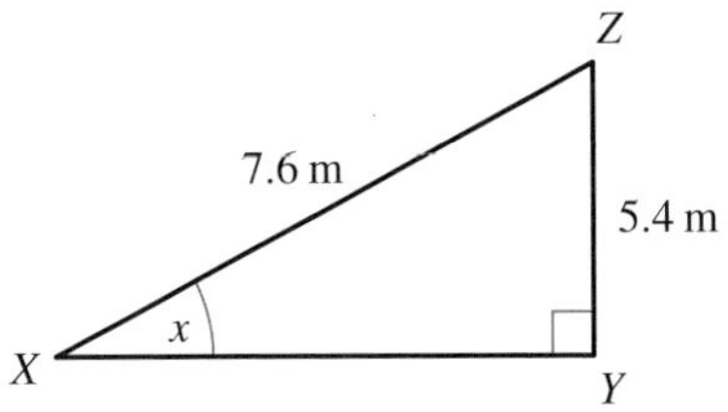

(3 marks)

9 Kari builds a skate ramp with 2 metres of wood.
She wants the vertical height of the ramp to be 1 metre.
What does the angle of elevation need to be?

(3 marks)

10 A ship is sighted from the top of a lighthouse.
The angle of depression from the lighthouse to the ship is 45°.
The distance from the top of the lighthouse directly to the ship is 4 miles.
Calculate the horizontal distance of the ship from the bottom of the lighthouse.
Give your answer correct to 2 decimal places.

(3 marks)

11 A rectangular lawn has a diagonal path running across it.
The lawn is 10 m wide and 15 m long.
Work out the length of the path.
Give your answer in surd form.

(3 marks)

12 The diagram shows 3 identical circles,
each with radius 4 cm.
Their centres are marked with the letters O, P and Q.
Each circle touches the other 2 circles, as shown in
the diagram.
Show that triangle OPQ has area $16\sqrt{3}$ cm².

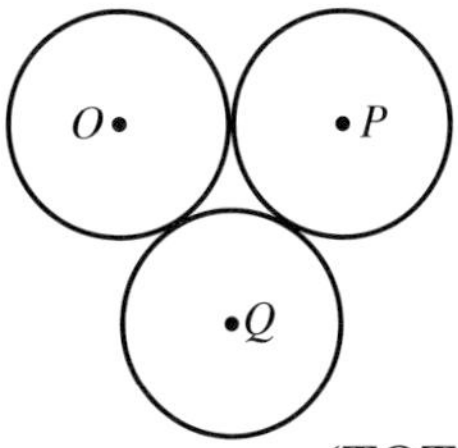

(3 marks)

(TOTAL: 40 marks)

13 Challenge The square and the isosceles triangle have the same area.
Find $\tan\theta$.

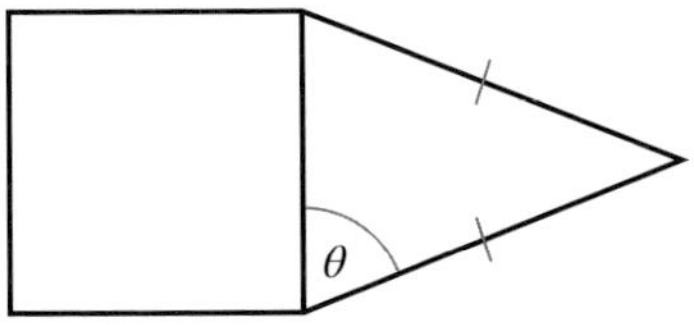

Not to scale

14 Reflect 'Notation' means symbols. Mathematics uses a lot of notation.
For example:

= means is equal to   ° means degrees   ⌐ means a right angle

Look back at this unit. Write a list of all the maths notation used.
Why do you think this notation is important?
Could you have answered the questions in this test without understanding the maths notation?

6 Graphs

6.1 Linear graphs

Prior knowledge

- Find the gradient and y-intercept from a linear equation.
- Rearrange an equation into the form $y = mx + c$.
- Compare two graphs from their equations.
- Plot graphs with equation $ax + by = c$.

Active Learn
Homework

Warm up

1 **Fluency a** Which graph has positive gradient? Which has negative?

b What are the x- and y-intercepts of each graph?

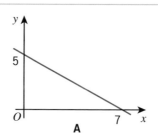

A

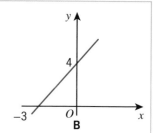

B

2 Rearrange $2x - y = 5$ to make y the subject.

3 For the equation $y - 3x = 6$

a when $x = 0$, what is the value of y **b** when $y = 0$, what is the value of x?

4 What is the gradient of each of these lines?

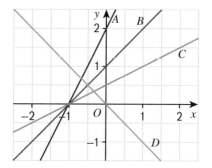

5 a Copy and complete this table for the graphs on the grid.

Equation of line	Gradient	y-intercept
A: $y = 2x + 4$		
B: $y = 2x$		
C: $y = 2x - 3$		
D: $y = -2x + 4$		

b Which line or lines

i pass through the origin

ii have the same y-intercept

iii are parallel?

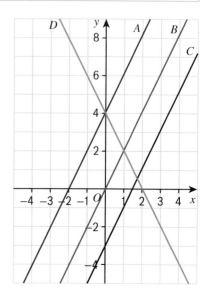

c Reflect Write a sentence describing how you can

  i tell if lines have the same y-intercept when given only the equation of the line

  ii tell if lines are parallel when given only the equation of the line

  iii find the gradient and the y-intercept when given only the equation of the line.

> **Key point**
>
> A **linear equation** generates a straight-line (linear) graph.
> The equation for a straight-line graph can be written as $y = mx + c$ where m is the gradient and c is the y-intercept.

Example

Write the equation of the line shown in the graph.

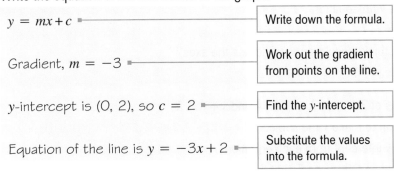

$y = mx + c$ — Write down the formula.

Gradient, $m = -3$ — Work out the gradient from points on the line.

y-intercept is $(0, 2)$, so $c = 2$ — Find the y-intercept.

Equation of the line is $y = -3x + 2$ — Substitute the values into the formula.

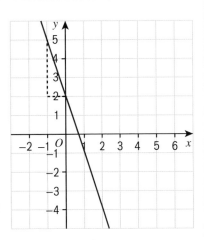

6 a Problem-solving Match each line with its equation.

$y = 3x + 1$	$y = 2x - 2$
$y = -x$	$y = 2x + 1$

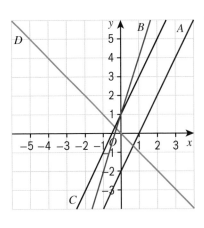

b Which line is the steepest?

c Reflect Write a sentence describing how you can tell which line is the steepest when given only the equations of the lines.

7 Problem-solving Write the equations of these lines.

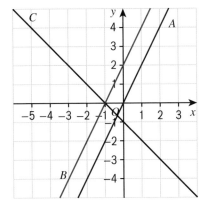

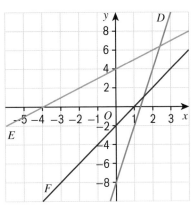

> **Q7 hint**
>
> Read the scales on both axes carefully.

8 **Reasoning** Here are the equations of some linear graphs.

A $y = 2x - 3$ **B** $y = 3x + 1$ **C** $y = x - 1$ **D** $y = 2x + 1$ **E** $y = -x$

Which of these graphs

a cross the y-axis at the same point **b** are parallel?

> **Key point**
>
> To find the y-intercept of a graph, find the y-coordinate where $x = 0$.
> To find the x-intercept of a graph, find the x-coordinate where $y = 0$.

9 **a** For the equation $2y - x = 3$

   i copy and complete the table of values

   ii plot the graph on suitable axes

x	0	
y		0

Repeat part **a** for the lines with equation

b $x + y = 4$ **c** $x + y = 7$

d **Reflect** Where do you think these graphs will cross the axes?

   i $x + y = 3$ **ii** $x + y = -1$

10 In **Q9** you drew the graphs of $2y - x = 3$, $x + y = 4$ and $x + y = 7$.

a Rearrange each equation to make y the subject.

b Read the gradient and y-intercept from each equation.

c Look back at your graphs in **Q9** to check that the gradients and y-intercepts are correct.

> **Key point**
>
> To compare the gradients and y-intercepts of two straight lines, make sure their equations are in the form $y = mx + c$.

11 **Reasoning** Which is the steepest line?

Rearrange to $y = mx + c$ if necessary.

A $y = \frac{1}{3}x - 2$ **B** $2y + 5x = 7$ **C** $3x + \frac{1}{2}y = 2$

D $y = 1 - 4x$ **E** $6x - 2y = 9$

> **Q11 hint**
>
> You might need to multiply or divide every term in the equation to get $y = $ ____ .

> **Exam-style question**
>
> **12** The equation of the line L_1 is $2y = 4x - 7$.
> The equation of the line L_2 is $3y - 6x + 2 = 0$.
> Show that these two lines are parallel. **(2 marks)**

> **Exam tip**
>
> When working with equations of graphs, always consider the form $y = mx + c$

13 **Problem-solving** Which of these lines pass through $(0, 3)$?

Show how you worked it out.

A $y = 3x - 3$ **B** $4y - 8x = 12$ **C** $5y = 3x - 15$ **D** $2x - y = 3$ **E** $3x + y = 3$

14 **Reasoning** The straight line L has the equation $2y - 5x + 1 = 0$.

The point P has coordinates $(0, -1)$.

Which of these lines are parallel to L and pass through P?

You must show your working.

A $y = 5x - 1$ **B** $y = \frac{5}{2}x$ **C** $5x - 2y = 2$ **D** $\frac{5}{2}x - y = 1$

6.2 More linear graphs

Active Learn
Homework

- Sketch graphs using the gradient and intercepts.
- Find the equation of a line, given its gradient and one point on the line.
- Find the gradient of a line through two points.

Warm up

1 **Fluency** Which lines are parallel? Which have the same y-intercept?

   A $y = 3x + 1$ **B** $y = -x + 1$ **C** $y = x + 2$ **D** $y = 5 - x$

2 On squared paper, draw a line with gradient

   a 5   **b** $\frac{1}{2}$ **c** -3

3 Write the equation of each line.

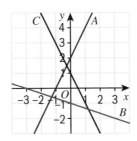

4 Write down the x-intercept of each line in **Q3**.

5 The equation of a line is $y = 3x + c$, and $y = 15$ when $x = 4$.
   Find the value of c.

Example

On the same grid, draw these graphs from their equations.

a $y = 2x - 1$ **b** $y = -x + 4$

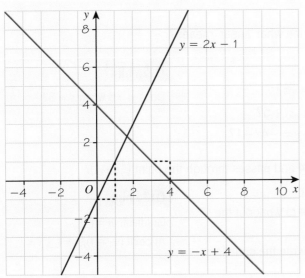

1 Plot the y-intercept.
2 Decide if the gradient is positive or negative.
3 Draw a line with this gradient, starting from the y-intercept.
4 Extend your line to the edges of the grid.
5 Label the line with its equation.

6 Draw these graphs from their equations.
Use a coordinate grid from −10 to +10 on both axes.

a $y = 2x + 4$ **b** $y = 2x - 3$ **c** $y = 3x$ **d** $y = \frac{1}{2}x + 2$ **e** $y = -3x + 2$

7 **Reasoning** Match each equation to one of the sketch graphs.

a $y = 5x + 1$ **b** $y = 2x + 3$ **c** $y = -x + 4$ **d** $y = -3x$ **e** $y = \frac{1}{2}x + 3$

8 **Reflect** Look at the sketches in **Q7**.
Write down the information you include on a sketch of a graph.
How is this different from plotting a graph?

> **Q9b hint**
>
> Mark the x- and y-intercepts and join with a straight line.
>
>

9 **a** Find the x-intercept and y-intercept of the graph with equation

    i $y = 2x$ **ii** $y = 3x + 1$

    iii $x + y = 5$ **iv** $3x + y = -6$

    v $y - x = 2$ **vi** $y - 2x = 4$

b Sketch the graphs.

Key point

A **linear function** has a graph that is a straight line.

---

10 **Reasoning** Which of these are linear functions?

A $y = -3x$ **B** $y = \frac{x}{4}$ **C** $y = 2x + 1$

D $3x + 2y = 5$ **E** $y = x^2 + 4$ **F** $y = \frac{4}{x}$

> **Q10 hint**
>
> Can you write them as $y = mx + c$?

11 **Reflect** $y = mx + c$ is a linear equation.
In your own words, how would you describe what 'linear' means?

12 **Reasoning**

a Does the point (3, 6) lie on the line $y = \frac{1}{2}x$?

b Does the point (2, 9) lie on the line $y = 2x + 5$?

c Does the point (−2, −7) lie on the line $y = -4x - 1$?

> **Q12a hint**
>
> Does $y = 6$ when $x = 3$?

13 A straight-line graph L has a gradient of 4 and passes through the point $(\frac{1}{2}, -1)$.

a Substitute these values into $y = mx + c$

b Solve the equation you wrote for part **a** to work out the value of c.

c Use your answers to parts **a** and **b** to write the equation of graph L.

> **Q13a hint**
>
> Gradient, $m = \square$
> At point $(\frac{1}{2}, -1)$, $x = \square$, $y = \square$

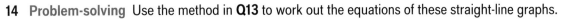

14 **Problem-solving** Use the method in **Q13** to work out the equations of these straight-line graphs.

a The line with gradient 3 that passes through the point $(0, 5)$

b The line with gradient -1 that passes through the point $(3, 0)$

c The line with gradient 2 that passes through the point $(4, 5)$

d The line with gradient $\frac{1}{2}$ that passes through the point $(6, 1)$

e The line with gradient -2 that passes through the point $(5, -4)$

15 Find the gradient of the line joining points $A(-3, -2)$ and $B(5, 4)$.

a by sketching a graph like this

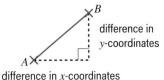

difference in y-coordinates

difference in x-coordinates

then using the formula

$$\text{gradient} = \frac{\text{difference in } y\text{-coordinates}}{\text{difference in } x\text{-coordinates}}$$

b by using the formula $m = \dfrac{y_2 - y_1}{x_2 - x_1}$ where $A = (x_1, y_1)$ and $B = (x_2, y_2)$

 $(-3, -2)$ $(5, 4)$

c **Reflect** Do you prefer the method in part **a** or part **b**? Explain why.

16 **Reasoning** P is the point $(-2, 6)$. Q is the point $(10, 0)$.

a Find the gradient of line PQ.

b Use your gradient from part **a** to write $y = mx + c$.
Substitute the coordinates of Q into this equation. Solve to find c.

c Write the equation of the line PQ.

17 Write the equation of the line that passes through points $A(1, -\frac{1}{2})$ and $B(-4, -3)$. **(3 marks)**

Exam tip

Make sure you do not ignore negative signs when working with coordinates.

18 To find the coordinates of the point where these graphs intersect
$\qquad y = 4x - 3 \qquad y = -x + 12$

a write the two equations equal to each other, $4x - 3 = -x + 12$, then solve to find x

b substitute x into one of the first equations to find y

c write the coordinates (x, y)

19 **Problem-solving** Find the coordinates of the point where these graphs intersect.
$\qquad y = -x + 2 \qquad 3x + 2y = 5$

Q19 hint

Write both equations in the form $y = mx + c$

20 Line L_1 passes through points $A(-2, -3)$ and $B(2, 5)$.
The equation of the line L_2 is $3y - 2x + 1 = 0$.
Find the coordinates of the point where the two lines intersect. **(5 marks)**

Q20 hint

The correctness of your final answer depends on finding the correct equation for L_1. So check your equation for L_1 by substituting the x-coordinates of points A and B and checking you get their y-coordinates.

6.3 Graphing rates of change

- Draw and interpret distance–time graphs.
- Calculate average speed from a distance–time graph.
- Understand velocity–time graphs.
- Find acceleration and distance from velocity–time graphs.

Active Learn
Homework

Warm up

1 **Fluency** A car travels 17 km in $\frac{1}{2}$ hour. What is its speed in km/h?

2 Find the area of each shape.
Give the correct units for your answers.

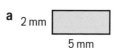

a 2 mm / 5 mm

b 3 cm / 7 cm

Key point

A **distance–time graph** represents a journey.
The vertical axis represents the *distance* from the starting point.
The horizontal axis represents the *time* taken.

---

3 Sophie cycles from her house to a cinema.
The distance–time graph shows her journey.

a How far is Sophie's house from the cinema?

b What time does Sophie arrive at the cinema?

c How long does she take to cycle to the cinema?

d For how long is she at the cinema?

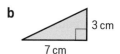

Sophie's trip to the cinema

4 Look back at Sophie's trip to the cinema in **Q3**.

a What was Sophie's speed in km/h

   i on the way to the cinema   ii on the way back from the cinema?

b **Reasoning** Work out the gradient for her cycles to and from the cinema. What do you notice?

5 **Reflect** Write a sentence describing

a what a horizontal line means on a distance–time graph

b what the gradient means on a distance–time graph

Key point

On a distance–time graph, the gradient is the speed.

---

6 **Problem-solving** Amal drives to her friend's house.
She drives 150 km in 2.5 hours. Then she stops for a half-hour break.
She then drives 70 km in 1 hour and arrives at her friend's house.

a On graph paper draw a horizontal axis from 0 to 4 hours and a vertical axis from 0 to 250 km.
Draw a distance–time graph to show Amal's journey.

b **Reasoning** Work out Amal's speed for the first part of the journey.

7 Problem-solving Kirsty is practising speed skating.
She covers the 1200 m straight course in 75 seconds.
She rests for 1 minute then skates back to the start line at 10 m/s.

  a Draw a distance–time graph to show Kirsty's skating practice.

  b Reasoning Work out the fastest speed she travelled, in m/s.

Q7 hint

Work out how far Kirsty travels in 1 second, or in 10 seconds. Plot this as a point.

Exam-style question

8 Here is a distance–time graph for a car's short journey from home.

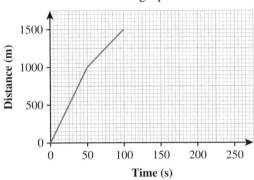

Exam tip

Exam papers are scanned and marked online. Therefore, when you use a pencil for drawing graphs, make sure *all* your pencil lines are clear. Use a pencil that is easy to see over the grid lines.

  a After 1500 m, the car stopped for 50 seconds.
The driver had left something at home.
The car returned home at a steady speed of 15 m/s.
Copy and complete the graph. **(2 marks)**

Q8a hint

'Steady speed' means travelling the same distance each minute.

  b Between which two times does the car travel at its greatest speed?
Explain how you know. **(1 mark)**

  c Work out this greatest speed. **(1 mark)**

Key point

$$\text{Average speed} = \frac{\text{total distance}}{\text{total time}}$$

Make sure your units match.

---

9 Problem-solving The table shows a train journey from Birmingham to Shrewsbury.
The train stops at Wolverhampton and Telford on the way.

When a train arrives at a station, it stays for 3 minutes before leaving for the next station.
There are 16 miles between each pair of stations.

Station	Time
Birmingham New Street (departing)	14:32
Wolverhampton (arriving)	14:42
Telford (arriving)	14:59
Shrewsbury (arriving)	15:19

  a Draw a distance–time graph for this journey.

  b Work out the speed of the train between Birmingham and Wolverhampton.

  c Work out the speed of the train between Telford and Shrewsbury.

  d What was the average speed for the whole journey?

  e Reflect Write a sentence explaining whether the average speed for the whole journey is always faster, slower or the same as the speed over each part of the journey.

10 Problem-solving Look at the graph you drew for **Q6**.
What was Amal's average speed for the whole journey?

 11 Problem-solving
Train A travels from Manchester to London.
Train B travels from London to Manchester.

Train journey to and from Manchester

a How far are the trains from London
when they pass each other?

b Which train travelled faster on average?

c Reflect Write a sentence commenting on whether these
distance–time graphs are good models for train journeys.

> **Q11c hint**
>
> Include any assumptions that
> are made.

> **Key point**
>
> A **rate of change graph** shows how a quantity changes over time.
> The gradient of a straight-line graph is the rate of change.

12 Reasoning Josh runs water into these four containers
at a constant rate.
This means that the same amount flows in every
second.

a In which container does the depth of water
increase by the same amount every second?

b Which graph shows the depth of water increasing steadily?

c Match each graph to one container.

d Reflect Write a sentence explaining why graphs **ii** and **iii** are curved.

13 Reasoning These three cylinders are vases.
They are all the same height.
Skye fills the vases with water at the same rate.

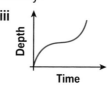

a Which vase will be full
　i first　　**ii** last?

b Draw axes showing depth against time.
On the same axes, sketch three graphs showing the rate at which water fills the vases A, B and C.

> **Key point**
>
> **Velocity** means speed in a particular direction.
> A **velocity–time graph** shows how velocity changes over time.

14 Reasoning Match each velocity–time graph to a description.

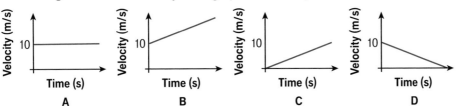

A   B   C   D

a Travels at a constant velocity of 10 m/s.

b Starts at 10 m/s and velocity steadily decreases.

c Starts from rest (0 m/s) and velocity steadily increases.

d Starts at 10 m/s and velocity steadily increases.

15 Future skills Sketch the velocity–time graph for a particle that starts from rest. Its velocity steadily increases to 20 m/s, then the particle travels at a steady velocity of 20 m/s.

> **Key point**
>
> On a velocity–time graph, the gradient is the rate of change of velocity, or **acceleration**.
> A positive gradient means an object is speeding up.
>
> $$\text{Acceleration} = \frac{\text{change in velocity}}{\text{time}}$$
>
> The area under a velocity–time graph is the distance travelled.

16 Problem-solving Gavin goes for a run. The graph shows his journey.

a What is Gavin's maximum velocity?

b When is Gavin running at a constant (steady) velocity?

c How many minutes did he run at 1.1 m/s?

> **Q16c hint**
>
> Read seconds from the graph and change to minutes.

Velocity–time graph of Gavin's run

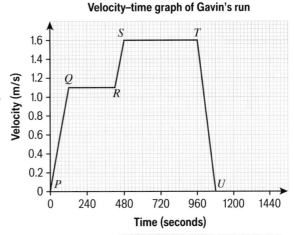

d Work out his acceleration for the first part of the journey, in m/s^2.

e Work out the distance Gavin ran during the last 120 seconds.

> **Q16e hint**
>
> Find the area of the triangle under the line segment TU.
>
>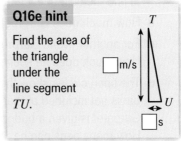

f Copy and complete this description of Gavin's run.
Gavin accelerated at ☐ m/s^2 for the first ☐ minutes, then ran at a constant velocity of ☐ m/s for ☐ minutes. Next ...

> **Q16f hint**
>
> Write about Gavin's **deceleration**. This is negative acceleration and means an object is slowing down.

17 Reflect Describe how you show constant speed, constant acceleration and constant deceleration on a velocity–time graph.

6.4 Real-life graphs

- Draw and interpret real-life linear graphs.
- Recognise direct proportion.
- Draw and use a line of best fit.

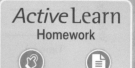

Active Learn
Homework

Warm up

1 **Fluency a** What type of graph is this?

b What type of correlation does it show?

c What name is given to the straight line drawn on the graph?

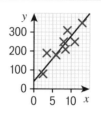

2 What is the equation of the line drawn on the graph in **Q1**?

3 The table shows the charge for using different numbers of units of electricity.

Units	0	200	500	700	900	1000
Charge (£)	12	40	82	110	138	152

a Plot these points on a grid.

b i Use your graph to find the charge for using 800 units of electricity.

ii Declan receives a bill for £60. How many units of electricity has he used?

Key point

Graphs can be used to display information from a variety of real-life situations.
Graph axes do not have to start at zero.
A discontinuity symbol ─╲╱─ shows that values have been missed out.

---

4 **Problem-solving** Gurpreet is buying some pens to give away at an exhibition.
The graph shows the price per pen depending on how many pens are ordered.

a Gurpreet buys 25 pens.
Read up from 25 on the axis for number of pens to find the cost of each of these 25 pens.

b How much does Gurpreet spend on his 25 pens?

c For another event, Gurpreet buys 60 pens.
How much does he spend altogether?

d The open circles show that the upper limit of each bar is not included at that price.
Gurpreet is given a budget of £75.
How many pens can he afford to buy?

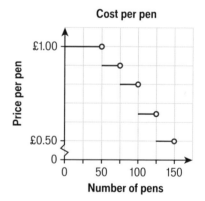

Cost per pen

---

5 **Problem-solving** This graph shows the conversion from euros (€) to Canadian dollars (C$).

a How many Canadian dollars do you get for €10?

b How many euros do you get for C$10?

c Work out the gradient of the graph.

d **Reflect** Copy and complete this sentence. The gradient of the graph represents the number of _____ per _____ .

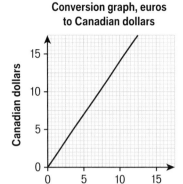
Conversion graph, euros to Canadian dollars

Exam-style question

6 This graph shows the charge to hire a van for a number of days.

a Find the gradient of the line. **(2 marks)**

b Explain what this gradient represents. **(1 mark)**

c The graph intersects the hire charge (£) axis at £40. Explain what this intercept represents. **(1 mark)**

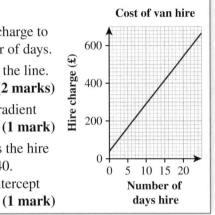
Cost of van hire

Exam tip

For real-life graphs, explain what the gradient and y-intercept mean in context. Here, it must be in the context of the cost of the van hire. Do not simply write about the gradient being the slope and the y-intercept being where $x = 0$.

Key point

When two quantities are in **direct proportion**
• their graph is a straight line through the origin
• when one variable is multiplied by n, so is the other.

---

7 **Reasoning** Which of these graphs show one variable in direct proportion to another?

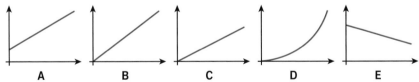

A   B   C   D   E

8 **Reasoning** Look at the graph you drew for **Q3**, and the graphs in **Q5** and **Q6**. Which show direct proportion? Explain.

9 **Reasoning** A recipe uses a spice mix including chilli powder and cumin in the ratio 2 : 5.

a Copy and complete this table.

b Draw a graph showing grams of cumin (y) against grams of chilli (x).

c Write the equation linking x and y.

d How much chilli would you need for a recipe using 85 g of cumin?

e Describe the relationship between x and y.

Chilli powder (grams)	1	4	10
Cumin (grams)			

Q9e hint

What can you say about two quantities that, when plotted one against the other, give a straight-line graph through the origin?

Unit 6 Graphs   173

10 **Reasoning** Zadie has a new freezer delivered to her house. She turns on the freezer and a sensor records the temperature inside the freezer.
The graph gives information about the temperature, $T°C$, of the air inside the freezer.

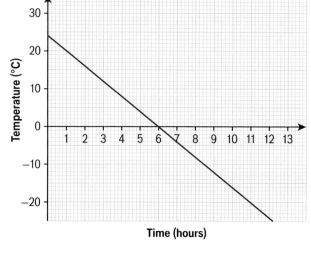

Temperature of air inside freezer

a What does
   i the y-intercept tell you
   ii the x-intercept tell you?

b Use the graph to estimate the temperature 3.5 hours after Zadie turns on the freezer.

c How much does the temperature fall over the first 5 hours?

d Is the rate of decrease of temperature constant? How can you tell from the graph?

11 **Reasoning** The table shows the largest quantity of a sugar, k grams, that will dissolve in a cup of coffee at temperature $t°C$.

t (°C)	44	50	62	70	78	85
k (grams)	265	300	360	400	440	475

a On a suitable grid, plot the points and draw a graph to illustrate this information.

b Use your graph to find
   i the lowest temperature at which 120 g of sugar will dissolve in the coffee
   ii the largest amount of sugar that will dissolve in the coffee at 81 °C

The equation of the graph is in the form $k = at + b$.

c Use your graph to estimate the values of the constants a and b.

d Will 4 teaspoons of sugar dissolve in the coffee at 90 °C? Use the equation to decide. Justify your answer.

Q11d hint

1 teaspoon of sugar = 5 grams

12 **Reasoning** The graph shows two different Pay As You Go mobile phone tariffs, Plan A and Plan B.

a What is the practical meaning of
   i the y-intercept value on Plan A
   ii the point where the two graphs intersect?

b Sally has Plan A. She makes two calls on Friday. The second call is an hour longer than the first. Work out the difference in cost between the two calls.

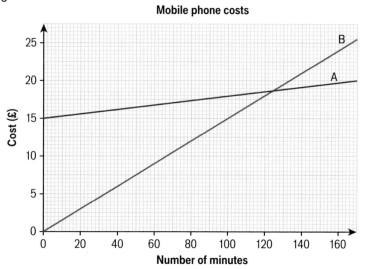

Mobile phone costs

c Another tariff, Plan C, is introduced.
On Plan C you will pay £18.50 per month for unlimited minutes.
Which plan should each person choose?
Molly: Average 150 minutes of calls per month.
Theo: Average 100 minutes of calls per month.

13 Problem-solving Beth wants to sell her car.
She has tracked the online sale price of the same model of car for a month.
Here are her results.

Car age (years)	1.1	3.0	2.0	5.0	4.2	1.7	5.5	2.5
Price (£)	11800	9000	10250	4900	6000	10700	4500	9800

a Plot a scatter graph of Beth's results.

b What type of correlation does this graph show?

c Draw a line of best fit.

d Write the equation of your line of best fit.

e Beth's car is $3\frac{1}{2}$ years old.
Use your equation to work out how much she should sell it for.

f **Reflect** Describe how you can use your equation to predict the price of a brand new car.

Exam-style question

14 The table shows life expectancy
(in years) for females born in the UK from 2006 to 2019.

Year of birth	Life expectancy (years)
2006	81.5
2007	81.6
2008	81.7
2009	82.2
2010	82.4
2011	82.7
2012	82.7
2013	82.8
2014	83.0
2015	82.7
2016	82.9
2017	83.0
2018	82.9
2019	83.4

Source: © ONS

Exam tip

You could draw a graph
to show the information.
For part **a**, you can either
use an equation of a line of
best fit or extend the graph.

a From this data, work out the life expectancy of a girl born in
  i 2022   **ii** 2050   **(4 marks)**

b Which answer is more reliable? Why?   **(2 marks)**

6.5 Line segments

- Find the coordinates of the midpoint of a line segment.
- Find the gradient and length of a line segment.
- Find the equations of lines parallel or perpendicular to a given line.

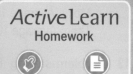

Active Learn
Homework

Warm up

1 **Fluency** Describe **a** parallel lines **b** perpendicular lines

2 What is the value half way between -2 and 4?

3 Here is a right-angled triangle.
Use Pythagoras' theorem to work out the length of side AB.

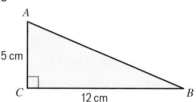

4 Rearrange the equation $y - 2x = -3$ into the form $y = mx + c$.
Then write down the gradient and y-intercept of the line $y = 2x - 3$.

Key point

A **line segment** has a start point and an end point.
The midpoint of a line segment is the point exactly in the middle of the line segment.

5 Draw a grid with axes from -2 to 10.

   a Plot and join each of these pairs of points with a straight line.

     i $A(6, 0)$ and $B(8, 4)$ **ii** $C(2, 9)$ and $D(9, 2)$ **iii** $E(3, 8)$ and $F(-1, 6)$

   b Write down the coordinates of the midpoint of each line segment in part **a**.

   c **Reasoning** Look at the coordinates of the start and end points of each line segment.
     What is the relationship of

     i the x-coordinates to the x-coordinate of its midpoint

     ii the y-coordinates to the y-coordinate of its midpoint?

Key point

The coordinates of the midpoint of a line segment are
$$\left(\frac{x_1 + x_2}{2}, \frac{y_1 + y_2}{2}\right)$$

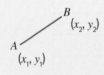

6 **Problem-solving** Work out the midpoint of a line segment PQ, where

   a P is $(0, 1)$ and Q is $(3, 10)$ **b** P is $(2, 3)$ and Q is $(6, -5)$

   c P is $(-3, 3)$ and Q is $(7, -2)$ **d** P is $(-7, -4)$ and Q is $(5, 0)$

7 Use the formula
$$\text{gradient} = \frac{\text{change in } y}{\text{change in } x} \quad \text{or} \quad m = \frac{y_2 - y_1}{x_2 - x_1}$$

   to work out the gradient of each line segment in **Q6**.

8 Use Pythagoras' theorem to work out the length of the line segment with end points

  a $A(-3, 1)$ and $B(0, -1)$

  b $C(-4, -1)$ and $D(2, 7)$

  c $E(-5, 3)$ and $F(8, -1)$

Q8a hint

Sketch a right-angled triangle.

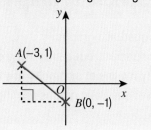

9 **Reasoning** A line is parallel to the line $y = 2x - 7$ and passes through the point $(2, -5)$.

  a Substitute the value of m for this line into $y = mx + c$.

  b Substitute the coordinates of the known point to work out the equation of the line.

10 **Problem-solving** Write the equation of a line parallel to $y = \frac{1}{3}x + 2$, which passes through the point $(9, -2)$.

11 Here are three pairs of perpendicular lines.

  a Write down the gradient of each line.

  b Multiply the gradients in each pair together. What do you notice?

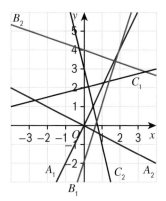

Key point

When two lines are **perpendicular**, the product of the gradients is −1.

When a graph has gradient m, a graph perpendicular to it has gradient $\frac{-1}{m}$.

12 **Reasoning** Write down the gradient of a line perpendicular to

  a $y = 3x - 1$ **b** $y = -\frac{1}{4}x + 2$ **c** $3y = 2x + 7$

Q12c hint

Rearrange as $y = mx + c$

13 **Problem-solving** Find the equation of a line that is

  a perpendicular to the line with equation $x + y = 6$ and passes through the point $(-3, -7)$

  b perpendicular to the line with equation $3y = 2x + 7$ and passes through the point $(-4, 1)$

Q13 hint

Use the gradient and the coordinates of the point to find c in $y = mx + c$

Exam-style question

14 $ABCD$ is a rhombus.

The coordinates of A are $(-2, 6)$.

The equation of the diagonal BD is $y = 2x$.

Find an equation of the diagonal AC. **(4 marks)**

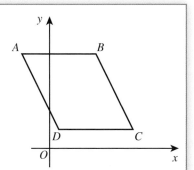

Exam tip

State any knowledge that you use. For example, what do you know about the diagonals of a rhombus?

6.6 Quadratic graphs

- Draw quadratic graphs.
- Solve quadratic equations using graphs.
- Identify the line of symmetry of a quadratic graph.
- Interpret quadratic graphs relating to real-life situations.

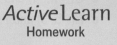

ActiveLearn
Homework

Warm up

1 Fluency What is the same and what is different about the graphs of $x = 2$ and $y = 2$?

2 Copy and complete the table of values for $y = x^2$

x	−4	−3	−2	−1	0	1	2	3	4
y	16								

3 Draw an x-axis from −5 to +5 and a y-axis from 0 to +20.
Plot the coordinates from your table of values in **Q2**.
Join the points with a smooth curve.
Label your graph $y = x^2$

> **Q3 hint**
>
> It is easier to draw a curve with your hand 'inside it' and moving outwards. Turn your paper round so you can draw the curve comfortably.

Key point

A **quadratic equation** contains a term in x^2 but no higher or negative powers of x.
The graph of a quadratic equation is a curved shape called a **parabola**.

4 a Copy and complete the table of values for $y = x^2 - 3$.

x	−3	−2	−1	0	1	2	3
y	6			−3			

  b Draw the graph of $y = x^2 - 3$ for values of x from −3 to 3.

5 Reasoning Jamie is asked to draw the graph of $y = x^2 - 4$ for $-2 \leqslant x \leqslant 2$.
This means plotting values of y for values of x from −2 to 2.
Here is his graph.

Write down one thing that is wrong with Jamie's graph.

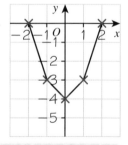

6 a Draw these graphs for $-3 \leqslant x \leqslant 3$.
  i $y = x^2 + 3$ **ii** $y = -x^2$
  iii $y = -x^2 + 3$

  b Reasoning Describe what you think these graphs will look like.
  i $y = x^2 + 5$ **ii** $y = x^2 - 5$
  iii $y = -x^2 - 5$

> **Q6a hint**
>
> Here are some common mistakes students make when drawing graphs.
>
> wobbly lines   feathering   flat bottom
>
>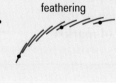

7 a Copy and complete the table of values for $y = 3x^2$

x	−2	−1	0	1	2
y					

b Draw the graph of $y = 3x^2$

> **Key point**
>
> A quadratic graph has either a **minimum point** or a **maximum point** where the graph turns.

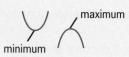

8 **Reasoning** Compare the graphs from **Q3**, **Q4**, **Q6** and **Q7**.

a What is the same about these graphs?

b Which ones have a minimum point? Which ones have a maximum point?

c Write the coordinates of the minimum/maximum point for each graph.

d Describe the symmetry of each graph by giving the equation of its mirror line.

9 **Problem-solving** Some maths students are investigating the effects of gravity on bottle rockets.
The students measure the rocket's height until it falls back to the ground.
The graph shows the rocket's height, h metres, at time t seconds after take-off.

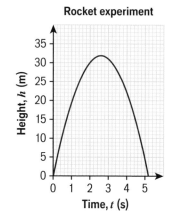

Rocket experiment

a What type of graph is this?

b When is the rocket travelling fastest?

> **Q9b hint**
>
> Faster speed = steeper gradient

c When is the rocket's speed zero?

d What is the maximum height that the rocket reaches?

e How long is the rocket in the air?

10 **Problem-solving** Carla throws a rounders ball.
This table gives data for the height, h metres, of the rounders ball at time t seconds after Carla throws it.

Time, t (seconds)	0	1	2	3	4
Height, h (metres)	1.2	3.7	4.7	4.2	2.2

a Use this data to draw a graph showing the trajectory (path) of the rounders ball.

b Continue the graph to predict when the rounders ball will land.

11 **Problem-solving** Here is the graph of $y = x^2 - 1$.
Use the graph to solve the equation

a $x^2 - 1 = 0$

b $x^2 - 1 = 3$

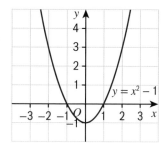

Example

Here is the graph of $y = x^2 - 3x - 2$.
Use the graph to find estimates of the solutions to the equation $x^2 - 3x - 8 = 0$.
Give your answers correct to 1 decimal place.

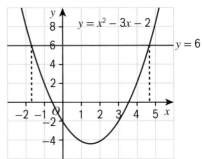

Rearrange the equation so that one side is $x^2 - 3x - 2$

$+6 \left(\begin{array}{l} x^2 - 3x - 8 = 0 \\ x^2 - 3x - 2 = 6 \end{array} \right) +6$ ⟵ $-8 + 6 = -2$

$x = -1.7$ ⟶ Find where $y = x^2 - 3x - 2$
$x = 4.7$ intersects $y = 6$.

12 **Reasoning** Solve these equations.

   a $2x - x^2 + 2 = 0$

   b $2x^2 + 4x - 3 = 0$

   c $1 - x^2 - 3x = 0$

   d **Reflect** Explain why $2x - x^2 = 3$ has no solutions.

13 **Reasoning** Ann is given the graph of $y = x^2 - 2x + 5$ for $-2 \leqslant x \leqslant 4$.
She is asked to draw a suitable straight line on the graph to find the solutions of $x^2 - 3x + 2 = 0$
Copy and complete Ann's working to find the straight-line graph she should draw.

$+\square+\square \left(\begin{array}{l} x^2 - 3x + 2 = 0 \\ x^2 - 2x + 5 = \square + \square \end{array} \right) +\square+\square$

Straight-line graph: $y = \square + \square$

Exam-style question

14 a Complete the table for $y = 2x^2 - x - 1$.   **(2 marks)**

x	-4	-3	-2	-1	0	1	2	3	4
y				2			5	14	

   b Draw the graph of $y = 2x^2 - x - 1$ for values of x from -4 to 4.   **(2 marks)**

   c By drawing a suitable line, use your graph to find estimates for the solutions of $2x^2 + x - 20 = 0$.   **(2 marks)**

Exam tip

Know the graph shapes to expect for different types of equations. This will help to ensure you draw graphs correctly. For example, this shows a miscalculated point.

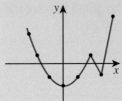

6.7 Cubic and reciprocal graphs

- Draw graphs of cubic functions.
- Solve cubic equations using graphs.
- Draw graphs of reciprocal functions.
- Recognise a graph from its shape.

*Active*Learn
Homework

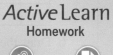

Warm up

1 **Fluency** What shape is **a** a linear graph **b** a quadratic graph?

2 Copy and complete this table of values for $y = x^3$

x	−3	−2	−1	0	1	2	3
y							

Key point

A **cubic function** contains a term in x^3 but no higher power of x. It can also have terms in x^2 and x and number terms.

3 Using your table of values from **Q1**, draw the graph of $y = x^3$ for $-3 \leqslant x \leqslant 3$.

Q3 hint

Your graph should be a smooth curve that looks like this.

4 **Reasoning** Miguel wants to use his graph of $y = x^3$ to estimate **a** 2^3 and **b** $\sqrt[3]{2}$
Choose the correct method to work out each estimate.

Method 1	**Method 2**
Read the value of x when $y = 2$	Read the value of y when $x = 2$

5 **Reasoning a** Use your graph from **Q3** to estimate   **i** 1.7^3 **ii** $\sqrt[3]{-11}$

   b Use a calculator to work out   **i** 1.7^3 **ii** $\sqrt[3]{-11}$

   c **Reflect** Which of your answers are most accurate? Explain.

6 **a** On the same axes, draw these graphs for $-3 \leqslant x \leqslant 3$.

   i $y = -x^3$ **ii** $y = x^3 + 1$ **iii** $y = x^3 - 2$

   b **Reflect** Write two sentences to compare your graph in **Q3** with your graphs in part **a**.

Q6a hint

Make a table of values like the one in **Q2**.

7 **Reflect** Describe what you think these graphs will look like.

   a $y = x^3 + 5$ **b** $y = x^3 - \frac{1}{2}$

Key point

A cubic equation can have 1, 2 or 3 solutions.

8 Use the graphs you drew in **Q6** to solve these equations.

   a $x^3 + 1 = 0$ **b** $x^3 - 2 = -3$

Q8 hint

Read off the x-values where the curve crosses $y = -3$.

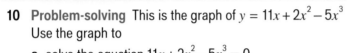

9 **a** Complete the table of values for $y = x^3 - 6x$.

x	-3	-2	-1	0	1	2	3
y			5	0			9

(2 marks)

b Draw the graph of $y = x^3 - 6x$ from
$x = -3$ to $x = 3$. **(2 marks)**

c Hence, or otherwise, solve $x^3 - 6x = 2$. **(2 marks)**

Exam tip

Think about what shape your graph should be. About where will it cross the axes? In part **c**, 'Hence or otherwise' means that it will be easier to answer this question using parts **a** and **b** (the graph you have drawn).

10 **Problem-solving** This is the graph of $y = 11x + 2x^2 - 5x^3$
Use the graph to

a solve the equation $11x + 2x^2 - 5x^3 = 0$

b solve the equation $11x + 2x^2 - 5x^3 = 8$

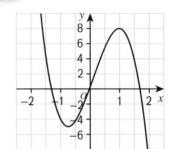

Key point

A **reciprocal function** is in the form $\frac{k}{x}$ where k is a number.

For reciprocal functions, the x- and y-axes are **asymptotes** to the curve. An asymptote is a line that the graph gets very close to, but never actually touches.

11 **a** Copy and complete the table of values for $y = \frac{1}{x}$

x	-3	-2	-1	$-\frac{1}{2}$	$-\frac{1}{4}$	$\frac{1}{4}$	$\frac{1}{2}$	1	2	3
y	$-\frac{1}{3}$			-2		4				

Q11b hint

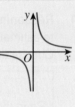

Plot the points. Join the two parts with smooth curves, so that your graph looks like this.

b Draw the graph of $y = \frac{1}{x}$, where $x \neq 0$, for $-3 \leqslant x \leqslant 3$.

12 **Reasoning**

a Draw a table of values for $y = -\frac{1}{x}$, where $x \neq 0$, for $-3 \leqslant x \leqslant 3$.

b Draw the graph of $y = -\frac{1}{x}$

c **Reflect** Write two sentences explaining what is same and what is different about
$y = \frac{1}{x}$ and $y = -\frac{1}{x}$

13 **a** Draw the graph of $y = \frac{3}{x}$, where $x \neq 0$, for $-4 \leqslant x \leqslant 4$.

b Use your graph to find the value of y when
i $x = -1$ **ii** $x = -2.5$

c Use your graph to find a solution to the equation $2.5x = 3$

Q13c hint

Rearrange as $2.5 = \dfrac{\square}{\square}$

6.8 More graphs

- Interpret linear and non-linear real-life graphs.
- Draw the graph of a circle.

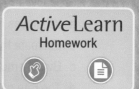
Warm up

1 **Fluency** From the graph, find
   a the value of x when $y = 5$
   b the value of y when $x = 4$

2 Construct a circle of radius 5 cm.

3 Write $\sqrt{8}$ in simplified surd form.

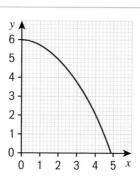

4 **Reasoning** The graph shows the count rate against time for magnesium-27, which is a radioactive material.
The count rate is the number of radioactive emissions per second.

   a Estimate the count rate after 20 minutes.

   b The **half-life** is the time it takes for the count rate to halve.
     After how many minutes is the count rate 30?

   c Estimate the half-life of magnesium-27.

   d **Reflect** Does the count rate ever reach zero? Explain.

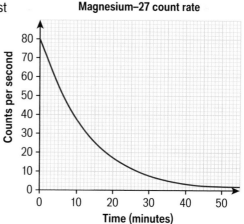

Magnesium–27 count rate

5 **Reasoning** Here are the cross-sections of three different concrete-transporter lorries.

   a 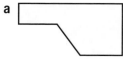   **b**    **c**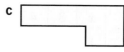

A builder empties the lorries by pumping out the concrete from the bottom at a steady rate.
Here are three sketch graphs showing the relationship between the depth of the concrete left in the lorry and the number of minutes since the pump was switched on.

Match each graph with one lorry.
For each match, write a sentence giving a reason for your answer.

6 **Problem-solving** The graph shows the value of an investment over a 5-year period.

a What was the initial value of the investment?

b Estimate the value of the investment after 5 years.

c By how much did the value increase in the first year?

d The rate of interest remained the same for the 5 years.
Work out the percentage interest rate.

Q6d hint

$$\frac{\text{actual change}}{\text{original amount}} \times 100$$

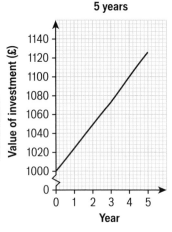

Investment over 5 years

7 **Reasoning** The distance–time graphs represent the journeys made by a bus and a car starting in Exeter, travelling to Swindon and returning to Exeter.

a Work out the greatest speed of the car during the journey.

The bus stopped at Bath on its journey.

b On the return journey, at what time did the bus reach Bath?

c Work out the average speed of the car over the whole journey.

d What does the change in gradient on the bus's journey from Bath to Swindon show?

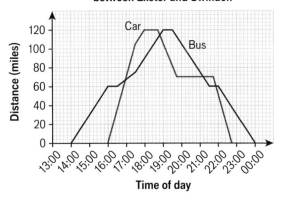

Distance–time graph for journeys between Exeter and Swindon

Key point

No correlation or weak correlation shows that there is *no* linear relationship between two quantities, because their graph is not close to a straight line.
When the points follow a curve, there might be a non-linear relationship between the quantities.

8 **Reasoning** Here are two sets of data.

Data set A

x	3	4	5	6	6	7	7	8	10
y	7	8	10	13	14	14	16	16	21

Data set B

x	3	3.6	4	4	4.5	4.7	5.1	5.3	5.6	5.7
y	9	13	15	14	21	23	26	27	31	33

a Plot each set of data on a scatter graph.

b Describe the correlation for each set.

c Draw a line of best fit for the graph for data set A. What does this show?

d Draw the graph of $y = x^2$ on the same grid as the graph for data set B.

e What do you notice from your graph? What do you think the relationship is between x and y in data set B?

Q8a hint

For the graph of data set B, make sure your y-axis extends to 40.

Q8d hint

Make a table of values from $3 \leqslant x \leqslant 6$.

9 **Reasoning** The petrol consumption of a car, in kilometres per litre (km/l), depends on the speed of the car.

The table gives some information about the petrol consumption of a car at different speeds.

Speed (km/h)	62	68	76	86	93	99	103
Petrol consumption (km/l)	12.6	13.9	14.7	15.0	14.6	13.7	12.2

a Draw axes on graph paper, using 5 cm to represent 20 km/h on the horizontal axis and 4 cm to represent 1 km/l on the vertical axis.

Start the horizontal axis at 60 and the vertical axis at 12.

Show the discontinuities clearly on the axes.

Plot the values from the table and join them with a smooth curve.

b From your graph, estimate

i the petrol consumption at 75 km/h

ii the speeds which give a petrol consumption of 13.5 km/l

Key point

The equation of a circle with centre $(0, 0)$ and radius r is $x^2 + y^2 = r^2$.

Example

Construct the graph of $x^2 + y^2 = 36$

$r = \sqrt{36} = 6$ ──────────── Compare $x^2 + y^2 = 36$ with $x^2 + y^2 = r^2$

Using compasses set to 6 units, draw a circle centre O.

10 On graph paper, draw the graphs of

a $x^2 + y^2 = 1$ **b** $x^2 + y^2 = 16$ **c** $x^2 + y^2 = 81$ **d** $x^2 + y^2 = 2.25$

Exam-style question

11 The equation of a circle is $x^2 + y^2 = 20$.
Find the radius of the circle.
Give your answer in simplified surd form. **(2 marks)**

Exam tip

Read the question carefully. It asks for only the radius. (You don't need to draw the circle.) It also asks for your answer in simplified surd form $\square\sqrt{\square}$

6 Check up

Active Learn
Homework

Linear graphs

1 A line has equation $2x + 3y = 7$.
Write down the gradient and y-intercept of the line.

2 Write down the equations of these lines.

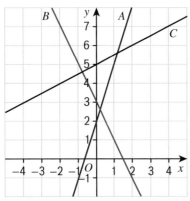

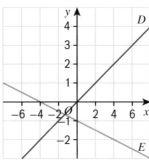

3 Draw a graph of the equation $y = -3x - 1$.
Do not use a table of values.

4 Without drawing a graph, write the equation of the line that passes through
   a $G(-4, 5)$ and $H(4, 1)$ **b** $P(1, -4)$ and $Q(4, 5)$

5 Draw the graph of $y = x^2 + 1$ for values of x from -3 to 3.

6 Hamzah goes for a bike ride.
The graph shows the four stages of his journey.

   a What is the gradient for the first stage of
      the bike ride? What does this represent?

   b Work out Hamzah's average speed for
      the whole journey, including any stops.

   c On which stage of the journey was he
      travelling fastest?

   d Work out his speed for that stage.

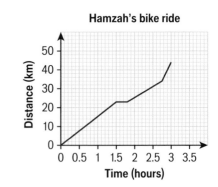

Hamzah's bike ride

7 Annie buys some cupcakes from the bakery.
The graph shows the pricing.

   a Explain what part A of the graph represents.

   b Explain what the gradient of part B represents.

   c Are x and y in direct proportion?
      Explain your answer.

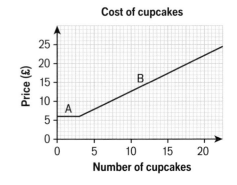

Cost of cupcakes

8 J is the point $(2, -5)$ and K is the point $(-3, -1)$. Work out

    a the midpoint of the line segment JK

    b the length of the line segment

9 The equation of a line is $y = 3x + 1$. Work out

    a the equation of a line parallel to $y = 3x + 1$ that goes through the point $(2, -7)$

    b the equation of any line perpendicular to $y = 3x + 1$ that does not share its y-intercept.

Non-linear graphs

10 Match each equation to one of the graphs below.

    a $y = x^2$ **b** $y = \dfrac{1}{x}$ **c** $y = -x^2$ **d** $x^2 + y^2 = 9$

    e $y = x^3$ **f** $y = -\dfrac{1}{x}$ **g** $y = -x^3$

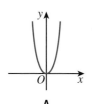

    A   B   C   D

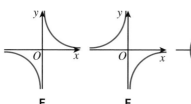

    E   F   G

11 The equation $-x^3 + 3x - 1 = 0$ has three solutions.

Use the graph of $y = -x^3 + 3x - 1$ to estimate all three solutions.

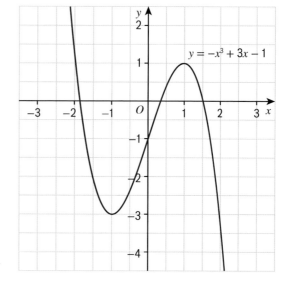

$y = -x^3 + 3x - 1$

12 The equation of a circle is $x^2 + y^2 = 49$. What is the radius of the circle?

Real-life graphs

13 Hannah is watering her garden.
The water coming out of the hosepipe forms a smooth curve.
This graph models the curve.

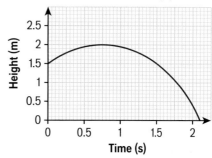

Water from a hosepipe

    a Give the coordinates of the maximum point of this graph.

    b What was the maximum height that the water reached?

    c How long did the water take to hit the ground after leaving the hosepipe?

    d What is the practical meaning of the starting point of the graph (the y-intercept)?

14 Mike fills these containers with water at a constant rate.
Match each container to a graph.

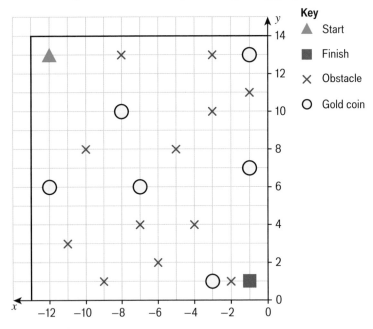

15 **Reflect** How sure are you of your answers? Were you mostly

Just guessing 🙁   Feeling doubtful 😐   Confident 🙂

What next? Use your results to decide whether to strengthen or extend your learning.

Challenge

16 Design a game where you have to get from the start to the finish, collecting all the gold coins and avoiding all the obstacles by travelling along graph lines.

Here is an example of a possible first two moves for this game:

- Walk 7 units in a negative direction along the line $x = -12$. Stop at $(-12, 6)$.
- Walk along the straight line $y = 6$ from $(-12, 6)$ to $(-7, 6)$.

Design your game within a border.
There must be at least 10 obstacles and 5 gold coins.
You cannot touch the borders of your grid to escape your obstacles. Record your moves.

After everyone has finished Check up, challenge a friend to complete your game in fewer moves.

6 Strengthen

Active Learn
Homework

Linear graphs

1 The diagram shows four straight-line graphs.

  a Which two lines have y-intercept $(0, 1)$?

  b What is the y-intercept of line D?

  c Which lines have a positive gradient, like this? (Think *uphill*.)

  d Which lines have a negative gradient, like this? (Think *downhill*.)

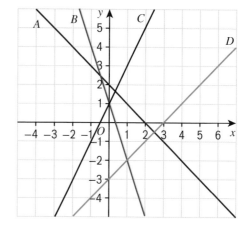

2 Look at the straight-line graphs in **Q1**. Match each equation with its line.

  a $y = x - 3$

  b $y = -3x + 1$

  c $y = 2x + 1$

  d $y = -x + 2$

> **Q2 hint**
>
> $$y = mx + c$$
>   gradient y-intercept
>
> Now look at the graphs. Find the y-intercept first. Then look for positive or negative gradients.

3 Ali goes for a bike ride.
The graph shows the three stages of his journey, AB, BC and CD.

Ali's bike ride

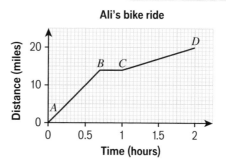

  a Here is the first stage of the bike ride.

    Work out the gradient.
    Use the dotted line to help you.

  b Look at the axes.
    Which of these correctly represents the gradient?

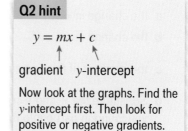

  c What else is represented by the division you wrote in part **b**?

  d What was the total distance Ali travelled on his bike ride?

  e What was the total time Ali took for his bike ride?

  f Work out Ali's average speed for his whole bike ride.

  g Which part of Ali's bike ride has the steepest gradient, and so the fastest travel?

  h Work out the speed for the fastest part of the ride.

4 On squared paper, draw lines with these gradients.

  a 4

  b −1

  c $\frac{1}{2}$

5 **a** Write down the gradient and y-intercept of the line with equation $y = 4x - 3$.

  b Draw a coordinate grid and mark the y-intercept from part **a**.

  c From the y-intercept, draw a line with the gradient from part **a**.

  d Label your line $y = 4x - 3$

6 Use the method in **Q5** to draw lines for these equations.

  a $y = 2x - 4$

  b $y = -x + 2$

  c $y = \frac{1}{2}x$

> **Q6b hint**
>
> $-x$ means '−1 lot of x'.

> **Q6c hint**
>
> What does it mean if there is not a number on the end of the equation?

7 The sketch graph shows the points $A(-3, 1)$ and $B(2, 6)$. From the sketch, work out

  a the change in x

  b the change in y

  c the gradient of this line segment, using $\dfrac{\text{change in } y}{\text{change in } x}$

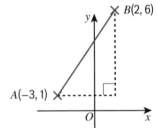

  d Substitute the x- and y-coordinates for point A and the gradient you found in part **c** into this equation for a straight-line graph:

$$y = mx + c$$

     ↑ gradient

  e Solve the equation you wrote in part **d** to find the value of c.

  f Substitute the gradient and your value of c into $y = mx + c$
    This is the equation of the line that passes through the points $A(-3, 1)$ and $B(2, 6)$.

  g Check that your equation is correct for point B: when $x = 2$, does $y = 6$?

8 Draw a sketch graph to show the points $C(-2, -1)$ and $D(1, 5)$.

  a Use your sketch to work out

    i the change in x **ii** the change in y

  b Use the method in **Q7** to write the equation of the line that passes through points C and D.

9 Copy and complete the calculation to work out the coordinates of M, the midpoint between points $E(-2, 3)$ and $F(1, 5)$.

$$(\; x \; , \; y \;)$$
$$E(-2 \; , \; 3 \;)$$
$$F(\; 1 \; , \; 5 \;)$$
$$M(\square , \square)$$
$$\dfrac{-2+1}{2} \qquad \dfrac{3+5}{2}$$

10 **a** For lines to be parallel, they must have the same gradient (but can have *any* value of *c*).
Choosing from these equations, which pairs of lines are parallel?

A $y = 2x - 3$ **B** $y = -x - 1$ **C** $y = -2x$

D $y = 4 - x$ **E** $y = x + 5$ **F** $y = 2x + 1$

b Write the equation of another line parallel to each pair.

11 **Reasoning**

a What is the gradient of any line parallel to $y = 3x - 3$?

b Write the equation of a line parallel to $y = 3x - 3$ that goes through $(-1, 7)$.

> **Q11b hint**
>
> Substitute the given values of x and y, and the value of m you found in part **a**, into $y = mx + c$. Solve to find c.

12 **a** Find the negative reciprocal of

  i 2

  ii $\frac{1}{2}$

  iii -2

  iv $\frac{1}{4}$

  v -1

b Look at these equations.

A $y = \frac{1}{4}x - 3$ **B** $y = 2x - 1$ **C** $y = -2x + 5$

D $y = 1 - x$ **E** $y = x + 6$ **F** $y = \frac{1}{2}x + 1$

G $y = -4x + 7$ **H** $y = -\frac{1}{2}x - 2$

Identify pairs with gradients where one is the negative reciprocal of the other.
These pairs of lines are perpendicular.

Non-linear graphs

1 **Reasoning**

a Graph A is quadratic. Which other graph has a similar curved shape and is quadratic?

b Graph B is cubic. Which other graph has a similar S shape and is cubic?

c Which graph is linear (a straight line)?

d The graph left over is reciprocal. Write a sentence describing the shape of a reciprocal graph.

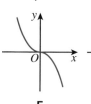

A   B   C   D   E   F

2 a Match each equation to one of these words.

A quadrant **B** cubic

C reciprocal **D** linear

Q2a hint

Linear equations contain x and no higher power.
Quadratic equations contain x^2 and no higher power.

i $y = x - 2$ **ii** $y = -x^2 + 4$ **iii** $y = -x^3$

iv $y = \frac{1}{x}$ **v** $y = x^2 + 1$ **vi** $y = x^3 - 2$

b Match each equation in part **a** with its graph in **Q1**.

3 The equation of a circle with centre (0, 0) and radius r is $x^2 + y^2 = r^2$

a Copy and complete the equation of a circle with radius 3 cm.
$$x^2 + y^2 = \square^2$$
$$x^2 + y^2 = \square$$

b The equation of a circle is $x^2 + y^2 = 100$.
Find the radius.

Q3b hint

$r^2 = 100$
$r = \square$

Real-life graphs

1 **Reasoning** Frankie kicks a rugby ball for a conversion after a try.
He kicks the ball from 6 m in front of the posts.
The graph shows the path followed by the rugby ball.

Path followed by a rugby ball

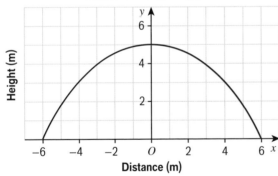

a What type of graph is this?
Explain your answer.

b What are the coordinates of the maximum point?

c What is the value of y when $x = 2$?

d What is the value of x when $y = 3.5$?

e What do the negative values of x mean in this context?

f Find the height of the ball as it goes past the posts.

g The bar on a rugby post is set at 3 m.
Assuming Frankie kicked the ball straight between the posts, has the ball gone over the bar?

Q1a hint

Think about the shape of the graph.

Q1b hint

Look carefully at the axes before you read the values.

Q1e hint

Read the question again for a reminder.

2   Here are two vases.

Vase 1   **Vase 2**

a Copy and complete this sentence with the words 'faster' or 'slower' for each vase, to describe how the water level changes as it fills up.

The water level in vase ☐ rises _____ first, then _____ .

b The graphs show the depth of water against time when water pours into the vases at a constant rate.
Which graph matches which vase?

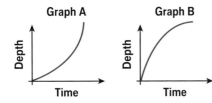

3   The graph shows the profit made on the sales of light bulbs by a company.
The line goes through the origin.

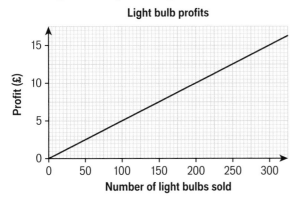

a Copy and complete.

   i   25 bulbs = £☐ profit

   ii £☐ profit = 175 bulbs

   iii ☐ bulbs = £4.80 profit

b Gradient = $\dfrac{\text{distance up}}{\text{distance across to the right}}$

Choose a distance from the horizontal axis (number of light bulbs sold).
Read across from this point on the graph to the vertical axis (profit).
Use these values to work out the gradient.

c Copy and complete this sentence.
The gradient represents the profit made per _____ .

d When two quantities are in direct proportion, their graph is a straight line through the origin.
Are profit and the number of light bulbs sold in direct proportion?

6 Extend

1 **Reasoning** Without plotting the graphs, work out which of these functions

  a have the same y-intercept   **b** have the same gradient

| **A** $y = \frac{1}{2}x + 4$ | **B** $y + 4x = 8$ | **C** $2y - x = 6$ | **D** $x + y = 3$ |

2 A pattern is made from squares.
Square $ABCD$ has vertices at the points (3, 4), (19, 4), (19, −12) and (3, −12).
Square $EFGH$ has vertices at the midpoints of AB, BC, CD and DA.
Square $IJKL$ has vertices at the midpoints of EF, FG, GH and HE.
Square $MNOP$ has vertices at the midpoints of IJ, JK, KL and LI.
The pattern continues with square $QRST$ inside square $MNOP$, and square $UVWX$ inside square $QRST$.
Work out the coordinates of the vertices of square $UVWX$.

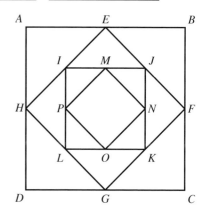

3 **a** Show that the equation $x^2 - 3x - 1 = 2x - 1$ can be rewritten as $x^2 - 5x = 0$.

  b Find the equation of the straight line shown.

  c Use the diagram to solve the equation $x^2 - 5x = 0$.

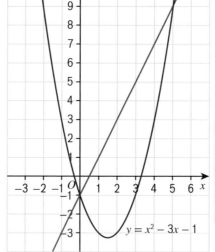

> **Q3c hint**
>
> You can solve the equation $x^2 - 5x = 0$ by finding the intersection of the graph of $y = x^2 - 3x - 1$ with the graph of a straight line.

4 **a** Copy and complete this table of values for the equation $y = 1 - \frac{2}{x}$, $x \neq 0$.

x	−3	−2	−1	−0.5	−0.1	0.1	0.5	1	2	3
y	1.7		3	5		−19				0.3

  b Draw the graph of $y = 1 - \frac{2}{x}$ for $-3 \leqslant x \leqslant 3$.

  c Write the equations of the two asymptotes for this graph.

> **Q4c hint**
>
> Asymptotes are straight lines that a graph approaches but never intersects.

5 The point $D(4, k)$ lies on the line $y = 3x - 5$.
Show that the point D also lies on the line $y = 2x - 1$.

6 A mobility scooter accelerates from rest at a constant rate of $1.2\,\text{m/s}^2$.

The distance, s, covered by the scooter is given by the formula $s = \frac{1}{2}at^2$, where a is the acceleration in m/s^2 and t is the time in seconds.

a Draw a graph of the distance covered by the scooter for values of t from 0 to 10 seconds.

b What is the distance covered after 4.5 seconds?

c How many seconds does the scooter take to cover 40 m?

Exam-style question

7 *ABCD* is a square.

C and *E* are points on the *y*-axis.
ABE is a straight line.
The equation of the line that passes through the points *A* and *B* is $y = \frac{1}{2}x + 1$.

P is a point on the *x*-axis at $(-\frac{1}{2}, 0)$.

Find the length of *CE*. **(4 marks)**

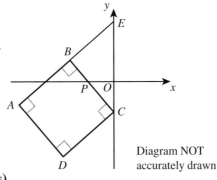

Diagram NOT accurately drawn

Q7 hint

Use the equation $y = \frac{1}{2}x - 1$ to work out the coordinates of *E*.

---

8 Reasoning

a Match each equation with its graph.

i $y = x^2 - 2$ **ii** $y = \frac{1}{x}$ **iii** $y = 2x^2 + 5$ **iv** $y = x^3 - 2$

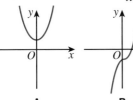

A

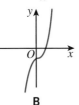

B

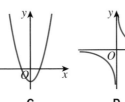

C

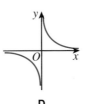

D

b Find the equation of any lines of symmetry for each graph.

Exam-style question

9 *ABCD* is a rectangle.

A, *E* and *B* are points on the line L_1 with equation $x + 4y = 12$.
A and *D* are points on the straight line L_2.
$AE : EB = 1 : 3$
Find an equation for L_2.   **(4 marks)**

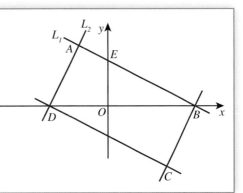

Working towards A level

10 The line L_1 has equation $3x - 7y - 8 = 0$ and crosses the *x*-axis at the point *P*.

The line L_2 is perpendicular to L_1 and passes through *P*.
Work out the equation of line L_2 in the form $ax + by + c = 0$, where a, b and c are integers.

This question is typical of the level of problem-solving required at A level. You often need to decide on a strategy before you start.

6 Test ready

Summary of key points

To revise for the test:

- Read each key point, find a question on it in the mastery lesson, and check you can work out the answer.

- If you cannot, try some other questions from the mastery lesson or ask for help.

Key points

1 A **linear equation** generates a straight-line (linear) graph.
   The equation for a straight-line graph can be written as $y = mx + c$
   where m is the gradient and c is the y-intercept.   → 6.1

2 **Parallel lines** have the same gradient.   → 6.1

3 To find the y-intercept of a graph, find the y-coordinate where $x = 0$.
   To find the x-intercept of a graph, find the x-coordinate where $y = 0$.   → 6.1

4 To compare the gradients and y-intercepts of two straight lines, make sure their
   equations are in the form $y = mx + c$ → 6.1

5 A **linear function** has a graph that is a straight line.   → 6.2

6 You can draw the graph of a linear function without drawing a table of values: plot the
   y-intercept and then draw a straight line from there with the correct gradient. → 6.2

7 A **distance–time graph** represents a journey.

   - Straight lines mean constant speed

   - Horizontal lines mean no movement

   - The gradient is the speed, since $\text{speed} = \dfrac{\text{distance}}{\text{time}}$ → 6.3

8 $\text{Average speed} = \dfrac{\text{total distance}}{\text{total time}}$ → 6.3

9 The gradient of a straight-line graph is the rate of change.   → 6.3

10 A **velocity–time graph** shows how velocity changes over time.

    - Straight lines mean constant acceleration.

    - Horizontal lines mean no change in velocity (i.e. travelling at a constant velocity).

    - The gradient is the acceleration, since $\text{acceleration} = \dfrac{\text{change in velocity}}{\text{time}}$.

    - The area under a velocity–time graph is the distance travelled.

11 Graph axes do not have to start at zero.
    A discontinuity symbol (zigzag line) —⋀— shows that values have been missed out. → 6.4

12 When two quantities are in **direct proportion**

    - their graph is a straight line through the origin

    - when one variable is multiplied by n, so is the other.   → 6.4

13 The midpoint of a line segment is the point exactly in the middle of the line segment. → 6.5

14 The coordinates of the midpoint of a line segment are

$$\left(\frac{x_1+x_2}{2}, \frac{y_1+y_2}{2}\right)$$

→ **6.5**

15 When two lines are **perpendicular**, the product of the gradients is −1.

When a graph has gradient m, a graph perpendicular to it has gradient $\dfrac{-1}{m}$. → **6.5**

16 A **quadratic equation** contains a term in x^2 but no higher or negative powers of x. The graph of a quadratic equation is a curved shape called a **parabola**.

17 A quadratic graph has either a **minimum point** or a **maximum point** where the graph turns. → **6.6**

18 A quadratic equation can have 0, 1 or 2 solutions. → **6.6**

19 A **cubic function** contains a term in x^3 but no higher power of x. It can also have terms in x^2 and x and number terms. → **6.7**

20 A cubic function can have 1, 2 or 3 solutions. → **6.7**

21 A **reciprocal function** is in the form $\dfrac{k}{x}$ where k is a number. → **6.7**

22 No correlation or weak correlation shows that there is *no* linear relationship between two quantities. → **6.8**

23 The equation of a circle with centre (0, 0) and radius r is $x^2+y^2=r^2$ → **6.8**

Sample student answer

Exam-style question

The point P has coordinates (5, 3).
The point Q has coordinates (a, b).
A line perpendicular to PQ is given by the equation $5x+2y=4$.
Find an expression for b in terms of a. **(5 marks)**

$5x+2y=4$
$\quad 2y=-5x+4$
$\quad\quad y=-\dfrac{5}{2}x+4$

So line PQ has gradient $-\dfrac{2}{5}$

and equation $y=-\dfrac{2}{5}x+c$

P has coordinates (5, 3),

so $3=-\dfrac{2}{5}\times 5+c$

$3=-2+c$
$5=c$

PQ has equation $y=-\dfrac{2}{5}x+5$

Q has coordinates (a, b), so $b=-\dfrac{2}{5}a+5$

This student would not get full marks for their answer, as their final answer was incorrect.

Copy the working. Write a tick beside each step of the method that the student got correct (HINT: The student may have used the correct method, but an incorrect value. Put a tick for correct method).

Identify the mistake that the student made.
Rewrite the method, correcting the mistake.

6 Unit test

Active Learn
Homework

1 On squared paper, draw the graph of $y = 2x - 1$ for $-2 \leqslant x \leqslant 5$.
(Do not use a table of values.) **(3 marks)**

2 Line segment *GH* is drawn on centimetre squared paper.
G is the point $(-1, 7)$. *H* is the point $(2, -2)$.

  a Find the gradient of the line segment *GH*. **(2 marks)**

  b Find the midpoint of the line segment *GH*. **(2 marks)**

  c Find the length of the line segment *GH*.
    Give your answer correct to 1 decimal place. **(2 marks)**

3 Here is a sketch of a scatter graph.

  Describe

    i the correlation and

    ii the relationship
      between *x* and *y*. **(2 marks)**

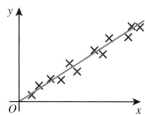

4 Elliot went for a cycle ride.
The travel graph represents part of
Elliot's cycle ride.

  At 12:45 pm Elliot stopped for a second
rest of 30 minutes.
Then he cycled home at a steady speed.
It took him 2.5 hours to get home.

  a Copy and complete the travel graph.
    (2 marks)

  b What speed did Elliot cycle at after his
    first rest? **(2 marks)**

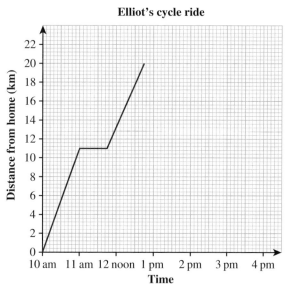

Elliot's cycle ride

5 A ball bearing rolls down a ramp and onto flat ground.
The graph shows its velocity for the first 20 seconds.

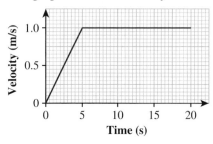

  a What was its acceleration in the first 5 seconds? **(2 marks)**

  b How long is the ramp? **(2 marks)**

6 Here is a scatter graph with the line of best fit drawn on.

a Work out the equation of the line of best fit. **(2 marks)**

b Explain what the gradient of the line of best fit represents. **(1 mark)**

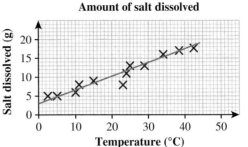

Amount of salt dissolved

7 **a** Copy and complete the table of values for $y = -\frac{2}{x}$ **(2 marks)**

x	−4	−2	−1	1	2	4
y						

b Draw the graph of $y = -\frac{2}{x}$, where $x \neq 0$, for $-4 \leqslant x \leqslant 4$. **(3 marks)**

c Use your graph to estimate a solution to the equation $1.5x = -2$. **(2 marks)**

8 The formula $KE = \frac{1}{2}mv^2$ gives the kinetic energy (in joules) of an object with mass m kg and velocity v m/s.

a Work out the kinetic energy of a ball with mass 1.5 kg, travelling at 3 m/s. **(1 mark)**

b Draw a graph of KE against v for values of v between 0 and 4 m/s. **(3 marks)**

c What is the velocity of the ball if its kinetic energy is 9 joules? **(1 mark)**

9 Write the equation of a line which is

a parallel to $y = 3x + 2$ **(1 mark)**

b parallel to $2y + 5x - 1 = 0$ **(2 marks)**

c perpendicular to $y = -2x + 1$ and passes through the point $(4, -3)$ **(2 marks)**

10 The diagram shows part of the graph of $y = 2x^2 - 4x$.

a What are the coordinates of the minimum point? **(1 mark)**

b What is the equation of the line of symmetry of the graph? **(1 mark)**

c Use the graph to find estimates for the solutions of $2x^2 - 4x - 1 = 0$.
Give your answers correct to 1 decimal place. **(2 marks)**

d Explain why $2x^2 - 4x + 3 = 0$ has no solutions. **(1 mark)**

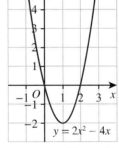

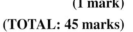

11 The equation of a circle is $x^2 + y^2 = 1.21$.
Find the radius of the circle. **(1 mark)**

(TOTAL: 45 marks)

12 Challenge

a Write the equation of a circle, and equations of one quadratic and two linear graphs that all touch the circle's circumference.

b Now try and include a cubic graph and reciprocal graph too.

13 Reflect Write a hint on how to remember the shapes of different types of graphs. Include sketches in your hints.

7 Area and volume

Prior knowledge

7.1 Perimeter and area

- Find the area and perimeter of compound shapes.
- Recall and use the formula for area of a trapezium.

*Active*Learn
Homework

Warm up

1 **Fluency** Which of these measurements are areas and which are perimeters?

$3\,\text{cm}^2$ $5\,\text{km}$ $32\,\text{mm}$ $7\,\text{m}^2$ $46\,\text{mm}^2$ $10\,\text{cm}$

2 Work out the area and perimeter of each shape.

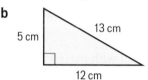
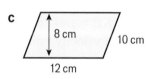

a 6 cm, 2 cm

b 5 cm, 13 cm, 12 cm

c 8 cm, 10 cm, 12 cm

3 Work out
  a the values of x and y
  b the perimeter
  c the area

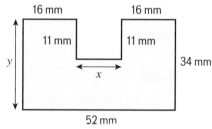

16 mm   16 mm
11 mm   11 mm
y x 34 mm
52 mm

Exam-style question

4 Here is a rectangle.

The length of the rectangle is 4 cm greater than the width of the rectangle.
4 of these rectangles are used to make this 8-sided shape.

The perimeter of the 8-sided shape is 40 cm.
Work out the area of the 8-sided shape. **(4 marks)**

Exam tip

Label lengths clearly on a copy of the diagram.

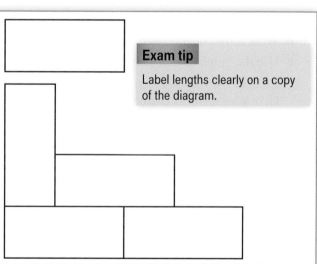

5 Work out the area and perimeter.

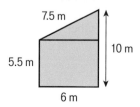

7.5 m
5.5 m
10 m
6 m

6 Work out the shaded area.
Give your answer to the nearest square mm.

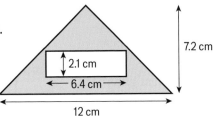

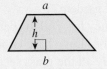
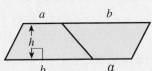
7 Calculate the areas of these trapezia.
Round your answers to 1 decimal place (1 d.p.) where necessary.

a 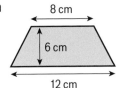   **b** 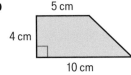   **c**   **d**

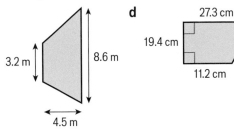

9 Calculate the area and perimeter
of this isosceles trapezium.

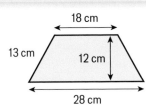

10 Lucy's garden is in the shape of a trapezium.

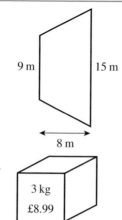

9 m   15 m

8 m

Lucy is going to plant grass seed over the whole garden.
Each box of grass seed costs £8.99.
1 kg of grass seed covers 5 m^2 of garden.
Lucy has £60 to spend on grass seed.
Does Lucy have enough money to buy all the grass seed she needs?
You must show how you get your answer.   **(5 marks)**

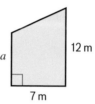

3 kg
£8.99

11 **Problem-solving** A trapezium has area 32 cm^2, and parallel sides 5.5 cm and 10.5 cm. Work out its height.

Example

This trapezium has area 70 m^2.
Find the length of the shorter parallel side.

a 12 m

7 m

$$70 = \frac{1}{2}(a + 12) \times 7$$
$\div 7$ ( ) $\div 7$

Substitute the values of h, b and A into the formula $A = \frac{1}{2}(a+b)h$

$$10 = \frac{1}{2}(a + 12)$$
$\times 2$ ( ) $\times 2$

Solve the equation.

$$20 = a + 12$$

$$a = 8\,cm$$

12 **Reasoning** Find the missing lengths.

a

a

Area 35 cm²   5 cm

8 cm

b

b

Area 8.4 m²   3.4 m

2.1 m

13 **Problem-solving** One corner of a rectangular piece of paper is folded up to make this trapezium.
Work out the area of the trapezium.

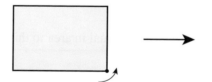

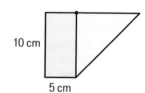

10 cm

5 cm

14 **Reflect** Write notes to help you remember the formula for the area of a trapezium.

7.2 Units and accuracy

- Convert between metric units of area.
- Write error intervals for rounded values.
- Calculate upper and lower bounds.

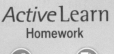
*Active*Learn
Homework

Warm up

1 Fluency Round each number to the level of accuracy given.

a 3.567 (1 d.p.)   **b** 320.6 (2 s.f.)   **c** 8.495 (2 d.p.)   **d** 15.721 (3 s.f.)

2 Work out

a i 10% of 25 kg   **ii** 10% less than 25 kg   **iii** 10% more than 25 kg

b i 5% of 40 m   **ii** 5% less than 40 m   **iii** 5% more than 40 m

3 a Explain why these two squares have the same area.
b Work out the area of each square.
c Copy and complete. $1\,\text{cm}^2 = \square\,\text{mm}^2$

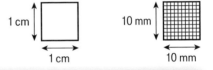

Key point

To convert from cm^2 to mm^2, multiply by 100.
To convert from mm^2 to cm^2, divide by 100.

4 Reasoning

a Sketch a square with side length 1 m and a square with side length 100 cm.
b Copy and complete. $1\,\text{m}^2 = \square\,\text{cm}^2$
c How do you convert from cm^2 to m^2?

5 Convert

a $250\,\text{mm}^2$ into cm^2 **b** $3.4\,\text{cm}^2$ into mm^2 **c** $20\,000\,\text{cm}^2$ into m^2

d $8\,\text{m}^2$ into cm^2 **e** $0.8\,\text{m}^2$ into cm^2 **f** $7000\,\text{cm}^2$ into m^2

g $7500\,\text{cm}^2$ into m^2 **h** $8.85\,\text{m}^2$ into cm^2 **i** $0.4\,\text{m}^2$ into cm^2

j $4000\,\text{cm}^2$ into mm^2 **k** $0.6\,\text{m}^2$ into mm^2 **l** $2\,800\,000\,\text{mm}^2$ into m^2

6 Calculate these areas, in the units given.

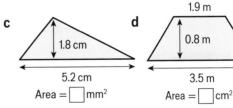

a 1.2 m, 50 cm, Area = $\square\,\text{m}^2$
b 16 mm, 3.4 cm, Area = $\square\,\text{mm}^2$
c 1.8 cm, 5.2 cm, Area = $\square\,\text{mm}^2$
d 1.9 m, 0.8 m, 3.5 m, Area = $\square\,\text{cm}^2$

e Reflect In part **c**, which was the easiest way to find the area in mm^2?

- Find the area in cm^2, then convert to mm^2.

- Convert the lengths to mm, then find the area.

f Reflect Which was the easiest way to find the area of part **d** in cm^2?

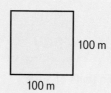
7 Here is the plan of a playing field.
Work out the area of the field in hectares.

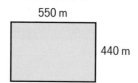

550 m

440 m

8 **Problem-solving** A farmer counts 2 wild oat plants in a 50 cm by 50 cm square of a field. The whole field has area 20 ha. Estimate the number of wild oat plants in the field.

9 **Reasoning**

  a Draw a square. Label each side 1 km.

  b Split the square into 100 m squares.

1 ha   100 m

100 m

  c Copy and complete.
    1 km^2 = ☐ ha

  d The area of Wales is 20 735 km^2. What is the area of Wales in hectares?

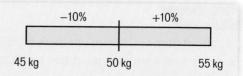
10 A factory makes bolts 30 mm long, with a 10% error interval.

  a Work out the largest and smallest possible lengths of the bolts.

  b Write the possible lengths as an inequality.
    ☐ mm ⩽ length ⩽ ☐ mm

11 Sweets are packed in 20 g bags, with a 5% error interval.
Work out the possible masses of the bags of sweets as an inequality.

12 **Reasoning a** Each measurement has been rounded to the nearest cm.
Write its smallest possible value.

   i 36 cm   **ii** 112 cm

  b Each measurement has been rounded to 1 decimal place.
Write its smallest possible value.

   i 2.5 cm   **ii** 6.7 kg

13 Write **i** the lower bound   **ii** the upper bound of each measurement.

   a 8 cm (to the nearest cm)   **b** 5.3 kg (to the nearest tenth of a kg)

   c 11.4 m (to 1 d.p.)   **d** 2.25 litres (to 2 d.p.)

   e 5000 m (to 1 s.f.)   **f** 32 mm (to 2 s.f.)

   g 1.53 kg (to 3 s.f.)   **h** 12.5 cm (to 3 s.f.)

14 Each measurement has been rounded to the accuracy given.
Write the error interval for each measurement.

   a x is rounded to 18 m (to the nearest metre)

   b y is rounded to 24.5 kg (to 1 d.p.)

   c z is rounded to 1.4 m (to 1 d.p.)

   d n is rounded to 5.26 km (to 2 d.p.)

Exam-style question

15 Jack rounds a number, n, to 1 decimal place.
The result is 3.7.
Write down the error interval for n.   **(2 marks)**

Exam tip

Write the error interval as an inequality.

---

16 A number, x, is rounded to 2 decimal places. The result is 4.28.
Using inequalities, write down the error interval for x.

17 **Reasoning** A number, y, is rounded to 2 significant figures. The result is 12.
Maisie writes this incorrect error interval for y.

$$11.5 \leqslant y \leqslant 12.5$$

Explain the mistake that Maisie has made.

Key point

To **truncate** a number to 1 digit, you remove the other digits *without* rounding.
5.694 truncated to 1 digit is 5.

---

18 Truncate each number to   **i** 1 digit   **ii** 2 digits.

   a 2.46   **b** 8.91   **c** 6.23   **d** 4.572

19 A number truncates to 5.

   a What is the lower bound for this number?   **b** What is the upper bound for this number?

Exam-style question

20 Josh truncates the number N to 1 digit. The result is 9.
Write down the error interval for N.   **(2 marks)**

Exam-style question

21 Amy used her calculator to work out the value of a number n.
The answer on her calculator display began
   4.2
Complete the error interval for n.
   _____ $\leqslant n <$ _____   **(2 marks)**

Example

The length of the side of a square is 5.34 cm to 2 d.p.
Work out the upper and lower bounds for the perimeter.
Give the perimeter to a suitable degree of accuracy.

> Use the upper and lower bounds of the side length to calculate the upper and lower bounds of the perimeter.

	Lower bound	Upper bound
Side length	5.335 cm	5.345 cm
Perimeter	5.335 × 4 = 21.34 cm	5.345 × 4 = 21.38 cm
Perimeter to 1 d.p.	21.3 cm	21.4 cm
Perimeter to nearest cm	21 cm	21 cm ✓

The perimeter is 21 cm, because the upper and lower bounds both round to 21 to the nearest whole cm.

> Round the upper and lower bounds until they give the same value.

 22 Reasoning A rectangle measures 17 cm by 28 cm to the nearest cm.
  a Work out the upper and lower bounds for the length and width.
  b Calculate the upper and lower bounds for the perimeter of the rectangle.
  c Give the perimeter to a suitable degree of accuracy.

 23 Reasoning A parallelogram has base length 9.4 m and height 8.5 m.
  Both measurements are given to 1 decimal place.
  Work out the upper and lower bounds for its area.

24 Reasoning A parallelogram has area 24 cm^2 to the nearest whole number.
  Its height is 6.2 cm (to 1 decimal place).
  a Write the upper and lower bounds for the area and the height.
  b Work out
  i $\dfrac{\text{upper bound for area}}{\text{upper bound for height}}$ **ii** $\dfrac{\text{upper bound for area}}{\text{lower bound for height}}$
  c Which calculation in part **b** gives the higher value?
    What is the upper bound for the base length of the parallelogram?
  d What is the lower bound for the base length of the parallelogram?
  e By considering bounds, write down the length of the base to a suitable degree of accuracy.

Exam-style question

 25 $y = \dfrac{k^2}{3x}$

  $k = 11.3$ to 3 significant figures
  $x = 1.4$ to 2 significant figures

> **Exam tip**
>
> Explain the reason clearly to get full marks.

  a Calculate the upper bound for the value of y.
    Give your answer to 5 significant figures. You must show all your working. **(5 marks)**
  b The lower bound for the value of y is 29.095 correct to 5 significant figures.
    By considering bounds, write down the value of y to a suitable degree of accuracy.
    You must give a reason for your answer. **(2 marks)**

7.3 Prisms

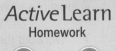
- Convert between metric units of volume.
- Calculate volumes and surface areas of prisms.

Warm up

1 Fluency Copy and complete.

   a 1 litre = ☐ ml   **b** 1 m = ☐ cm

2 Work out the volume of this 3D solid made from two cuboids.

3 Solve

   a $9b = 72$

   b $\frac{25}{2}h = 50$

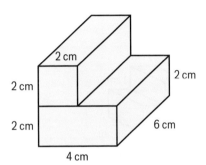

Key point

The **dimensions** of a cuboid are its length, width and height.
The **surface area** of a 3D solid is the total area of all its faces.

4 Reasoning a Sketch a cuboid with dimensions 4 cm by 5 cm by 7 cm.

   b Work out the area of the top of your cuboid.
   Which other face of the cuboid is identical to this one?

   c Work out the area of the front and side of your cuboid.
   Which other faces of the cuboid are identical to them?

   d Work out the total surface area of your cuboid.

   e Reflect Explain how you can calculate the surface area of a cuboid without drawing its net.

5 Calculate the surface area of a cuboid with dimensions 3 cm × 2 cm × 6 cm.

Key point

A **prism** is a 3D solid that has the same cross-section all through its length.

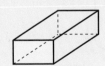 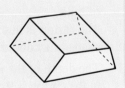

---

6 Reasoning

   a Is the 3D solid in **Q2** a prism? Explain your answer.

   b Work out the area of the cross-section of the solid in **Q2**.

   c Multiply the area of the cross-section by the length of the solid. What do you notice?

   d Reflect For a cuboid, why is multiplying the area of the cross-section by the length the same as multiplying length × width × height?

Key point

Volume of a prism = area of cross-section × length

7 Work out the volume of each prism.

a

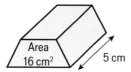

Area
16 cm²

5 cm

b

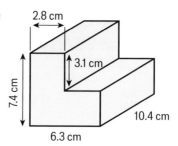

2.8 cm

3.1 cm

7.4 cm

6.3 cm

10.4 cm

c

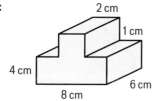

2 cm

1 cm

4 cm

6 cm

8 cm

d

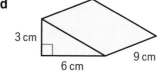

3 cm

6 cm

9 cm

8 **Reasoning** These chocolate bars are packed into cuboid-shaped boxes for transport.

Sketch how you could pack six of these bars to take up as little room as possible.
What size box do you need for 48 chocolate bars?

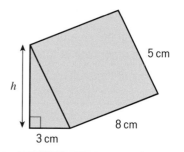

2.1 cm

3 cm

12 cm

9 **Reasoning** This triangular prism has volume 48 cm³.

a Write and solve an equation to work out its height, h.

b Sketch its net and work out its surface area.

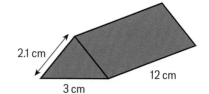

h

3 cm

8 cm

5 cm

Exam-style question

10 Sadie buys a carton of milk.
The carton is in the shape of a cuboid.
The depth of the milk in the carton is 9 cm.
Sadie pours all the milk into this cuboid-shaped tray.

Work out the depth of milk in the tray. **(3 marks)**

Diagram NOT accurately drawn

22 cm

Milk

10 cm

5 cm

Exam tip

Add extra information, such as drawing the level of milk, to the diagram.

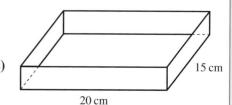

15 cm

20 cm

Key point

Volume is measured in mm^3, cm^3 or m^3.

11 **Reasoning a** Sketch a cube with side length 1 cm and a cube with side length 10 mm.

    b Copy and complete. $1 cm^3 = \square mm^3$

    c How do you convert from mm^3 to cm^3?

12 **Reasoning a** Work out the volumes of a cube with side length 1 m and a cube with side length 100 cm.

    b How do you convert from m^3 to cm^3?

13 Convert

    a $5 cm^3$ into mm^3 **b** $52 cm^3$ into mm^3 **c** $4000 mm^3$ into cm^3

    d $400 mm^3$ into cm^3 **e** $3421 mm^3$ into cm^3 **f** $3 m^3$ into cm^3

    g $4.5 m^3$ into cm^3 **h** $6000 cm^3$ into m^3 **i** $9\,500\,000 cm^3$ into m^3

Key point

Capacity is the amount of liquid a 3D object can hold. It is measured in ml and litres.

$1 cm^3 = 1 ml$

$1000 cm^3 = 1$ litre

14 Copy and complete.

    a $5200 cm^3 = \square ml = \square$ litres   **b** 0.7 litres $= \square ml = \square cm^3$

    c $175 ml = \square cm^3$ **d** $1750 ml = \square cm^3$

    e $2 m^3 = \square cm^3 = \square ml = \square$ litres   **f** $3 m^3 = \square$ litres

15 **Future skills** A water tank is a cuboid 140 cm tall, 80 cm wide and 2 m long. Kate paints all the faces except the base.

    a Work out the total area she paints, in square metres.

    b One tin of paint covers $4 m^2$. How many tins of paint does Kate need?

16 **Problem-solving** A cube has surface area $507.8 cm^2$ to 1 decimal place. What is the length of one side of the cube? Give your answer to 1 decimal place.

17 **Future skills** A scientist collects a sample of leaf mould 20 cm deep from a $0.25 m^2$ area in a wood.

    a By modelling the sample as a cuboid, calculate the volume of leaf mould she collects.

    b In the leaf mould sample, she counts 12 worms. Estimate the number of worms in the top 20 cm of leaf mould in 2 hectares of the wood.

Exam-style question

18 A container is in the shape of a cuboid.

The container is $\frac{4}{5}$ full of water.
A bucket holds 1.2 litres of water.
What is the greatest number of buckets that can be completely
filled with water from the container? **(4 marks)**

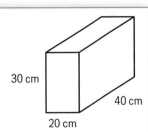

30 cm

40 cm

20 cm

7.4 Circles

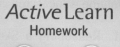
*Active*Learn
Homework

- Calculate the area and circumference of a circle.
- Calculate area and circumference in terms of π.

Warm up

1 Fluency a What is the radius of each circle?

b What is the diameter?

5 cm   62 mm

2 Solve

a $35 = 7r$ **b** $64 = r^2$ **c** $75 = 3r^2$

3 Make x the subject of

a $y = mx$ **b** $t^2 = x^2$ **c** $p = x^2$

Key point

The **circumference** of a circle is its perimeter.

---

4 Reasoning The table gives the diameter and circumference of some circles.

a Work out the ratio $\dfrac{\text{circumference}}{\text{diameter}}$ for each one.
What do you notice?

Diameter	Circumference
10 cm	31.4 cm
54 m	169.6 m
36 mm	113 mm

b The ratio $\dfrac{\text{circumference}}{\text{diameter}}$ of a circle is represented by the Greek letter π (pi).
Find the π key on your calculator.
Write the value of π to 8 decimal places.

c Reflect Explain how you can work out the circumference of a circle if you know its diameter.
What if you know its radius?

Key point

For any circle
Circumference $= \pi \times$ diameter
$C = \pi d$ or $C = 2\pi r$

---

5 Work out the circumference of each circle.
Give your answers to 1 decimal place, and the units of measurement.

a
9 cm

b
4.7 m

c
12 mm

d
3.4 cm

e Reflect Do you need to remember both formulae for the circumference of a circle, or just one?

---

6   Ali walks once round a circle with diameter 60 metres.
     There are 5 points equally spaced on the circumference of
     the circle.

     Find the distance Ali walks between one point and the next point.
     Give your answer to 2 decimal places.   **(2 marks)**

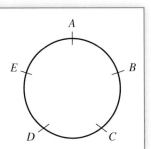

Key point

The formula for the area, A, of a circle with radius r is $A = \pi r^2$

7   Find the area of each circle.
     Give your answers to 1 decimal place, and the units of measurement.

a   b   c   d

4 cm   1.2 m   7 m   5.2 cm

8   **Reflect** One of these expressions is for the area of a circle and one is for the circumference.

     $2\pi r$ πr^2

     Think about the units of area and circumference.
     How can you remember which expression is for area and which is for circumference?

9   **Reasoning** The areas and circumferences of these circles
     are given in terms of π.
     Match each circle to its area and circumference.

Q9 hint

'In terms of π' means π is in the answer.

a   b

5 cm   7 cm

c   d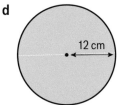

10 cm   12 cm

Q9 hint

Substitute the radius into the circumference and area formulae.

| 49π cm^2 | 100π cm^2 | 144π cm^2 | 25π cm^2 |

| 10π cm | 20π cm | 24π cm | 14π cm |

10   **Reasoning**

     a   Work out the area and circumference of a circle with radius 6 cm
         i   in terms of π ii   to 2 significant figures
     b   Which values for the area and circumference are the most accurate?

11 Work out the shaded area, to the nearest square centimetre.

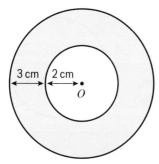

12 The diagram shows a pattern made from 3 circles.

Each circle has centre O.
Maria says that exactly $\frac{1}{3}$ of the pattern is shaded.
Show that Maria is correct.
You must show all your working. **(3 marks)**

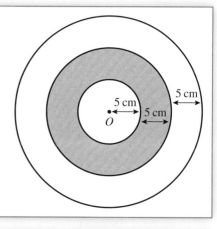

13 Dane's garden is in the shape of a rectangle.
In the garden there is a patio in the shape of a rectangle and a circular pond with diameter 2.4 m.
The rest of the garden is grass.

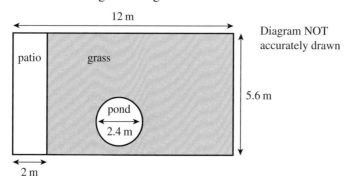

Diagram NOT accurately drawn

Exam tip

Show clearly which areas you are working out. You could use:

Area ☐ =

Area ◯ =

Dane is going to put lawn feed on all the grass.
One box of lawn feed will cover $12\,\text{m}^2$ of grass.
Dane buys 3 boxes of lawn feed.
Is this enough?
You must show your working. **(5 marks)**

14 Problem-solving
A bicycle wheel has radius 32 cm.
How many complete revolutions does the wheel make in 1 km?

15 The circumference of a circle is 104 cm.

a Substitute the value for C into the formula $C = \pi d$.

b Solve the equation to find the diameter to 1 decimal place.

16 Problem-solving
Find the radius of a circle with circumference 24 cm.

Example

A circle has area $50\,\text{m}^2$. Find its radius, to the nearest cm.

$50 = \pi r^2$	Substitute $A = 50$ into the area formula.
$\dfrac{50}{\pi} = r^2$	Rearrange to make r^2 the subject.
$\sqrt{\dfrac{50}{\pi}} = r$	Square root both sides to find r.

$r = 3.9894...\,\text{m} = 399\,\text{cm (nearest cm)}$

---

17 Problem-solving

a Find the radius of a circle with area $520\,\text{m}^2$.
Give your answer to the nearest cm.

b Find the diameter of a circle with area $630\,\text{cm}^2$.
Give your answer to the nearest mm.

18 Tim is using circles in a scale diagram.
The area of each circle represents the number of people in a group.

Circle	Number of people	Area of circle
X	40	$40\,\text{cm}^2$
Y	25	$25\,\text{cm}^2$
Z	70	$70\,\text{cm}^2$

a Copy and complete to make r the subject of the formula for area of a circle.

$A = \pi r^2$

$\dfrac{A}{\square} = r^2$

$\sqrt{\dfrac{A}{\square}} = \square$

b Use your formula for r from part **a** to work out the radii of circles X, Y and Z to the nearest mm.

Q18b hint

'Radii' is the plural of 'radius'.

7.5 Sectors of circles

- Calculate the perimeter and area of semicircles and quarter circles.
- Calculate arc lengths, angles and areas of sectors of circles.

Warm up

1 **Fluency** What fraction of the whole circle is each sector?

a
45°

b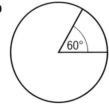
60°

2 Find the circumference and area of this circle
  a in terms of π
  b correct to 3 significant figures

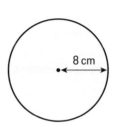
8 cm

3 Simplify, by collecting like terms
  a $2x + 2x$
  b $2\pi + 2\pi$
  c $2\pi + 6 + 4.2$
  d $5 + 3\pi + 2$

Key point

An **arc** is part of the circumference of a circle.
A **sector** is a slice of a circle, between an arc and two radii.

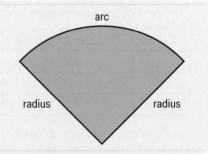
arc
radius   radius

---

4 Work out the area, in terms of π, of
  a the semicircle
  b the quarter circle
  by first working out the area of the whole circle.

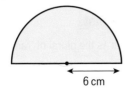
6 cm

10 cm

Q4 hint

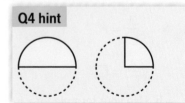

  c Work out your answers to parts **a** and **b** correct to 3 significant figures.

5 Work out the perimeter of each semicircle, in terms of π, by

  • finding half the circumference of the whole circle

  • adding the diameter to it

a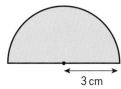

3 cm

b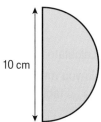

10 cm

c Work out your answers to parts **a** and **b** correct to 1 decimal place.

6 **Problem-solving** Work out the perimeter of this quarter circle

a in terms of π

b to 1 decimal place

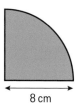

8 cm

7 **Problem-solving** A window is made from a rectangle and a semicircle. Work out the area and perimeter of the window correct to 2 decimal places.

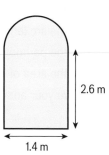

2.6 m

1.4 m

8 **Problem-solving** Four quarter circles are cut from a 10 cm square like this.

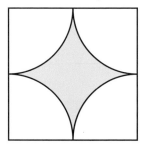

Work out the shaded area.

Exam-style question

9 The diagram shows a square $ABCD$ with sides of length 8 cm. It also shows a semicircle and an arc of a circle.

AD is the diameter of the semicircle.

AC is the arc of a circle with centre D.

Show that $\dfrac{\text{area of unshaded region}}{\text{area of square}} = \dfrac{\pi}{8}$ **(4 marks)**

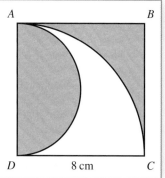

A   B

D   8 cm   C

10 Problem-solving The area of this semicircle is 15 cm² to the nearest whole number.

a Find the radius of the semicircle.
Write all the numbers on your calculator display.

b How many decimal places could you measure to, with a ruler?
Round your answer to part **a** to a suitable degree of accuracy.

Key point

For a sector with angle $x°$ of a circle with radius r

Arc length $= \dfrac{x}{360} \times 2\pi r$

Area of sector $= \dfrac{x}{360} \times \pi r^2$

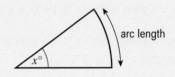

Example

Work out

  a the arc length

  b the perimeter

  c the area of this sector

Give your answers to 3 significant figures.

a   Arc length $= \dfrac{x}{360} \times 2\pi r$

$= \dfrac{40}{360} \times 2 \times \pi \times 10$ ← Write the formula, substitute the angle x and radius.

$= 6.9813... = 6.98\,\text{cm (3 s.f.)}$

b   Perimeter $= 6.98 + 10 + 10$ ← Perimeter = arc length + 2 radii

$= 26.98 = 27.0\,\text{cm (3 s.f.)}$

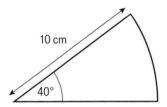

c   Area $= \dfrac{x}{360} \times \pi r^2$

$= \dfrac{40}{360} \times \pi \times 100$ ← Write the formula, substitute the angle x and radius.

$= 34.9065... = 34.9\,\text{cm}^2 \text{ (3 s.f.)}$

Exam-style question

11 OAB is a sector of a circle, centre O.

The radius of the circle is 12 cm.
The angle of the sector is 20°.

Calculate the area of sector OAB.

Give your answer correct to 3 significant figures.

Diagram NOT accurately drawn

(2 marks)

Exam tip

Write the formula you are using and show how you will substitute the given numbers into it.
Make sure you write down your unrounded answer from your calculator before rounding.

---

12 Work out the arc length and perimeter of the sector in **Q11**.
Give your answers to 3 significant figures.

13 **Problem-solving**
   a Work out the arc length and area of this sector.
   b The radius of the circle was measured to the nearest cm.
   Work out the error interval for the area of the sector.

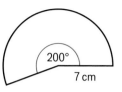

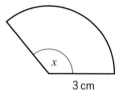

14 The area of this sector is $10\,\text{cm}^2$.
   a Substitute $r = 3$ and area $= 10$ into the formula
   $$\text{Area} = \frac{x}{360} \times \pi r^2$$

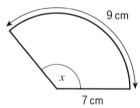

   b Solve your equation from part **a** to find the angle of the sector,
   to the nearest degree.

15 **Problem-solving** Find the angle of this sector.

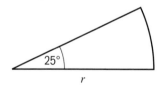

16 **Problem-solving** This sector has area $16\,\text{m}^2$.
Find the radius.
Give your answer to a suitable degree of accuracy.

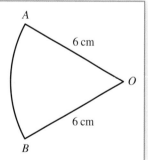

Exam-style question

17 OAB is a sector of a circle with centre O and radius 6 cm.
The area of the sector is $35\,\text{cm}^2$.
Calculate the perimeter of the sector.
Give your answer correct to 3 significant figures.   **(4 marks)**

---

18 **Problem-solving** Angle AOB is $45°$.
The sector AOB has area $5\pi\,\text{cm}^2$.
Find the length of the arc AB, giving your answer to a suitable
degree of accuracy.

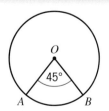

7.6 Cylinders and spheres

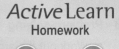
*Active*Learn
Homework

- Calculate volume and surface area of a cylinder and a sphere.
- Solve problems involving volumes and surface areas.

Warm up

1 **Fluency** What are the area and circumference of this circle in terms of π?

7 cm

2 Sketch the net of a cylinder.

3 Find the value of r. Give your answers to 1 decimal place where appropriate.

 a $72 = 2r^2$ **b** $54 = \frac{2}{3}r^2$ **c** $32 = 4\pi r^2$ **d** $30\pi = 3\pi r^3$

4 **Reasoning** You can think of a cylinder as being like a prism.

 a Write an expression for the area of its cross-section.

 b Write a formula, $V =$ ____ $\times h$, for its volume.

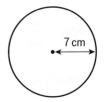

Key point

The volume of a cylinder of radius r and height h is $V = \pi r^2 h$

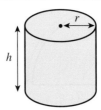

5 Work out the volume of each cylinder. Give your answers to 1 decimal place.

 a 3 cm / 7 cm **b** 32 mm / 52 mm **c** 5 m / 13 cm

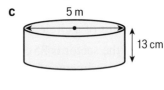

6 **Problem-solving** A scientist cuts a circular section of ice, with diameter 1 m.
The mean thickness of the ice is 34 cm.
Estimate the volume of ice in the sample. Give your answer in m^3.

7 A cylinder has radius 3.5 cm and volume 125 cm^3.

 a Substitute the values into the volume formula.

 b Work out its height.

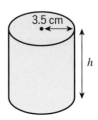
3.5 cm / h

Example

Calculate the total surface area of this cylinder.
Give your answer to 1 decimal place.

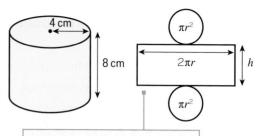

Area of each circle = $\pi \times 4^2 = 16\pi$

Area of rectangle = $2\pi rh = 2 \times \pi \times 4 \times 8 = 64\pi$

Surface area = $2 \times 16\pi + 64\pi$

$\qquad = 32\pi + 64\pi$

$\qquad = 96\pi$

$\qquad = 301.5928... = 301.6 \text{ cm}^2$ (1 d.p.)

Sketch a net.
Each circle has area πr^2.
The length of the rectangle is the circumference of the circle, $2\pi r$.
The width of the rectangle is the height of the cylinder, h.

Two circles plus rectangle.

Key point

The total surface area of a cylinder of radius r and height h is $2\pi r^2 + 2\pi rh$

8 Calculate the total surface area of each cylinder in **Q5**.

Exam-style question

9 Lucas has to cover 4 pillars completely with paint.
Each pillar is in the shape of a cylinder with a top and a bottom.
Each pillar has a diameter of 0.3 m and a height of 1.4 m.
Lucas has 2 tins of paint. Each tin of paint covers 3 m².
Has Lucas got enough paint to completely cover the 4 pillars?
You must show how you get your answer. **(5 marks)**

10 Problem-solving A cylinder has total surface area 3900 mm²
and radius 15 mm. Work out its height, to the nearest mm.

Q10 hint

Substitute the values into the surface area formula and solve.

11 Problem-solving When 120 ml of water is poured into a
cylinder, it reaches a height of 8 cm.

a Work out the radius of the cylinder.

More water is poured into the cylinder, until it reaches a height of 20 cm.

b How much water is in the cylinder now?

Key point

For a sphere of radius r
Surface area = $4\pi r^2$
Volume = $\frac{4}{3}\pi r^3$

12 Calculate the surface area and volume of each sphere. Give your answers in terms of π.

a

9 mm

b

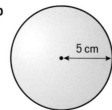

5 cm

13 Here is a hemisphere of radius 8 cm.

Calculate

a the volume of the hemisphere

b the area of its curved surface

c its total surface area (flat surface + curved surface)

Give your answers to 2 decimal places.

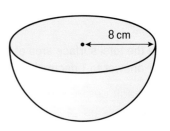

Exam-style question

14 The diagram shows a solid glass paperweight, made from a hemisphere on top of a cylinder.

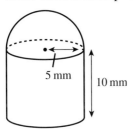

5 mm

10 mm

Exam tip

Exam questions on spheres give you the volume and surface area formulae.

Volume of sphere $= \frac{4}{3}\pi r^3$

Surface area of sphere $= 4\pi r^2$

The height of the cylinder is 10 mm.
The radius of the cylinder is 5 mm.

a Calculate the total volume of the paperweight.
Give your answer correct to 3 significant figures. **(3 marks)**

b Calculate the surface area of the paperweight.
Give your answer correct to 3 significant figures. **(3 marks)**

15 **Problem-solving** A spherical ball bearing is made from 20 ml of molten steel.
Work out its radius, to the nearest millimetre.

16 **Problem-solving** What is the radius of a sphere with surface area 500 m²?

Exam-style question

17 Shape S is one quarter of a solid sphere, centre O.

Shape S

Volume of sphere $= \frac{4}{3}\pi r^3$

Surface area of sphere $= 4\pi r^2$

The volume of S is 243π cm³
Find the surface area of S.
Give your answer correct to 3 significant figures.
You must show your working. **(5 marks)**

18 **Reflect** Do you need to remember the cylinder formulae, or can you work them out using what you know about prisms and circles?

7.7 Pyramids and cones

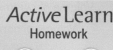

Active Learn
Homework

- Calculate volume and surface area of pyramids and cones.
- Use a flow diagram to help you solve problems.

Warm up

1 Fluency

   a What is the volume of a cube of side 5 mm?

   b A cube has volume 64 cm^3. How long is one of its sides?

2 Work out the area of each triangle.

   a

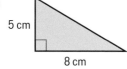

5 cm
8 cm

   b

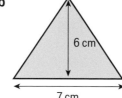

6 cm
7 cm

3 Use Pythagoras' theorem to work out the length of the sloping side in the triangle in **Q2a**.
   Give your answer to 1 decimal place.

4 Here is a square-based pyramid.

   a Sketch a net of this pyramid.

   b Work out the area of each face.

   c Calculate the surface area of the pyramid.

   d **Reflect** Do you need to sketch the net to work out the surface area of this pyramid? Explain.

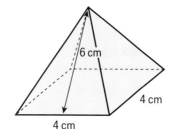

6 cm
4 cm
4 cm

Exam-style question

5 Here is a solid square-based pyramid *ABCDE*.

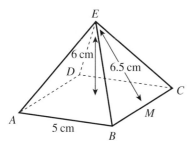

E
6 cm
D
6.5 cm
C
A
5 cm
M
B

The base of the pyramid is a square of side 5 cm.
The height of the pyramid is 6 cm.
M is the midpoint of *BC* and *EM* = 6.5 cm.
Work out the total surface area of the pyramid.   **(4 marks)**

Key point

Volume of pyramid $= \frac{1}{3} \times$ area of base $\times$ vertical height

Volume of cone $= \frac{1}{3} \times$ area of base $\times$ vertical height

$$= \frac{1}{3}\pi r^2 h$$

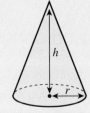

6 This pyramid has a square base of side 8 cm, and vertical height 10 cm.
Calculate its volume to 3 significant figures.

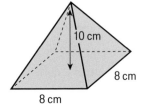

Exam-style question

7 This solid is made from a square-based pyramid and a cube.
The square-based pyramid is 12 cm high,
and has volume 300 cm³.

Find

a the length of one side of the square base **(3 marks)**

b the total volume of the solid **(3 marks)**

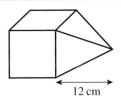

8 A cone has base radius 6 cm and height 8 cm.
Calculate its volume

a in terms of π

b to 3 significant figures

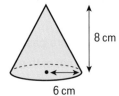

Key point

Curved surface area of a cone $= \pi r l$, where r is the base radius
and l is the slant height.
Total surface area of a cone $= \pi r l + \pi r^2$

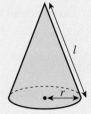

9 A cone has base radius 5 cm and slant height 13 cm.
Calculate, in terms of π

a the area of its base

b its curved surface area

c its total surface area

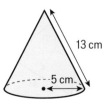

10 Reasoning

a Show that the slant height of this disposable paper cup is $\sqrt{97}$ cm.

b Work out the area of card used to make the cup.

c Max used $l = \sqrt{97}$ in his area calculation. Lois used $l = \sqrt{97} = 9.45$ (2 d.p.).
Which value of l gives the more accurate calculation for surface area?

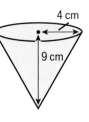

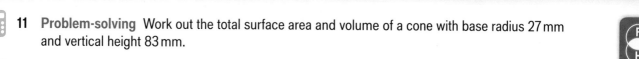

11 Problem-solving Work out the total surface area and volume of a cone with base radius 27 mm and vertical height 83 mm.

12 Problem-solving An ice-cream cone of radius 3 cm holds 100 ml of ice cream.
What is the height of the cone?

13 Problem-solving A medium ice-cream cone has a radius of 3 cm and a vertical height of 17.5 cm.
A large cone has a vertical height of 18 cm.
The volume of the large cone is 40% bigger than the medium cone.

a Draw a picture to show all the information in the question.

b Use your picture to help you complete this flow diagram and working to find the diameter of the large cone.

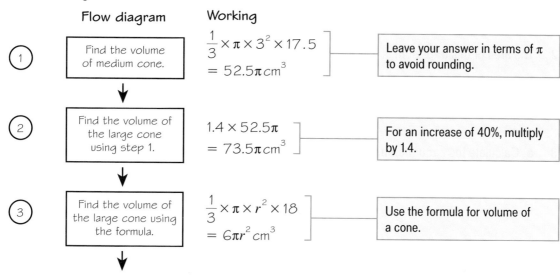

Flow diagram | Working

① Find the volume of medium cone.

$\frac{1}{3} \times \pi \times 3^2 \times 17.5$
$= 52.5\pi \text{ cm}^3$

Leave your answer in terms of π to avoid rounding.

② Find the volume of the large cone using step 1.

$1.4 \times 52.5\pi$
$= 73.5\pi \text{ cm}^3$

For an increase of 40%, multiply by 1.4.

③ Find the volume of the large cone using the formula.

$\frac{1}{3} \times \pi \times r^2 \times 18$
$= 6\pi r^2 \text{ cm}^3$

Use the formula for volume of a cone.

14 Problem-solving A sphere of plastic with volume 600 cm³ is melted and used to make a cone of the same radius. Work out the height of the cone.

15 The top 8 cm of this cone is cut off, to leave a 3D solid called a frustum.
Volume of frustum = volume of whole cone − volume of top cone
Work out the volume of the frustum, in terms of π.

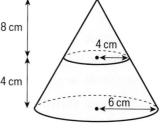

8 cm
4 cm
4 cm
6 cm

Exam-style question

16 Calculate the volume of this 3D solid, in terms of π.

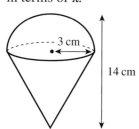

3 cm
14 cm

(4 marks)

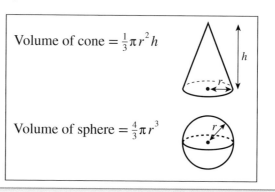

Volume of cone $= \frac{1}{3}\pi r^2 h$

h
r

Volume of sphere $= \frac{4}{3}\pi r^3$

r

7 Check up

Active Learn
Homework

2D shapes

1 Work out the shaded area.

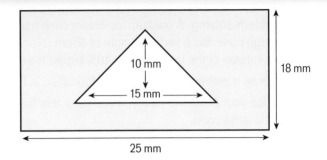

2 The area of this trapezium is $45\,\text{cm}^2$. Find x.

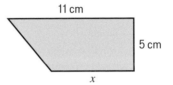

3

   a Calculate the circumference of this circle. Give your answer to 1 decimal place.

   b Find the area of the circle in terms of π.

4 Work out the perimeter of this semicircle. Give your answer correct to 1 decimal place.

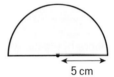

5 Calculate

   a the area

   b the arc length of this sector

   Give your answers correct to 1 decimal place.

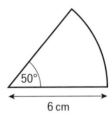

Accuracy and measures

6 Copy and complete.

   a $4\,\text{m}^2 = \square\,\text{cm}^2$ **b** $5600\,\text{cm}^2 = \square\,\text{m}^2$

   c $9\,500\,000\,\text{cm}^3 = \square\,\text{m}^3$ **d** $4\ \text{litres} = \square\,\text{ml} = \square\,\text{cm}^3$

7 Write an inequality to show the error interval for each measurement.

   a 36 m rounded to the nearest metre.

   b 23.6 km rounded to 1 decimal place.

   c 9.2 cm rounded to the nearest mm.

3D solids

8 Work out the volume of this triangular prism.

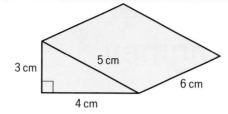

3 cm
5 cm
6 cm
4 cm

 9 Calculate the surface area of this cylinder, with radius 5.3 cm and height 9.5 cm.

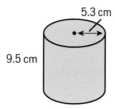

5.3 cm
9.5 cm

10 A sphere has radius 3 cm. Work out its volume in terms of π.

3 cm

Volume of sphere $= \frac{4}{3}\pi r^3$

Surface area of sphere $= 4\pi r^2$

11 Calculate the volume and surface area of this square-based pyramid.

12 cm 13 cm

10 cm

 12 Calculate the volume of this cone.

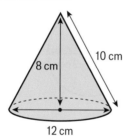

8 cm
10 cm
12 cm

Volume of cone $= \frac{1}{3}\pi r^2 h$

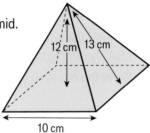

h

r

13 Reflect How sure are you of your answers? Were you mostly

Just guessing 😟   Feeling doubtful 😐   Confident 🙂

What next? Use your results to decide whether to strengthen or extend your learning.

Challenge

14 These two cardboard boxes each hold 4 tennis balls, with diameter 6.5 cm. Which shape would you recommend to the manufacturer, and why?

> **Q14 hint**
>
> You could think about:
> - stacking and transport
> - eye catching design
> - amount of card needed to make the box
> - amount of empty space inside, around the tennis balls.

7 Strengthen

Active Learn
Homework

2D shapes

1 a Measure the perpendicular height of this trapezium.

   b Work out the perimeter.
   Use a ruler to measure the lengths you need.

   c Sketch the trapezium.
   Label the parallel sides a and b. Label the perpendicular height h.

   d Use Area $= \frac{1}{2}(a+b)\,h$ to find the area of this trapezium.

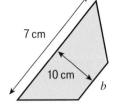

2 Reasoning This trapezium has area $55\,\text{cm}^2$.

   a Sketch the diagram and label a, b and h.

   b Substitute the values for A, a and h into the formula $A = \frac{1}{2}(a+b)\,h$

   c Simplify the right-hand side of your equation from part **b**.
   Multiply out the brackets.

   d Solve the equation to find b.

3 The formulae for circumference are $C = \pi d$ $C = 2\pi r$

   a Write down the formula to use if you are given the radius.

   b Work out the circumference of each circle

      i in terms of π $C = \pi \square = \square \pi$

      ii correct to 1 decimal place

A
2 cm

B
12 cm

4 Here are two expressions used with circles.

   $2\pi r$ πr^2

   a Match each expression to the correct measurement.

   area = 34 cm²   circumference = 19.5 cm

   b Write the formula for area of a circle.

   c Write the formula for circumference of a circle.

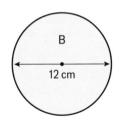

Q4 hint

Circumference is in cm: $2\pi r$
Area is in cm²: πr^2

5 Work out the area of each circle in **Q3**

   a in terms of π $A = \pi \square^2 = \square \pi$

   b correct to 1 decimal place

6 Here is a semicircle with radius 7 cm.

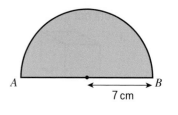

  a What fraction of a circle is a semicircle?

  b Work out, giving your answers to 1 decimal place

    i the area of a full circle with radius 7 cm

    ii the area of this semicircle with radius 7 cm

    iii the circumference of a full circle with radius 7 cm

    iv the arc length AB

    v the diameter AB

    vi the perimeter of the semicircle

7 Copy and complete the fraction of each circle that is marked.

a
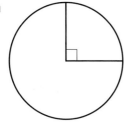

$$\frac{\square}{360} = \frac{\square}{\square}$$

b
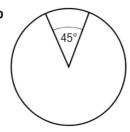

$$\frac{\square}{360} = \frac{\square}{\square}$$

c
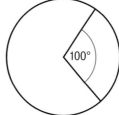

$$\frac{\square}{360} = \frac{\square}{\square}$$

8 Here is a sector of a circle with radius 8 cm.

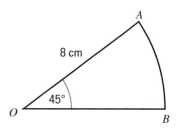

  a What fraction of a circle is this sector?

  b Work out, giving your answers 1 decimal place

    i the area of a full circle with radius 8 cm

    ii the area of this sector with radius 8 cm

    iii the circumference of a full circle with radius 8 cm

    iv the arc length AB

    v the total length from A to O to B

    vi the perimeter of the sector

Accuracy and measures

1 **a** Work out the area of each shape in cm^2.

   i

   ii
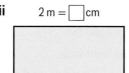

  b Copy and complete this double number line for cm^2 and m^2.
    Use the areas of the rectangles from part **a**. Follow the pattern.

2 **a** Work out the volume of each cuboid in cm³.

i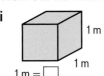
1 m
1 m
1 m = ☐

ii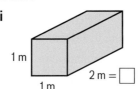
1 m
1 m
2 m = ☐

b Copy and complete this double number line for cm³ and m³.

c Copy and complete this number line.

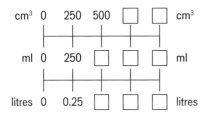

3 **a** A pen is 23 cm long, to the nearest cm.
The diagram shows the measurements that round to 23 cm, to the nearest cm.

Write an inequality to show the upper and lower bounds of this measurement.
Use *l* for the length of the pen.

b A pencil sharpener is 32 mm long, to the nearest mm.
Write an inequality to show the upper and lower bounds of this measurement.
Use *l* for the length of the pencil sharpener.

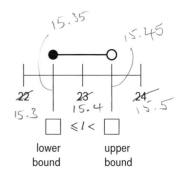
☐ ≤ *l* < ☐
lower bound   upper bound

3D solids

1 **a** Sketch the front face of each of these solids.

i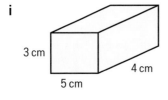
3 cm
4 cm
5 cm

ii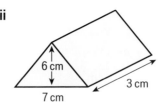
6 cm
3 cm
7 cm

iii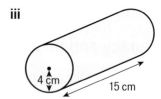
4 cm
15 cm

b Work out the volume of each solid by
- working out the area of the front face
- multiplying the area by the length of the solid

2 **a** Sketch the net of this cylinder.

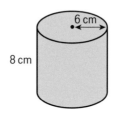
6 cm
8 cm

b Work out (giving your answers to 1 decimal place)

   i the area of the circle

   ii the length of the rectangle

   iii the area of the rectangle

   iv the total surface area of the cylinder

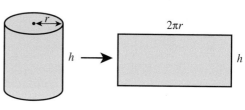

3 **a** Write the formula for surface area
      of a sphere.

   b Work out the surface area of a sphere
      of radius 6 cm.

   c Write the formula for the volume
      of a sphere.

   d Work out the volume of a sphere of radius 6 cm.

   Give your answers to parts **b** and **d** to 2 decimal places.

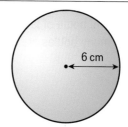

Surface area of sphere $= 4\pi r^2$

Volume of sphere $= \frac{4}{3}\pi r^3$

6 cm

4 Here is a square-based pyramid.

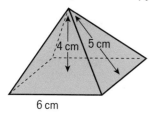

4 cm 5 cm

6 cm

   a Work out the area of its base.

   b What is the vertical height?

   c Work out Volume $= \frac{1}{3} \times$ area of base $\times$ vertical height

   d Sketch a triangular face of the pyramid.
      Label the base and height of the triangle.

   e Work out the area of

      i one triangular face

      ii 4 triangular faces

   f Work out the surface area of the pyramid.

5 Here is a cone.

   a What is its vertical height?

   b What is its slant height?

   c Use the formula to work out the volume of the cone.
      $V = \frac{1}{3}\pi r^2 h$, where h is vertical height.

   d Use the formula to work out the surface area of the cone.
      Surface area $= \pi r^2 + \pi r l$, where l is the slant height.

   Give your answers correct to 1 decimal place.

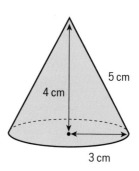

5 cm

4 cm

3 cm

7 Extend

1 Write an expression for
   a the area of the cross-section of this prism in mm^2
   b the volume of the prism in mm^3

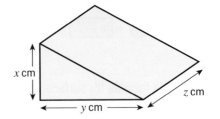

$$a \quad \frac{1}{2} \times 10x \times 10y = 50xy$$

$$b \quad 50xy \times 10z = 500xyz$$

2 **Problem-solving** The diagram shows a lawn with a wall along one side.
   a Show that the wall is 4 m long.
   b A 500 ml bottle of lawn feed treats 20 m^2 of lawn.
      How many bottles are needed to treat this lawn?

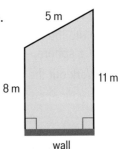

3 The graph shows the velocity of a remote-controlled car during a test. Work out the distance the car travelled during the test.

Q3 hint

Distance = area under velocity–time graph.

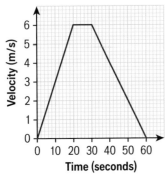

Velocity of remote-controlled car

4 **Problem-solving** A cylindrical water tank has height 1.2 m and radius 50 cm. Water flows into the tank at a rate of 300 ml per second. How long will it take for the tank to fill? Give your answer to the nearest minute.

5 What percentage of this diagram is shaded?

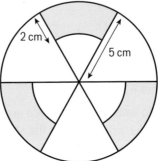

6 **Problem-solving** The diagram shows a trapezium.
All the lengths are in centimetres.
The area of the trapezium is $144\,\text{cm}^2$.
Show that $3x^2 - 6x = 144$.

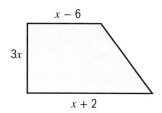

Exam-style question

7 A square, with sides of length $x\,\text{cm}$, is inside a circle.
Each vertex of the square is on the circumference of the circle.
The area of the circle is $80\,\text{cm}^2$.
Work out the value of x.
Give your answer correct to 3 significant figures. **(4 marks)**

8 **Problem-solving** A paintbrush is 30 cm long.
It just fits diagonally inside a cylindrical paint tin.
The tin is 24 cm high.
What is the capacity of the tin, to the nearest litre?

9 The diagram shows a solid cylinder.

The cylinder has base radius 3 cm and height 9 cm.
The total surface area of the cylinder is $n\pi\,\text{cm}^2$, where n is an integer.
Find the value of n.

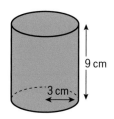

9 cm

3 cm

10 $x = 15.6$ $y = 4.2$ $z = 5.8$
All values have been rounded to 1 decimal place.
Work out the upper bound of

a $x + y$ **b** yz **c** xyz **d** $\dfrac{x}{y}$

11 $d = 520$ (2 s.f.) $e = 13.55$ (4 s.f.)
Write the value of each expression to a suitable degree of accuracy.

a de **b** $\dfrac{d^2}{e}$

12 **Problem-solving** The diameter of the Moon is 3.5×10^6 metres.
Calculate its surface area. Assume the Moon is a sphere.
Give your answer in standard form.

Working towards A level

13 The diagram shows a cone with base radius $r\,\text{cm}$,
perpendicular height $h\,\text{cm}$ and slant height $l\,\text{cm}$.
The curved surface area of the cone is $60\pi\,\text{cm}^2$.
The slant height and the radius of the base are
in the ratio $l : r = 5 : 2$.

Work out the perpendicular height of
the cone.
Give your answer, fully simplified,
in the form $a\sqrt{b}$, where a and b
are integers.

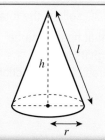

Q13 hint

Curved surface area
of a cone $= \pi r l$

At A level you often need to use a combination of
different mathematical skills. Here, you need to know
about the geometry of a cone, to use Pythagoras'
theorem and ratio, and to be confident handling surds.

7 Test ready

Summary of key points

To revise for the test:

- Read each key point, find a question on it in the mastery lesson, and check you can work out the answer.

- If you cannot, try some other questions from the mastery lesson or ask for help.

Key points

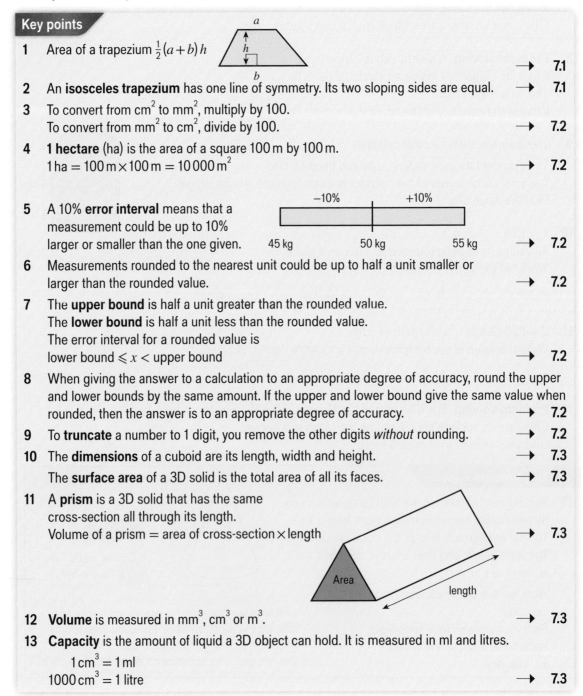

1 Area of a trapezium $\frac{1}{2}(a+b)h$ → **7.1**

2 An **isosceles trapezium** has one line of symmetry. Its two sloping sides are equal. → **7.1**

3 To convert from cm^2 to mm^2, multiply by 100.
   To convert from mm^2 to cm^2, divide by 100. → **7.2**

4 **1 hectare** (ha) is the area of a square 100 m by 100 m.
   $1\,ha = 100\,m \times 100\,m = 10\,000\,m^2$ → **7.2**

5 A 10% **error interval** means that a
   measurement could be up to 10%
   larger or smaller than the one given. → **7.2**

6 Measurements rounded to the nearest unit could be up to half a unit smaller or
   larger than the rounded value. → **7.2**

7 The **upper bound** is half a unit greater than the rounded value.
   The **lower bound** is half a unit less than the rounded value.
   The error interval for a rounded value is
   lower bound $\leqslant x <$ upper bound → **7.2**

8 When giving the answer to a calculation to an appropriate degree of accuracy, round the upper
   and lower bounds by the same amount. If the upper and lower bound give the same value when
   rounded, then the answer is to an appropriate degree of accuracy. → **7.2**

9 To **truncate** a number to 1 digit, you remove the other digits *without* rounding. → **7.2**

10 The **dimensions** of a cuboid are its length, width and height. → **7.3**

    The **surface area** of a 3D solid is the total area of all its faces. → **7.3**

11 A **prism** is a 3D solid that has the same
    cross-section all through its length.
    Volume of a prism = area of cross-section × length → **7.3**

12 **Volume** is measured in mm^3, cm^3 or m^3. → **7.3**

13 **Capacity** is the amount of liquid a 3D object can hold. It is measured in ml and litres.
    $1\,cm^3 = 1\,ml$
    $1000\,cm^3 = 1\,litre$ → **7.3**

Key points

14 The **circumference** of a circle is its perimeter.
For any circle
Circumference $= \pi \times$ diameter
$C = \pi d$ or $C = 2\pi r$
The formula for the area, A, of a circle with radius r is $A = \pi r^2$.

→ **7.4**

15 An **arc** is part of the circumference of a circle.
A **sector** is a slice of a circle, between an arc and two radii.

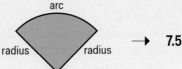

arc

radius   radius

→ **7.5**

16 For a sector with angle $x°$ of a circle with radius r
Arc length $= \dfrac{x}{360} \times 2\pi r$
Area of sector $= \dfrac{x}{360} \times \pi r^2$

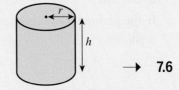

arc length

$x°$

→ **7.5**

17 The volume of a cylinder of radius r and height h is $V = \pi r^2 h$.
The total surface area of a cylinder of radius r and height h
is $2\pi r^2 + 2\pi rh$.

h

→ **7.6**

18 For a sphere of radius r
Surface area $= 4\pi r^2$
Volume $= \frac{4}{3}\pi r^3$

r

→ **7.6**

19 Volume of pyramid $= \frac{1}{3} \times$ area of base $\times$ vertical height

→ **7.7**

20 Volume of cone $= \frac{1}{3} \times$ area of base $\times$ vertical height $= \frac{1}{3}\pi r^2 h$
Curved surface area of a cone $= \pi r l$, where r is the base radius
and l is the slant height.
Total surface area of a cone $= \pi r l + \pi r^2$

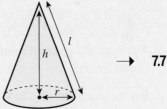

h l

r

→ **7.7**

Sample student answer

Exam-style question

The diagram shows a sector of a circle, centre O.

The radius of the circle is 9 cm.
The angle of the sector is $100°$.
Calculate the area of the sector.
Give your answer correct to 3 significant figures.

(2 marks)

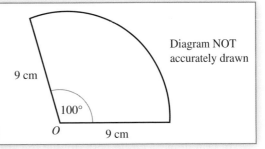

Diagram NOT
accurately drawn

9 cm

$100°$

O 9 cm

$$\dfrac{100}{360} \times \pi \times 9^2 = 70.685\,83\ldots$$
$$= 70.686 \text{ cm}^2$$

Has the student answered the question fully?

7 Unit test

Active Learn
Homework

1   Here are a rectangle and a triangle.

$PR = 8\,\text{cm}$
$BC = PQ$
The perimeter of $ABCD$ is $26\,\text{cm}$.
The area of PQR is $14\,\text{cm}^2$.
Find the length of AB.   **(4 marks)**

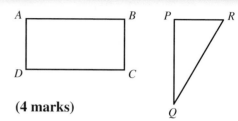

 2   A circle has diameter $90\,\text{cm}$.
Work out the circumference of the circle.
Give your answer correct to 3 significant figures.   **(2 marks)**

3   Work out
   a the area   **(1 mark)**
   b the perimeter of this trapezium   **(2 marks)**

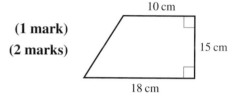

4   A trapezium of area $60\,\text{cm}^2$ has parallel sides of length $12\,\text{cm}$ and $8\,\text{cm}$.
What is the perpendicular distance between the two parallel sides?   **(3 marks)**

 5   The diagram shows a solid metal triangular prism.
The areas of two of the faces are marked on
the diagram.

The metal prism is melted and made into cubes.
Each of the cubes has side length $3.5\,\text{cm}$.
Work out the greatest number of these cubes that
can be made.   **(6 marks)**

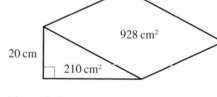

6   Sophie calculates V, the volume of a sphere.
The first two digits of her answer are
   9.2
Write down the error interval for V.   **(2 marks)**

 7   Calculate the perimeter of this shape.
Give your answer to 3 significant figures.   **(2 marks)**

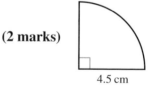

 8   **a** What is the area of a circle with radius $8\,\text{cm}$?
      Give your answer in terms of π.   **(1 mark)**

   b Dan draws a circle with double the area of the circle in part **a**.
      What radius does he use?
      Give your answer to a suitable degree of accuracy.   **(2 marks)**

 9   A cylindrical water tank holds 26 litres when full.
The water tank is $36\,\text{cm}$ tall.
Work out the radius of the tank to 2 decimal places.   **(4 marks)**

10 Calculate the volume of a hemisphere of radius 5.6 cm.
Give your answer to 3 significant figures.
(2 marks)

Volume of sphere $= \frac{4}{3}\pi r^3$

Surface area of sphere $= 4\pi r^2$

11 This solid is made from a cone and a cylinder of radius 4 cm.
Find the total surface area of the solid, including the base, in terms of π.
(4 marks)

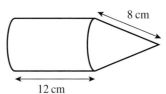

8 cm

12 cm

12 The perimeter of this sector is 16 cm.
Find the area of the sector.
(3 marks)

x

5 cm

13 The lengths of this square-based pyramid are given to 1 decimal place.
Calculate the upper and lower bounds for its volume. **(3 marks)**

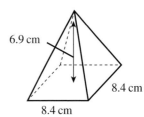

6.9 cm

8.4 cm

8.4 cm

14 The diagram shows a solid shape.
The shape is a cone on top of a hemisphere.

The total surface area of the shapes is $k\pi$ cm^2, where k is an integer.
Work out the value of k. **(4 marks)**

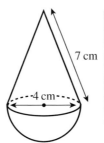

7 cm

4 cm

Curved surface area of cone $= \pi r l$

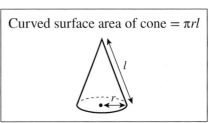

l

r

(TOTAL: 45 marks)

15 **Challenge** Sketch three copies of this net for a triangular prism.

a On one net, shade an area given by the expression ax.

b On the second net, shade an area given by the expression $(a+b)x$.

c On the third net, shade an area given by the expression $\frac{1}{2}bc$.

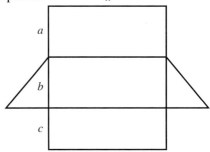

x

a

b

c

16 **Reflect** Look back at this unit.
Which lesson made you think the hardest? Write a sentence to explain why.
Begin your sentence with, 'Lesson _____ made me think the hardest because _____'.

Mixed exercise 2

Active Learn
Homework

1   Work out the size of the angle marked x.
    Give reasons for your answer.

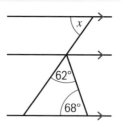

2   Here are some scatter graphs.
    A line of best fit is drawn on each graph.

      Graph A   **Graph B**   **Graph C**

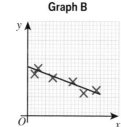
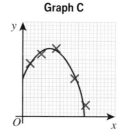

Which of these equations best matches each line of best fit?

  i $y = 20 - \frac{1}{2}x$ **ii** $y = -\frac{1}{2}x$ **iii** $y = \frac{1}{2}x + 20$

  iv $y = \frac{1}{x}$ **v** $y = 10x - 3x^2$ **vi** $y = 3x^2 + 10x$

Exam-style question

3   The diagram shows a cube and a cuboid.

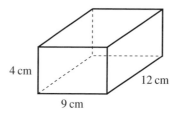

The total surface area of the cube is equal to the total surface area of the cuboid.
Ali says, 'The volume of the cube is equal to the volume of the cuboid.'
Is Ali correct? You must give reasons for your answer.   **(5 marks)**

---

4   **Problem-solving / Reasoning** The diagram shows two identical
    regular pentagons that overlap.
    Work out the size of angle a.

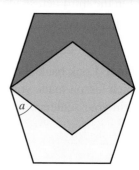

5 **Problem-solving** The diagram shows a solid triangular prism.
All of the measurements are given in cm.
The volume of the prism is $V\,\text{cm}^3$.
Show that $V = 5x^2 + 75x + 180$.

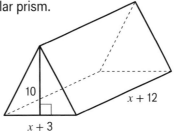

10

$x + 12$

$x + 3$

6 **Problem-solving** The diagram shows part of a regular decagon
and a line of symmetry.
Work out the size of angle x.

x

7 **Reasoning** P is the point with coordinates $(4, 5)$.
Q is the point with coordinates $(1, -1)$.
The straight line L goes through both points P and Q.
Is the line with equation $2y = 6x - 3$ parallel to line L? Give reasons for your answer.

8 **Problem-solving** The diagram shows a sphere and a solid cylinder.

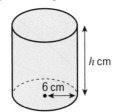

9 cm

h cm

6 cm

Surface area of sphere $= 4\pi r^2$
Volume of sphere $= \frac{4}{3}\pi r^3$

The total surface area of the cylinder is double the surface area of the sphere.
Work out the ratio of the volume of the sphere to the volume of the cylinder.
Write your ratio in the form $1:n$. Give your answer to 3 significant figures.

9 **Problem-solving** The diagram shows the line ABC with equation $y = \frac{1}{2}x + 3$.

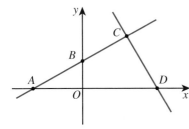

B is the midpoint of AC.
D is the point with coordinates $(10, 0)$.
Find an equation of the line CD.

10 The diagram shows a logo.
The logo is a grey semicircle with radius 7.5 cm with
a white sector with radius 5 cm.
Angle $AOB = 100°$
What percentage of the logo is grey?
Give your answer to 3 significant figures.

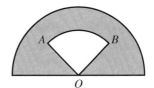

A B

O

11 **Problem-solving** The diagram shows a square $ABCD$ and a straight line CBN.

The equation of the line that passes through the points A and B is $y = 2x - 6$.

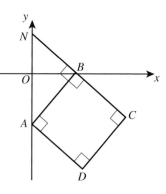

  a Find the length of BC.

     Give your answer in simplified surd form.

  b Find the length of AN.

12 The diagram shows points P, Q and R on the circle $x^2 + y^2 = 81$.

M is the midpoint of PQ.

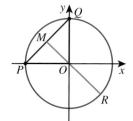

  a Work out the coordinates of P.

  b Work out the coordinates of Q.

  c **Problem-solving** What is the equation of the line segment MR?

Exam-style question

13 The diagram shows triangle XYZ.

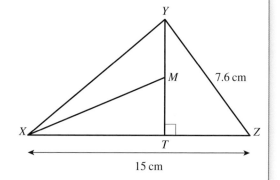

  XTZ and YMT are straight lines.

  $XZ = 15$ cm

  $YZ = 7.6$ cm

  The length of XT : the length of $TZ = 2:1$

  M is the midpoint of YT.

  Work out the size of angle MXT.

  Give your answer to 1 decimal place.

  You must show all your working.

                                  (4 marks)

Exam-style question

14 Here is a speed–time graph for a train journey between two stations.

The journey took 300 seconds.

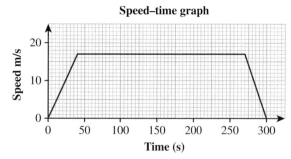

Speed–time graph

  a Calculate the time taken by the train to travel half the distance between the two stations.

    You must show all your working.   **(4 marks)**

  b Compare the acceleration of the train during the first part of its journey with the acceleration of the train during the last part of its journey.   **(1 mark)**

15 The volume of a sphere is 120 cm^3 correct to the nearest cm^3.
Calculate the surface area of the sphere to an appropriate degree of accuracy.

16 **Problem-solving** The diagram shows a square inside a circle.
All four vertices of the square lie on the circle.
The radius of the circle is 10 cm.
Work out the total area of the shaded regions.
Give your answer correct to 3 significant figures.

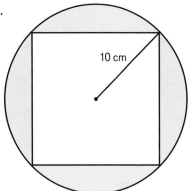

10 cm

17 The diagram shows a sector $OACB$ of a circle with centre O.
The point C is the midpoint of the arc AB.
The diagram also shows a hollow cone with vertex O.
The cone is formed by joining OA and OB.

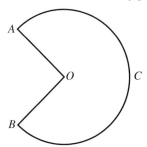
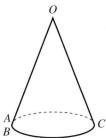

Volume of cone $= \frac{1}{3}\pi r^2 h$
Curved surface area of cone $= \pi r l$

The cone has volume 68.6 cm^3 and height 4.8 cm.
Calculate the size of angle AOB of sector $OACB$.
Give your answer correct to 3 significant figures.
You must show all your working.

(5 marks)

18 The straight line L_1 has equation $2x + y = 3$.
The point A has coordinates $(0, -2)$.
The straight line L_2 is perpendicular to L_1 and passes through A.
Line L_1 crosses the y-axis at the point B.
Lines L_1 and L_2 intersect at the point C.
Work out the area of triangle ABC.
You must show all your working.

(5 marks)

8 Transformations and constructions

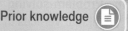
8.1 3D solids

ActiveLearn
Homework

* Draw plans and elevations of 3D solids.

Warm up

1 Fluency What are the dimensions of the top, side and front of this cuboid?

2 cm
4 cm
3 cm

2 Work out the length of the diagonal of the top face of the cuboid in **Q1**.

3 On an isometric grid, draw

   a a cube   **b** a cuboid   **c** a triangular prism.

4 Here is one plane of symmetry for a cuboid.
How many planes of symmetry does the cuboid have in total?

Key point

The **plan** is the view from above the solid.
The **front elevation** is the view of the front of the solid.
The **side elevation** is the view of the side of the solid.

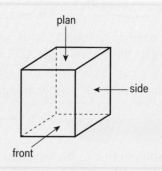

plan
side
front

Example

Draw the **plan, front elevation** and **side elevation** of this solid on squared paper.

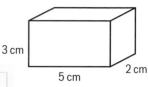

3 cm
5 cm
2 cm

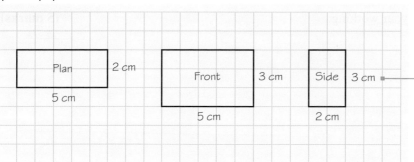

| Plan | 2 cm |
| 5 cm | |

Front 3 cm
5 cm

Side 3 cm
2 cm

Use a ruler.
Measure accurately.
Label the lengths.

5 On squared paper, draw and label the plan, front elevation and side elevation of these solids.

a

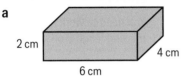

2 cm
4 cm
6 cm

b

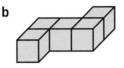

c

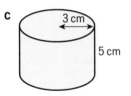

3 cm
5 cm

> **Q5c hint**
>
> You will need a ruler and compasses.

6 **Reasoning** Sketch the solids represented by these plans and elevations.

a

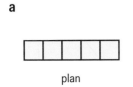
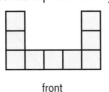

plan front elevation side elevation

b

plan side elevation front elevation

c

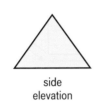
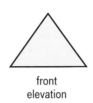

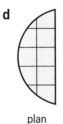

plan side elevation front elevation

d

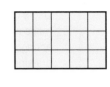

plan front elevation side elevation

7 **Reflect** What do the diagonals on the plan in **Q6c** represent?

8 **Problem-solving** Here is the side elevation of a 3D solid. Sketch three possible 3D solids it could belong to.

9 **Reasoning** The diagram shows a prism. Which of these shows the front elevation of the prism?

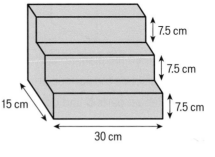

7.5 cm
7.5 cm
15 cm
7.5 cm
30 cm

A

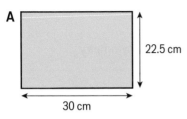

22.5 cm
30 cm

B

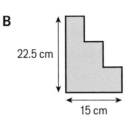

22.5 cm
15 cm

C

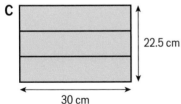

22.5 cm
30 cm

D

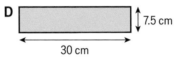

7.5 cm
30 cm

10 Problem-solving Make an accurate drawing of the front elevation, side elevation and plan of this solid.

Q10 hint

You need to work out the missing lengths on some faces.

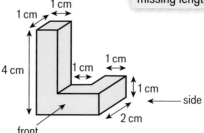

Exam-style question

11 The diagram shows a solid prism. On a centimetre-square grid, draw an accurate side elevation and front elevation of the prism. **(4 marks)**

Exam tip

Use a ruler and pencil, and make sure the lines are dark enough to be seen. When drawing the front elevation, you must include the horizontal line that shows the top edge of the front face.

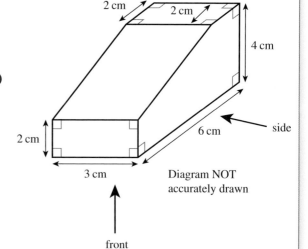

Diagram NOT accurately drawn

12 Problem-solving / Reasoning A cube has side length 4 cm.

a Calculate the surface area of the cube.

b The cube is cut in half along its horizontal plane of symmetry.

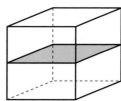

Sketch the plan, front elevation and side elevation of each of the new 3D solids.

c Calculate the surface area of each of the new solids.

d Repeat parts **b** and **c** for the cube cut along this diagonal plane of symmetry.

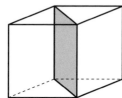

e Reflect Explain why the total surface area of the two half-cubes is not equal to the surface area of the original cube.

8.2 Reflection and rotation

- Reflect a 2D shape in a mirror line.
- Rotate a 2D shape about a centre of rotation.
- Describe reflections and rotations.
- Carry out and describe combinations of reflections.

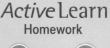 *Active* Learn
Homework

Warm up

1 Fluency

  a When you reflect a shape, are the original shape and the reflected shape congruent?

  b When you rotate a shape, are the original shape and the rotated shape congruent?

2 Draw a coordinate grid from -5 to $+5$ on both axes. Draw these straight lines.

  a $y = -3$ **b** $x = 4$ **c** $y = x$ **d** $y = -x$ **e** $x = 1.5$

Key point

Reflections and rotations are types of **transformation**.
Transformations move a shape to a different position.
An original shape is called an **object**.
When the object is transformed, the resulting shape is called an **image**.

3 Draw a coordinate grid from -5 to $+5$ on both axes.

  a Draw rectangle Q with vertices at coordinates (1, 1), (1, 3), (5, 3) and (5, 1).

  b Reflect rectangle Q in the x-axis. Label the image R.

  c Reflect rectangle R in the line $x = 1$. Label the image S.

  d Reflect rectangle S in the x-axis. Label the image T.

  e **Reasoning** Describe the single reflection that maps rectangle T to rectangle Q.

4 Draw a coordinate grid from -3 to $+3$ on both axes.

  a Draw triangle A with coordinates $(-1, -1)$, $(-1, 2)$ and $(2, -1)$.

  b Reflect triangle A in the line $y = 1$. Label the image B.

  c Reflect triangle A in the line $y = x$. Label the image C.

  d **Reflect** What do you notice about your answer to part **c**? Explain why this happens.

5 Draw a coordinate grid from -8 to $+8$ on both axes.

  a Draw triangle A with coordinates (1, 1), (1, 5) and (4, 5).

  b Rotate triangle A

    i 90° clockwise about (1, 1)   **ii** 180° about (1, 0)

    iii 90° anticlockwise about (0, 1)   **iv** 180° about $(-2, 1)$

    v 90° clockwise about (2, 5)   **vi** 180° about (2, 3)

    Label your results **i**, **ii** etc.

> **Q5b hint**
>
> Use tracing paper to help.

  c **Reflect** Explain why you don't need to give the direction for a rotation of 180°.

6 Look at the diagram.
   Which shapes are
   a reflections of P
   b rotations of P?

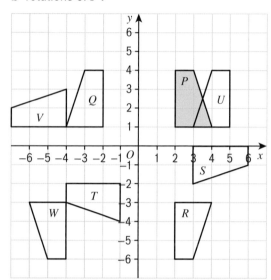

7 Look at the diagram in **Q6**.
   Describe fully the single
   transformation that maps
   a P to Q
   b P to R
   c P to S
   d P to T
   e P to U
   f P to V
   g P to W

Q7c hint

For a rotation,
trace the original shape.
Rotate the tracing paper
about different fixed points
with your pencil. Repeat
until your tracing ends up
on top of the image.

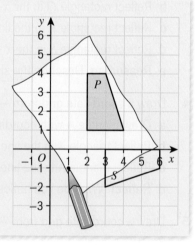

8 **Problem-solving** Describe fully the single transformation that maps

   a *A* to *B*

   b *A* to *C*

   c *D* to *E*

   d *D* to *F*

   e *G* to *H*

   f *H* to *I*

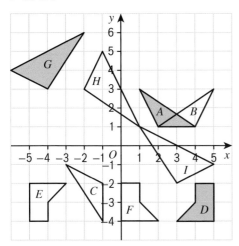

9 **Reasoning** Draw a coordinate grid from −5 to +5 on both axes.
Square *A* has vertices at (−1, 2), (−1, 4), (1, 4) and (1, 2).
Square *A* is reflected in the line *y* = *x* to give square *B*.
Square *B* is reflected in the line *y* = −1 to give square *C*.
Square *C* is reflected in the line *x* = 1.5 to give square *D*.
Describe fully the single transformation that maps shape *D* to shape *A*.

11 **Reasoning** 'A reflection in one axis followed by a reflection in the other axis is the same
as a rotation.'
Decide whether this statement is sometimes true, always true or never true.

8.3 Enlargement

Active Learn
Homework

• Enlarge shapes by fractional and negative scale factors about a centre of enlargement.

Warm up

1 Fluency

a What is the scale factor of the enlargement of shape A to shape B?

b Which vertex on shape B corresponds to F on shape A?

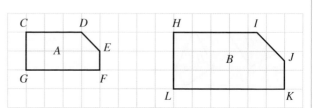

2 Copy and complete this diagram to draw an enlargement of triangle A with scale factor 3, centre (0,0).

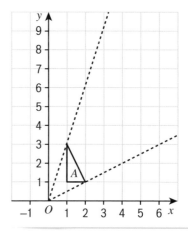

Key point

An enlargement is a transformation where all the side lengths of a shape are multiplied by the same **scale factor**.

3 Copy the diagram.
Enlarge the triangle by scale factor 2, with these centres of enlargement.

a (3, 5)

b (4, 3)

c (2, 2)

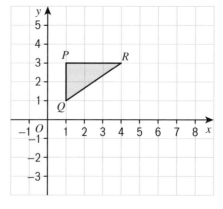

Key point

To fully describe a single transformation involving an **enlargement** on a coordinate grid, you must state it is an enlargement and give the scale factor and the coordinates of the **centre of enlargement**.

4 Triangle ABC has been enlarged to give triangle PQR.

a What is the scale factor of the enlargement?

b Copy the diagram. Join corresponding vertices on the object and the image with straight lines. Extend the lines until they meet at the centre of enlargement.

c Write down the coordinates of the centre of enlargement.

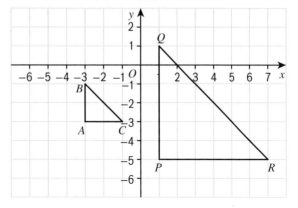

d Copy and complete to fully describe the enlargement from A to B.
Enlargement by scale factor ____ , centre (____ , ____).

5 **Problem-solving** Draw a rectangle A, with base 3 cm and height 2 cm.

a Work out the area of the rectangle.

b Shape A is enlarged by scale factor 2 to make shape B.
Work out the area of shape B.

c Shape A is enlarged by scale factor 3 to make shape C.
Work out the area of shape C.

Shape	Scale factor	Area of enlarged shape / Area of shape A
B	2	
C	3	
D	4	

d Shape A is enlarged by scale factor 4 to make shape D. Work out the area of shape D.

e Copy and complete the table.

f **Reflect** When a shape is enlarged by scale factor k, what happens to its area?

Key point

To enlarge a shape by a **fractional scale factor**, multiply all the side lengths by the scale factor.

6 Copy these diagrams. Enlarge each shape by the scale factor given.

a scale factor $\frac{1}{2}$

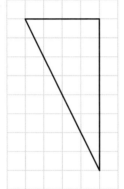

b scale factor $\frac{1}{3}$

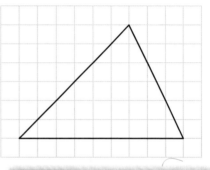

Q6b hint

Divide the base and vertical height by 3.

7 **Reflect** Describes what happens when, for scale factor k,

  a $k < 1$

  b $k > 1$

  c $k = 1$

8 **a** Copy and enlarge each shape by the given scale factor about the centre of enlargement shown.

> **Q8a hint**
>
> Multiply the distance from the centre to each vertex of the shape by the scale factor.

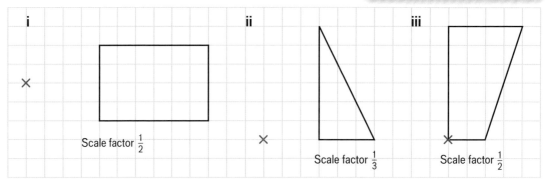

i Scale factor $\frac{1}{2}$

ii Scale factor $\frac{1}{3}$

iii Scale factor $\frac{1}{2}$

  b **Reasoning** When a shape is enlarged by scale factor $\frac{1}{2}$, what is its area enlarged by?

9 **Problem-solving** Draw a coordinate grid from −1 to 10 on both axes.
Draw a trapezium with vertices at (3, 2), (3, 10), (7, 10) and (7, 6).
Enlarge the trapezium by scale factor $\frac{1}{4}$, centre (−1, 0).

10 **Problem-solving** For each diagram, describe the enlargement that maps shape P to shape Q.

a
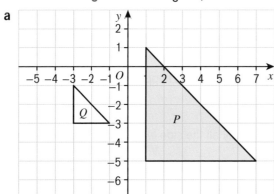

b
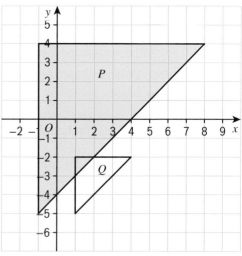

  c **Reflect** Explain how you can tell from the diagram that the transformation is an enlargement with a fractional scale factor.

Key point

A **negative scale factor** takes the image to the opposite side of the centre of enlargement.

Example

Enlarge triangle A by scale factor -2, with centre of enlargement $(-1, 2)$.

Mark the centre of enlargement.

Count the squares from the centre of enlargement to each vertex of triangle A.

Multiply by the scale factor and use the opposite directions:
- Instead of 1 down, 4 left , go 2 up, 8 right.
- Instead of 2 left, go 4 right.

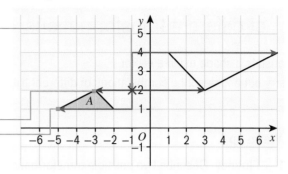

11 **Problem-solving** Draw a coordinate grid from -12 to $+12$ on both axes.
Join the points $(1, 2)$, $(4, 4)$ and $(4, 1)$ to make a triangle.
Enlarge the triangle by scale factor -2, with centre of enlargement

  a $(-1, 0)$ **b** $(-1, 3)$ **c** $(4, 4)$

12 Copy the diagram.

  a Enlarge shape T by scale factor $-\frac{1}{2}$, with centre of enlargement $(-2, 3)$. Label the image shape U.

  b Which vertex on shape S corresponds with each of these vertices on shape T?

    i A **ii** B **iii** C **iv** D

  c Explain how you can tell from the diagram that the transformation from shape T to shape S is an enlargement with a negative scale factor.

  d Describe fully the single transformation that maps shape S to shape T.

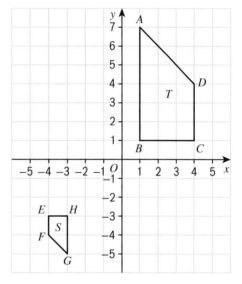

> **Q12d hint**
>
> Draw lines through corresponding vertices to find the centre of enlargement.

Exam-style question

13 Describe fully the single transformation that maps shape B to shape A.   **(3 marks)**

> **Exam tip**
>
> Notice the question asks for a single transformation. Also notice it asks for the map from shape B to shape A (not from shape A to shape B).

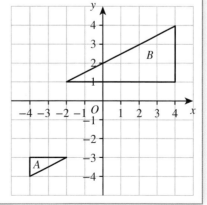

8.4 Translations and combinations of different transformations

Active Learn
Homework

- Translate a shape using a vector.
- Carry out and describe combinations of different transformations.

Warm up

1 Fluency Describe two possible transformations that could take shape A to shape B.

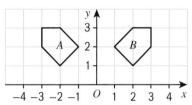

2 Describe the translation that takes each shape to its image.

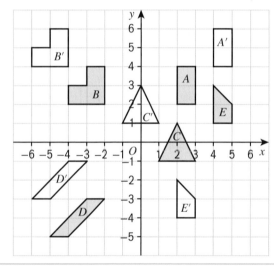

Q2 hint

☐ squares right/left,
☐ squares up/down.

Key point

In a **translation**, all the points on the shape move the same distance in the same direction.
You can describe a translation by using a **column vector**.

The column vector for a translation 2 squares right and 3 squares down is $\begin{pmatrix} 2 \\ -3 \end{pmatrix}$.

The top number gives the movement parallel to the x-axis.
The bottom number gives the movement parallel to the y-axis.

Translate triangle A by the vector $\begin{pmatrix} -3 \\ 2 \end{pmatrix}$.

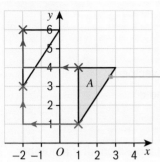

Move each point on the original shape 3 squares left and 2 squares up.

3 Copy this diagram.
Translate shape A by the vectors

a $\begin{pmatrix} 2 \\ 3 \end{pmatrix}$ to B

b $\begin{pmatrix} 3 \\ -4 \end{pmatrix}$ to C

c $\begin{pmatrix} -2 \\ 0 \end{pmatrix}$ to D

d $\begin{pmatrix} 0 \\ 3 \end{pmatrix}$ to E

e $\begin{pmatrix} -1 \\ -4 \end{pmatrix}$ to F

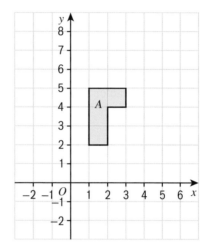

4 **Reasoning** Describe these translations using column vectors.

a B to A

b A to C

c B to E

d D to E

e E to D

f **Reflect** Describe how you can use your answer to part **d** to help you find the answer to part **e**.

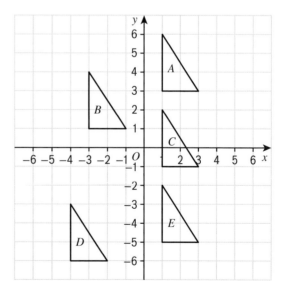

5 **Reasoning** A shape is translated by vector $\begin{pmatrix} a \\ b \end{pmatrix}$.
What vector would translate the shape back to its original position? Explain your answer.

6 Draw a coordinate grid from −6 to +6 on both axes.

  a Plot a triangle with vertices at (1, 1), (3, 1) and (1, −2). Label the triangle P.

  b i Translate triangle P by vector $\begin{pmatrix} 1 \\ 4 \end{pmatrix}$. Label the image Q.

    ii Translate triangle Q by vector $\begin{pmatrix} -2 \\ 1 \end{pmatrix}$. Label the image R.

  c Describe the translation of triangle P to triangle R, using a single vector.

  d Reflect Describe what you notice about the vectors in parts **b** and **c**

Key point

The **resultant vector** is the vector that moves the original shape to its final position after a number of translations.

7 Reasoning

  a A shape is translated by vector $\begin{pmatrix} 3 \\ 4 \end{pmatrix}$ followed by a translation by vector $\begin{pmatrix} 1 \\ -3 \end{pmatrix}$.

    What is the resultant vector?

  b What is the resultant vector for a translation of $\begin{pmatrix} a \\ b \end{pmatrix}$ followed by a translation of $\begin{pmatrix} c \\ d \end{pmatrix}$?

    Explain your answer.

Exam-style question

8 Shape A is transformed to shape B by a reflection in the line $y = -1$ followed by a translation $\begin{pmatrix} c \\ d \end{pmatrix}$

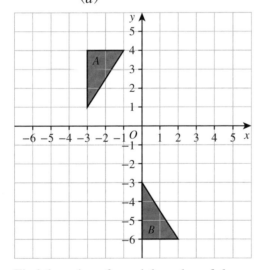

Exam tip

Deal with one piece of information at a time. Reflect triangle A in the line $y = -1$ first. Then work out the translation.

Find the value of c and the value of d. **(3 marks)**

9 a Draw a trapezium with vertices at (3, 2), (3, 4), (5, 4) and (6, 2). Label the trapezium P.

  b Reflect trapezium P in the line $y = 1$. Label the image Q.

  c Rotate trapezium Q 180° about point (1, −1). Label the image R.

  d Translate trapezium R by vector $\begin{pmatrix} 2 \\ 4 \end{pmatrix}$. Label the image S.

  e Reasoning Describe fully the reflection that maps trapezium P to trapezium S.

10 James rotates triangle P 180° about (1, 1) to get triangle Q.
He then reflects triangle Q in the line $y = x$ to get triangle R.
Arabee reflects triangle P in the line $y = x$ to get triangle S.
She then rotates triangle S 180° about (1, 1) to get triangle T.
Arabee says that triangle T should be in the same position as triangle R.
Is Arabee correct? You must show how you got your answer. **(3 marks)**

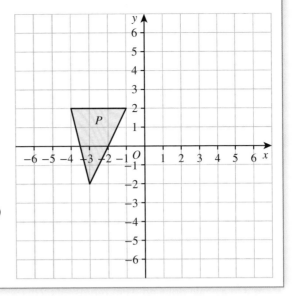

11 a Draw a triangle with vertices at (1, 2), (1, 5), and (3, 3) on a coordinate grid from −6 to +6 on both axes. Label the triangle V.

b Triangle V is reflected in the line $y = x$. Label this triangle W.

c Triangle W is translated $\begin{pmatrix} -4 \\ -2 \end{pmatrix}$ and then rotated 90° anticlockwise about point (−2, 2).
Show this combined transformation and label the final image X.

d Describe fully the single transformation that maps triangle V to triangle X.

12 Reasoning In **Q11**, one point on triangle V is invariant under the transformation that gives triangle W. Find the coordinates of this point.

13 Future skills A company has based its logo on a triangle.
Draw a coordinate grid from −6 to +6 on both axes.

a Plot the points (0, 0), (1, 2) and (2, 2) and join them to make a triangle.

b Reflect the triangle in the line $y = x$

c Draw more reflections to complete the logo.

d The company now wants to make a version of the logo 12 units tall, to go on a desk sign.
What transformation will convert the original logo into the larger one?

14 Reflect Adam says, 'A shape and its transformed image are always congruent.'
Do you agree with this statement?
If not, give a counter example and explain your answer.

Q14 hint

A counter example is an example where the statement is not true.

8.5 Scale drawings and bearings

- Draw and use scales on maps and scale drawings.
- Solve problems involving bearings.

Warm up

1 Fluency Find the size of each angle labelled with a letter.

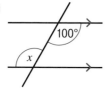 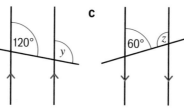 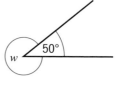

a   b   c   d

2 a On a scale drawing, 1 cm represents 2 m.
What does 10 cm on the drawing represent?

  b On a map, 1 cm represents 10 km. A road is 25 km long.
What is the length of this road on the map?

3 a Make an accurate scale drawing
of this triangular garden.
Use a ruler and protractor.
Use a scale of 1 cm to 1.5 m.

  b What is the perimeter of the
real-life garden?

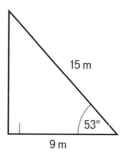

15 m

53°

9 m

Example

A map has a scale of 1 : 50 000.
What is the real-life distance in kilometres for 6 cm on the map?

> Map ratios have no units.
> 1 : 50 000 means that
> 1 cm represents 50 000 cm.

    Map   Real Life

      1 : 50 000
×6 ⎛   ⎞ ×6
      6 : 300 000

6 cm represents 6 × 50 000 = 300 000 cm
300 000 cm = 300 000 ÷ 100 = 3000 m   →   Convert cm to m.
3000 m = 3000 ÷ 1000 = 3 km   →   Convert to km.

4 Future skills Paul is using a map with a scale of 1 : 50 000.
He measures these distances.
What are the distances in real life? Write your answers in kilometres.

  a 10 cm   **b** 5 cm   **c** 2.5 cm   **d** 0.5 cm

5   **Future skills** The scale on a map is 1 : 200 000.

  a Copy and complete.
     Map : Real life
     1 cm : 200 000 cm = ☐ m = ☐ km

  b What is the distance on the map, in cm, for a real distance of
     i   20 km
     ii 10 km
     iii 8 km?

6   **Future skills** The scale on a map is 1 : 25 000.

  a On the map, the distance between two schools is 10 cm.
     Work out the real distance between the schools. Give your answer in km.

  b The real distance between two farms is 4 km.
     Work out the distance between the farms on the map. Give your answer in cm.

7   **Reasoning** Here is a map of part of a town.

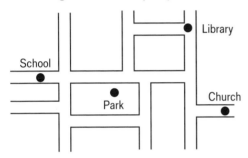

   The real-life distance between the school and the library 'as the crow flies' is 480 m.

  a Measure the distance between the school and the library.
     What scale has been used on the map?

  b From the map, estimate the distance as the crow flies between
     i   the church and the park
     ii the church and the school

  c John can walk 100 m in 40 seconds.
     How long will it take him to walk from the library to the school?
     Write your answer in minutes.

8   **Future skills** The diagram shows two satellites A and B detecting
    an aeroplane (C).

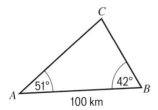

  a Make an accurate scale drawing using a scale of 1 : 2 000 000.

  b Work out the real distances AC and CB.

9 Write the bearing of B from A in each diagram.

a

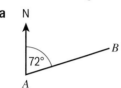

b

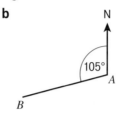

10 Plot a point A. Plot a point B on a bearing of 285° from A.

11 **Problem-solving** The distance between Manchester Airport and Luton Airport is 215 km.
The bearing of Luton Airport from Manchester Airport is 135°.
Make an accurate scale map of the locations of the two airports, using a scale of 1 cm to 40 km.

12 **Problem-solving** A plane is 80 km west of an airport.
The plane then flies on a bearing of 050° for 120 km.

  a Make an accurate scale drawing. Use a scale of 1 cm to 20 km.

  b What is the bearing of the airport from the plane?

  c How far is the plane from the airport?

13 **Problem-solving** A ship sails for 24 km on a bearing of 060°.
It then turns and sails for 18 km on a bearing of 160°.

  a Use a scale of 10 cm to 30 km to draw an accurate scale drawing of the journey of the ship.

  b How far is the ship from its starting point? Give your answer to the nearest kilometre.

  c On what bearing should the ship sail to return to its starting point?

Exam-style question

14 The diagram shows the
position of two boats, B and C.

Boat Q is on a bearing of 045° from boat B.
Boat Q is on a bearing of 260° from boat C.
Draw an accurate diagram to show the position of boat Q.
Mark the position of boat Q with a cross (×).
Label it Q.   **(3 marks)**

Exam tip

Use a sharp pencil. Draw angles
accurately.

15 The bearing of Palermo Airport from Paris Airport is 143°.

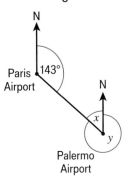

a Find angle x.

b Find angle y.

c Write the bearing of Paris Airport from Palermo Airport.

16 Problem-solving

a The bearing of B from A is 080°. Sketch a diagram. Work out the bearing of A from B.

b The bearing of C from D is 230°. Work out the bearing of D from C.

17 Problem-solving The diagram shows points A, B and C on a map.

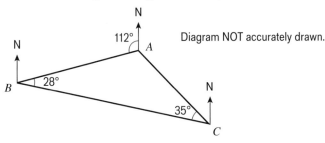

Diagram NOT accurately drawn.

Work out the bearing of A from C.

Exam-style question

18 The diagram shows the positions of three towns, Ashdale (A), Borton (B) and Carford (C).

Diagram NOT accurately drawn

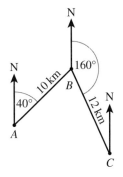

a Work out the bearing of A from B. **(2 marks)**

b Draw the diagram accurately using a scale of 1 cm to 2 km. Find

i the distance in km from C to A

ii the bearing of A from C

iii the bearing of C from A **(4 marks)**

8.6 Constructions 1

- Construct triangles using a ruler and compasses.
- Construct the perpendicular bisector of a line.
- Construct the shortest distance from a point to a line using a ruler and compasses.

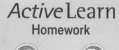

*Active*Learn
Homework

Warm up

1 Fluency What do these words mean?

  a perpendicular   **b** arc

2 Use a ruler and a protractor to make an accurate drawing of this triangle.

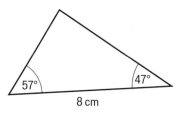

3 a Reasoning Make an accurate drawing of a triangle with these three angles.

  b Reflect Can you draw a different triangle with the same angles?

Key point

To **construct** means to draw accurately using a ruler and compasses.

Example

Construct a triangle with sides 11 cm, 8 cm and 6 cm.

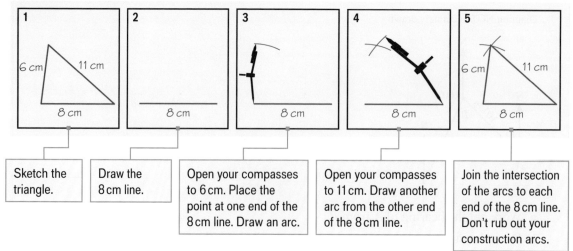

1	2	3	4	5
Sketch the triangle.	Draw the 8 cm line.	Open your compasses to 6 cm. Place the point at one end of the 8 cm line. Draw an arc.	Open your compasses to 11 cm. Draw another arc from the other end of the 8 cm line.	Join the intersection of the arcs to each end of the 8 cm line. Don't rub out your construction arcs.

4 Construct an accurate drawing of this triangle.

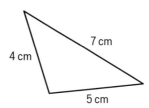

5 Sketch each triangle ABC and label the lengths.
Then construct each triangle.
  a $AB = 5\,cm$, $BC = 6\,cm$, $AC = 7\,cm$
  b $AB = 10\,cm$, $AC = 5\,cm$, $CB = 6\,cm$
  c $AB = 8.5\,cm$, $BC = 4\,cm$, $AC = 7.5\,cm$

6 **Problem-solving** Construct an equilateral triangle with sides 6.5 cm.
Check the angles using a protractor.

7 **Reasoning** By drawing suitable diagrams, explain why it is impossible to construct a triangle
with sides 6 cm, 4.5 cm, 11 cm.

8 The diagram shows the side elevation of a house roof.
Using a scale of 1 cm to 2 m, construct an accurate scale drawing of
this elevation.

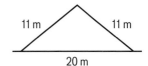

9 **Problem-solving** This chocolate box is in the shape of a tetrahedron.
Each face is an equilateral triangle with side length 24 cm.
Construct an accurate scale drawing of a net for the box.
Use a scale of 1 cm to 4 cm.

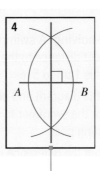

Key point

A **perpendicular bisector** cuts a line in half at right angles.

Example

Draw a line AB 9 cm long. Construct its perpendicular bisector.

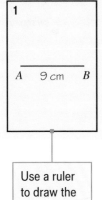

Use a ruler to draw the line.

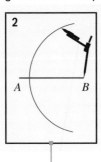

Open your compasses to more than half the length of the line. Place the point at B and draw an arc above and below.

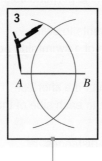

Keeping the compasses open to the same distance, move the point of the compasses to A and draw a similar arc.

Join the points where the arcs intersect. Don't rub out your construction arcs.

10 **a** Draw a line AB 7 cm long.
     Construct the perpendicular bisector of AB.

   b Use a ruler and protractor to check that it bisects your line at right angles.

   c Mark any point P on your perpendicular bisector.
     Measure its distance from A and from B.

   d **Reflect** Explain how you can find a point the same distance from A as from B.

11 **Problem-solving** Two jet skis, S and T, are 50 m apart. Jet ski S is north of jet ski T.

   a Using a scale of 1 cm to 5 m, draw an accurate scale drawing of the jet skis.

   b A lifeboat is equidistant from both jet skis. The lifeboat is less than 90 m from each jet ski.
     Construct a line to show where the lifeboat could be.

12 Follow these instructions to draw the perpendicular
   from point P to the line AB.

   a Draw a line segment AB and a point P above the line.

   b Open your compasses and draw an arc with centre P.
     Label the two points S and T where the arc intersects
     the line AB.

   c Construct the perpendicular bisector of the line ST.

   d **Reasoning** What is the shortest distance from P to AB?

13 Follow these instructions to construct the perpendicular at point P on a line.

   a Draw a line segment and point P on the line.

   b Open your compasses. Put the point on P and draw arcs on the line on either side of point P.
     Label the points X and Y where the arcs intersect the line.

   c Construct the perpendicular bisector of XY.

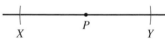

14 **Problem-solving** A swimmer wants to swim
   the shortest distance to the edge of a swimming pool.
   The scale is 1 cm to 5 m.

   a Trace the diagram and construct the shortest
     path for the swimmer to swim to each side of the
     swimming pool.

   b Work out the difference in the distances.

   c The swimmer swims 2 m every second.
     How long would the shortest distance take?

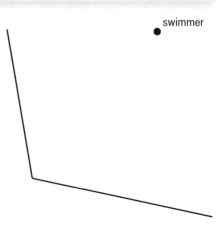

swimmer

8.7 Constructions 2

- Bisect an angle using a ruler and compasses.
- Construct angles using a ruler and compasses.
- Construct shapes made from triangles using a ruler and compasses.

Active Learn
Homework

Warm up

1 **Fluency** Use a protractor to draw an angle of 45°.

2 **a** Construct a triangle with sides 10 cm, 8 cm, 6 cm using a ruler and compasses.
   b What type of triangle have you drawn?

3 **a** Construct an equilateral triangle with side 5 cm using a ruler and compasses.
   b What is the size of each interior angle in your triangle?

Key point

An **angle bisector** cuts an angle exactly in half.

Example

Draw an angle of 80°.
Construct the **angle bisector**.

1   Draw an angle of 80° using a protractor.

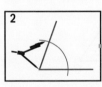

2   Open your compasses and place the point at the vertex of the angle.
Draw an arc that crosses both arms of the angle.

3   Keep the compasses open to the same distance. Move them to one of the points where the arc crosses an arm. Make an arc in the middle of the angle.

4   Do the same for where the arc crosses the other arm.

5   Join the vertex of the angle to the point where the two small arcs intersect.
This line is the angle bisector. Don't rub out your construction arcs.

4 For each angle
   i   trace the angle
   ii construct the angle bisector using a ruler and compasses
   iii check your two smaller angles using a protractor

a    b

5 **Reasoning**
   a What size is the angle bisector of a straight line?
   b Use a ruler and compasses to construct these angles.
      i   90°
      ii 45°
   c **Reflect** Compare the methods for constructing a perpendicular bisector from a point on a line (**Q13** in 8.6) and constructing the angle bisector of a straight line.
     What do you notice?

6 **Reasoning**
   a What 2D shape has 60° angles?
   b Use a ruler and compasses to construct these angles.
      i   60°
      ii 30°

7 **Problem-solving** Use a ruler and compasses to construct a 120° angle.

8 Follow these instructions to construct triangle PQR.
   a Draw line RQ and extend it beyond R.

   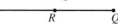

   b Use your method from **Q5** to construct a 90° angle at R.
   c Construct a 60° angle at Q, using your method from **Q6**.
   d Extend your line from Q to meet the vertical line from R.

   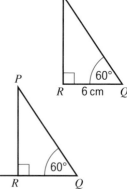

   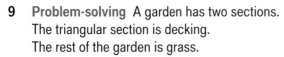

9 **Problem-solving** A garden has two sections.
   The triangular section is decking.
   The rest of the garden is grass.
   a Use a ruler and compasses to make a scale drawing of the garden.
     Use a scale of 1 cm to 4 m.
   b Calculate the area of the decking.

   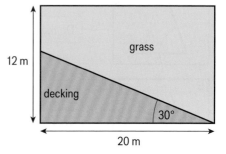

10 Problem-solving Four pairs of wires connect a flagpole to the ground.
The lower wire BD bisects angle ABC.

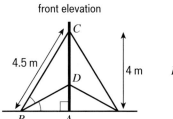

front elevation

4.5 m

C

D

4 m

B   A

plan

B ——— C

a Construct a scale drawing of the front elevation. Choose a suitable scale.

b Measure the length of the wire BD.

c How much wire is used in total?

11 Problem-solving

a Use a ruler, protractor and compasses to construct the triangle ABC.

b Construct a perpendicular line from C to AB.

c Calculate the area of the triangle to the nearest cm.

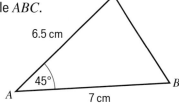

C

6.5 cm

45°

A   7 cm   B

12 a Construct a triangle with sides 5 cm, 8 cm and 10 cm.

b Construct the bisector of each angle.

c The three angle bisectors cross at the same point.
Label this point O.

d Construct the perpendicular to one of the sides from
the point you found in part **c**.
Label the point where the perpendicular meets the side, A.

e Draw a circle with radius OA.
What do you notice about your circle?

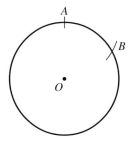

5 cm   8 cm

10 cm

13 Reasoning

a Draw a circle with centre O and radius 5 cm.
Mark a point A on its circumference.

b Keep the compasses the same size as the radius
and draw an arc from point A.
Label the point where the arc cuts the circle, B.

c Keeping the compasses the same, repeat from point B.
Repeat until you have six points on the circumference.

d Join the points and name the shape that you have drawn.

e **Reflect** What is the size of angle AOB? Explain why.

A

B

O

14 Problem-solving A regular octagon can be divided into eight congruent triangles.
Construct a regular octagon in a circle of radius 5 cm.

8.8 Loci

- Draw a locus.
- Use loci to solve problems.

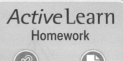

Active Learn
Homework

Warm up

1 Fluency Are all the points on the dotted line the same distance from the solid line?

2 Draw a small cross. Mark ten points which are 4 cm from it.
What shape do they make?

Key point

A **locus** is the set of all points that obey a certain rule. Often a locus is a continuous path.
A circle is the locus of a point that moves so that it is always a fixed distance from a fixed point.

3 A teacher asks some children to sit 5 m from her while she reads a story.
Sketch the locus of where the children sit.

4 Reasoning Draw a line 6 cm long.

  a Use compasses to draw points 3 cm from each end.

  b Draw the locus of all points which are 3 cm from the line.

5 Problem-solving The diagram shows a fenced area in a park.

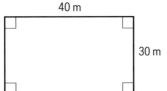

40 m

30 m

> **Q5 hint**
>
> Think carefully about what happens at the corners.

  a Draw a plan of the fenced area on squared paper. Use a scale of 1 cm to 5 m.

A runner runs round the outside of the fenced area, staying exactly 10 m from the fence.

  b Construct the locus of his path.

6 Reasoning

  a Draw two points 10 cm apart and label them A and B.

  b i Mark a point which is 5 cm from A and 5 cm from B.

    ii Mark two points which are 6 cm from A and 6 cm from B.

    iii Mark two points which are 7 cm from A and 7 cm from B.

  c Join the points with a straight line.

  d Reflect Can you use this line to show *all* the points that are equidistant from A and B?
Explain.

Key point

Points equidistant from two points lie on the perpendicular bisector of the line joining the two points.

7   **Problem-solving** A library is to be built equidistant from two railway stations, Arton and Borham. The stations are 2 km apart.
Using a scale of 1 cm to 250 m, construct the locus of the places where the library can be built.

Key point

Points equidistant from two lines lie on the angle bisector.

8   **Problem-solving** Clare wants to place a lamp in her living room so that it is equidistant from the two marked walls.

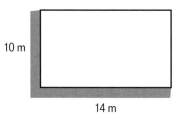

10 m

14 m

   a Copy the diagram using a scale of 1 cm to 2 m.

   b Construct the locus of the places where she can position the lamp.

9   **Problem-solving** Rectangle $ABCD$ is rotated 90° clockwise about D. Copy the diagram.

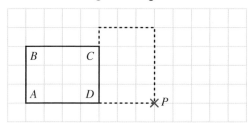

   a The rectangle is then rotated 90° clockwise about P. Add this to the diagram.

   b Draw the locus of vertex A.

   c Draw the locus of vertex B.

Example

A and B are two points 4 cm apart.
Shade the region of points that are less than 3 cm from A and less than 2 cm from B.

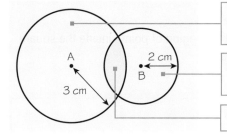

| Draw a circle at A with radius 3 cm. All the points inside this circle are less than 3 cm from A. |

| Draw a circle at B with radius 2 cm. All the points inside this circle are less than 2 cm from B. |

| Shade the region which satisfies both rules. |

10 **Problem-solving** Radio masts A and B are 120 km apart.
The bearing of radio mast B from radio mast A is 120°.
The radio masts each transmit a signal over a distance of 80 km.
Draw an accurate scale drawing of the radio masts using a scale of 1 cm to 20 km.
Shade the region which can receive signals from both radio masts.

11 P, Q and R are three points on a map. 1 cm represents 500 m.
Point T is 1.5 km from point P.
Point T is equidistant from point Q and point R.

×Q

×P

×R

a Trace the map.

b On your map from part **a**, show one of the possible positions for point T.

12 **Problem-solving** Make an accurate scale drawing of this garden.
Use a scale of 1 cm to 4 m.

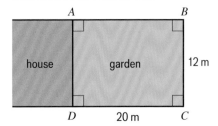

A tree can be planted between 10 m and 4 m from corner C.
It must be planted at least 14 m from the house.
Accurately shade the region where the tree could be planted.

13 **Problem-solving** Draw a square $ABCD$ with side length 8 cm on cm squared paper.
Shade the region that is less than 5 cm from A and closer to side AB than to side AD.

14 **Problem-solving**

a Draw a square $ABCD$ with side length 7 cm. Construct the region of points inside the square that are more than 3.5 cm from any vertex of the square.

b Calculate the area of this region.

Exam-style question

15 A graph $x^2 + y^2 = 16$ shows the boundary of the region covered by a fire engine, where x and y are in km.
What area does the fire engine cover? **(3 marks)**

8 Check up

Active Learn
Homework

Transformations

1 Enlarge this shape by scale factor $\frac{1}{3}$ with centre of enlargement S.

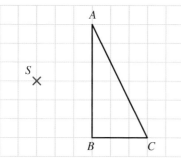

2 Describe fully the single transformation that maps

    a shape P to shape Q

    b shape Q to shape R

    c shape R to shape S

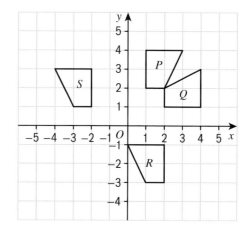

3 Describe fully the transformation that maps

    a shape A to shape B

    b shape A to shape C

    c shape B to shape D

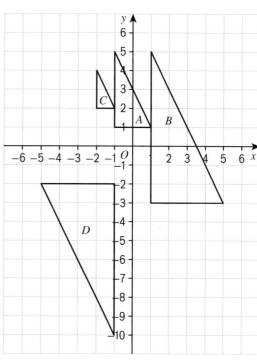

4 **a** Copy the diagram onto a coordinate grid from −6 to +6 on both axes.
Reflect shape A in the line $y = -1$.
Label the image B.

b Rotate shape B by $180°$ about point $(2, 0)$.
Label the image C.

c Translate shape C by vector $\begin{pmatrix} -6 \\ -2 \end{pmatrix}$.
Label the image D.

d Describe fully the single transformation that maps shape A to shape D.

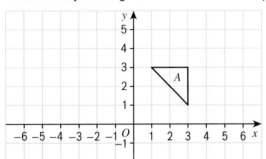

Drawings and bearings

5 Make an accurate drawing of the front elevation, side elevation and plan of this solid.

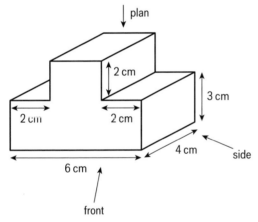

6 A map has a scale of 1 : 100 000. Two villages are 4 km apart.
Work out the distance between the two villages on the map.

7 The bearing of a ship from a lighthouse is $110°$.
What is the bearing of the lighthouse from the ship?

8 A plane flies 250 km from an airport on a bearing of $130°$.
The plane then turns and travels for 200 km on a bearing of $050°$.

a Using a scale of 1 cm to 50 km, draw an accurate scale drawing of the flight of the plane.

b Work out the distance of the plane from the airport.

c Find the bearing that the plane must travel on to return to the airport.

Constructions and loci

9 Draw a line AB 10 cm long.
Construct its perpendicular bisector using a ruler and compasses.

10 Trace this angle. Bisect the angle
using a ruler and compasses.

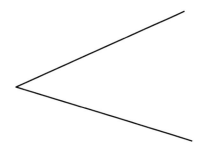

11 Three radio stations A, B and C can each transmit signals up to 100 km.
The diagram shows the distances between them.

   a Using a scale of 1 cm to 20 km, construct this
diagram accurately.

   b Shade the region that receives signals from all
three radio stations.

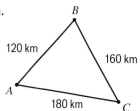

12 **Reflect** How sure are you of your answers? Were you mostly

Just guessing 😞   Feeling doubtful 😐   Confident 🙂

What next? Use your results to decide whether to strengthen or extend your learning.

Challenge

13 **a** Follow these instructions to construct a square.

     • Draw one side of your square, AB.

     • Extend this line segment through B.
Construct a perpendicular line through B.

     • Open your compasses to the length of AB.
With the point of your compasses at B, draw
an arc through the perpendicular line
to find vertex C.

     • Finally, set the point of your compasses at A
and then C, drawing an arc each time to locate
the final vertex of the square.
Label the intersection of these arcs D and draw in the remaining lines.

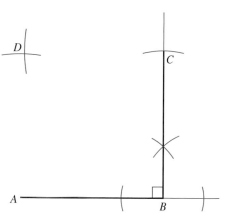

   b Draw a circle that passes through all four vertices of your square.

   c How could you use your square to construct a regular octagon?

8 Strengthen

Active Learn
Homework

Transformations

1 Joanne has started to reflect the triangle in the line $y = x$

  a Copy the diagram.

  b Turn the page so the mirror line is vertical. Then continue the reflection by reflecting each vertex in the mirror line.

  c Trace your completed diagram. Fold your diagram along the line $y = x$. What happens to the image and the object?

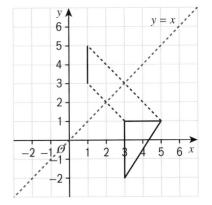

2 Draw a coordinate grid from −6 to +6 on both axes.

  a Plot and join the points (−1, 1), (−1, 4), (1, 4) and (1, 1).

  b Draw the lines

    i $y = -1$ **ii** $y = -x$

  c Use the method in **Q1b** to reflect the shape from part **a** in the line

    i $y = -1$ **ii** $y = -x$

3 Shape A is reflected to give image B.

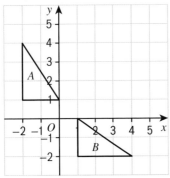

  a Join corresponding vertices on the object and the image and find the midpoints. Join the midpoints to find the mirror line.

  b Copy and complete. Shape A is reflected in the line $y = $ _____ to give image B.

4 Write these as column vectors.

  a 3 right, 2 up   **b** 5 right, 1 up

  c 2 right, 1 down   **d** 3 left, 2 up

  e 6 left, 2 down   **f** 3 right, 4 down

> **Q4 hint**
>
> The vector is $\begin{pmatrix} \text{horizontal movement} \\ \text{vertical movement} \end{pmatrix}$.
> Right → and up ↑ are positive.
> Left ← and down ↓ are negative.

5 a Copy the coordinate grid and shape A only.
Translate shape A by these vectors.

   i $\begin{pmatrix} 3 \\ 2 \end{pmatrix}$ Label the image B.

   ii $\begin{pmatrix} 2 \\ -1 \end{pmatrix}$ Label the image C.

   iii $\begin{pmatrix} -3 \\ 2 \end{pmatrix}$ Label the image D.

   iv $\begin{pmatrix} -6 \\ -3 \end{pmatrix}$ Label the image E.

b Choose one vertex on shape A.
Identify the corresponding vertex on shape F.
Describe the translation that takes the vertex
on A to the corresponding vertex on F.
Check this translation works for other
corresponding vertices on shapes A and F.

Q5a hint

Use your answers to **Q4** to help you.
Translate one vertex of shape A at a time.

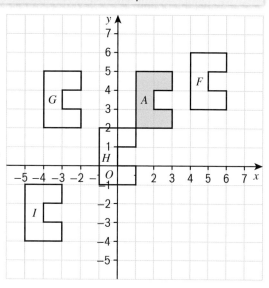

Q5b hint

You might choose the bottom right vertex on
shape A.
So identify the bottom right vertex on
shape F.

c Use the method in part **b** to describe the
translation that takes

   i A to G **ii** A to H **iii** A to I

6 Copy the diagram.

a Mark a centre of rotation at $(-1, 4)$.

b Trace triangle S and, with your tracing still in place,
put your pencil tip on $(-1, 4)$.

c When triangle S is rotated 90° anticlockwise
about $(-1, 4)$, the image is triangle T.
Turn your tracing paper to work out the position
of triangle T.

d Triangle S is rotated 90° clockwise to give
triangle U.
Use your tracing of triangle S to work out if A,
B or C is the centre of rotation.

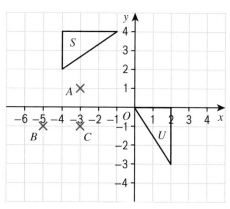

7 Describe the rotation that takes shape A to

a shape B

b shape C

c shape D

Q7 hint

Rotation of $\square°$ _____
about $(\square, \square)$.

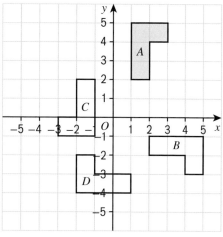

8 Fernando has enlarged rectangle R to give rectangle S.
Copy the diagram.

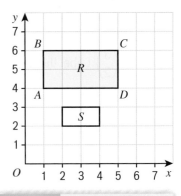

a A is the bottom left vertex of rectangle R.
Label the bottom left vertex of rectangle S with A'.

b Label the other corresponding vertices on rectangle S
with B', C' and D'.

c What is the scale factor of enlargement for
corresponding sides?

d Join corresponding vertices with straight lines.
Extend the straight lines till they meet.
This is the centre of enlargement.

Q8c hint

Length of AB × scale factor =
length of $A'B'$

e Copy and complete to describe fully the enlargement from
R to S.
Enlargement by scale factor ☐ with centre of enlargement
(☐, ☐).

9 Copy the diagram in the top right of a 20×14 square grid.

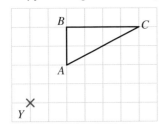

a Work out the distances from the centre of enlargement, Y, to each vertex.
The first one is done for you.
  A 2 right, 2 up B C

b Use your answer to part **a** to work out the distances from Y when

  i enlarging by scale factor $\frac{1}{2}$
    A 1 right, 1 up B C

  ii enlarging by scale factor -1
    A 2 left, 2 down B C

Q9b ii and iii hint

The negative sign tells you to
change direction.

  iii enlarging by scale factor -2
    A 4 left, 4 down B C

c Use your answers to part **b** to enlarge triangle ABC by

  i scale factor $\frac{1}{2}$ with centre of enlargement Y

  ii scale factor -1 with centre of enlargement Y

  iii scale factor -2 with centre of enlargement Y

10 Copy this diagram in the top right of a 22×14 square grid.
Enlarge the shape by scale factor -3
with centre of enlargement O.

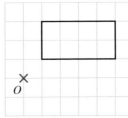

Q10 hint

Write down the distances from
the centre of enlargement to the
vertices of the rectangle.

11 Look at the diagram.

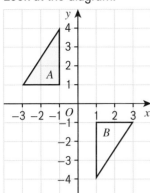

a Explain how you know that

   i triangle B is *not* a reflection of triangle A

   ii triangle B is *not* a translation of triangle A

b Explain how you can show that triangle B is a rotation of triangle A.

Q11a i hint

Trace triangle A. Fold your diagram along different horizontal and vertical lines, as well as $y = x$ and $y = -x$. Does A fit on top of B?

12 Copy and complete the list of information needed to describe:

Reflection   line of reflection

Rotation   _____ , _____ and _____

Translation   _____ and _____ (or _____)

Enlargement   _____ and _____

Drawings and bearings

1 Simeon starts to draw the plan and elevations of this solid. Copy and complete Simeon's drawings.

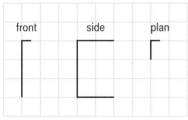

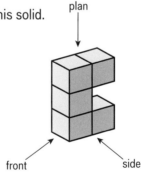

2 Look at the diagram of a solid.

  a Work out length a.

  b Work out length b.

  c Make an accurate drawing of the side elevation of this solid.

  d Reflect Here is the plan view for this solid.

    Explain what the line that splits the rectangle in two represents.

  e Make an accurate drawing of the front elevation of this solid.

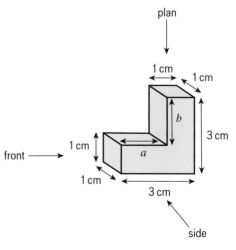

3 A map has a scale of 1 : 50 000.

    a Copy and complete. 1 cm represents _____

    b Copy and complete this double number line.

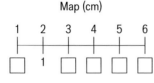

Real life (km)

    c What real distances do these map distances represent?

      i 2 cm   **ii** 5 cm   **iii** 12 cm   **iv** 8.5 cm

4 **Reasoning** The bearing of B from A is 115°.
Copy and complete the working to find the
bearing of A from B. Give the reason for each step.

$x = \square°$ (_____)

$y = 360° - x$ (_____) $= 360° - \square° = \square°$

Bearing of A from B is $\square°$.

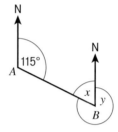

5 A ship sails 20 km from port on a bearing of 050°.
It then turns and sails for 30 km on a bearing of 160°.

    a Copy and complete the sketch of the ship's journey.

    b Make an accurate scale drawing using a scale of 1 cm to 5 km.

    c Draw a line to represent the shortest distance from the ship to the port.

    d Use your diagram to work out

      i how far the ship is from port, to the nearest km

      ii the bearing the ship needs to sail on to get back to port

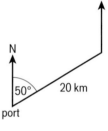

Constructions and loci

1 Follow the instructions to construct this triangle.

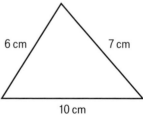

a Use a ruler to draw the 10 cm side accurately.

b The 6 cm side starts at the left-hand end of this line. Open your compasses to exactly 6 cm and draw an arc from the left-hand end of the line.

c Open your compasses to exactly 7 cm and draw an arc from the other end.

d Use the point where the arcs cross to create the finished triangle.

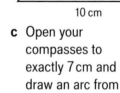

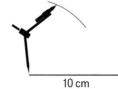

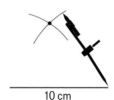

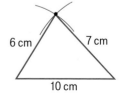

2 Construct this triangle.

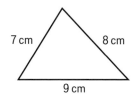

7 cm   8 cm

9 cm

3 Draw a line 12 cm long. Follow these instructions to construct the perpendicular bisector.

  a Draw the line. Open your compasses to more than half the length of the line.

  b Draw the first arc.

  c Draw the second arc.

  d Draw the perpendicular bisector.

12 cm

4 Draw a line 7 cm long. Construct the perpendicular bisector.

5 Use a protractor to draw an angle of 60°.
Follow these instructions to construct the angle bisector.

  a Draw the angle.

  b Draw an arc from the vertex of the angle.

  c Draw another arc between the two sides of the angle.

  d Draw a second arc.

  e Draw the angle bisector.

60°

6 Use a protractor to draw an angle of 100°.
Construct the angle bisector using a ruler and compasses.

Q6 hint

Remember this diagram

7 **a** Draw a dot in the middle of a blank piece of paper.
Draw as many dots as you can exactly 4 cm from your dot.

  b What shape have you created?

  c Copy and complete.
Points that are equidistant from a centre make a _____ .

8 Draw two crosses 6 cm apart. Label them A and B.

  a Mark all the points which are 4 cm from cross A.
Shade lightly the region that is less than 4 cm from A.

  b Mark all the points which are 4 cm from cross B.
Shade lightly the region that is less than 4 cm from B.

  c Shade darkly the region which is less than 4 cm from cross A and less than 4 cm from cross B.

Q8c hint

Shade darkly the region that has been lightly shaded from both A and B.

8 Extend

1 **Problem-solving** Triangle P with vertices at $(-1, 0)$, $(-1, 3)$ and $(1, 0)$ is transformed to give triangle Q with vertices at $(-1, 0)$, $(-1, -6)$ and $(-5, 0)$.
Describe fully the single transformation that maps triangle P to triangle Q.

2 **Problem-solving** Draw a coordinate grid from -4 to $+4$ on both axes.
 a Plot the points $A(1, 2)$, $B(3, 4)$ and $C(2, -1)$.
 b Reflect points A, B and C in the x-axis.
 c What do you notice about the coordinates of A, B and C when they are reflected in the x-axis?
 d Repeat parts **a** and **b**, reflecting in the y-axis.
 e What would be the coordinates of the point (p, q) if it was reflected in
  i the x-axis
  ii the y-axis
  iii the x-axis, then the y-axis?

3 **Problem-solving** Draw a coordinate grid from -4 to $+4$ on both axes.
 a Plot the points $A(1, 3)$, $B(-4, -2)$, $C(-1, 3)$ and $D(1, -2)$.
 b Reflect points A, B, C and D in the line $y = x$.
 c Reflect points A, B, C and D in the line $y = -x$.
 d What would be the coordinates of the point (p, q) if it was reflected in
  i the line $y = x$
  ii the line $y = -x$
  iii the line $y = x$, then the line $y = -x$?
 e **Reflect** Compare your answer to part **d iii** with your answer to **Q2e iii**.
  What do you notice?

Exam-style question

4 Quadrilateral A with vertices at $(2, 1)$, $(4, 1)$, $(3, 5)$, $(5, 5)$ is reflected in the x-axis to give image B.
Quadrilateral B is reflected in the y-axis to give image C.
Without drawing, work out the vertices of image C. **(3 marks)**

---

5 **Problem-solving** The point $S(4, 3)$ is reflected to give point T.
Point T is reflected to give point U. The coordinates of U are $(-3, 4)$.
Without drawing, find two combinations of reflections that could map point S to point U.

6 **Problem-solving** Draw a coordinate grid from -4 to $+4$ on both axes.
 a Plot the points $A(-1, 3)$ and $B(3, -1)$.
 b Work out the equation of line AB.
 c What is the gradient of a line perpendicular to AB?
 d Construct the perpendicular bisector of line AB.
  Check that its gradient matches your answer to part **c**.

7   The bearing of a ship from port is $a°$, where $0 < a < 180$.

    a Show that the bearing of the port from the ship is $(180+a)°$. **(2 marks)**

    b Work out the bearing of the port from the ship when $180 < a < 360$. **(2 marks)**

8   The diagram shows three sides of a regular hexagon. *ABP* is a straight line.
    The length of each side is 4 cm.

    a Work out the marked exterior angle.

    b Draw accurately sides *AB* and *BC*.

    c Continue in the same way to draw the hexagon.

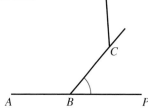

9   Here is a rectangle.
    Using a ruler and compasses, construct a triangle with the same
    area as this rectangle. **(3 marks)**

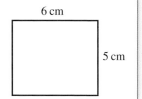

6 cm

5 cm

10 **a** A firework rocket reaches a height of 100 m before exploding in all directions to a distance of
        20 m. What 3D shape does the burst form?

    b What is the 2D shape of the burst as seen from the ground?

11 This solid is rotated 90° anticlockwise
    about a vertical axis of rotation.
    Draw an accurate plan, front elevation and side
    elevation of the rotated solid. **(3 marks)**

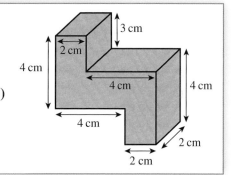

3 cm
2 cm
4 cm
4 cm
4 cm
4 cm
2 cm
2 cm

12 Draw a coordinate grid from −8 to +8 on both axes.

    a Plot the points $A(-5, 6)$ and $B(3, -2)$.

    b Find where the perpendicular bisector of AB intersects the graph $x^2+y^2 = 25$.

13 **Problem-solving** A ship *S* is 23.5 km from a port *A*,
    on a bearing of 307° from *A*.
    The ship is sailing on a bearing of 144° at a speed of 26 km/h.
    How long does it take, to the nearest minute, for the ship to
    reach a point *B*, the point on its path closest to port *A*?

    Q13 hint

    Draw a diagram showing points
    S, *A* and *B*. Triangle *SBA* will
    be right-angled at *B*. Work out
    angle *ASB* and use trigonometry
    to find the distance *SB*. Then
    work out the time.

8 Test ready

Summary of key points

To revise for the test:

- Read each key point, find a question on it in the mastery lesson, and check you can work out the answer.

- If you cannot, try some other questions from the mastery lesson or ask for help.

Key points

1 The **plan** is the view from above a solid.
The **front elevation** is the view of the front of the solid.
The **side elevation** is the view of the side of the solid. → **8.1**

2 **Reflections**, **rotations**, **translations** and **enlargements** are types of **transformation**.
Transformations move a shape to a different position.
An original shape is called an **object**.
When the object is transformed, the resulting shape is called an **image**. → **8.2, 8.3, 8.4**

3 To fully describe a single transformation

- involving a **reflection** on a coordinate grid, you must state it is a reflection and give the equation of the **mirror line**

- involving a **rotation** on a coordinate grid, you must state it is a rotation and give the angle, direction and **centre of rotation** (no direction is needed for a rotation of 180°)

- involving an **enlargement** on a coordinate grid, you must state it is an enlargement and give the scale factor and the coordinates of the **centre of enlargement**. → **8.2, 8.3**

4 An **enlargement** is a transformation where all the side lengths of a shape are multiplied by the same **scale factor**. → **8.3**

5 To find the **centre of enlargement**, join corresponding points of the object and the image. → **8.3**

6 To enlarge a shape by a **fractional scale factor**, multiply all the side lengths by the scale factor. → **8.3**

7 A **negative scale factor** takes the image to the opposite side of the centre of enlargement. → **8.3**

8 When a shape is enlarged the area increases by $(\text{scale factor})^2$. → **8.3**

9 In a **translation**, all the points on the shape move the same distance in the same direction. You can describe a translation by using a **column vector**.

The column vector for a translation 2 squares right and 3 squares down is $\begin{pmatrix} 2 \\ -3 \end{pmatrix}$.

The top number gives the movement parallel to the x-axis.
The bottom number gives the movement parallel to the y-axis. → **8.4**

10 The **resultant vector** is the vector that moves the original shape to its final position after a number of translations or other transformations. → **8.4**

11 In reflections, rotations and translations, the object and the image are **congruent**, as the lengths of the sides and the angles do not change.
In an enlargement, the object and the image are **similar**. → **8.4**

12 An **invariant point** on a line or a shape is a point that does not vary (move) under a single transformation or combined transformations. → **8.4**

13 A **bearing** is an angle in degrees, clockwise from north.
A bearing is always written using three digits, e.g. 090° or 127°. → **8.5**

14 To **construct** means to draw accurately using a ruler and compasses. → **8.6**

15 A **perpendicular bisector** cuts a line in half at right angles. → **8.6**

16 **Equidistant** means 'at equal distance'. → **8.6**

17 The shortest path from a point to a line is perpendicular to the line. → **8.6**

18 An **angle bisector** cuts an angle exactly in half. → **8.7**

19 A **locus** is the set of all points that obey a certain rule.
Often the locus is a continuous path. → **8.8**

20 A circle is the locus of a point that moves so that it is always a fixed distance from a fixed point. → **8.8**

21 Points equidistant from two points lie on the perpendicular bisector of the line joining the two points. → **8.8**

22 Points equidistant from two lines lie on the angle bisector. → **8.8**

Sample student answers

Exam-style question

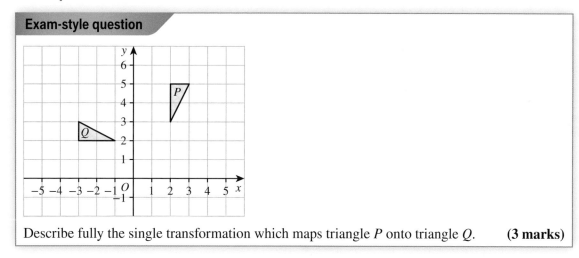

Describe fully the single transformation which maps triangle P onto triangle Q. **(3 marks)**

Here are three students' attempts to answer this question.

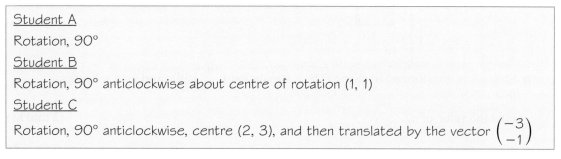

Student A
Rotation, 90°
Student B
Rotation, 90° anticlockwise about centre of rotation (1, 1)
Student C
Rotation, 90° anticlockwise, centre (2, 3), and then translated by the vector $\begin{pmatrix} -3 \\ -1 \end{pmatrix}$

Which student gives the best answer and why?

8 Unit test

*Active*Learn
Homework

1   The diagram shows the plan, front elevation and side elevation of a solid shape drawn on a centimetre grid.

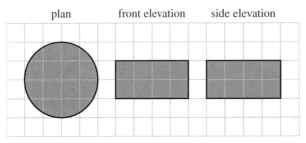

plan   front elevation   side elevation

Draw a sketch of the solid shape. Give the dimensions of the solid on your sketch. **(2 marks)**

2   Construct this triangle using a ruler and compasses.

(2 marks)

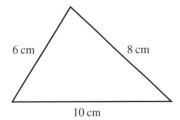

6 cm   8 cm

10 cm

3   **a** Describe fully the single transformation that maps

   i A to B

   ii B to C

   iii C to D **(7 marks)**

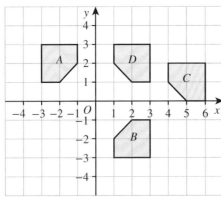

b Shape A is transformed to shape C by a translation $\binom{n}{-1}$ followed by a reflection in $x = 2.5$

Find the value of n.   **(2 marks)**

4 Copy this diagram.

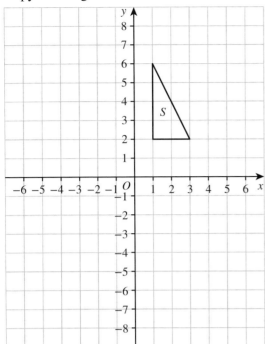

a Enlarge triangle S by scale factor $1\frac{1}{2}$ about point $(1, 0)$. Label the image T. (**2 marks**)

b Enlarge triangle S by scale factor $-\frac{1}{2}$ about point $(-1, -2)$. Label the image U. (**2 marks**)

5 Describe the enlargement from shape A to shape B.

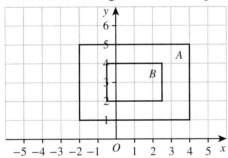

(**3 marks**)

6 Alistair's garden is in the shape of a trapezium.

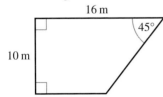

a Using a ruler and compasses, construct an accurate scale drawing of the garden.
Use a scale of 1 cm to 2 m. (**3 marks**)

b Find the perimeter of the garden. (**1 mark**)

7   *ABCD* is a square of side 10 cm.
    Work out the area of the region of points that are

    • more than 6 cm from *B* **and**

    • closer to *BC* than to *DC*   **(3 marks)**

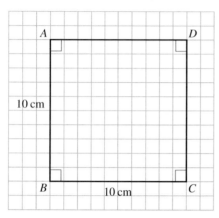

8   A map has a scale of 1 : 200 000.
    The length on the map is 4 cm. What is the real distance in km?   **(1 mark)**

9   A ship sails 120 km from the port on a bearing of 200°.
    The ship turns and travels for 160 km on a bearing of 040°.

    a Using a scale of 1 cm to 20 km, draw an accurate scale drawing of the path of
    the ship.   **(2 marks)**

    b What is the bearing that the ship must travel on to return to the port?   **(1 mark)**

10 A helicopter, *H*, is on a bearing of 255° from a ship, *S*.
    What is the bearing of the ship *S* from the helicopter *H*?   **(2 marks)**

11 Point (2, 3) is reflected in the *x*-axis and then in the line $y = x$
    Without drawing, write the coordinates of the image.   **(2 marks)**

                                                                (TOTAL: 35 marks)

12 **Challenge** Draw a coordinate grid from −5 to +5 on both axes.
    Join the points (1, 1), (1, 3) and (4, 1) to make triangle *M*.

    a Enlarge triangle *M* by scale factor −1 about the origin. Label the new triangle *N*.

    b What rotation also maps triangle *M* to triangle *N*?

    c Does this always work? Try other shapes.

13 **Reflect** In this unit, you have done a lot of drawing.
    Write down at least three things to remember when doing drawings in mathematics.
    Compare your list with a classmate.
    What else can you add to your list?

9 Equations and inequalities

Prior knowledge

9.1 Solving linear inequalities

Active Learn
Homework

- Solve inequalities and show the solution on a number line and using set notation.

Warm up

1 **Fluency** Which is true for $-2 < x < +2$?

A x lies between -2 and $+2$ but is equal to neither.

B x is greater than $+2$ and less than -2.

C x is greater than or equal to -2 and less than or equal to $+2$.

D x is equal to either -2 or $+2$.

2 Write the inequalities that these number lines represent for x.

a 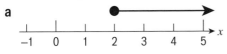 **b**

c

3 Solve to find x.

a $5 - 4x = 3$ **b** $4 - 2x = 6 - 3x$

c $4x = 2(2 - x)$ **d** $9 - 5x = 21 + x$

4 Write down the integers that satisfy each inequality.

a $-5 < x \leqslant 3$

b $0 < x \leqslant 4$

c $-3 \leqslant x < 3$

d $-2 < x \leqslant 1$

Exam-style question

5 **a** $-3 < n \leqslant 1$ where n is an integer.

Write down all the possible values of n. **(2 marks)**

b Write down the inequality represented on the number line.

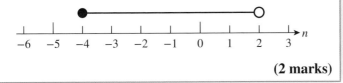

(2 marks)

Exam tip

The number line is labelled n, so use n in your inequality.

Key point

You can solve an inequality in the same way as you solve an equation.

6   Solve these inequalities, by rearranging to $x < \square$ or $x > \square$
   a $x + 2 > 3$ **b** $x - 1 < 0$
   c $3x + 1 > 4$ **d** $5x - 3 < 2$

Key point

You can write the solution to an inequality using **set notation**.

$$\{x : x > 2\}$$

the set of x such that

7   $\{x : x > 3\}$ means 'the set of all x values such that x is greater than 3'.
   Write the meaning of each of these sets.
   a $\{x : x < 2\}$ **b** $\{x : x \leqslant -2\}$
   c $\{x : x \geqslant 0\}$ **d** $\{x : x > -1\}$

Example

Solve $3x - 2 \geqslant 6 - x$
Write the solution set using set notation.

$3x \geqslant 6 - x + 2$ ── Add 2 to both sides.

$4x \geqslant 8$ ── Add x to both sides.

── Divide both sides by 4.

$x \geqslant 2$

In set notation: $\{x : x \geqslant 2\}$ ── This tells us that there is a set of values of x, not just one value.

8   Solve each inequality and show your answer on a number line.
   Write the solution set using set notation.
   a $4x > 12$ **b** $5x + 3 \geqslant 13$
   c $3x - 5 > 4$ **d** $2x + 3 \leqslant 7$

Exam-style question

9   $2x + 5 \geqslant 10$, where x is an integer.
   Find the smallest value of x.   **(3 marks)**

Exam tip

Use the inequality symbol on each line of your working.

10 Solve these inequalities and write the solution using set notation.
   a $3(x - 2) > 6$ **b** $4x - 5 \leqslant 2x + 9$
   c $2(x - 1) < 5x + 7$ **d** $2(3x + 4) > 4x - 3$
   e $3(4 - 2x) \leqslant 2(2x - 3)$ **f** $2(7 - 3x) \geqslant 6(3x + 1)$

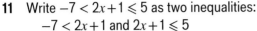

Key point

When inequalities have a lower limit and an upper limit, solve the two sides separately.

11 Write $-7 < 2x+1 \leqslant 5$ as two inequalities:
    $-7 < 2x+1$ and $2x+1 \leqslant 5$
    Solve each one separately.
    Then combine the solutions to $\square < x \leqslant \square$

12 Solve each inequality and write the solution using set notation.

    a $-5 < 2x+1 \leqslant 9$ **b** $-2 \leqslant \dfrac{2x}{3} \leqslant 6$ **c** $-1 < \dfrac{3x-1}{4} \leqslant 2$

Exam-style question

13 **a** Solve $10x < 7x+9$.   **(2 marks)**

    b On a copy of the number line below, show the set of values for which
    $$-3 < x+1 \leqslant 2$$
    (3 marks)

---

14 **Problem-solving** A ball thrown in the air travels at speed $s = (20 - 4t)$ metres per second, where t is the time after being thrown.
    For which values of t is the speed between $5\,\text{m/s}$ and $15\,\text{m/s}$?

15 **a** Multiply both sides of the inequality $5 > 3$ by -1.
        Is the inequality still true?

    b Divide both sides of the inequality $8 < 16$ by -2.
        Is the inequality still true?

    c **Reflect** Explain what happens when you multiply or divide an inequality by a negative number.

Key point

When you multiply or divide an inequality by a negative number, reverse the inequality signs.

16 Solve these inequalities.

    a $11 - x \geqslant 7$
    b $-3x < 9$
    c $6 - 5x \leqslant 2$
    d $-8 < -x < -2$
    e $-4 < -2x < 10$
    f $-8 < 4 - 3x \leqslant 10$

17 Solve these inequalities and write the solution using set notation.

    a $3(x+2) \geqslant 2x+3$
    b $-3 < 2x+1 \leqslant 9$
    c $-2 > 4(1-x) \geqslant -8$

18 Find the integer values of x that satisfy both of these inequalities.
    $4 - 3x < 5$ and $2x - 3 \leqslant 4$

9.2 Solving quadratic equations 1

- Rearrange and solve quadratic equations.
- Find the roots of quadratic equations.

Warm up

1 **Fluency** Write the two square roots of these numbers.

    a 100   **b** 144   **c** 49

2 Find two integers whose product is -12 and whose sum is 4.

3 Factorise

    a $x^2 - 5x$ **b** $y^2 - 4$ **c** $x^2 + 3x - 10$

Key point

Solving a quadratic equation means finding values for the unknown that fit.

4 Solve to find the value of z, following these steps.
    1 Rearrange each equation to make z^2 the subject.
    2 Square root both sides to find two possible values of z.
    a $3z^2 = 108$ **b** $2z^2 + 1 = 33$ **c** $4z^2 - 100 = 0$

5 Solve these quadratic equations.
    a $4x^2 = 64$ **b** $2x^2 + 3 = 101$ **c** $7x^2 - 175 = 0$

6 **Reasoning** Show that $x = -3$ is a solution of the equation $2x^2 - 3 = 15$

Example

Solve $x^2 + 2x - 8 = 0$

$(x + 4)(x - 2) = 0$ — Factorise.

So either $x + 4 = 0$ or $x - 2 = 0$ — The product of the factors is 0 so one or both factors equals 0.

$x = -4$ or $x = 2$ — Solve the linear equations.

Key point

You can solve equations of the form $x^2 + bx + c$ by factorising.

7 Solve

    a $x^2 - 10x + 24 = 0$ **b** $x^2 + 2x - 24 = 0$ **c** $x^2 + 10x + 24 = 0$

    d $x^2 + x - 30 = 0$ **e** $x^2 - x - 30 = 0$ **f** $y^2 + y - 2 = 0$

    g $y^2 + 3y + 2 = 0$ **h** $y^2 - y - 2 = 0$ **i** $y^2 - 3y - 10 = 0$

8 **a** Use this graph to solve the equation $x^2 + x - 6 = 0$.

   b Factorise $x^2 + x - 6 = 0$ to show that you get the same solution.

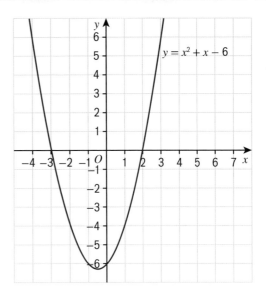

9 **Reasoning**

   a Show that $x^2 + 5x = 0$ is equivalent to $x(x+5) = 0$

   b Explain why $x(x+5) = 0$ implies that either $x = 0$ or $x + 5 = 0$

   c Show that $x = 0$ and $x = -5$ both satisfy the equation $x^2 + 5x = 0$

10 Solve

   a $x^2 + 7x = 0$ **b** $y^2 - 4y = 0$ **c** $2y^2 - 8y = 0$ **d** $12y + 3y^2 = 0$

11 **Reasoning**

   a Use this graph to explain why $x^2 - 4x + 4 = 0$ has only one solution.

   b Factorise $x^2 - 4x + 4 = 0$ to show that you get the same solution.

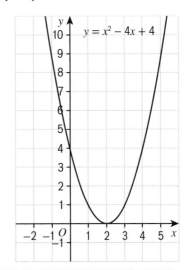

12 Solve

   a $x^2 - 6x + 9 = 0$ **b** $x^2 + 6x + 9 = 0$

   c $x^2 - 10x + 25 = 0$ **d** $x^2 + 14x + 49 = 0$

   e $x^2 + 22x + 121 = 0$ **f** $x^2 - 18x + 81 = 0$

Key point

The **roots** of a quadratic function are its solutions when it is equal to zero.

13 Factorise each function to find its roots.

   a $x^2 - 16$ **b** $4 - y^2$ **c** $x^2 - x$ **d** $x^2 - 2x$

   e $t^2 + 5t + 6$ **f** $2r - 8 + r^2$ **g** $12 - 7s + s^2$ **h** $m^2 + 3m - 10$

14 Solve

   a $x^2 + 7x = -6$ **b** $x^2 + x = 12$

   c $x^2 + 8 = 6x$ **d** $x^2 = 7x$

Q14a hint

Rearrange into the form $x^2 + \square x + \square = 0$

15 **Problem-solving** Write any function that has the roots $x = 4$ and $x = -6$.

9.3 Solving quadratic equations 2

ActiveLearn
Homework

- Solve more complex quadratic equations.
- Use the quadratic formula to solve a quadratic equation.

Warm up

1 Fluency What two values of x satisfy

 a $x^2 = 25$ **b** $x^2 = 64$ **c** $x^2 = 225$?

2 Solve

 a $x^2 + 4x + 3 = 0$ **b** $x^2 + 5x + 4 = 0$ **c** $x^2 - x - 6 = 0$

3 Expand and simplify

 a $(2x+1)(x+3)$ **b** $(3x-1)(x+2)$ **c** $(2x+2)(x-4)$ **d** $(4x-3)(x+4)$

4 Use your calculator to evaluate each expression.
 Give your answers correct to 2 decimal places.

 a $\dfrac{-3+\sqrt{28}}{6}$ **b** $\dfrac{5-\sqrt{12}}{10}$

5 Simplify

 a $\sqrt{24}$ **b** $\sqrt{28}$ **c** $\sqrt{40}$ **d** $\dfrac{-3+3\sqrt{2}}{3}$ **e** $\dfrac{-4+2\sqrt{3}}{4}$

6 a Reasoning Write and solve an equation to find x.

 b Reflect Explain why only one of the solutions is a value for x.

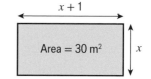

7 Problem-solving Rugs are rectangles of different sizes.
 A small rug has dimensions $a \times a$.
 A large rug has dimensions $2a \times (a+1)$.
 The area of the large rug is $12\,\text{m}^2$.
 What are the dimensions of the small rug?

Example

Solve $(x+2)^2 = 7$.

$x + 2 = \pm\sqrt{7}$ ← Square root both sides. $\pm$ means 'plus or minus'.

$x = -2 + \sqrt{7}$ ← $+\sqrt{7}$ gives one solution.

or $x = -2 - \sqrt{7}$ ← $-\sqrt{7}$ gives the other solution.

8 Write two solutions in surd form for each equation.

 a $x^2 = 5$ **b** $(x+1)^2 = 5$ **c** $(x-1)^2 = 5$ **d** $2(x-1)^2 = 5$

9 Solve $(x-3)^2 = 7$.

Give your solutions correct to 3 significant figures.

(2 marks)

Key point

A **quadratic expression** is in the form $ax^2 + bx + c$, where a, b and c are numbers.

10 Copy and complete to factorise $2x^2 + 3x - 5$.

a $a = 2, b = 3, c = -5$ — Compare with $ax^2 + bx + c$

$ac = \square$

b $\square \times \square = -10$

$\square + \square = 3$ — Find two factors whose product is ac and whose sum is b.

c $\quad 2x^2 + 3x - 5$

$2x^2 + 5x - 2x - 5$ — Use the two factors to split the x term.

Factorise each pair of terms.

d $x(2x + \square) - (2x + \square)$

e $(2x + \square)(x - 1)$ — Factorise.

11 For **Q10c** Casey wrote
Show that this expression
factorises to $(2x + 5)(x - 1)$.

$2x^2 + 3x - 5$

$2x^2 - 2x + 5x - 5$

12 Factorise

a $2x^2 + x - 3$ **b** $2x^2 + 5x - 3$ **c** $5x^2 + 7x + 2$

d $5x^2 + 11x + 2$ **e** $3x^2 - 17x + 10$ **f** $3x^2 - 11x + 10$

13 **a** **Reasoning** Show that the method used in **Q10** works to factorise $x^2 + x - 42$.

b **Reflect** Explain which method you prefer for factorising quadratic expressions $ax^2 + bx + c$ where $a = 1$, and why.

14 Solve

a $(2a + 5)(a - 8) = 0$ **b** $(2x - 9)(3x + 12) = 0$

c $(3y - 4)(2y + 5) = 0$ **d** $(4b - 3)(3b - 8) = 0$

15 **a** Copy and complete to solve $5x^2 + 15x + 10 = 0$.

$5x^2 + 15x + 10 = 0$

$5(x^2 + \square + \square) = 0$ — Take out the common factor.

$x^2 + \square + \square = 0$ — $5 \neq 0$, so $x^2 + \square + \square = 0$

$(x + \square)(x + \square) = 0$

$x = \square$ or $x = \square$

b Solve

i $4x^2 - 6x - 18 = 0$ **ii** $6x^2 + 9x - 15 = 0$ **iii** $4x^2 - 6x - 4 = 0$

16 Problem-solving Gerri has a patio that is $4\,\text{m} \times 5\,\text{m}$.
She has $10\,\text{m}^2$ of turf and wants to use it to make a border
round the patio that is the same width all round.

   a Write an equation for the area of the grass border.

   b Gerri uses all her turf. Solve to find x.

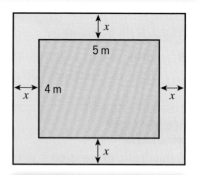

Key point

You can use the **quadratic formula** $x = \dfrac{-b \pm \sqrt{b^2 - 4ac}}{2a}$ to find the solutions to a quadratic equation $ax^2 + bx + c = 0$.

Example

Solve $x^2 + 4x + 2 = 0$. Give your solutions in surd form.

$a = 1, b = 4, c = 2$

> Compare with $ax^2 + bx + c$. Write the values of a, b and c.

$x = \dfrac{-4 \pm \sqrt{4^2 - 4 \times 1 \times 2}}{2 \times 1}$

> Substitute a, b and c into the quadratic formula.

$= \dfrac{-4 \pm \sqrt{8}}{2}$

> You are asked to give your solutions in surd form, so simplify the surd.

$= \dfrac{-4 \pm 2\sqrt{2}}{2} = -2 \pm \sqrt{2}$

The solutions are $x = -2 + \sqrt{2}$ and $x = -2 - \sqrt{2}$

> $+$ gives one solution and $-$ gives the other.

18 Solve these equations, giving your solutions in surd form.

   a $x^2 + 5x + 5 = 0$ **b** $x^2 + 7x + 2 = 0$ **c** $x^2 + 2x - 2 = 0$ **d** $x^2 - 2x - 6 = 0$

   e $3x^2 + 9x + 5 = 0$ **f** $3x^2 + 9x - 5 = 0$ **g** $3x^2 - 9x - 5 = 0$ **h** $5x^2 - 8x + 2 = 0$

19 Solve these equations using the quadratic formula. Give your solutions correct to 2 decimal places.

   a $x^2 + 6x - 10 = 0$ **b** $2x^2 - 5x - 6 = 0$ **c** $3x^2 + 2x - 2 = 0$

   d $2x^2 + 3x - 8 = 0$ **e** $8x^2 - 15x + 3 = 0$ **f** $6x^2 + 7x - 1 = 0$

20 a Rearrange $2x^2 - 7x = 15$ so the right-hand side is 0.

   b Solve your equation from part **a**

   i by finding factors of -15 **ii** by using the quadratic formula

   c **Reflect** Does it matter which method you use? When is it better to use the formula?

9.4 Completing the square

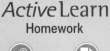
Active Learn
Homework

- Complete the square for a quadratic expression.
- Solve quadratic equations by completing the square.

Warm up

1 Fluency What is an integer?

2 Expand and simplify

  a $(x+4)^2$ **b** $(x-3)^2$ **c** $(2x+3)^2$ **d** $(x+2)^2+4$ **e** $(x+1)^2+7$

3 Which of these expand and simplify to give an x term of $2x$?

  A $(x+4)^2$ **B** $(x+2)^2$ **C** $(x+1)^2$ **D** $(x-2)^2$ **E** $(x-4)^2$

4 Simplify these surds.

  a $\sqrt{45}$ **b** $\sqrt{32}$ **c** $\sqrt{48}$ **d** $\sqrt{90}$ **e** $\sqrt{75}$

5 Solve these equations, giving your answers in surd form.

  a $(x+1)^2=7$ **b** $(x-3)^2=7$ **c** $2(x-3)^2=7$

6 Write a quadratic expression for the area of the large square.

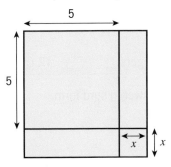

Key point

Expressions such as $(x+2)^2$, $(x-1)^2$ and $\left(x+\frac{1}{2}\right)^2$ are called **perfect squares**.

7 Write these as perfect squares, $(x+p)^2$

  a x^2+6x+9 **b** $x^2+8x+16$
  c $x^2+10x+25$ **d** $x^2-12x+36$

8 **a** Expand and simplify $(x+2)^2$

  b Write these expressions in the form $(x+2)^2+q$

    i x^2+4x+5

    ii x^2+4x+6

    iii x^2+4x-1

Write $x^2 + 2x + 7$ in the form $(x+p)^2 + q$, where p and q are integers.

$[x^2 + 2x] + 7$

$x^2 + 2x \equiv (x+1)^2 - 1$

So $[x^2 + 2x] + 7 = [(x+1)^2 - 1] + 7$

$= (x+1)^2 + 6$

So $p = 1$ and $q = 6$

> Separate the x terms from the number term.

> Find the perfect square that gives the correct x^2 and x terms, then subtract the number term to make the identity true.

> Substitute the identity into the original expression.

> Simplify the expression.

> Compare $(x+1)^2 + 6$ with $(x+p)^2 + q$ and write down the values.

Key point

$x^2 + bx + c$ can be written in the form $\left(x + \dfrac{b}{2}\right)^2 - \left(\dfrac{b}{2}\right)^2 + c$

This is called **completing the square**.

9 Write these in the form $(x+p)^2 + q$, where p and q are integers.

a $x^2 + 2x - 1$

b $x^2 + 8x$

c $x^2 + 12x$

d $x^2 + 6x + 11$

e $x^2 - 6x + 11$

Exam-style question

10 Write $x^2 + 14x - 1$ in the form $(x+a)^2 + b$, where a and b are integers. **(2 marks)**

11 Copy and complete to solve the quadratic equation, giving your answer in surd form.

$x^2 + 4x + 1 = 0$

$(x + \square)^2 - \square + 1 = 0$

$(x + \square)^2 = \square$

> Complete the square.

> Solve this equation.

12 Solve these quadratic equations, giving your answers in surd form where necessary.

a $x^2 + 2x - 5 = 0$ **b** $x^2 - 2x - 5 = 0$

c $x^2 + 6x + 7 = 0$ **d** $x^2 - 6x - 7 = 0$

e $x^2 + 8x + 9 = 0$ **f** $x^2 - 8x - 9 = 0$

13 Copy and complete to write the expression $3x^2 - 12x - 1$ in the form $a(x+p)^2 + q$.

$3x^2 - 12x - 1 = 3[\square - \square] - 1$

$= 3[(x - \square)^2 - \square] - 1$

$= 3(x - \square)^2 - 12 - 1$

$= 3(x - \square)^2 - \square$

> Take out $a = 3$ as a common factor of the x^2 and x terms.

> Complete the square for the expression inside the brackets.

> Simplify to $a(x+p)^2 + q$

14 Write these in the form $a(x+p)^2 + q$.

   a $2x^2 + 12x + 1$ **b** $2x^2 - 12x + 1$ **c** $3x^2 - 6x + 5$

   d $3x^2 - 6x - 5$ **e** $5x^2 + 10x + 25$ **f** $4x^2 + 12x - 7$

15 Solve these equations by completing the square.
   Give your answers in surd form.

   a $2x^2 - 12x + 7 = 0$ **b** $3x^2 + 12x - 1 = 0$ **c** $5x^2 + 10x + 3 = 0$

16 **a** Divide all the terms of $4x^2 - 8x - 16 = 0$ by the common factor of $4x^2$, $-8x$ and -16.

   b Solve the resulting equation by completing the square.
   Give your answer correct to 2 decimal places.

   c **Reflect** Which is more accurate, giving an answer as a surd or to 2 decimal places?

17 Solve these quadratic equations by completing the square.
   Give your answers correct to 2 decimal places.

   a $2x^2 + 4x - 8 = 0$ **b** $3x^2 + 6x - 10 = 0$ **c** $4x^2 + 6x - 5 = 0$

18 Copy and complete to solve the quadratic equation. Give your answer correct to 2 decimal places.

$$6x^2 + 3x - 1 = 0$$

$$6\left[\square + \tfrac{1}{2}x\right] - 1 = 0 \quad \longleftarrow \boxed{\text{Take out } a = 6 \text{ as a common factor.}}$$

$$6\left[\left(x+\tfrac{1}{4}\right)^2 - \dfrac{\square}{\square}\right] - 1 = 0 \quad \longleftarrow \boxed{\text{Complete the square.}}$$

$$6\left(x+\tfrac{1}{4}\right)^2 - \dfrac{6}{16} - 1 = 0$$

$$6\left(x+\tfrac{1}{4}\right)^2 - \dfrac{3}{\square} - 1 = 0 \quad \longleftarrow \boxed{\text{Simplify } \dfrac{6}{16}}$$

$$6\left(x+\tfrac{1}{4}\right)^2 = \dfrac{\square}{8} \quad \longleftarrow \boxed{\text{Collect like terms.}}$$

$$\left(x+\tfrac{1}{4}\right)^2 = \dfrac{11}{\square} \quad \longleftarrow \boxed{\text{Divide both sides by 6.}}$$

$$x + \dfrac{\square}{\square} = \pm\sqrt{\dfrac{\square}{48}} \quad \longleftarrow \boxed{\text{Square root both sides.}}$$

$$x = \sqrt{\dfrac{11}{48}} - \square \text{ or } x = -\square - \square$$

$$x = \square \text{ or } x = \square \text{ (to 2 d.p.)}$$

Exam-style question

19 Solve $6x^2 + 3x - 13 = 0$ by completing the square.
   Give your answer correct to 3 significant figures.

   (3 marks)

Exam tip

When you are told the method to use, make sure you use this method.

9.5 Solving simple simultaneous equations

Active Learn
Homework

- Solve simple simultaneous equations.
- Solve simultaneous equations for real-life situations.

Warm up

1 Fluency Which of these have the value 0 for *any* value of the variable?

A $-3y + (-3y)$ **B** $2y - (-2y)$ **C** $-4x + 4x$ **D** $-3z - (-3z)$

2 Rearrange these equations to make b the subject.

a $b - 12 = 2a$ **b** $2b + 6c = 10$ **c** $5a - 3b = 5$

3 Write an equation for each of these.

a The sum of x and y is 12.   **b** The difference between x and y is 4.

4 Draw graphs to solve these simultaneous equations.
$$x + y = 7$$
$$2x - y = 8$$

Example

Solve these simultaneous equations algebraically.
$$x + y = 6 \text{ and } 3x - y = 10$$

	$x + y = 6$	(1)
	$3x - y = 10$	(2)

Write the equations one above the other and number them.

(1)	$x + y = 6$
(2)	$3x - y = 10$
(1) + (2)	$4x + 0 = 16$
	$x = 4$

The y terms have opposite signs, so add the equations to eliminate them.

Solve to find x.

$$4 + y = 6$$
$$y = 2$$

Substitute the x-value into one of the equations and solve to find y.

$$x = 4, y = 2$$

Write both the solutions.

Check: $3 \times 4 - 2 = 10$ ✓

Check the solutions satisfy the other equation.

Key point

When there are two unknowns, you need two equations to find their values.
These are called **simultaneous equations**.

5 a Solve these simultaneous equations algebraically.
$$x + y = 7$$
$$2x - y = 8$$

b In **Q4** you solved these equations using graphs. Are your solutions the same?

6 Solve these simultaneous equations algebraically.
Start by adding the two equations to eliminate terms.

a $2x - y = 4$
$3x + y = 11$

b $x + 2y = 9$
$3x - 2y = -5$

c $-x + 5y = 4$
$x - 2y = 2$

d $2x + 3y = 0$
$-2x + 8y = 22$

7 Solve these simultaneous equations algebraically. First eliminate terms by adding or subtracting.

a $5x + y = 15$
$2x + y = 3$

b $2x + 3y = 18$
$-2x + 5y = 14$

c $3x + 2y = 10$
$3x - 4y = 16$

d $4x - y = 1$
$x - y = 7$

e $4x - 3y = 10$
$5x - 3y = 14$

f $4x - y = 0$
$2x + y = 3$

g $3y + x = 6$
$6y - x = -3$

h $4x - 3y = 4$
$12x + 3y = 8$

8 Problem-solving The sum of two numbers is 23 and their difference is 5.
Let the two numbers be x and y.
Write two equations and solve them to find the two numbers.

> **Key point**
>
> You can solve simultaneous equations by
> **Elimination** – making the coefficients of one variable the same in both equations, and then either adding or subtracting the equations to eliminate this variable
> **Substitution** – substituting an expression for x or y from one equation into the other equation.

9 Anthony solves simultaneous equations using this substitution method.

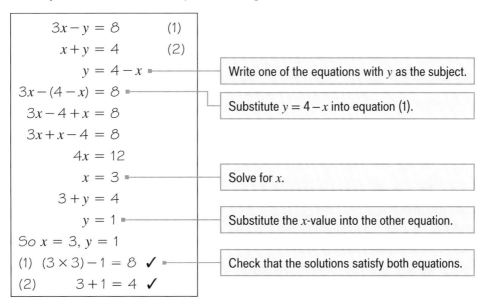

Solve these simultaneous equations using Anthony's method.

a $y = -6$
$3x + 2y = 30$

b $y = x + 3$
$x + y = 20$

c $y - 3x = 0$
$2x + 2y = 24$

d $2x - y = 0$
$5x + 4y = 26$

10 Problem-solving Two meals and a bottle of mineral water cost £29.
A meal costs £10 more than the bottle of mineral water.

a Let the cost of a meal be x and the water be y. Write an equation for the first sentence.

b Write an equation for the second sentence.

c How much is one meal?

d How much is a bottle of water?

11 Copy and complete to solve the simultaneous equations.

a $4x - 2y = 14$ (1)

     $3x + y = 18$ (2)

     $\times 2 \left(\right) \times 2$

     $\square x + 2y = \square$ (3)

b Add equations (1) and (3). Find x.

     $4x - 2y = 14$ (1)

     $\underline{\square x + 2y = 36}$ (3)

     $\square x + 0 = \square$

     $x = \square$

c Substitute your value of x into equation (1) to find y.

12 Use the method in **Q11** to solve these simultaneous equations.

  a $5x - 3y = 23$ **b** $3x + y = 4$ **c** $4x - 2y = 1$ **d** $3x + 2y = 3$

   $2x + y = 18$ $5x + 2y = 10$ $6x - 4y = 1$ $6x + 3y = 4$

Exam-style question

13 Solve the simultaneous equations

  $4x + 3y = 5$

  $2x + y = 3$ **(3 marks)**

Exam tip

Substitute your values of x and y back into each equation to check they fit.

---

14 $5x + y = 0$

  $x + 5y = 0$

  a First solve the simultaneous equations by multiplying the first equation by 5.

  b Solve by multiplying the second equation by 5.

  c **Reflect** Does it matter which equation you multiply?

15 Solve these simultaneous equations.

  a $3x - 2y = -12$ **b** $5x - 3y = 7$ **c** $6x + y = 6$ **d** $4x + 4y = 1$

   $x + 4y = 10$ $x + 6y = -25$ $10x + 2y = 11$ $2x - 8y = 8$

 16 **Problem-solving** Pete buys 2 lamb chops and 2 burgers and pays £7 for them.
At the same shop Jamie buys 3 lamb chops and 4 burgers and pays £11.
How much does a burger cost?

17 **Future skills** A telephone company charges £x per month for a basic line rental and
then £y per 100 minutes.
Justin pays £18 for 200 minutes. Teresa pays £21 for 300 minutes.

  a Work out the cost of the monthly rental.

  b How much would Caron pay for 400 minutes?

Exam-style question

18 5 teas and 4 biscuits have a total cost of £12.10.
3 teas and 2 biscuits have a total cost of £6.90.
Work out the cost of one tea and the cost of one biscuit.   **(4 marks)**

9.6 More simultaneous equations

- Use simultaneous equations to find the equation of a straight line.
- Solve linear simultaneous equations where both equations are multiplied.
- Write equations involving two unknowns to describe real-life situations, and then solve them.

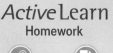

Active Learn
Homework

Warm up

1 **Fluency** What is the equation of a straight line?

2 Multiply each equation by 4.   **a** $2x + 3y = 6$ **b** $x - 6y = 7$

3 Solve these simultaneous equations.   **a** $y + 2x = 8$ **b** $3y + 2x = 14$
                                         $2y - 2x = 4$ $5y + x = 14$

4 Follow these steps to find the equation of the line through the points (2, 5) and (3, 8).

   a Write the equation of a line through (2, 5), by substituting $x = 2$ and $y = 5$ into $y = mx + c$.

   b Write the equation of a line through (3, 8).

   c Solve your simultaneous equations from parts **a** and **b** to find m and c.

   d Substitute your values of m and c from part **c** into $y = mx + c$.

5 Find the equation of the line through the points (6, −3) and (−2, 5).

Exam-style question

6 A is the point with coordinates (3, 11). B is the point with coordinates (d, 17).
    The gradient of line AB is 3. Work out the value of d.   **(3 marks)**

Key point

To solve simultaneous equations, you may need to multiply the equations by different numbers so that you can add or subtract to eliminate a variable.

Example

Solve these simultaneous equations. $5x + 2y = 16$
                                            $4x - 3y = -1$

(1) $5x + 2y = 16$ (1) × 3: $15x + 6y = 48$ (3)
(2) $4x - 3y = -1$ (2) × 2: $8x - 6y = -2$ (4)

> Multiply equation (1) by 3 and equation (2) by 2 to make the coefficients of y equal.

                (3) + (4): $23x = 46$

> Add the equations to eliminate y.

                         $x = 2$
               $10 + 2y = 16$

> Substitute the x-value into one of the original equations.

                     $2y = 6$
                       $y = 3$

> Write both the solutions.

$x = 2, y = 3$
Check: $4 \times 2 - 3 \times 3 = 8 - 9 = -1$ ✓

> Check the solutions satisfy the other equation.

7 Solve these simultaneous equations.
Give your answers as decimals where necessary.

a $5x + 3y = 13$
  $4x - 2y = 6$

b $3x + 2y = 13$
  $4x + 3y = 18$

c $4x - 7y = 1$
  $3x - 10y = 15$

d $2x + 5y = 24$
  $3x - 7y = -22$

e $4x + 1.5y = 7$
  $5x + 2y = 8$

f $3.6x + 5y = 28$
  $4.8x - 7y = 10$

g $2x + 5y = 19.6$
  $3x - 2y = 0.9$

h $5x - 3y = -11.25$
  $7x + 4y = -9.6$

8 **Problem-solving** Hire charges for a mini bus consist of £x fixed charge + y pence for each mile of the journey.
A hire for 20 miles costs £25.
A hire for 30 miles costs £30.
How much would a hire for 50 miles cost?

 9 **Problem-solving** Daniel pays for two children and four adults to go into a sports centre.
His friend pays for three adults and three children.
Daniel pays £9.20 for the tickets and his friend pays £8.40.
How much is an adult ticket and how much is a child's ticket?

 10 **Problem-solving** Amy buys two bananas and three pears in a shop and pays £1.95.
At the same shop Jacob buys three bananas and five pears and pays £3.05.
What is the cost of a pear? What is the cost of a banana?

Exam-style question
11 Solve the simultaneous equations $3x - 4y = 5.4$ $9x + 5y = 8.55$ **(3 marks)**

Exam tip

Number the equations and show any multiplying, adding or subtracting clearly.

12 **Problem-solving** A van can carry 300 kg.
Two possible maximum loads are 4 bags of cement and 7 bags of sand, or 6 bags of cement and 3 bags of sand.
What is the mass of a bag of sand? What is the mass of a bag of cement?

13 The diagram shows a rectangle with all measurements in metres.

a Write down a pair of simultaneous equations in a and b.
Rearrange your equations so that they are both $\square a + \square b = \square$

b Solve the equations.

c Give the dimensions of the rectangle.

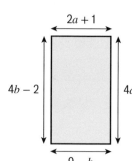

9.7 Solving linear and quadratic simultaneous equations

Active Learn
Homework

- Solve simultaneous equations with one quadratic equation.

Warm up

1 **Fluency** Which of these equations is

   a linear   **b** quadratic   **c** a circle?

$$x^2 - 4x + 2 = 0$$

$$y = 4 - 3x$$

$$x^2 + y^2 = 16$$

$$y + x = 4$$

2 Solve these quadratic equations.

   a $x^2 + 3x - 4 = 0$ **b** $2x^2 - x - 3 = 0$ **c** $6x^2 + 10x - 4 = 0$

3 Use the quadratic formula to solve these equations.
Give your answers correct to 2 decimal places.

   a $x^2 + 3x - 5 = 0$ **b** $3x^2 - x - 3 = 0$ **c** $2x^2 + 5x - 3 = 0$

Example

Solve these simultaneous equations.
$$2x + y = 3 \quad (1)$$
$$x^2 + y = 6 \quad (2)$$

$y = 3 - 2x$ ━━━ Rearrange the linear equation to make y the subject.

$x^2 + (3 - 2x) = 6$ ━━━ Substitute $y = 3 - 2x$ into the quadratic equation.

$x^2 - 2x + 3 = 6$

$x^2 - 2x - 3 = 0$ ━━━ Expand the bracket then rearrange so the right-hand side is 0.

$(x + 1)(x - 3) = 0$ ━━━

So either $x + 1 = 0$ or $x - 3 = 0$

$x = -1$ or $x = 3$ ━━━ Solve the quadratic equation by factorising.

$2 \times (-1) + y = 3$ ━━━ Substitute $x = -1$ into the linear equation to find one value of y.

$-2 + y = 3$

$y = 5$

$2 \times 3 + y = 3$ ━━━ Substitute $x = 3$ into the linear equation to find the second value of y.

$6 + y = 3$

$y = -3$

So the solutions are $x = -1$, $y = 5$
and $x = 3$, $y = -3$ ━━━ Write the pairs of solutions.

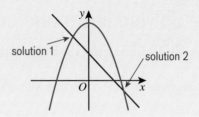
4 Solve these simultaneous equations.
Give your answers correct to 2 decimal places where appropriate.

a $y = x$
$x^2 + y = 12$

b $2x - y = 7$
$x^2 - 15 = y$

c $y - 4x = 6$
$y = 2x^2 + 3x + 5$

d $y = 5x - 3$
$y = 3x^2 + 6x - 7$

e $y + 3x = 8$
$y = x^2 + 2x + 4$

f $2y - 4x = 6$
$y = x^2 + x - 5$

5 **Reasoning** The diagram shows a sketch of the curve $y = 4(x^2 - x)$.
The curve crosses the straight line with equation $y = 4 - 4x$ at two points.
Find the coordinates of the points where they intersect.

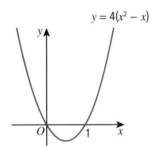

$y = 4(x^2 - x)$

6 Solve these simultaneous equations.

a $y = 2x^2 + x - 2$
$x + y = 2$

b $y = 4x^2 - x - 6$
$y = 2 - x$

c $y = x^2 + 6x + 5$
$y = 5 + x$

d $y = 3x^2 - 4x - 2$
$2x - y = 3$

e $y = 2x - 1$
$4x - y^2 = -13$

f $3y = x + 6$
$-2x + y^2 = 7$

7 **Reasoning** The diagram shows a rug laid on a wooden floor.
Its width is 2 m less than the width of the room.

a Write an equation to represent the width of the room (y).

b Write an equation to represent the area of the rug, which is $3\,m^2$.

c Use these two equations to find the value of x and hence the width of the room (y).

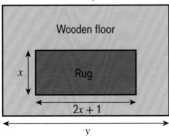

Wooden floor

x

Rug

$2x + 1$

y

8 **Problem-solving** A curve with equation $y = x^2 - 4x - 1$ crosses a straight line with equation $y = 2x - 1$ in two places.
Find the coordinates of the points where they intersect.

9 C is the curve with equation $y = x^2 - 6x + 6$.
L is the straight line with equation $y = 2x - 9$.
L intersects C at two points, A and B.
Calculate the exact length of AB. **(6 marks)**

10 **Reasoning** The diagram shows a circle of diameter 4 cm with centre at the origin.

a Write the equation for the circle.

b Use an algebraic method to find the points where the line $y = 2x - 1$ crosses the circle.

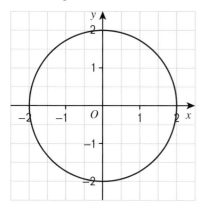

11 Solve these simultaneous equations.
Give your answers correct to 3 significant figures.

a $x^2 + y^2 = 28$
$y = x + 3$

b $x^2 + y^2 = 35$
$5x - y = -2$

c $x^2 + y^2 = 50$
$y - 2x = 3$

12 **a** On graph paper, draw the graph of $x^2 + y^2 = 6.25$. **(2 marks)**

b Hence find estimates for the solutions of the simultaneous equations
$x^2 + y^2 = 6.25$
$3x - y = 1$ **(3 marks)**

13 Solve algebraically the simultaneous equations
$x^2 - 3y^2 = 6$
$2x + 5y = 1$ **(5 marks)**

9 Check up

Inequalities

1 Find the possible integer values for x that satisfy the inequality $-10 < -5x \leqslant 25$.

2 **a** Solve the inequality $-3 < 2x - 3 \leqslant 6$.
   b Write the solution using set notation.

Quadratic equations

3 Write and solve an equation to find x.

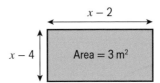

$x - 2$
$x - 4$
Area = $3\,\text{m}^2$

4 Solve
   a $x^2 + 3x = 0$ **b** $2x^2 + 2x - 12 = 0$

5 Factorise $3x^2 - 4x - 4$.

6 Use the quadratic formula to solve $x^2 - 2x - 6 = 0$.
   Give your answer in surd form.

7 Write $x^2 + 6x + 3$ in the form $(x + p)^2 + q$.

8 Solve $x^2 + 6x - 3 = 0$ by completing the square, giving your answer in surd form.

Simultaneous equations

9 Solve these simultaneous equations.
   a $2x + y = 12$ **b** $2x - 3y = 10$
        $3x + 2y = 17$ $3x + 2y = -4.5$

10 Find the equation of the straight line through the points $(4, 5)$ and $(0, -3)$.

11 Solve these simultaneous equations.
       $2x + y = 5$
       $x^2 + 2x = y$

12 **Reflect** How sure are you of your answers? Were you mostly

Just guessing 🙁   Feeling doubtful 😐   Confident 🙂

What next? Use your results to decide whether to strengthen or extend your learning.

Challenge

13 **a** My daughter's age in 3 years' time will be the square of her age 3 years ago.
     How old is she now?

   b Write a problem like this for a friend.
     Check that it works and that you can find the answer.

9 Strengthen

Active Learn
Homework

Inequalities

1 **a** Solve $-6 < 3x \leqslant 3$, by dividing each term by 3.

  b Solve $-8 \leqslant -4x < 12$, by

   i dividing each term by -4 and reversing the signs, $\square \geqslant x > \square$

   ii then rewriting in numerical order, $\square < x \leqslant \square$

  c Solve these inequalities, by dividing each term by -1.

   i $2 < -x \leqslant 5$ **ii** $-3 \leqslant -x < 2$ **iii** $-5 < -x \leqslant -1$

2 **a** Solve $2 < 3x - 1$

  b Solve $3x - 1 < 11$

  c Use your answers from parts **a** and **b** to write $\square < x < \square$
Find the possible integer values for x that satisfy $2 < 3x - 1 < 11$

3 Find the possible integer values for $4 < 2x + 5 \leqslant 9$.

> **Q3 hint**
>
> Follow the method used in **Q2**.

4 In set notation, $x \leqslant \frac{2}{3}$ is $\left\{ x : x \leqslant \frac{2}{3} \right\}$.
Write these inequalities in set notation.

  a $x > 4$ **b** $x < \frac{7}{8}$ **c** $0 \leqslant x < 3.5$ **d** $-2 < x \leqslant 5$

Quadratic equations

1 $x(x + 7) = 0$
This means that either $x = 0$ or $x + 7 = 0$.
Write two possible values of x.

2 **a** Factorise $x^2 + 5x$

  b $x^2 + 5x = 0$
Copy and complete.
This means that either $x = 0$ or $\square + \square = 0$
Write two possible values of x.

3 **a** Find two numbers whose product is -12 and whose sum is -1.

  b Use your answer to part **a** to factorise $x^2 - x - 12$.
$(x + \text{one factor})(x - \text{other factor})$

  c Solve $x^2 - x - 12 = 0$

4 Solve

  a $x^2 + 3x - 18 = 0$ **b** $x^2 - 7x + 12 = 0$ **c** $x^2 + 2x - 15 = 0$

5 **a** A rectangle is x cm long and $(x - 2)$ cm wide. Write an expression for its area.

  b A square has side $(x + 4)$. Write an expression for its area.

6 The diagram shows a rectangle.

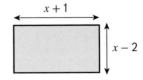

  a Write an expression for the area of the rectangle.

  b The area of the rectangle is $4\,\text{m}^2$. Write an equation for this.

  c Rearrange your equation so you have 0 on the right-hand side.

  d Solve this equation to find x.

7 **a** Write down the factor pairs of -6.

  b Try each factor pair in these brackets.
  $$(2x+\square)(x+\square)$$
  Which pair gives $2x^2+x-6$ when you expand?

  c Solve $2x^2+x-6=0$

8 Solve

  a $3x^2+5x-12=0$ **b** $3x^2-2x-8=0$

  c $4x^2-14x+12=0$ **d** $4x^2-19x+12=0$

9 A quadratic equation is in the form $ax^2+bx+c=0$, where a, b and c are numbers. What are the values of a, b and c in each of these equations?

  a $2x^2+3x+1=0$

  b $2x^2-4x-6=0$

  c $3x^2+4x-1=0$

10 What is the value of b^2-4ac for each equation in **Q9**?

11 Use the quadratic formula $x=\dfrac{-b\pm\sqrt{b^2-4ac}}{2a}$ to solve the equations in **Q9**.

12 **a** Expand

  i $(x+3)^2$

  ii $(x-5)^2$

  b Predict what the x term will be when you expand $(x+6)^2$

  c Expand to check your prediction.

13 **a** Copy and complete.
  $$(x+\square)^2=x^2+4x+\square$$
  $$(x+\square)^2-\square=x^2+4x$$

  b Write $x^2+4x=8$ as $(x+2)^2-\square=8$
  Simplify to $(x+2)^2=\square$

  c Solve your equation from part **b**.

14 **a** Copy and complete.
  $$(x-\square)^2=x^2-6x+\square$$
  $$(x-\square)^2-\square=x^2-6x$$

  b Solve $x^2-6x=9$ by completing the square.

Simultaneous equations

1 $3x + y = 10$
Find the value of y when $x = 2$.

2 For each pair of equations
   i copy the equations and circle the terms that have the same number in both
   ii if both circled numbers have the same sign, subtract one equation from the other; if the circled numbers have different signs, add the two equations
   iii find the values of x and y.
The first pair is started for you.

  a $2x + \textcircled{3}y = 7$ **b** $4x - 3y = 7$ **c** $5x - 2y = 13$ **d** $-3x + y = -7$
    $5x + \textcircled{3}y = 13$ $2x + 3y = 17$ $3x - 2y = 7$ $3x - 2y = 2$

3 For each pair of simultaneous equations
   i write down what you need to multiply equation (2) by, to get the same number in front of both y terms
   ii multiply equation (2) by this number to produce equation (3)
   iii solve equations (1) and (3)

  a $3x + \textcircled{2}y = 17$ (1)   **b** $5x + \textcircled{3}y = 26$ (1)
          $2x + y = 11$ (2) $2x - y = 6$ (2)
    $\times \square \, \big(\underset{\square + \textcircled{2}y = \square}{} \big) \times \square$ (3)

  c $7x - 5y = 9$ (1)   **d** $3x - 8y = 11$ (1)
     $3x + y = 7$ (2) $5x - 2y = 41$ (2)

4 Here are two simultaneous equations.
                                      $5x + \textcircled{2}y = 17$ (1)
  a What is the LCM of the two circled numbers?
                                        $4x + \textcircled{3}y = 15$ (2)
  b Multiply equation (1) so that the number in front of the y is your answer to part **a**.
  c Repeat part **b** for equation (2).
  d Solve your pair of equations from parts **b** and **c**.

5 Here are two simultaneous equations. $x^2 - 2x - y = 6$
                                                $5x + y = 4$

  a Rearrange $5x + y = 4$ to make y the subject.
  b Substitute your answer to part **a** in place of y in $x^2 - 2x - y = 6$
  c Simplify the equation by collecting the x terms.
  d Rearrange so the right-hand side is 0.
  e Solve the quadratic equation.
  f Substitute both values of x into $5x + y = 4$ to find both values of y.

6 Solve these simultaneous equations. $x^2 + 4x - y = 4$
                                             $y + x = 2$

9 Extend

1   The product of two consecutive positive numbers is 30.

   a Write this using algebra.

   b Solve your equation to find the two numbers.

> **Q1a hint**
>
> Use x for the first number.
> The next consecutive number is $x + \square$

 2 A lawn is 4 m longer than it is wide. The total area of the lawn is $30\,\text{m}^2$.
What is its perimeter? Give your answer correct to 2 decimal places.

3   Write $3x^2 + 2.4x$ in the form $a(x+p)^2 + q$. State the values of a, p and q.

 4 **Reasoning** The football pitch in the diagram has area $7140\,\text{m}^2$.
What are the dimensions of the pitch?

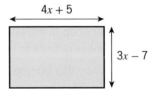

5   The diagram shows a 6-sided shape.
All the corners are right angles and all the measurements are in centimetres.
The area of the shape is $75\,\text{cm}^2$.

   a **Reasoning** Show that $2x^2 + 5x - 75 = 0$.

   b Solve the equation $2x^2 + 5x - 75 = 0$.

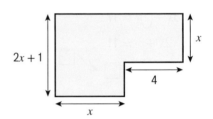

6   **Reasoning** The diagram shows a rectangle.
All sides are measured in centimetres.

   Jean says the perimeter of the rectangle is more than 75 cm.
Show that Jean is correct.

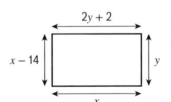

> **Q6 hint**
>
> Write two simultaneous questions and solve them.

Exam-style question

7   The straight line L_1 passes through the points with coordinates (2, 2) and (5, 11).
The straight line L_2 passes through the origin and has gradient -2.
The lines L_1 and L_2 intersect at point P.
Find the coordinates of P. **(4 marks)**

Exam-style question

8   The nth term of a sequence is given by $an^2 + bn$ where a and b are integers.
The 2nd term of the sequence is 8.
The 4th term of the sequence is 40.
Find the 6th term of the sequence. **(4 marks)**

---

9 **Reasoning** This trapezium has area $20\,\text{m}^2$.
The area of a trapezium is given by the
formula $A = \frac{1}{2}(a+b)h$.
Find the value of x.

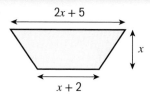

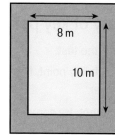

10 **Problem-solving** A pond is 8 m wide by 10 m long.
It has a path around it that is exactly the same width all round.
The area of the path is 80% of the area of the pond.
How wide is the path?

11 Solve these simultaneous equations.
$y = x+3$ and $x-2y = -1$

12 Solve $x-4 < 3x+6 \leqslant 9$.
Write the solutions using set notation.

13 a **Reasoning** Expand and simplify the left-hand side to show that
$(x+p)^2 + q = x^2 + 2px + p^2 + q$
b Jake uses this method to write $x^2 + 4x + 5$ in the form $(x+p)^2 + q$.

> $(x+p)^2 + q = x^2 + 2px + p^2 + q = x^2 + 4x + 5$
> Comparing the x terms: $2px = 4x$ so $2p = 4$, $p = 2$
> Comparing number terms: $p^2 + q = 5$
> $\qquad\qquad\qquad\qquad\quad 4 + q = 5$
> $\qquad\qquad\qquad\qquad\qquad\; q = 1$
> So $(x+p)^2 + q = (x+2)^2 + 1$

Use Jake's method to write these expressions in the form $(x+p)^2 + q$
i $x^2 + 6x + 15$ **ii** $x^2 + 8x - 3$ **iii** $x^2 - 4x + 2$ **iv** $x^2 + 3x + 7$

Exam-style question

14 The table shows some values
of x and y that satisfy the equation
$y = a\sin x° + b$
Find the value of y when $x = 45$.

x	0	30	60	90	120	150	180
y	3	4	$\sqrt{3}+3$	5	$\sqrt{3}+3$	4	3

(4 marks)

Working towards A level

15 Given that $x^2 - bx + 9a \equiv (x-2a)^2 + 5$, work out the **two** pairs of values of a and b.

> In some A level questions it isn't immediately obvious
> what strategy to use.

Q15 hint

In an identity the algebraic expressions on
both sides are equivalent. The coefficients
of like terms are equal. Set up equations
in a and b and solve them simultaneously.

16 a Factorise $y^2 - 13y + 36$.

b By factorising fully, simplify $\dfrac{x^4 + x^3 - 6x^2}{x^4 - 13x^2 + 36}$

> At A level, the answer to one part of a question is
> often linked to a later part. Here the answer to part **a** is
> directly related to factorising the denominator in part **b**.

Q16b hint

The denominator is a quadratic in x^2, so
replace y in the factors from part **a** by x^2.

9 Test ready

Summary of key points

To revise for the test:

- Read each key point, find a question on it in the mastery lesson, and check you can work out the answer.

- If you cannot, try some other questions from the mastery lesson or ask for help.

Key points

1 You can solve an inequality in the same way as you solve an equation. → **9.1**

2 You can write the solution to an inequality using **set notation**. $\{x : x > 2\}$

the set of x such that → **9.1**

3 When inequalities have a lower limit and an upper limit, solve the two sides separately. → **9.1**

4 When you multiply or divide an inequality by a negative number, reverse the inequality signs. → **9.1**

5 **Solving** a quadratic equation means finding values for the unknown that fit. → **9.2**

6 You can solve equations of the form $ax^2 + bx + c$ by factorising. → **9.2**

7 The **roots** of a quadratic function are its solutions when it is equal to zero. → **9.2**

8 A **quadratic expression** is in the form $ax^2 + bx + c$, where a, b and c are numbers. → **9.3**

9 You can use the **quadratic formula**

$$x = \frac{-b \pm \sqrt{b^2 - 4ac}}{2a}$$

to find the solutions to a quadratic equation $ax^2 + bx + c = 0$ → **9.3**

10 Expressions such as $(x + 2)^2$, $(x - 1)^2$ and $\left(x + \frac{1}{2}\right)^2$ are called **perfect squares**. → **9.4**

11 $x^2 + bx + c$ can be written in the form $\left(x + \frac{b}{2}\right)^2 - \left(\frac{b}{2}\right)^2 + c$

This is called **completing the square**. → **9.4**

12 $ax^2 + bx + c$ can be written as $a\left(x^2 + \frac{b}{a}x\right) + c$ before completing the square for the expression inside the brackets. → **9.4**

13 When there are two unknowns, you need two equations to find their values. These are called **simultaneous equations**. → **9.5**

14 You can solve simultaneous equations by
Elimination – making the coefficients of one variable the same in both equations, and then either adding or subtracting the equations to eliminate this variable.
Substitution – substituting an expression for x or y from one equation into the other equation. → **9.5**

15 To solve simultaneous equations, you may need to multiply the equations by different numbers so that you can add or subtract to eliminate a variable. → **9.6**

16 A pair of quadratic and linear simultaneous
    equations can have two possible solutions.

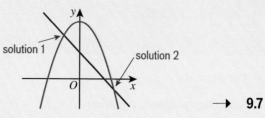

→ 9.7

17 To find the coordinates where two graphs intersect,
    solve their equations simultaneously.

→ 9.7

Sample student answers

Exam-style question

Solve algebraically the simultaneous equations
$$x^2 + y^2 = 41$$
$$y - 2x = 14$$

(5 marks)

Three students' attempts to answer the question are shown.

Student A
$$x^2 + y^2 = 41$$
$$x + y = \sqrt{41}$$

Student B
$$y = 2x + 14$$
$$x^2 + (2x + 14)^2 = 41$$
$$x^2 + 4x^2 + 196 = 41$$

Student C
$$y = 2x + 14$$
$$x^2 + (2x + 14)^2 = 41$$
$$x^2 + 4x^2 + 56x + 196 - 41 = 0$$
$$5x^2 + 56x + 155 = 0$$
$$x = \frac{-56 \pm \sqrt{56^2 - 4 \times 5 \times 155}}{10} = -5 \text{ or } -\frac{31}{5}$$

---

a Explain what Students A and B have done wrong.

b Why is Student C unlikely to gain full marks?

9 Unit test

1 Factorise $9x^2 - 3x - 2$. **(2 marks)**

2 Solve the quadratic equation $15 = 2x^2 - 7x$. **(3 marks)**

3 **a** One side of a rectangular room is $2\,m$ longer than the other side.
   Write the area of the room as an expression in x (the length of the shorter side). **(1 mark)**

   b The area of the room is $15\,m^2$. What is the value of x? **(3 marks)**

4 Solve the equation $3x^2 - 2x - 2 = 0$.
   Give your solutions correct to 3 significant figures. **(3 marks)**

5 A picture frame is designed to take a $6\,cm \times 8\,cm$ picture.

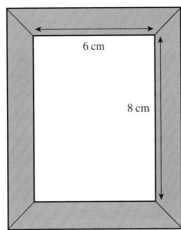

6 cm

8 cm

   The border is exactly the same width all round and its area is $32\,cm^2$.
   How wide is the border? **(4 marks)**

6 Solve these simultaneous equations.

   a $3x - 2y = 12$
      $4x + 2y = 9$ **(3 marks)**

   b $x + 2y = 18$
      $2x + 3y = 5$ **(3 marks)**

7 Jay buys 2 apples and 3 pears in a supermarket and pays £1.90.
   He later returns and buys 4 pears and 5 apples and pays £3.35.
   Find the cost of one apple and the cost of one pear. **(4 marks)**

8 Find the integer x that satisfies both the inequalities
   $x + 4 > 5$ and $3x - 4 < 5$ **(3 marks)**

9 **a** Solve the inequality $2y + 6 < 4y + 7$. **(2 marks)**

   b Solve the inequality $-3 < 2(4 - x) \leqslant 6$.
      Write the solution using set notation. **(3 marks)**

10 Solve these simultaneous equations algebraically.
$$x^2 + y^2 = 25$$
$$y - 2x = -10$$ **(5 marks)**

11 This trapezium has area $3\,\text{m}^2$.

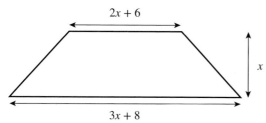

The area of a trapezium is given by the formula $A = \frac{1}{2}(a+b)h$
Find the value of x. **(4 marks)**

12 Write $2x^2 + 12x + 13$ in the form $a(x+p)^2 + q$. **(3 marks)**

13 The diagram shows a sketch of the curve $y = 2x^2 + 4x - 2$.

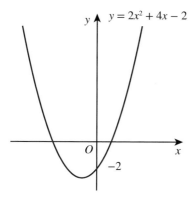

The line $y = 6 - x$ crosses the curve at points A and B.
Use an algebraic method to find the coordinates of A and B.
Give your answers to 1 decimal place. **(4 marks)**

(TOTAL: 50 marks)

14 Challenge Show that the line $x + y = 7$ does not intersect the circle $x^2 + y^2 = 12$.

15 Reflect For this unit, copy and complete these sentences.
I showed I am good at _____
I found _____ hard
I got better at _____ by _____
I was surprised by _____
I was happy that _____
I still need help with _____

10 Probability

10.1 Combined events

Prior knowledge

- Use the product rule for finding the number of outcomes for two or more events.
- Use two-way tables and sample space diagrams to solve probability problems.

Active Learn
Homework

Warm up

1   Fluency For a fair coin, what is P(head)?

2   Jess is buying a car. She has a choice of 3 colours, red, blue and silver, and a choice of 2 models, an estate and saloon.

   a How many possible combinations of colour and model are there?

   b How many combinations are there for 4 colours and 2 models?

   c How many combinations are there for 5 colours and 2 models?

   d How many combinations are there for 6 colours and 3 models?

   e How many combinations are there for m colours and n models?

3   The table gives the numbers of boys and girls in a group who wear glasses.

	Glasses	No glasses	Total
Boys		10	
Girls	6		18
Total			32

   a Copy and complete the table.

   A person is picked at random.
   What is the probability the person is

   b a boy without glasses

   c a girl?

Key point

Probability = $\dfrac{\text{number of successful outcomes}}{\text{total number of possible outcomes}}$

A **sample space diagram** shows all the possible outcomes of two events.

Example

Lisa spins these two spinners and adds the scores.

Both spinners are fair.

Find the probability that the total score is greater than 6.

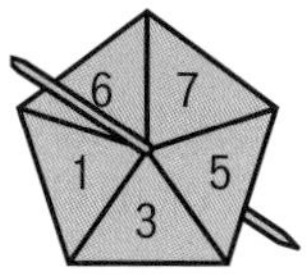

6
7
1
5
3

Spinner 1

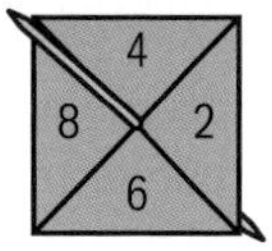

4
8
2
6

Spinner 2

Draw a sample space diagram.

		Spinner 2			
		2	4	6	8
Spinner 1	1	3	5	7	
	3	5	7		
	5	7			
	7	9			
	9				

If you notice that all the numbers in the blank squares will be greater than 6, you don't need to work them out.

$\frac{17}{20}$

$\frac{\text{number of scores} > 6}{\text{total number of outcomes}}$

4 Two fair 5-sided spinners are spun and the results are added together.
Work out the probability of getting

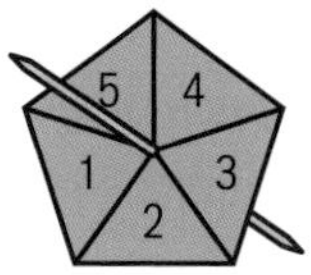

5
4
1
3
2

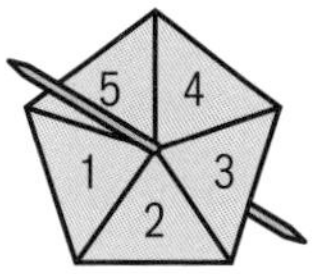

5
4
1
3
2

a a total of 2

b a total of 6

c a total that is a prime number

d a total that is less than 8

5 **a** From this set menu of 5 main courses and 3 desserts, write all the combinations of main courses and desserts.

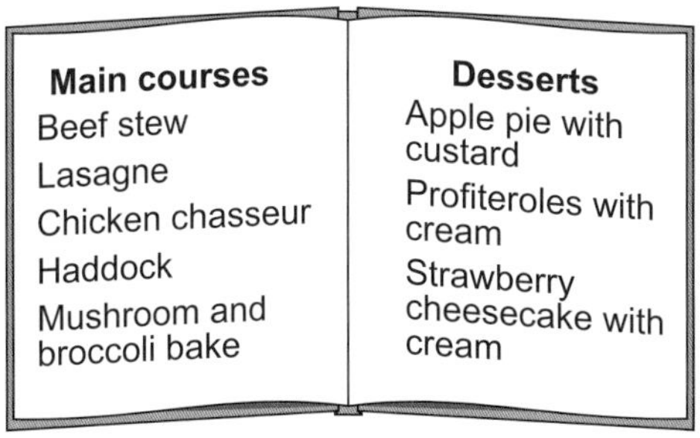

Main courses
Beef stew
Lasagne
Chicken chasseur
Haddock
Mushroom and broccoli bake
Desserts
Apple pie with custard
Profiteroles with cream
Strawberry cheesecake with cream

b How many possible combinations are there?

c Lasagne and profiteroles is 1 combination out of a total of □ combinations.
What is the probability that a combination picked at random from the menu is lasagne and profiteroles?

d What is the probability that the combination picked is haddock and a dessert served with cream?

6 **Problem-solving** Two fair coins are flipped at the same time.
Work out

a P(two tails)

b P(head and tail)

Exam tip

Organise the information in a table or diagram.

Exam-style question

7   80 people were asked if they prefer to go on holiday in Britain or in France or in Germany.
43 of the people were female.
12 of the 30 people who said Britain were male.
19 females said France.
4 males said Germany.
One of the people is chosen at random.
What is the probability that this person is a male who said France? **(4 marks)**

8   Sasha rolls two fair 6-sided dice.

   a Work out the probability of getting

   i a total of 3

   ii a total that is even

   iii a total greater than 8

   b What total are you most likely to get when rolling two 6-sided dice?

9   Two of Amy, Beth, Callum, Dan and Ellie are picked at random.

   a Draw a sample space diagram to show all the possible combinations of two people.

   b How many combinations of two people are there?

   c What is the probability that Amy is one of the people picked?

   d What is the probability that Callum and Dan are both picked?

10   Chloe has two bags of sweets, A and B.
In bag A she has a strawberry flavour, an orange flavour, a lime flavour and a blackcurrant flavour sweet.
In bag B she has a strawberry flavour, a blackcurrant flavour and a lime flavour sweet.
Chloe takes a sweet at random from each bag.
Work out the probability that the sweets will be

   a both strawberry flavour

   b the same flavour

   c different flavours

11   **Problem-solving** Harry flips a fair coin three times.
Work out the probability that the coin lands heads up for all three flips.

12   Jade, Kieran, Laura, Marco and Nicola take part in a chess tournament.
Each player in the tournament plays every other player.
There are 10 matches altogether.
Two players are picked at random to play the first game.
Work out the probability that the first game will be played by a male player and a female player.

10.2 Mutually exclusive events

- Identify mutually exclusive outcomes and events.
- Find the probabilities of mutually exclusive outcomes and events.
- Solve probability problems.

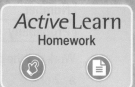

Active Learn
Homework

F
H

Warm up

1 **Fluency** Boys and girls in a class are in the ratio of 1 : 2.
What fraction of the class are boys?

2 A fair 6-sided dice is rolled once. What is the probability of rolling

   a a square number   **b** a multiple of 2   **c** a multiple of 3?

Key point

Two events are **mutually exclusive** if they cannot happen at the same time.

3 Which two events from **Q2** are mutually exclusive?

Key point

When events are mutually exclusive you can add their probabilities.
For mutually exclusive events $P(A \text{ or } B) = P(A) + P(B)$
A set of events is **exhaustive** when the events include every possible outcome.
The probabilities of an exhaustive set of mutually exclusive events sum to 1.

4 There are only red cubes and blue cubes in a bag.
A cube is taken from the bag at random. $P(\text{red}) = 0.2$

   a What fraction of the cubes are red?

   b Jenny says, 'There are 22 cubes in the bag.'
      Explain why Jenny must be wrong.

5 The numbered cards are shuffled. A card is taken at random.

   a Work out the probability of taking a square number or a prime number or a multiple of 6.

   b Are the events 'taking a square number, a prime number or a multiple of 6' exhaustive?
      Explain.

6 **Problem-solving** A and B are two mutually exclusive events.
$P(A) = 0.25$ and $P(A \text{ or } B) = 0.6$
Work out the value of $P(B)$.

7 **Problem-solving** The table gives the probability of getting each of 1, 2, 3 and 4 on this biased 4-sided spinner.

Number	1	2	3	4
Probability	$4x$	$3x$	$2x$	x

Work out the probability of getting

a 2 or 4   **b** 1 or 2 or 3

Exam-style question

8 There are only blue balls, red balls and yellow balls in a bag. There are

- twice as many blue balls as red balls

- three times as many yellow balls as blue balls.

Millie takes at random a ball from the bag.
Work out the probability that Millie takes a red ball.

(3 marks)

Exam tip

Represent the relationships between the numbers of balls of each colour using diagrams, ratios or algebra.

Key point

For mutually exclusive events A and not A, P(not A) = 1 − P(A)
A and not A are always mutually exclusive.

---

9 The probability that it will rain tomorrow is 0.88.
Work out the probability that it will not rain tomorrow.

10 A bag contains 20 counters. 7 of the counters are red.
A counter is taken at random from the bag.
Work out the probability that the counter will be

a red   **b** not red

11 **Problem-solving** C and D are two mutually exclusive events.
P(D) = 0.4 and P(C or D) = 0.78
Work out P(not C).

Example

There are only red, blue, green and yellow counters in a bag.
The table shows the probabilities of picking each colour.

Colour	red	blue	green	yellow
Probability	0.15	0.4	0.25	0.2

What is the smallest possible number of counters in the bag?

$$P(red) = 0.15 = \frac{15}{100} = \frac{3}{20}$$

If there are 20 counters:

red	blue	green	yellow
3	$0.4 \times 20 = 8$	$0.25 \times 20 = 5$	$0.2 \times 20 = 4$

Smallest number of counters = 20

Write the lowest probability as a fraction.

Check the probabilities give a whole number of counters for each colour.

12 A bag contains only red counters, blue counters and green counters.
A counter is picked at random from the bag.
$P(red) = \frac{1}{4}$ and $P(blue) = \frac{3}{8}$

   a Work out   **i** P(not red)   **ii** P(blue or red)   **iii** P(green)

   b What is the smallest possible number of counters in the bag?

Exam-style question

13 There are only red cubes, white cubes and blue cubes in a box. The table shows the probability of taking at random a red cube from the box.

Colour	red	white	blue
Probability	0.4		

The number of white cubes in the box is the same as the number of blue cubes in the box.

   a Copy and complete the table.   **(2 marks)**

There are 15 blue cubes in the box.

   b Work out the total number of cubes in the box.   **(2 marks)**

> **Exam tip**
>
> Write down your calculations even if you work out the answer mentally.

Exam-style question

14 There are only black counters, white counters, green counters and yellow counters in a bag.

Colour	black	white	green	yellow
Probability	0.1	0.45	0.4	

A counter is taken at random from the bag.
The table shows the probabilities of getting a black counter or a white counter or a green counter.

   a Work out the probability of getting a yellow counter.   **(1 mark)**

   b What is the least possible number of counters in the bag? You must give a reason for your answer.   **(2 marks)**

> **Exam tip**
>
> Give your reason for part **b**. The correct answer without a reason is unlikely to get full marks.

---

15 A box contains only milk, plain and white chocolates in the ratio 4 : 3 : 2.
Anna picks a chocolate at random. Work out

   a the fraction of the chocolates that are white

   b the probability that Anna will pick a chocolate that is not white.

Exam-style question

16 There are only blue counters, green counters and red counters in a box.
The ratio of the number of blue counters to green counters is 3 : 2.
The ratio of the number of green counters to red counters is 5 : 1.
There are less than 120 counters in the box.
What is the greatest possible number of red counters in the box?   **(3 marks)**

Exam-style question

17 There are only red cubes, white cubes and blue cubes in a box.
The ratio of the number of red cubes to the number of white cubes is 1 : 9.
Tim takes a cube at random from the box.
The probability that the cube is blue is 0.4.
Work out the probability that Tim takes a red cube.   **(3 marks)**

> **Exam tip**
>
> Check your calculations carefully.

10.3 Experimental probability

- Estimate the expected results for experimental and theoretical probabilities.
- Compare real results with theoretical expected values to decide if a game is fair.

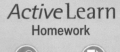 *Active* Learn
Homework

Warm up

1 Fluency Work out   **a** 50×0.3 **b** 200×0.7 **c** $210 \times \frac{1}{3}$ **d** $150 \times \frac{4}{5}$

2 Josh uses this spinner for a game.

  a What is the theoretical probability that the spinner will land on the letter B?

  Josh is going to spin this spinner 300 times.

  b Estimate how many times the spinner will land on the letter B.

Key point

Experimental probability of an outcome = $\dfrac{\text{frequency of outcome}}{\text{total number of trials}}$

Expected number of outcomes = number of trials × probability

---

3 Ella dropped a drawing pin on the table lots of times. It landed either point up or point down. She recorded her results in a frequency table.

  a Work out the total number of trials.

  b Work out the experimental probability of the drawing pin landing

Position	Frequency
point up	43
point down	7

  i point up   **ii** point down

  c Ella drops the drawing pin 100 times. How many times do you expect it to land point up?

  d **Reflect** When you repeat an experiment, will you get exactly the same results? Why is experimental probability only an estimate? How can you improve the accuracy of the estimate?

Exam-style question

4 The table shows the probabilities that a biased dice will land on 2, on 3, on 4, on 5 and on 6.

Number on dice	1	2	3	4	5	6
Probability		0.18	0.15	0.13	0.08	0.2

> **Exam tip**
>
> Once you have found your answer, read the question again. Have you really answered the question?

Zack rolls the biased dice 200 times.
Work out an estimate for the total number of times the dice will land on 1 or 4.   **(3 marks)**

---

5 **Problem-solving** There are red, blue and yellow counters in a bag in the ratio 5 : 6 : 1.

  a What is the probability of picking a red counter?

  A counter is picked at random from the bag and then replaced. This is done 180 times.

  b Work out an estimate for the total number of times a red counter is picked.

6 The probability of England losing their next football match is 0.28.
The probability of England drawing their next football match is 0.36.
Work out an estimate for the number of times England will win in their next 50 football matches.

Exam-style question

7 Sean, Tina and Naveen each dropped a drawing pin a number of times.
The table shows the number of times the drawing pin landed point down

	Sean	Tina	Naveen
Point down	25	57	10
Point up	6	18	4

and the number of times it landed point up, for each person.
Katy is going to drop the drawing pin once.
Use all the results in the table to work out an estimate for the probability that the drawing pin will land point up. **(1 mark)**

Example

The table shows the results of spinning a 4-sided spinner.
Is the spinner fair? Give a reason for your answer.

Number	1	2	3	4
Frequency	19	27	21	5

On a fair 4-sided spinner:

$P(1) = P(2) = P(3) = P(4) = \dfrac{1}{4} = 0.25$ ◄───── Calculate the theoretical and experimental probabilities.

On this spinner:

$P(1) = \dfrac{19}{72} = 0.2638...$ $P(2) = \dfrac{27}{72} = 0.375$ ◄

$P(3) = \dfrac{21}{72} = 0.2916...$ $P(4) = \dfrac{5}{72} = 0.0694...$

The spinner is not fair because the experimental probability for 4 is 0.0694..., which is very different from the theoretical probability of 0.25 for a score of 4. ◄─── Explain whether or not the experimental probabilities are close to the theoretical probabilities.

8 Reasoning The table shows the results of spinning a 5-sided spinner.
Is the spinner fair? Give a reason for your answer.

Number	1	2	3	4	5
Frequency	46	39	37	40	38

9 Reasoning The table shows the results of rolling a 6-sided dice.
Is the dice fair? Give a reason for your answer.

Number	1	2	3	4	5	6
Frequency	23	22	21	18	9	7

10 Reasoning The probability of winning a prize in a raffle is $\frac{1}{200}$.
Deepak says, 'If I buy 200 tickets I will win a prize.'
Is he right? Give a reason for your answer.

11 Reasoning Ben rolls two dice 180 times.
How many times would you expect him to get

a a total of 12   **b** a total of 7   **c** a total that is a prime number?

10.4 Independent events and tree diagrams

- Draw and use frequency trees.
- Calculate probabilities of independent events.
- Use probability tree diagrams to solve problems.

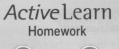

Active Learn
Homework

Warm up

1 Fluency Work out

a $\frac{2}{5}+\frac{1}{5}$ b $\frac{4}{9}+\frac{3}{9}$ c $\frac{1}{2}+\frac{1}{4}$ d $\frac{3}{8}+\frac{1}{4}$

2 Work out these calculations. Give your answers in their simplest form.

a $\frac{7}{10}\times\frac{2}{9}$ b $\frac{5}{9}\times\frac{3}{4}$ c 0.4×0.2 d 0.6×0.7

Key point

A **frequency tree** shows two or more events and the number of times they occurred.

3 In a football tournament 20 matches were played.
In 8 of the matches Team A scored the first goal.
In 5 of these matches they also scored the second goal.
Team B scored the first two goals in 3 of the matches.
Copy and complete the frequency tree for the 20 matches played.

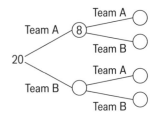

4 A garage records the MOT test results on 40 cars.
Of the 40 cars tested, 15 of them are less than 5 years old.
11 of the cars under 5 years old passed.
28 cars passed altogether.

a Copy and complete the frequency tree.

b Work out the probability that a car fails its MOT.

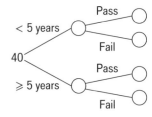

5 80 people with similar symptoms were tested for a virus using a new trial medical test.
19 of the people tested showed a positive result.
The virus only developed in 11 of the people who tested positive.
A total of 67 people did not develop the virus at all.

a Draw a frequency tree for this information.

b Work out the probability that a person develops the virus.

c Draw a two-way table for this information.

d **Reflect** Which diagram did you find easier to draw and use: the frequency tree or the two-way table?

6 **Problem-solving** Jin and Ryan race in a 100 metre sprint and a 100 metre swim.
The probability that Jin will win the sprint is 0.3. The probability that Jin will win the swim is 0.8.
Assuming that the two events are independent, work out the probability that Jin will win both races.

7 **Reasoning** There are two sets of traffic lights on Matthew's car journey to school.
The probability that he has to stop at the first set of traffic lights is 0.45.
The probability that he has to stop at the second set of traffic lights is 0.35.
Work out the probability that he will not stop at

   a the first set of traffic lights   b the second set of traffic lights   c either set of traffic lights

   d **Reflect** What assumption did you make to answer parts **a**, **b** and **c**?

8 Joe plays a spin-the-wheel game at the fair. The probability that he wins is $\frac{1}{4}$.
Calculate the probability that he wins three successive games.

Example

This fair 5-sided spinner is spun twice.

a What is the probability of both spins landing on red?

b What is the probability of landing on one red and one blue?

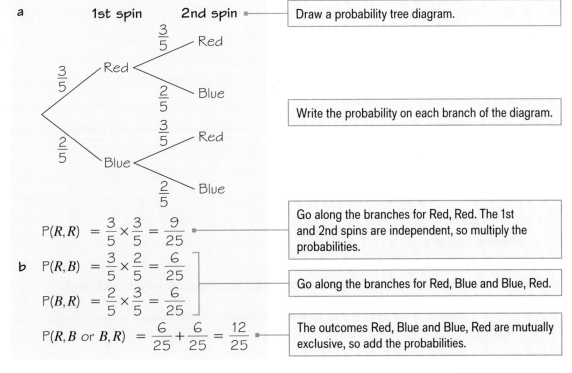

Draw a probability tree diagram.

Write the probability on each branch of the diagram.

$$P(R, R) = \frac{3}{5} \times \frac{3}{5} = \frac{9}{25}$$

Go along the branches for Red, Red. The 1st and 2nd spins are independent, so multiply the probabilities.

b $$P(R, B) = \frac{3}{5} \times \frac{2}{5} = \frac{6}{25}$$
$$P(B, R) = \frac{2}{5} \times \frac{3}{5} = \frac{6}{25}$$

Go along the branches for Red, Blue and Blue, Red.

$$P(R, B \text{ or } B, R) = \frac{6}{25} + \frac{6}{25} = \frac{12}{25}$$

The outcomes Red, Blue and Blue, Red are mutually exclusive, so add the probabilities.

9 On a hook-a-duck game at a fundraising event you win a prize if you pick a duck with an '×' on its base. Aaron picks a duck at random, replaces it and then picks another one.

a Copy and complete the probability tree diagram.

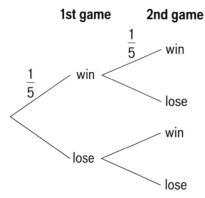

b What is the probability of
  i winning two prizes
  ii winning nothing
  iii winning one prize
  iv winning at least one prize?

> **Q9b iv hint**
>
> Winning 'at least one' means winning one or more.

10 Megan has two bags of counters, labelled A and B.
In bag A there are 3 red and 5 green counters.
In bag B there are 1 red and 5 green counters.
A counter is taken at random from each bag.

a Copy and complete the probability tree diagram to show the probabilities.

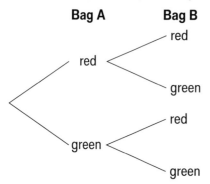

b Work out the probability of taking
  i two counters the same colour
  ii one counter of each colour
  iii no red counters
  iv at least one red counter

c **Reflect** How did you calculate P(at least one red)? Show another way to calculate it.

11 There are only red and yellow marbles in a bag.
    There are 5 red marbles and 3 yellow marbles.
    Ethan takes a marble from the bag at random,
    notes the colour and then puts the marble back in the bag.
    Ethan then repeats this process.
    Work out the probability that Ethan takes marbles of different colours.

Q11 hint

Draw a probability tree diagram.

12 **Problem-solving** Caitlin spins two spinners.
    On spinner 1, P(pink) = 0.2.
    On spinner 2, P(pink) = 0.35.

    a Work out the probability that only one spinner lands on pink.

    b Work out the probability that both spinners land on pink.

    c If each spinner was spun 500 times, how many times would you expect them both to land
       on pink?

Exam-style question

13 Bina has two spinners, spinner A and spinner B.
    Each spinner can land on only blue or yellow.
    The probability that spinner A will land on blue is 0.4.
    The probability that spinner B will land on blue is 0.75.
    The probability tree diagram shows this information.

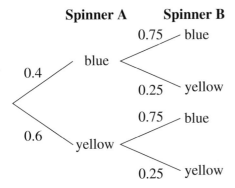

Bina spins spinner A once and she spins spinner B once.
She does this a number of times.
The number of times **both** spinners land on blue is 84.
Work out an estimate for the number of times **both** spinners land on yellow.   **(3 marks)**

Exam tip

You can write probabilities on
the diagram as you find them,
but make sure you show how
you calculated them.

10.5 Conditional probability

- Decide if two events are independent.
- Draw and use tree diagrams to solve conditional probability problems.
- Use two-way tables to calculate conditional probability.

Active Learn
Homework

Warm up

1 Fluency There are 4 red counters in a bag of 10 counters.
What is **a** P(red) **b** P(not red)?

2 The two-way table shows the subjects students like best.
Work out the probability that a student picked at random

a likes English best

b does not like science best

	English	Maths	Science	Total
Male	15	23	22	60
Female	32	17	21	70
Total	47	40	43	130

Key point

If one event depends upon the outcome of another event, the two events are **dependent events**. For example, taking a red ball from a bag of red and blue balls reduces the chance of taking another red ball.

3 For each of these events, state if the events are independent or dependent.

a Randomly picking a chocolate from a box, eating it, and then picking another.

b Rolling two 6-sided dice.

c Flipping a coin three times.

d Randomly taking a counter from a bag, replacing it and then taking another counter.

e Randomly taking a counter from a bag, not replacing it, and then taking another counter.

Key point

A **conditional probability** is the probability of a dependent event. The probability of the second outcome depends on what has already happened in the first outcome.

4 Future skills The two-way table shows the number of deaths and serious injuries caused by road traffic accidents in Great Britain in 2013.

Work out an estimate for the probability

		Speed limit			
		20 mph	30 mph	40 mph	Total
Type of injury	**Fatal**	6	520	155	681
	Serious	420	11 582	1662	13 664
	Total	426	12 102	1817	14 345

a that the accident is fatal given that the speed limit is 30 mph

b that the accident happens at 20 mph given that the accident is serious

c that the accident is serious given that the speed limit is 40 mph

Give your answers to 3 decimal places.

Example

There are 10 pencils in Toby's pencil case. Seven of the pencils are HB pencils.
Toby takes two pencils out of his pencil case.
Work out the probability that he picks out at least one HB pencil.

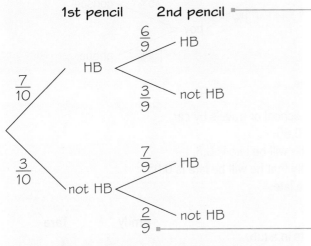

Draw a tree diagram to show all the possible outcomes.

Taking two pencils from the pencil case at the same time is the same as taking one pencil, then another (without replacement).

For the 2nd pencil, there are only 9 to choose from.

b P(at least one HB) = $1 - $ P(no HB)

P(not HB, not HB) $= \dfrac{3}{10} \times \dfrac{2}{9} = \dfrac{6}{90} = \dfrac{1}{15}$

P(at least one HB) $= 1 - \dfrac{1}{15} = \dfrac{14}{15}$

You don't need to simplify probability fractions, but sometimes it makes calculations easier.

5 Chris has a bag containing 5 red and 3 orange sweets. He picks a sweet at random and eats it. He then picks another sweet at random.

a Copy and complete the probability tree diagram to show all the probabilities.

b Work out the probability that the sweets will be

  i the same colour

  ii one of each colour

  iii not orange

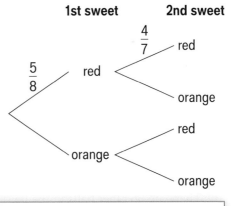

Exam-style question

6 There are 28 students in Jack's class.
15 of the students are boys.
Two students from the class are chosen at random.
Jack draws this probability tree diagram for this information.

Write down **one** thing that is wrong with the probabilities in the probability tree diagram. **(1 mark)**

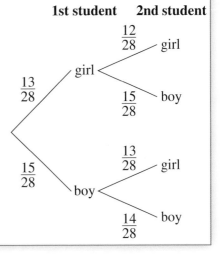

7 **Reasoning** In a group of students, 55% are girls. 30% of these girls prefer to play games on their phones. 75% of the boys prefer to play games on their games consoles.

a Copy and complete the probabilty tree diagram.

b One student is selected at random. Find the probability that this is a boy who prefers to play games on his phone.

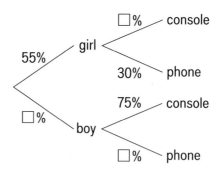

8 **Problem-solving** Callum either walks to school or travels by car.
The probability that he walks to school is 0.65.
If he walks to school, the probability that he will be late is 0.3.
If he travels to school by car, the probability that he will be late is 0.05.
Work out the probability that he will not be late.

9 Emily and Tara have 5 chocolate biscuits, 3 shortbread biscuits and 2 ginger biscuits in a tub. Emily takes a biscuit, at random, from the tub. Then Tara takes a biscuit.

a Copy and complete the diagram to show the probabilities of taking the same type of biscuit.

b Work out the probability that they both pick the same type of biscuit.

c **Reflect** Explain why your tree diagram does not need to show *all* the probabilities, to answer part **b**.

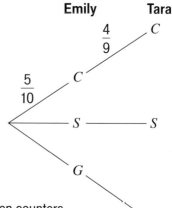

10 **Problem-solving** A bag contains 4 red, 3 blue and 2 green counters.
Jamie takes two counters, at random, from the bag.
Work out the probability that his two counters are the same colour.

Exam-style question

11 There are 9 balls in a bag.
There are equal numbers of green balls, white balls and pink balls in the bag.
There are no other balls in the bag.
3 balls are taken at random from the bag.

a Work out the probability of taking 3 green balls. **(2 marks)**

The 3 balls are put back into the bag.
Some more balls are now put into the bag.
There are still equal numbers of green balls, white balls and pink balls in the bag.
There are no balls of any other colour in the bag.

b Is it now less likely or equally likely or more likely that the 3 balls taken at random will be green?
You must show how you get your answer. **(2 marks)**

Exam tip

In part **b**, just stating the correct answer, without showing working to support it, is likely to lose marks.

10.6 Venn diagrams and set notation

Active Learn
Homework

- Use set notation.
- Use Venn diagrams to solve conditional probability problems.

Warm up

1 **Fluency** What are the integer values in each set?

a $\{x : 0 < x \leqslant 5\}$ **b** $\{x : -3 < x < 2\}$

2 Amber surveyed Year 10 students to see how many had smartphones and tablets.
The Venn diagram shows her results.

  a How many students did not have either a smartphone or a tablet?

  b How many students had a tablet?

  c How many students took part in Amber's survey?

  d What is the probability that one of these students picked at random had a smartphone and a tablet?

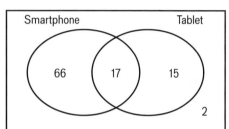

Key point

Curly brackets { } show a set of values.
$\in$ means 'is an **element** of'. An element is a 'member' of a set.
$\mathscr{E}$ means the **universal set** – all the elements being considered.

3 $A = \{$positive even numbers $< 10\}$
$B = \{$prime numbers $< 10\}$

  a List the numbers in each set.
    $A = \{2, ...\}$ $B = \{...\}$

  b Write 'true' or 'false' for each statement.

    i $6 \in A$ **ii** $1 \in B$ **iii** $5 \in B$

4 The Venn diagram shows two sets, P and Q, and the set of all numbers being considered, $\mathscr{E}$.

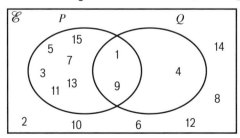

  a Write all the elements of each set inside curly brackets { }.

    i P **ii** Q **iii** $\mathscr{E}$

  b Which set is $\{$square numbers $< 16\}$?

  c Write descriptions of the other two sets.

$A \cap B$ means "A intersection B".
This is all the elements that are in A *and* in B.

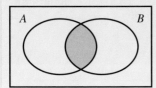

$A \cup B$ means "A union B".
This is all the elements that are in A *or* B *or both*.

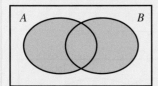

A' means the elements *not* in A.

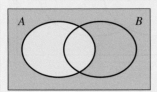

5 For the Venn diagram in **Q4**, write the elements of each set.

    a $P \cup Q = \{1, \ldots\}$ **b** $P \cap Q$ **c** P'

    d Q' **c** $P' \cap Q$ **f** $Q' \cap P$

$\mathscr{E} = \{$numbers less than $15\}$
$A = \{1, 4, 9\}$
$B = \{1, 3, 5, 8\}$
Draw a Venn diagram to represent this information.

> 1 Label $\mathscr{E}$ and the sets A and B.

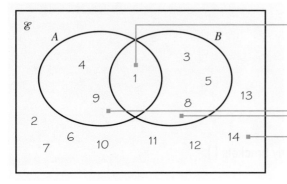

2 Write in the elements in A **and** B.

3 Write in the elements in A but not in B.

4 Write in the elements in B but not in A.

5 Write in the elements of $\mathscr{E}$ but not in A or B.

6 $\mathscr{E}$ = {even numbers less than 25}
A = {4, 8, 12, 16, 20, 24}
B = {10, 20}

a Copy and complete the Venn diagram to
represent this information. **(4 marks)**

A number is chosen at random from the
universal set, $\mathscr{E}$.

b What is the probability that the number is in the set $A \cup B$? **(2 marks)**

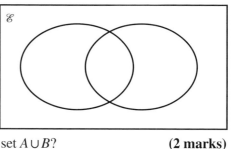

Exam tip

Write out all the elements of $\mathscr{E}$.
Check you have included all of
them in the Venn diagram.

7 The Venn diagram shows two events when
a 12-sided dice is rolled.
X = {number is prime}
Y = {number is a multiple of 2}
Work out

a $P(X)$ **b** $P(Y)$

c $P(X \cap Y)$ **d** $P(X \cup Y)$

e $P(X')$ **f** $P(Y')$

g $P(X \cap Y')$ **h** $P(X' \cup Y)$

8 **Reasoning** Charlie asks the 30 students in his class if they
passed their English and maths tests.
21 students passed both their English and maths tests.
2 students didn't pass either test.
25 students passed their maths test.
One of the students is selected at random.
Work out the probability that this student passed the English test but not the maths test.

Q8 hint

Draw a Venn diagram.

9 **Reasoning** Lucy asked 150 students if they play an instrument (I) and/or play for a school
sports team (S).
63 students play for a school sports team.
27 students play an instrument and play for a school sports team.
72 students do not play an instrument or play for a school sports team.

a Work out the probability that a student plays an instrument.

b Work out the probability that a student plays an instrument
given that they play for a school sports team.

Q9b hint

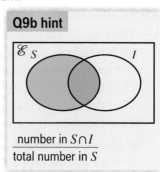

$\dfrac{\text{number in } S \cap I}{\text{total number in } S}$

10 Problem-solving Caitlin did a survey of pet
owners owning cats (C), dogs (D) and fish (F).
The Venn diagram shows her results.
One of the pet owners is selected at random.

a Work out the probability that this pet owner
does not own a fish.

b A dog owner is selected at random.
Work out the probability that this dog owner
also owns a cat, but not a fish.

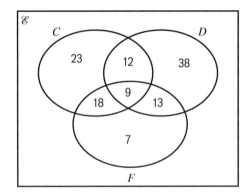

11 $\mathcal{E}$ = {odd numbers less than 20}
$A = \{1, 3, 5, 7\}$
$B = \{5, 9, 13, 17\}$
$C = \{1, 5, 15, 17\}$

a Complete the Venn diagram for this
information. **(4 marks)**

A number is chosen at random from $\mathcal{E}$.

b Find the probability that the number is a
member of $A \cap C$. **(2 marks)**

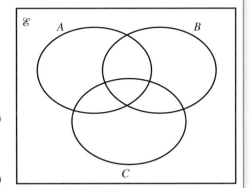

Key point

$P(A \cap B | B)$ means the probability of A and B given B.

Q11a hint

Write the element in
$A \cap B \cap C$ first.

12 Problem-solving The Venn diagram shows people's
choices of chocolate (C), strawberry (S) and
vanilla (V) ice cream flavours for the 'three scoops'
dessert.
Work out

a $P(C \cap S \cap V)$

b $P(S \cap V)$

c $P(S \cap V | S)$

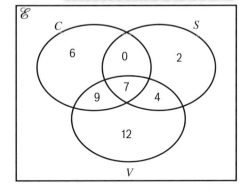

Exam-style question

13 There are 80 students at a language school.
All 80 students learn at least one language from French, Italian and Spanish.
7 of the students learn French, Italian and Spanish.
15 of the students learn French and Italian. 26 of the students learn French and Spanish.
17 of the students learn Italian and Spanish.
41 of the students learn French. 52 of the students learn Spanish.

a One of the students is chosen at random.
Work out the probability that this student learns French but not Italian. **(4 marks)**

b Two of the students are chosen at random.
Work out the probability that they both learn only Italian. **(2 marks)**

10 Check up

Calculating probability

1 Ewan spins the spinner and rolls the 6-sided dice.
   He finds the total of the outcomes.

   a Draw a sample space diagram to show all the
      possible outcomes.

   b Work out the probability of scoring

      i a total of 8

      ii a total of a multiple of 3

      iii a total of more than 9

2 A bag contains toy animals.
   Emma takes an animal from the bag at random.

   a The probability of picking a sheep is $\frac{1}{5}$.
      What is the probability of picking an animal that is not a sheep?

   b The probability of picking a horse is $\frac{1}{2}$.
      What is the probability of picking a sheep or a horse?

3 The probability that it will rain today is 0.3.
   The probability that it will rain tomorrow is 0.25.
   The two probabilities are independent.

   a Work out the probability that it will not rain tomorrow.

   b Work out the probability that it will rain today and tomorrow.

4 A and B are mutually exclusive. $P(B) = 0.45$, $P(A \text{ or } B) = 0.6$
   Work out $P(A)$.

5 Jane records the hair colour of students in her class and whether they wear glasses.
   The two-way table shows her results.
   A dark-haired student is selected at random.
   What is the probability that they wear glasses?

	Hair colour			
	Fair	**Dark**	**Ginger**	**Total**
Wears glasses	0	2	1	3
Does not wear glasses	13	15	1	29
Total	13	17	2	32

Experimental probability

6 The table shows the probability of each number on a 6-sided spinner.
The spinner is equally as likely to land on 3 as it is to land on 5.

Number	1	2	3	4	5	6
Probability	0.2	0.3		0.15		0.15

a Copy and complete the table.

The spinner is spun 300 times.

b How many times would you expect the spinner to land on 4?

c Is the spinner fair? Explain your answer.

Tree diagrams and Venn diagrams

7 $\mathscr{E}$ = {numbers less than 12}
A = {2, 4, 6, 8, 10}
B = {1, 2, 3, 4, 5}
C = {4, 6, 7, 11}
Copy and complete the Venn diagram for this information.

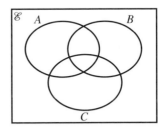

8 Grace spins two spinners, A and B.
The probability of getting an even number on spinner A is 0.4.
The probability of getting an even number on spinner B is 0.65.

a Copy and complete the probability tree diagram.

b Work out the probability of getting an even number on

   i neither spinner   **ii** only one spinner

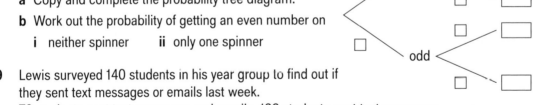

9 Lewis surveyed 140 students in his year group to find out if they sent text messages or emails last week.
79 students sent text messages and emails. 126 students sent text messages.
All students sent either a text message or an email.

a Draw a Venn diagram to show Lewis's data.

A student is selected at random.

b Work out the probability that the student sent an email last week.

c Given that the student sent a text message, work out the probability that they sent an email.

10 Reflect How sure are you of your answers? Were you mostly

Just guessing 🙁   Feeling doubtful 😐   Confident 🙂

What next? Use your results to decide whether to strengthen or extend your learning.

Challenge

11 a Use the numbers 1 to 6 to fill in the sectors of these two spinners so that when the results are added together the probability of getting a total of 7 is $\frac{3}{20}$.

   b Both of your spinners are spun once and the results are added together.
Work out the probability of spinning a total of 9.

10 Strengthen

Active Learn
Homework

Calculating probability

1 Here are some lettered tiles.

One of these tiles is picked at random. Work out

a P(I)   **b** 1 − P(I)   **c** P(not I)

d What do you notice about your answers to parts **b** and **c**?

e Use your answer to part **d** to help you work out

  i P(T)   **ii** P(not T)

2 Using the tiles in **Q1**, work out

a P(A)   **b** P(S)   **c** P(A or S)

d Explain why 'picking an A' and 'picking an S' are mutually exclusive.

e What do you notice about your answers to parts **a**, **b** and **c**?

f Use your answer to part **e** to help you work out P(I or T).

3 The probability of getting a letter S on a tile in a word game is 0.05.
The probability of getting tiles S or E is 0.2.
Work out the probability of getting the tile E.

$$P(S \text{ or } E) = P(S) + P(E)$$

4 Brad spins these two fair spinners.

Spinner A   Spinner B

a Copy and complete the sample space diagram to show all the possible outcomes

		Spinner B				
		0	**2**	**4**	**6**	**8**
	1	1, 0	1, 2			
Spinner A	**2**	2, 0				
	3					

b How many possible outcomes are there?

c Work out the probability of

  i one number being 3

  ii one number being double the other

d Brad spins the two spinners and adds the two numbers together.
Draw a new sample space diagram to show the scores.

e Some scores are most likely. Which scores?

f What is the probability of scoring at least 6?

5 Mohammed surveyed the students in his year group to see who had school dinners and who had a packed lunch. The two-way table shows his results.

	School dinner	Packed lunch	Total
Male	27	46	73
Female	36	41	77
Total	63	87	150

  a How many female students are there?

  b What fraction of females have packed lunches?

One of the female students is selected at random.

  c What is the probability that this female student has a packed lunch?

6 **a** Two events A and B are mutually exclusive.
    $P(A) = 0.3$ $P(B) = 0.5$
    Work out $P(A \text{ or } B)$.

  b Two events C and D are independent.
    $P(C) = 0.1$ $P(D) = 0.7$
    Work out $P(C \text{ and } D)$.

  c **Reflect** When do you add probabilities and when do you multiply?

Experimental probability

1 Dylan makes this 6-sided spinner.
He spins it 180 times and gets 15 threes.

  a How many threes would you expect in 180 spins of a *fair* spinner?

  b Is the actual number of threes close to the expected number? Do you think Dylan's spinner is fair? Explain.

2 Megan spins a spinner 80 times. The table shows her results.

  a Copy the table. Work out the total frequency.
    Add an extra column to the table to work out the experimental probability of each number.

  b Megan spins the spinner another 150 times. How many times would you expect it to land on 1 in these 150 spins?

Number	Frequency
1	16
2	12
3	14
4	17
5	21

Tree diagrams and Venn diagrams

1 There are only red and blue counters in a bag.
One counter is taken and then replaced in the bag.
A second counter is taken.
The tree diagram shows the probabilities.

  a Copy and complete the diagram and calculations to show all the probabilities.

  b Which two outcomes have exactly *one* red counter?

  c Work out the probability of picking exactly one red counter.

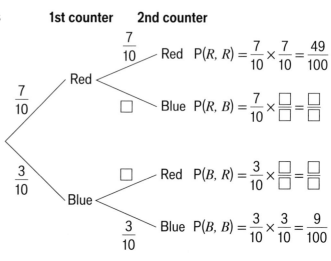

2 $\mathscr{E} = \{$even numbers less than 20$\}$
$A = \{10, 12, 14\}$
$B = \{2, 8, 12\}$
$C = \{2, 12, 18\}$

a Copy the Venn diagram. Copy sets A, B and C.
Cross the numbers off in your sets as you write them in the diagram in parts **b** to **f**.

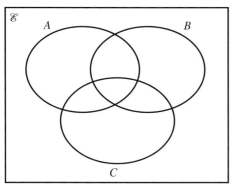

b Which number is in A, B and C?
Write it where all three circles overlap.

c There is no other number in both A and B or in both A and C. Leave these sections empty.

d Which other number is in B and C?

e Write the remaining numbers in A only, B only, and C only.

f Write the remaining numbers in $\mathscr{E}$.

3   Rachel surveys people swimming at her local swimming pool.
15 people swim front crawl.
12 people swim breaststroke.
7 people swim both front crawl and breaststroke.

a Draw a Venn diagram.

　i Write the number for front crawl and breaststroke
　　in the section where the circles overlap.

　ii The total in the whole front crawl circle needs to be 15.
　　How many people need to go in the rest of the front crawl circle?

　iii How many people need to go in the rest of the breaststroke circle?

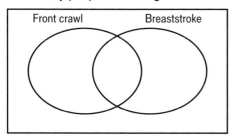

b Work out the total number of people in the Venn diagram.

c What is the probability that a person picked at random

　i swims front crawl and breaststroke

　ii swims front crawl only?

d Given that a person picked at random swims front crawl,
what is the probability that they also swim breaststroke?

Q3d hint

What fraction of 'front crawl'
people also swim breaststroke?

10 Extend

1   Design a set of counters so that P(red) = P(green) = $\frac{1}{5}$ and P(blue) = $\frac{1}{2}$, and there are half as many yellow counters as red ones.

Exam-style question

2   Amy and Mel play netball.
The probability that Amy will score a goal in the next match is 0.7.
The probability that Mel will score a goal in the next match is 0.2.
Amy says, 'The probability that we will both score a goal in the next match is $0.7 + 0.2$.'
Is Amy right? Give a reason for your answer.   **(1 mark)**

Exam-style question

3   There are 15 girls and 13 boys in Mr Martin's class.
Mr Martin is going to choose at random 3 children from his class.
Work out the probability that he will choose exactly 2 girls and 1 boy.   **(4 marks)**

4   **Problem-solving** Ali has a bag of red, yellow and blue counters in the ratio 2 : 1 : 3.
Brad has a bag of red, yellow and blue counters in the ratio 4 : 3 : 1.
Ali and Brad have 12 red counters each. Ali takes a counter out of his bag and puts it into Brad's bag. Brad then takes a counter out of his bag at random.
Work out the probability that they both take a counter of the same colour.

5   **Reasoning** Tom has a bag with these shapes in.

Tom drops the bag and two shapes fall out.

a Work out the probability that the two shapes are not regular polygons.

b Work out the probability that the two shapes have an interior angle sum of 540°.

c Work out the probability that the one of the shapes has an interior angle sum of 360° and the other has an interior angle sum of 540°.

Exam-style question

6   A factory makes 360 doughnuts a day.
The doughnuts are jam doughnuts or chocolate doughnuts.
Each day Sarah takes a sample of 12 doughnuts to check.
The proportion of the jam doughnuts in the sample needs to be the same as the proportion of jam doughnuts made that day.
On Monday Sarah calculated that she needed exactly 3 jam doughnuts in her sample.

a Work out the total number of jam doughnuts that were made on Monday.   **(2 marks)**

On Tuesday the number of jam doughnuts Sarah needs in her sample is 5 correct to the nearest whole number. Sarah takes at random a doughnut from the 360 doughnuts made on Tuesday.

b Work out the lower bound of the probability that the doughnut is a jam doughnut.   **(2 marks)**

7   There is an 85% chance that a battery will last longer than the advertised life of the battery.
The batteries are sold in packets of two.
A shop has 200 packets of the batteries.
Find an estimate for the number of packets that will have exactly one battery that lasts
longer than the advertised life of the battery. **(3 marks)**

8   **Reasoning** Mike is a stamp collector.
The Venn diagram shows information about his
stamp collection.
$\mathcal{E} = \{$Mike's full collection of 750 stamps$\}$
$C = \{$stamps from the 20th century$\}$
$B = \{$British stamps$\}$
Mike has 30 stamps that are neither British nor from
the 20th century.
Given that a stamp selected at random is from the 20th century,
work out the probability that it is British.

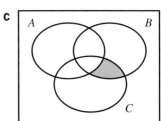

9   Use set notation to describe the shaded area in each Venn diagram.

a 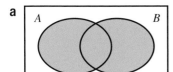 b 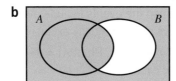 c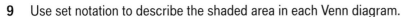

10 There are only b blue counters and y yellow counters in a bag.
A counter is taken at random from the bag.
The probability that the counter is blue is $\frac{4}{11}$.
The counter is put back in the bag.
2 more blue counters and 1 more yellow counter are put in the bag.
A counter is taken at random from the bag.
The probability that the counter is blue is $\frac{2}{5}$.
Find the number of blue counters and the number of yellow counters
that were in the bag originally. **(5 marks)**

Working towards A level

11 A sample of 72 students was taken from a college.
The students were asked whether they studied maths or geography.
One-fifth of the students who studied maths also studied geography.
One-eighth of the students who studied geography also studied maths.
24 students studied neither maths nor geography.

   a Draw a Venn diagram to show this information.

   b Find the probability that one of the 72 students,
      chosen at random, studied both maths and geography.

Q11b hint

Set up an equation to find x,
where x is the number studying
both maths and geography.

10 Test ready

Summary of key points

To revise for the test:

- Read each key point, find a question on it in the mastery lesson, and check you can work out the answer.

- If you cannot, try some other questions from the mastery lesson or ask for help.

Key points

1 Probability $= \dfrac{\text{number of successful outcomes}}{\text{total number of possible outcomes}}$

   A **sample space diagram** shows all the possible outcomes of two events. → **10.1**

2 Two events are **mutually exclusive** if they cannot happen at the same time. → **10.2**

3 When events are mutually exclusive you can add their probabilities.
   For mutually exclusive events $P(A \text{ or } B) = P(A) + P(B)$
   A set of events is **exhaustive** when the events include every possible outcome.
   The probabilities of an exhaustive set of mutually exclusive events sum to 1. → **10.2**

4 For mutually exclusive events A and not A, $P(\text{not } A) = 1 - P(A)$
   A and not A are always mutually exclusive. → **10.2**

5 Experimental probability of an outcome $= \dfrac{\text{frequency of outcome}}{\text{total number of trials}}$
   Expected number of outcomes $=$ number of trials $\times$ probability → **10.3**

6 As the number of experiments increases, the experimental probability gets closer and closer to the theoretical probability. → **10.3**

7 A **frequency tree** shows two or more events and the number of times they occurred. → **10.4**

8 Two events are **independent** if one event does not affect the probability of the other.
   For example, flipping heads with a coin has no effect on rolling an even number with a dice, so they are independent events.
   To find the probability of two independent events, multiply their probabilities.
   $P(A \text{ and } B) = P(A) \times P(B)$ → **10.4**

9 A **probability tree diagram** shows two or more events and their probabilities. → **10.4**

10 If one event depends upon the outcome of another event, the two events are **dependent events**. For example, taking a red ball from a bag of red and blue balls reduces the chance of taking another red ball. → **10.5**

11 A **conditional probability** is the probability of a dependent event.
   The probability of the second outcome depends on what has already happened in the first outcome. → **10.5**

12 Curly brackets $\{\,\}$ show a set of values.
   $\in$ means 'is an **element** of'. An element is a 'member' of a set.
   $\mathscr{E}$ means the **universal set** – all the elements being considered. → **10.6**

13 $A \cap B$ means "A intersection B".
This is all the elements that are in A *and* in B.

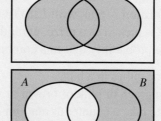

$A \cup B$ means "A union B".
This is all the elements that are in A *or* B *or* both.

A' means the elements *not* in A.

→ **10.6**

14 $P(A \cap B | B)$ means the probability of A and B given B.

→ **10.6**

Sample student answers

Matt has a bag of 9 sweets.
In the bag, there are
    2 orange flavoured sweets
    7 strawberry flavoured sweets.
Matt takes two of the sweets at random.
He eats the sweets.
Work out the probability that at least one of the sweets Matt eats is orange flavoured. **(5 marks)**

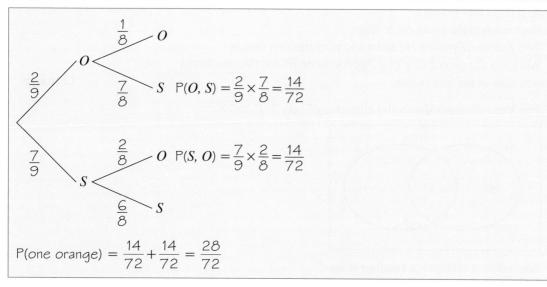

a Has the student found the probability of at least one orange sweet?

b Work out the correct answer.

10 Unit test

Active Learn
Homework

1 A phone is made in five different colours and three different memory sizes.

    a How many combinations of colour and memory size are there? **(2 marks)**

    b One combination is pink with 128 GB of memory.
      One phone is picked as a prize, at random.
      What is the probability that this combination is picked? **(2 marks)**

2 There are some cubes in a bag.
The cubes are green or pink or brown or white.
Lee is going to take a counter at random from the bag.
The table shows each of the probabilities
that the cube will be brown or will be white.
There are 20 counters in the bag.

Colour	Green	Pink	Brown	White
Probability			0.15	0.25

The probability that the counter Lee takes
will be pink is twice the probability that the counter will be green.

    a Work out the number of green counters in the bag. **(4 marks)**

    A cube is going to be taken at random from a bag of cubes.
    The probability that the counter will be blue is 0.5.
    There must be an even number of cubes in the bag.

    b Explain why. **(1 mark)**

3 Holly flips two coins 160 times.
She gets two tails 75 times.
Do you think the coins are both fair?
Give a reason for your answer. **(3 marks)**

4 There are five football teams in a tournament: Brazil, England, Scotland,
Argentina and France.
Each team plays every other team.
Two teams are picked at random to play the first match.
Work out the probability that Argentina **or** Brazil (but not both)
will play in the first match. **(3 marks)**

5 The Venn diagram shows the elements of sets A, B and $\mathscr{E}$.

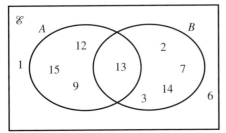

A number is selected at random from $\mathscr{E}$.
Find the probability that the number is an element of $A \cup B'$. **(2 marks)**

6 A and B are two mutually exclusive events.
$P(A) = 0.35$ and $P(A \text{ or } B) = 0.8$.
Work out $P(\text{not } B)$. **(2 marks)**

7 There are only white cubes and black cubes in a bag.
Marie takes at random a cube from the bag.
The probability that the cube is white is 0.45.
Marie puts the cube back in the bag.
Seb takes at random a cube from the bag.
He puts the cube back in the bag.

a What is the probability that Marie and Seb take cubes of different colours? **(2 marks)**

b There are 36 white cubes in the bag.
How many black cubes are there in the bag? **(2 marks)**

8 The Venn diagram shows customers' choices of
cheese (*C*), tomato (*T*) and lettuce (*L*) fillings for a
sandwich in a cafe.

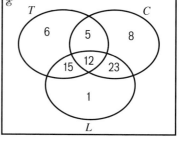

a How many people chose all three fillings? **(1 mark)**

b A customer is selected at random.
Work out the probability that this customer had tomato
and lettuce fillings. **(1 mark)**

c A customer who had lettuce was selected at random.
Work out the probability that this customer also had cheese. **(2 marks)**

9 There are 10 cubes in a bag. 6 of the cubes are red. 4 of the cubes are white.
Daisy takes at random two cubes from the bag.
Work out the probability that Daisy takes at least one red cube.
You must show your working. **(4 marks)**

10 A class of 27 students is split between boys and girls in the ratio 5 : 4.
Work out the probability that two students selected at random are both boys. **(4 marks)**

(TOTAL: 35 marks)

11 Challenge Two players are playing a card game with these sets of cards.

Player A

Player B

Both players shuffle their cards and turn over the top card.
Make up a rule for each player to win so that the game is fair.
Use probability to show that the game is fair.

12 Reflect Write down a word that describes how you feel

a before a maths test

b during a maths test

c after a maths test

> **Q12 hint**
>
> Here are some possible words:
> OK, worried, excited, calm.

Beside each word, draw a face, or 😞 to show if it is a good or a bad feeling.

Discuss with a classmate what you could do to change 😞 feelings to 🙂 feelings.

Exam-style question

1   Here is a solid square-based pyramid, *ABCDE*.

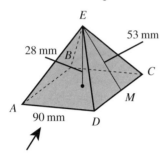

The base of the pyramid is a square of side 90 mm.
The height of the pyramid is 28 mm.
M is the midpoint of *CD*.
EM = 53 mm
Using compasses and a ruler, construct the front elevation of the pyramid
from the direction of the arrow.   **(3 marks)**

2   **Reasoning** Here are two different inequalities:

$2 < 2x \leqslant 10$
$2 \leqslant 2x < 10$

Jamal says, 'The two inequalities are the same because the values for x range from 1 to 5.'
Ahmed says, 'The two inequalities are different as the range of values for each inequality
is different.'
Who is correct? Give a reason for your answer.

Exam-style question

3   Zach is asked to enlarge triangle *ABC* with centre *O* and scale factor $1\frac{1}{2}$.
Zach draws triangle *A′B′C′*:

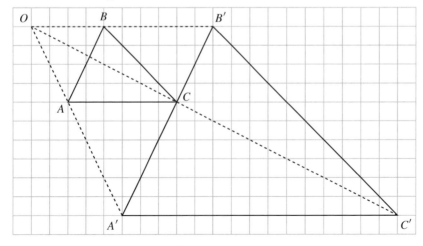

Explain why Zach's diagram is not correct.   **(1 mark)**

4 **Problem-solving** There are 108 male members and 112 female members of a leisure centre. 73 of these members are enrolled onto weekly fitness classes. Twice as many females as males are not enrolled onto weekly fitness classes. Copy and complete the frequency tree.

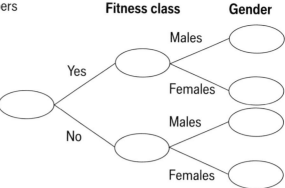

Fitness class   Gender

Yes — Males / Females

No — Males / Females

5 **Reasoning** Nadia is asked to solve the quadratic equation $5x^2 + 4x = 0$.
Nadia writes:

$$5x^2 + 4x = 0$$
$-4x \big($ $\quad\quad\quad\quad$ $\big) -4x$
$$5x^2 = -4x$$
$\div x \big($ $\quad\quad\quad\quad$ $\big) \div x$
$$5x = -4$$
$\div 5 \big($ $\quad\quad\quad\quad$ $\big) \div 5$
$$x = \frac{-4}{5}$$

a Nadia is incorrect. Explain why.
b Solve the quadratic equation $5x^2 + 4x = 0$.

6 **Problem-solving** Joe spins a spinner.
The spinner can land on red, yellow or blue.
The probability that the spinner will land on red is 0.4.
The probability that the spinner will land on yellow is x.
Joe spins the spinner 120 times.
Give an expression, in terms of x, for an estimate of the number of times the spinner will land on blue.

7 **Problem-solving** Gary buys three mobile phone cases and two charging leads and pays £29.50.
Gary's friend buys two mobile phone cases and takes a charging lead back to the shop.
The friend gets a full refund on the charging lead and pays £11.50 in total.
What is the cost of a mobile phone case? What is the cost of a charging lead?

8 **Reasoning**
Shape A is rotated 90° clockwise about the point $(-2, 1)$ to give shape B.
Shape B is translated by the vector $\begin{pmatrix} 3 \\ -1 \end{pmatrix}$ to give shape C.
Describe fully the single transformation that maps shape A onto shape C.

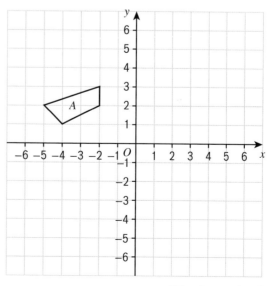

9 The diagram shows a right-angled triangle.
All the measurements are in centimetres.
The area of the triangle is $19.5\,\text{cm}^2$.
Work out the length of the shortest side of the triangle.
You must show all your working. **(4 marks)**

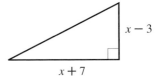

10 **Problem-solving** A school has 934 students.
558 students are in Key Stage 3 and 376 are in Key Stage 4.
$\frac{2}{3}$ of the students in Key Stage 3 live in the catchment area.
75% of the students in Key Stage 4 live in the catchment area.

  a Copy and complete the Venn diagram,
  where $\mathscr{E}$ = number of students in the school,
  $KS3$ = number of students in Key Stage 3
  and C = number of students living in the
  catchment area.

  b One student who lives in the catchment area is
  chosen at random.
  Work out the probability that the student is in
  Key Stage 3.

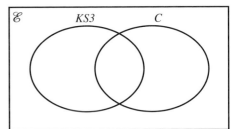

11 **Problem-solving** Here is a sketch of a rectangular garden $ABCD$,
where $AD = 5\,\text{m}$ and $AB = 6\,\text{m}$.

A gardener is putting a bird feeder in the garden.
The bird feeder needs to be:
  more than $4\,\text{m}$ from point C
  nearer to CD than to BC
  and less than $3\,\text{m}$ from DC.
Using a scale of $1\,\text{cm}$ to represent 1 metre, draw the garden and then shade the region where the
gardener can put the bird feeder.

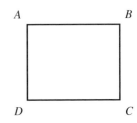

12 **Problem-solving** The Venn diagram shows some
information about a class of 30 students.
C = students who have a cat
D = students who have a dog

The probability of a student with a dog also having
a cat is $\frac{1}{5}$.
Work out the value of y.

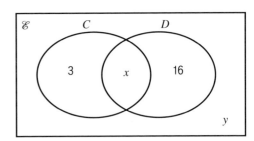

13 There are some circles and some squares in a bag.
The shapes are red or the shapes are blue.
The ratio of the number of circles to the number of squares is $5 : 4$.
The ratio of the number of red shapes to the number of blue shapes is $2 : 9$.

  a Explain why the least possible number of cubes in the bag is 99. **(1 mark)**

All the circles are blue.

  b Work out the least possible number of blue squares in the bag. **(3 marks)**

14 **Reasoning** The area of this trapezium is $266\,\text{cm}^2$.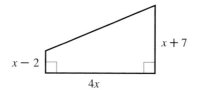
   a Show that $2x^2 + 5x - 133 = 0$
   b Work out the value of x.

---

15 When a biased coin is thrown 3 times, the probability of getting 3 heads is $\frac{64}{125}$.
   Work out the probability of getting 3 tails when the coin is thrown 3 times. **(2 marks)**

---

16 **Problem-solving** The quadratic formula is used to solve a quadratic equation.

Substituting the values into the formula gives $x = \dfrac{-9 \pm \sqrt{81 - 48}}{6}$

Work out the quadratic equation that is being solved.
Give your answer in the form $ax^2 + bx + c = 0$, where a, b and c are integers.

---

17 Rectangle $ABCD$ is transformed by a combined transformation of a reflection in the line $y = -1$ followed by a rotation.
Under the combined transformation, two vertices of the rectangle $ABCD$ are invariant.
Describe fully one possible rotation.

(2 marks)

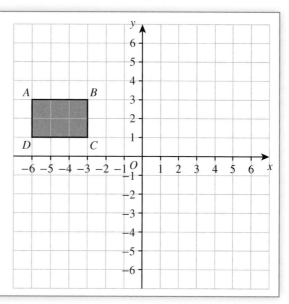

---

18 **Problem-solving** Maisie has 10 pens in her pencil case.
Four of the pens are blue and the rest of the pens are black.
Maisie takes a pen from her pencil case at random.
She lends this pen to a friend.
She then takes another pen from the pencil case at random.
Work out the probability that Maisie takes one pen of each colour.

19 **Reasoning** A curve C has equation $y = 4x^2 + 13x + 10$.
A line L has equation $y = x + 1$.
Solve the equations simultaneously to show that the curve and the line have only one point of intersection.

20 **Reasoning** A circle C has equation $x^2 + y^2 = 97$.
A line L has equation $y = 2x + k$.
The circle and the line intersect at points P and Q.
   a Solving the equations simultaneously, show that $5x^2 + 4kx + k^2 - 97 = 0$.
   b Given that $k = 1$, work out the coordinates of points P and Q.

Answers

UNIT 1 Number

1.1 Number problems and reasoning

1 12

2 a 2, 1   4, 1   6, 1
   2, 3   4, 3   6, 3
   2, 5   4, 5   6, 5
   2, 7   4, 7   6, 7
   2, 9   4, 9   6, 9

  b 15

3 a 6   **b** 2   **c** 3   **d** 5

  e Students' own answers, for example, There are 12 possible outcomes when rolling a dice and flipping a coin, and this is the same as the product of the possible outcomes of each event.

4 a 4, 4, 4   4, 4, 2, 2   4, 3, 3, 2   4, 2, 2, 2, 2
   3, 3, 3, 3   3, 3, 2, 2, 2   2, 2, 2, 2, 2, 2

  b Students' own answer   **c** 6

5 VP, VB, VC, VL, SP, SB, SC, SL, MP, MB, MC, ML

6 a 15

  b 3 starters and 4 mains: 12 combinations
   3 starters and 5 mains: 15 combinations
   a starters and b mains: $a \times b$ combinations

7 a 24   **b** Students' own answer

8 No, e.g. $196 \div 16$ is not a whole number.

9 a 10   **b** 10 000   **c** 5000

10 a ABC, ACB, BAC, BCA, CAB, CBA

  b Yes

  c i 24   **ii** 720   **iii** 3 628 800

11 a i 1 000 000 **ii** 6 760 000 **iii** 118 813 760
  b i 151 200   **ii** 3 276 000 **iii** 78 936 000

1.2 Place value and estimating

1 $10.15 \div 2.9 = 3.5$ and $10.15 \div 3.5 = 2.9$

2 a i 900 000 **ii** 870 000 **iii** 873 000
  b i 2000   **ii** 2000   **iii** 2020
  c i 0.007 **ii** 0.0071 **iii** 0.007 06

3 a 27   **b** 49   **c** 5

4 10

5 a 364.82   **b** 0.364 82   **c** 0.364 82

  d Students' own answers, for example, The number of digits after the decimal point in the answer is the same as the sum of the number of digits after the decimal point in each number.

6 a 3.7   **b** 37   **c** 0.986

7 a Students' own answer
  b Students' own answer
  c Students' own answer
  d It must use the digits 399492, so it must end in a 2.

8 0.006 93

9 a 2.2   **b** 2.4   **c** 2.6   **d** 2.8

10 The correct answers are given here. 0.1 out in either direction is acceptable.
  a 6.9   **b** 4.7   **c** 9.2
  d 11.3   **e** 3.2   **f** 6.3

11 The correct answers are given here. 1 out in either direction is acceptable.
  a 10   **b** 22   **c** 3
  d 50   **e** 40   **f** 96

12 a 16   **b** 4

13 a 0.4   **b** 11   **c** 1
  d 0.4, 11.2, 1.1 **e** Students' own answer
  f Students' own answer

14 $9.2^2 \approx 85$; $85 \times 6 = 510 \, \text{cm}^2$

15 $\sqrt{80} \approx 8.9$; $8.9 \times 4 = 35.6 \, \text{cm}$

16 a 4.5 cm, accept 4.4 or 4.6

17 a i £200   **ii** £100   **iii** £100
  b i £189.50 **ii** £98.54 **iii** £94.75
  c Students' own answers, for example, It is better to overestimate a cost, because if you underestimate it, you might not have enough money to pay.

1.3 HCF and LCM

1 a 1, 2, 4, 5, 10, 20   **b** 2 and 5

2 a 2, 3, 5, 7, 11, 13, 17, 19   **b** 1, 2, 3, 4, 6, 8, 12, 24

  c

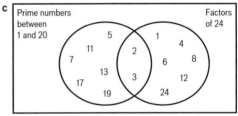

3 6

4 a 5^3 **b** 2^5 **c** $2 \times 3 \times 5^2$
  d $2^3 \times 3^2$ **e** 125, 32, 150, 72

5 a, b

  c $40 = 2 \times 2 \times 2 \times 5$
  d $40 = 2^3 \times 5$

6

  $75 = 3 \times 5 \times 5 = 3 \times 5^2$

7 a $60 = 2 \times 2 \times 3 \times 5 = 2^2 \times 3 \times 5$
  b $60 = 2 \times 2 \times 3 \times 5 = 2^2 \times 3 \times 5$

8 Answers to parts **a** and **b** are the same.

9 a Students' own answers, for example,
   $48 = 12 \times 4 = 6 \times 8 = 3 \times 16 = 2^4 \times 3$
  b Students' own answers, for example, It doesn't make any difference which factors you start with, as you get the same answer.

10 Students' own answers

11 a 2×3^2 **b** $2 \times 3 \times 7$ **c** 5^2
   d $2^2 \times 3^2$ **e** $2^3 \times 3$ **f** $2^4 \times 5$

12 $m = 3, n = 3, p = 5$

13 a $2^4 \times 5$
   b i $160 = 2 \times 80$ so $160 = 2 \times 2^4 \times 5 = 2^5 \times 5$
     ii $40 = 80 \div 2$ so $40 = 2^4 \times 5 \div 2 = 2^3 \times 5$

14 a No, Yes, Yes
   b $792 = 2^3 \times 3^2 \times 11$ so $12 = 2^2 \times 3$ divides into 792 exactly.
   c Yes. $132 = 2^2 \times 3 \times 11$
   d No. $27 = 3^3$ and 792 only contains 3^2

15 a HCF = 6; LCM = 120   **b** HCF = 2; LCM = 420
   c HCF = 2; LCM = 72   **d** HCF = 15; LCM = 45
   e HCF = 9; LCM = 108   **f** HCF = 33; LCM = 66

16 a Students' own answer   **b** Students' own answer

17 a $2^2 \times 3$ **b** $2^4 \times 3^2$

18 a $2^2 \times 3^4 \times 5$ **b** $2^3 \times 3^6 \times 5^2$

19 a $2^2 \times 5 \times 7$ **b** $2^3 \times 5^2 \times 7^2$
   c i $(2 \times 5 \times 7)$ **d ii** $(2^6 \times 5^2 \times 7^2)$

20 a 3.10 pm   **b** 4

21 12 cm tiles

22 Students' own answer

23 a 1, 2, 3, 6, 9   **b** The factors of 18 other than 18

1.4 Calculating with powers (indices)

1 11, −11

2 a 27   **b** 16   **c** −1   **d** 64
   e 25   **f** 0.008   **g** 12   **h** 72

3 a 16   **b** 27

4 a 2   **b** 3   **c** 4   **d** 1

5 a 3   **b** −1   **c** 10   **d** −5
   e Students' own answer

6 a 40   **b** 19   **c** 5   **d** 4
   e 5   **f** 15   **g** −72   **h** −0.1

7 a 64   **b** 8   **c** 2

8 a 2   **b** 3   **c** 10

9 a i 100 000   **ii** 100 000
    iii 100 000 000   **iv** 100 000 000
   b Add the indices together.
   c i 10^7 **ii** 10^6 **iii** 10^{-5}

10 a 3^6 **b** 4^{10} **c** 9^7 **d** 5^9

11 a 3   **b** 2   **c** 7

12 a 3^8 **b** 4^6 **c** 5^4
   d 2^7 **e** 2^9 **f** 3^6

13 a i 5^3 **ii** $5^5 \div 5^2 = 5^3$
   b 4^4 **c** $6^1 = 6$ **d** Subtract the indices.

14 a 7^4 **b** 4^2 **c** $3^1 = 3$

15 a 2   **b** 4   **c** −3

16 a i 1, 2, 9; 1, 3, 8; 1, 4, 7; 1, 5, 6;
     2, 3, 7; 2, 4, 6; 3, 4, 5
    ii 4, 4, 4
   b i Any two numbers where one is 6 more than the other,
     e.g. 41 and 35
    ii 12, 6 or −6, −12

17 a 5^6 **b** 6^8 **c** 5^2 **d** 8^1

18 a 16   **b** $\frac{1}{2}$

19 a 2^{15} **b** 6^{12} **c** 8^{14}
   d Students' own answers, for example, The power in the final
    answer is the product of the powers in the question.

20 a 2^{12} **b** 6^{10} **c** 4^{-6} **d** 5^{12}

21 a Alison added the indices instead of multiplying.
   b Students' own answer

22 a i 10^8 **ii** 10^{12} **iii** 10^{20}
    iv 10^6 **v** 10^{12} **vi** 10^{24}
   b i The power of 10 is half the power of 100.
    ii The power of 10 is one-third the power of 1000.

23 3

24 a 2^{11} **b** 5^5 **c** $4^3 = 2^6$

1.5 Zero, negative and fractional indices

1 a 36   **b** 8   **c** 3   **d** 2

2 a $\frac{5}{3}$ **b** $\frac{6}{5} = 1\frac{1}{5}$ **c** $\frac{2}{3}$ **d** $-\frac{7}{20}$

3 a 3^{10} **b** 2^2 **c** 2^7
   d 3^5 **e** 3^3

4 a 5^8 (390 625) **b** $\frac{1}{4}$ **c** $\frac{4}{9}$
   d $\frac{1}{5}$ **e** $-\frac{2}{3}$

5 a 3   **b** 4   **c** 6   **d** 3

6 a i 0.5   **ii** 0.25
    iii 0.2   **iv** 0.1
   b i $\frac{1}{2}$ **ii** $\frac{1}{4}$
    iii $\frac{1}{5}$ **iv** $\frac{1}{10}$
   c i 0.25   **ii** 0.0625
    iii 0.04   **iv** 0.01
   d i $\frac{1}{4}$ **ii** $\frac{1}{16}$
    iii $\frac{1}{25}$ **iv** $\frac{1}{100}$
   e i 2   **ii** $\frac{16}{9} = 1.\dot{7}$
   f 1 divided by the positive power.

7 a $\left(\frac{1}{4}\right)^{-2} = 16$, $\frac{1}{3^5} = 3^{-5}$, $\frac{3}{2} = \left(\frac{2}{3}\right)^{-1}$, $\frac{1}{2^4} = 2^{-4}$, $\frac{1}{5^3} = 5^{-3}$
   b $3^{-8} = \frac{1}{3^8}$, $\frac{1}{8^3} = 8^{-3}$
   c $\left(\frac{2}{3}\right)^{-1} = \frac{3}{2}$, so $\left(\frac{a}{b}\right)^{-1} = \frac{b}{a}$

8 a 6^{12} **b** 5^{-4} **c** 8^{-1}

9 a $2^3 \div 2^3 = 2^0$ **b** 8   **c** $2^3 \div 2^3 = 8 \div 8 = 1$
   d $2^3 \div 2^3 = 2^0 = 1$
   e $7^5 \div 7^5 = 7^0 = 1$
   f $a^0 = 1$

10 a $\frac{1}{3}$ **b** $\frac{1}{16}$ **c** $\frac{1}{100\,000}$ **d** $\frac{4}{3}$
   e $\frac{100}{49}$ **f** $\frac{125}{64}$ **g** $\left(\frac{1}{5}\right)^0 = 1$ **h** $7^1 = 7$

11 a $\frac{4}{5}$ **b** $\frac{16}{121}$ **c** $\frac{25}{144}$ **d** $\frac{27}{1000}$

12 a $\frac{10}{7}$ **b** 100 000   **c** $\frac{125}{8}$ **d** $\frac{25}{36}$

13 a i 7   **ii** 4   **iii** 11   **iv** $\frac{2}{5}$
   b square root
   c i 3   **ii** 10   **iii** −1   **iv** $\frac{1}{10}$
   d cube root
   e i 5   **ii** 2

14 a 6   **b** 9   **c** $\frac{1}{3}$
   d $\frac{7}{10}$ **e** $\frac{4}{5}$ **f** $\frac{8}{7}$
   g −2   **h** $\frac{1}{3}$ **i** $-\frac{4}{5}$

15 He has multiplied 64 by $-\frac{1}{4}$ instead of finding 1 divided by the fourth root.

16 a $\frac{1}{5}$　　**b** $\frac{1}{4}$　　**c** $\frac{5}{3}$　　**d** $\frac{3}{2}$

17 a 16　　**b** 1000　　**c** 64　　**d** 16
  e $\frac{8}{27}$　　**f** $\frac{1}{9}$　　**g** $-\frac{1}{27}$　　**h** $\frac{4}{9}$

18 a 9　　**b** $\frac{125}{12}$　　**c** $\frac{125}{8}$

19 a 4　　**b** $\frac{1}{3}$　　**c** -2
  d $-\frac{1}{2}$　　**e** $\frac{7}{2}$　　**f** $\frac{7}{4}$

20 a $\frac{1}{5} \times 16 = \frac{16}{5}$　　**b** He said $25^{-\frac{1}{2}} = 5$ but it is $\frac{1}{5}$

21 a $2^{\frac{3}{4}}$　　**b** $2^{\frac{6}{5}}$　　**c** $2^{-\frac{4}{5}}$　　**d** $2^{\frac{15}{4}}$

22 $-\frac{9}{10}$

1.6 Powers of 10 and standard form

1 A and C

2 a 4500　　**b** 0.63　　**c** 6.94　　**d** 0.8453

3 a 10 000　　　　　　　**b** 10^3
  c 1　　　　　　　　　**d** $\frac{1}{10} = 0.1$
  e $\frac{1}{100} = 0.01$　　　　**f** $\frac{1}{1000} = 0.001$
  g $\frac{1}{10\,000} = 0.000\,01$　　**h** 10^{-6}

4 a 5.67　　**b** 4.908 34

5 Answers in bold

Prefix	Letter	Power	Number
tera	T	10^{12}	1 000 000 000 000
giga	G	10^9	**1 000 000 000**
mega	M	**10^6**	1 000 000
kilo	k	10^3	**1000**
deci	d	**10^{-1}**	0.1
centi	c	10^{-2}	**0.01**
milli	m	**10^{-3}**	0.001
micro	μ	10^{-6}	**0.000 001**
nano	n	**10^{-9}**	0.000 000 001
pico	p	10^{-12}	**0.000 000 000 001**

6 a 0.015 g　　　　　　**b** 0.000 000 007 m
  c 0.0017 kg　　　　　**d** 0.000 000 000 0073 s

7 a 0.000 0012 m　　　　**b** 0.000 000 000 025 m
  c 0.000 000 000 9 m

8 a $4.5 \times 10\,000$　　**b** 10^4　　**c** 4.5×10^4
  d 4.5×0.001　　**b** 10^{-3}　　**c** 4.5×10^{-3}

9 A, D, F

10 a 8.7×10^4　　**b** 1.042×10^6　　**c** 1.394×10^9
  d 7×10^{-3}　　**e** 2.84×10^{-6}　　**f** 1.003×10^{-4}

11 a 400 000　　**b** 350　　**c** 6780
  d 0.062　　**e** 0.000 0893　　**f** 0.004 04

12 D, B, C, A

13 a $\neq$　　**b** $\neq$　　**c** $=$
  d $\neq$　　**e** $\neq$　　**f** $=$
  g No, 1.999×10^4 is smaller than 1.9×10^5

14 a 4.5×10^{12}, 7×10^{-5}
  b Calculator says 4.5 E +12, for example.
    Calculator says 7 E −05
  c Students' own answers

15 a 6×10^7, 60 000 000　　**b** 2×10^{11}, 200 000 000 000
  c 4.8×10^6, 4 800 000　　**d** 2×10^3, 2000
  e 3×10^{-8}, 0.000 000 03　　**f** 2.5×10^{-5}, 0.000 025
  g 2.5×10^7, 25 000 000　　**h** 6.4×10^{-5}, 0.000 064

16 0.51 kg

17 No. 1.28×10^9 is less than $10 \times 1.5 \times 10^8 = 1.5 \times 10^9$

18 a i 80 000　　**ii** 300
  b 80 300, 8.03×10^4

19 a 4.07×10^5　　**b** 9.778×10^4
  c 7.2162×10^2　　**d** $8.325\,993 \times 10^5$

20 $x = 5$, $y = 1$, $z = -2$

1.7 Surds

1 $-3, 5$

2 The digit 5 is recurring, 0.555 555...

3 a 4　　**b** 25　　**c** 8　　**d** 10

4 a $3, -3$　　**b** $4, -4$　　**c** $4, -4$
  d $6, -6$　　**e** $5, -5$

5 a 2.24　　**b** 2.65　　**c** 4.36　　**d** 7.28
  e Square root

6 a i 2.449 48...　　　　　**ii** 2.449 48...
  b i 3.872 98...　　　　　**ii** 3.872 98...
  c Answers to parts **i** and **ii** are the same.
  d i 12　　**ii** 5　　**iii** 5

7 a 2　　**b** 5　　**c** 8　　**d** 6

8 a $2\sqrt{5}$　　**b** $10\sqrt{3}$　　**c** $2\sqrt{11}$
  d $5\sqrt{10}$　　**e** $20\sqrt{2}$　　**f** $12\sqrt{14}$

9 a $5\sqrt{3}$　　**b** 8.66 (2 d.p.)

10 a Students' own answer, e.g. $\sqrt{80}$
  b Students' own answer

11 a $\frac{\sqrt{7}}{2}$　　**b** $\frac{\sqrt{5}}{3}$　　**c** $\frac{2\sqrt{5}}{7}$
  d $\frac{3\sqrt{2}}{5}$　　**e** $\frac{3}{8}$

12 $\sqrt[3]{6}$, $\sqrt{8}$, $\sqrt{17}$

13 a $x = \pm 3\sqrt{10}$
  b Students' own answers, for example, You can't solve $x^2 + 90 = 0$ in the same way because you need to solve $x^2 = -90$ or $x = \sqrt{-90}$ which can't be done.

14 a $x = \pm 5\sqrt{2}$　　**b** $x = \pm 4\sqrt{10}$　　**c** $x = \pm 2\sqrt{3}$　　**d** $x = \pm 2\sqrt{7}$

15 a i $60\sqrt{6}$　　**ii** $48\sqrt{15}$　　**iii** $180\sqrt{2}$
  iv 144　　**v** 605　　**vi** $24\sqrt{3}$

16 a $\frac{\sqrt{7}}{7}$　　**b** $\frac{\sqrt{5}}{5}$　　**c** $\frac{\sqrt{5}}{10}$　　**d** $\frac{\sqrt{2}}{2}$
  e $\frac{\sqrt{15}}{5}$　　**f** $\frac{8\sqrt{10}}{5}$　　**g** $\sqrt{11}$

17 $\left(\frac{2}{\sqrt{10}}\right)^3 = \frac{8}{10\sqrt{10}} = \frac{8\sqrt{10}}{100} = \frac{2\sqrt{10}}{25}$

18 $a = 7$, $b = 343$

19 $4\sqrt{5}$ cm

20 a $\frac{\sqrt{3}}{2}$　　**b** $\frac{16}{7}$　　**c** $\frac{15}{4}$

1 Check up

1 60

2 a 1536.4　　**b** 0.92

3 7.3

4 a i 4　　**ii** $\frac{1}{2}$
  b i 3.8　　**ii** 0.5

5 $2 \times 3^2 \times 5$

6 HCF = 2; LCM = 126

7 a $2\times5^2\times7^2$ **b** $2^3\times5^2\times7^3$

8 a $10^3=1000$ **b** $2^4=16$
c $\sqrt[3]{-27}=-3$ **d** $5^0=1$

9 a 2 **b** 144 **c** 1

10 a 9^4 **b** 3^8 **c** 5^5
d 2^7 **e** 2^{12} **f** 4^{-2}

11 a $\frac{1}{16}$ **b** 125 **c** $\frac{8}{27}$
d $\frac{1}{4}$ **e** $\frac{1}{4}$

12 a $3\sqrt{7}$ **b** $50\sqrt{10}$

13 a $\frac{10}{\sqrt{10}}$ **b** $\frac{\sqrt{6}}{3}$ **c** $\frac{\sqrt{6}}{12}$
d $\sqrt{2}$ **e** $\frac{\sqrt{6}}{36}$

14 a 3.204×10^7 **b** 7×10^{-4}

15 a 56 000 **b** 0.001 09

16 a 4.5×10^{12} **b** 5×10^2 **c** 8.6×10^3

18 30

1 Strengthen

Calculations, factors and multiples

1 a C, 1, R C, 1, B C, 1, W
C, 2, R C, 2, B C, 2, W
S, 1, R S, 1, B S, 1, W
S, 2, R S, 2, B S, 1, W
b Students' own answer

2 a 11.172, 111.72, 1117.2, 111 720
b 63.5, 635, 6350, 635 000

3 a 641.69 **b** 64 169 **c** 0.641 69

4 a $64.169\div7.21=8.9$
b i 89 **ii** 8.9 **iii** 0.89

5 a

b i 7.1 **ii** 7.7 **iii** 8.7

6 a i 6 **ii** 20 **iii** 12 **iv** 2
b i 6.1 **ii** 19.7 **iii** 12.0 **iv** 2.1

7 a $2^3\times3^2$ **b** $2^2\times3\times5$ **c** $3^4\times7^2$

8 a
```
        60
       /  \
      6   [10]
     / \   / \
   [2][3][2][5]
```
b $60=2\times2\times3\times5$
c $60=2^2\times3\times5$

9 a
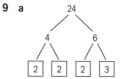
b
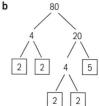

c

d

e
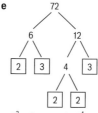

10 a $2^3\times3$ **b** $2^4\times5$ **c** $2\times3\times5$
d 2^4 **e** $2^3\times3^2$

11 a $18=2\times3\times3$ **b** $45=3\times3\times5$
c
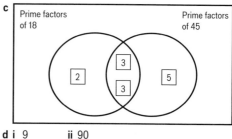

d i 9 **ii** 90

12 a HCF = 10; LCM = 60 **b** HCF = 7; LCM = 84
c HCF = 5; LCM = 75 **d** HCF = 4; LCM = 396

Indices and surds

1 a $2^3=8$ **b** $5^2=25$ **c** $(-3)^3=-27$

2 a 16 **b** 125 **c** 6 **d** 3

3 a 21 **b** 32 **c** −24
d −20 **e** 63 **f** 150

4 a 27 **b** 169 **c** 3

5 a $3^5\times3^3=3^8$ **b** $4^4\times4^6=4^{10}$
c 6^2 **d** $\frac{7^6}{7^3}=7^3$
e To multiply powers of the same number, **add** the indices.
To divide powers of the same number, **subtract** the indices.

6 a 5^9 **b** 7^{11} **c** 5^5
d 9^6 **e** 8^{-2} **f** 7^7

7 a 2^7 **b** 5^7 **c** 2^{13} **d** 3^8

8 a 4^6 **b** 6^{12} **c** 7^{10} **d** 8^{21}
e To work out a power in a bracket raised to a power, **multiply** the indices.

9 a i 1 **ii** 1 **iii** 1 **iv** 1
b i 1 **ii** 1 **iii** 1 **iv** 1

10 a i 13 **ii** 13
b i 8 **ii** 5 **iii** 9 **iv** 12
c i 8 **ii** 8
d i 5 **ii** 3 **iii** 10 **iv** 2
e $\sqrt[4]{16}=2$

11 a i 4 **ii** 16
b i 25 **ii** 9 **iii** 100 **iv** 4
c 8

12 a i $\frac{1}{4^3}$ **ii** 10^{-5} **iii** 2^{-1}

iv $\frac{1}{3^{\frac{1}{3}}}$ **v** $\left(\frac{7}{6}\right)^{-2}$

b i $\frac{1}{4}$ **ii** $\frac{1}{100}$ **iii** $\frac{1}{6}$ **iv** $\frac{1}{5}$

13 a $50 = 25 \times 2$, so $\sqrt{50} = \sqrt{25} \times \sqrt{2} = 5\sqrt{2}$
b $84 = 4 \times 21$, so $\sqrt{84} = \sqrt{4} \times \sqrt{21} = 2\sqrt{21}$
c i $4\sqrt{6}$ **ii** $5\sqrt{7}$ **iii** $8\sqrt{2}$

14 a 9 **b** 36 **c** 17 **d** 21

15 a $\frac{\sqrt{17}}{17}$ **b** $\frac{\sqrt{21}}{7}$ **c** $\frac{\sqrt{2}}{4}$ **d** $\frac{3\sqrt{5}}{5}$

Standard form

1 a Yes **b** No; 32 is not between 1 and 10.
c No; cannot have millions.
d No; 0.8 is not between 1 and 10.

2 a 6.8×10^4 **b** 9.4×10^7 **c** 8.01×10^5
d 4×10^{-6} **e** 3.9×10^{-3} **f** 5.3×10^{-8}

3 a 8×10^9 **b** 6×10^{14} **c** 6×10^2
d 4.8×10^{13} **e** 5.6×10^{10} **f** 4.8×10^{-5}

4 a 25 000, 0.013 **b** 25 000.013

1 Extend

1 a Square A **b** Square B

2 $27 = 3^3$; $(3^3)^2 = 3^6$
$9 = 3^2$; $(3^2)^3 = 3^6$

3 36 and 108

4 a $48 = 2 \times 2 \times 2 \times 2 \times 3$
$90 = 2 \times 3 \times 3 \times 5$
$150 = 2 \times 3 \times 5 \times 5$
b HCF = 6; LCM = 3600 **c** Students' own answer

5 a 300 minutes = 5 hours
b He is partly correct: teaching times of 10, 15, 20, ... hours would also work in theory but be too long in practice.

6 a Numbers ending in zero are multiples of 10.
$10 = 2 \times 5$
b 4 **c** $2^5 \times 9 \times 5^5 = 900\,000 = 9 \times 10^5$

7 a $2^8 \times 5^9$ **b** $2^7 \times 3^6$ **c** $2^6 \times 3^5 \times 5^7$
d $2^{10} \times 3^9 \times 5^7$

8 a 11 881 376 **b** 4 084 101

9 625

10 a i 116 460 km **ii** 1.1646×10^5 km
b i 227 900 000 000 m **ii** 2.279×10^{11} m
c i 0.000 004 m **ii** 4×10^{-6} m
d i 0.000 000 000 1 m **ii** 1×10^{-10} m

11 1.7962×10^8 kg

12 a 0.000 6265 **b** −428 560 000

13 a $\frac{7\sqrt{2}}{2}$ **b** $-\frac{\sqrt{2}}{6}$

14 $\frac{\sqrt{3}}{3}$

15 One course : $5 + 7 + 3 = 15$
Two courses: $35 + 15 + 21 = 71$
Three courses: 105
Total: $15 + 71 + 105 = 191$

16 a 9 000 000 **b** 800 **c** 0.000 008

17 a 20 **b** 3 **c** 19
d 3 **e** 2 **f** 2

18 a e.g. $x = 1$, $y = -3$, $z = 2$
b x and y can take any values that satisfy $x + y + 3 = 1$

19 −3

20 Students' own answers, e.g. $\frac{1}{\sqrt{7}}$, $\frac{2}{\sqrt{28}}$

1 Test ready

Sample student answers

1 The student has not written the answer in standard form.

2 In the first line, the student should have multiplied by $\frac{\sqrt{6}}{2}$. Their answer is in the correct form, however.

1 Unit test

1 a 1 multiplication with an answer of 33.642,
e.g. 62.3×0.54 or 0.623×54
b 1 division with an answer of 0.623 e.g. $33.642 \div 54$

2 $\sqrt[3]{27}$, $\sqrt{69}$, 3.4^2, 13.74

3 a $2 \times 3 \times 7$ **b** $84^3 = 2^6 \times 3^3 \times 7^3$

4 HCF = 15, LCM = 150

5 1.15 pm

6 a 48 **b** 46.2

7 a $a = 6$ **b** $a = 3$ **c** $a = 2$

8 3^{30}

9 $18 = 2 \times 3 \times 3$
$2520 = 2 \times 3 \times 3 \times 140$.
Conclusion: yes.

10 a 6.5×10^{-7} **b** 3.2×10^9 **c** 9×10^5

11 $\frac{9}{16}$

12 a 1.8×10^5 **b** 6×10^4
c 7.2×10^9 **d** 5×10^{-1}

13 a 20 **b** 1000

14 a 12 **b** $\frac{7}{6}$

15 $15\sqrt{6}$ units^2

16 4500

17 $\frac{4\sqrt{6}}{3}$

18 The tray is not deep enough.
One sheet of paper is 0.009 cm thick.
500 sheets is 4.5 cm thickness in total.
4.5 cm > 4 cm.

19 a e.g. $a = 2$, $b = -8$, $c = 2$
b a and b as long as $a + b = -6$

20 Students' own answers

UNIT 2 Algebra

2.1 Algebraic indices

1 a 4 **b** 2 **c** 2 **d** 2

2 a 2^7 **b** 2^3 **c** 2^{12} **d** 2^{-1}

3 a 10^5 **b** 5^2 **c** 5^3 **d** 3^3

4 a x^7 **b** x^7 **c** a^{11}
d y^9 **e** t^9

5 a $6a^8$ **b** $8c^6$ **c** $40n^7$ **d** $7v^5$
e $15s^5t^6$ **f** $30p^6q^6$

6 a x^2 **b** x^3 **c** p^3 **d** y^6
e r **f** t^2 **g** n^2

7 a $2g^2$ **b** $3f^4$ **c** $3x^2$ **d** $3w^2$
e $2a$ **f** $5ab$ **g** $4mt^3$ **h** $3r^2s^2$

8 a x^6 **b** x^{18} **c** t^9 **d** j^{18}

9 $(3x^2)^3$ and $27x^6$, $(3x^3)^2$ and $(-3x^3)^2$

10 a $8r^6$ **b** $9f^8$ **c** $\dfrac{b^6}{8}$ **d** n^2p^2

  e n^3p^3 **f** n^6p^3 **g** $8x^3y^3$ **h** $8x^3y^{12}$

11 a t^8 **b** $64x^3y^6$ **c** $3a^2b^2$

12 a Clockwise for multiply: $3x^4y^3$, $18x^7y^5$, $72x^8y^5$, $12x^5y^3$
  Divide: $4x$, $6x^3y^2$

  b Students' own answers.

13 a $8x^6y^9$ **b** $36x^{10}y^4$ **c** $81x^8y^4$ **d** $\dfrac{4x^6y^4}{9}$

14 a $x^3 \div x^3 = x^{3-3} = x^0$

  $x^3 \div x^3 = \dfrac{x^3}{x^3} = 1$

  Therefore $x^0 = 1$

  b $x^3 \div x^4 = \dfrac{x \times x \times x}{x \times x \times x \times x} = \dfrac{1}{x}$

  $x^3 \div x^4 = x^{3-4} = x^{-1}$

  Therefore $x^{-1} = \dfrac{1}{x}$

  c $x^3 \div x^5 = \dfrac{x \times x \times x}{x \times x \times x \times x \times x} = \dfrac{1}{x^2}$

  $x^3 \div x^5 = x^{3-5} = x^{-2}$

  Therefore $x^{-2} = \dfrac{1}{x^2}$

15 a $\dfrac{1}{b}$ **b** $\dfrac{1}{h^2}$ **c** $\dfrac{1}{y^3}$ **d** 1

  e a^2 **f** a^4 **g** $2x^2y^2$ **h** $8x$

16 a $12c^3d$ **b** 3 **c** -4

17 a $\dfrac{1}{t^6}$ **b** x^2 **c** 1 **d** w

18 a 1 **b** $\dfrac{1}{e^2f^3}$ **c** $\dfrac{1}{4p^{10}q^2}$ **d** $\dfrac{5v^3}{2u^4}$

  e $\dfrac{a^2}{b}$ **f** $\dfrac{q^8}{9p^2}$ **g** $\dfrac{s^6}{4t^2}$ **h** $\dfrac{s^6}{25t^4}$

19 a x **b** x^2 **c** $3x$ **d** $3x^2$

  e $2x^3$ **f** $2x^4$ **g** $6xy^2$ **h** $4x^2y^3$

20 a $x^{\frac{1}{2}} \times x^{\frac{1}{2}} = x^{\frac{1}{2}+\frac{1}{2}} = x^1 = x$

  $\sqrt{x} \times \sqrt{x} = x$

  Therefore $x^{\frac{1}{2}} = \sqrt{x}$

  b $x^{\frac{1}{3}} \times x^{\frac{1}{3}} \times x^{\frac{1}{3}} = x^{\frac{1}{3}+\frac{1}{3}+\frac{1}{3}} = x^1 = x$

  $\sqrt[3]{x} \times \sqrt[3]{x} \times \sqrt[3]{x} = x$

  Therefore $x^{\frac{1}{3}} = \sqrt[3]{x}$

21 a $x^{\frac{3}{2}}$ **b** x^2 **c** y **d** $y^{\frac{5}{3}}$

22 a $4b$ **b** $2c$ **c** $4c^3$ **d** $\dfrac{1}{4c^3d^2}$

  e $\dfrac{x}{2y^4}$ **f** $\dfrac{1}{2d}$ **g** $\dfrac{y}{2x^2}$

23 a 1 **b** x **c** $r^{\frac{3}{2}}$ **d** $r^{\frac{1}{2}}$

  e $\dfrac{3}{p}$ **f** $2p$ **g** $8a^3$ **h** $27a^3b^6$

2.2 Expanding and factorising

1 a $4x+8$ **b** $3q-15$ **c** $14m+7$ **d** $-2y-12$

2 a $9a+5$ **b** $x+4$ **c** $5s$

3 a $5(x+3)$ **b** $5(2y+5)$ **c** $x(x-1)$ **d** $y(3y+1)$

4 a $2(x+5)$ **b** $2x, 10$

  c The answers to part **b** add up to give the answer to part **a**.

5 a, **b** and **d** are all identities; **c** is an equation.

  a $x \times x \equiv x^2$ **b** $3x+4x-x \equiv 6x$ **d** $\dfrac{6x}{3} \equiv 2x$

6 a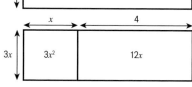

  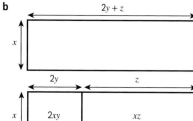

  b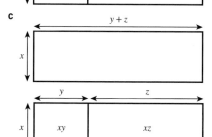

  c

7 a x^2+7x **b** y^3-3y **c** $2y^3-6y$
  d $2t^2-4t$ **e** $2t^2-wt$ **f** $st+stw$
  g $3st^2w+9st$ **h** $3s^2t^2+15st$

8 a $8e+18$ **b** $8y+14$ **c** $2x-10$
  d $9m+27$ **e** $x+1$ **f** $13x+8y$

9 a $4y^2-5y$ **b** $10t^2-6t$
  c $8t^2-3t-2$ **d** $2p^2+pq+q^2$
  e $3w^2+w$ **f** $5e^2+3ef+2f^2$

10 $10x+13$

11 a $2x$ **b** x **c** $4y$ **d** $5xy$

12 a $2(x+6)$ **b** $2(2x+3y)$ **c** $2x(2+3y)$
  d $b(3a-5)$ **e** $7x(y+z)$ **f** $ab(1-c)$
  g $t^2(t+2)$ **h** $3pq(2p-3)$ **i** $3xz(x+4)$
  j $5jk(4k-3j)$ **k** $2pq(6r-5s)$ **l** $2def(4d+5f)$

13 a $8x^2-20xy$ **b** $2cp(2-3p)$ **c** $3m^2n^3$

14 a $4(s+2t)$
  b $= 4(s+2t)[(s+2t)-2]$
    $= 4(s+2t)(s+2t-2)$

15 a $7(p+1)(2p+5)$ **b** $5(c+1)(c-1)$
  c $4(y+4)(3y+10)$ **d** $(a+3b)(a+3b-2)$
  e $5(f+5)(2f+1)$ **f** $5(a+b)(a+b-2)$

16 a Students' own answers

b One of the numbers is even so can be written as $2m$.
One of the other numbers is a multiple of 3 so can be written as $3n$.
If the other number is p, their product is $2m \times 3n \times p = 6mnp$ so is divisible by 6.

c One of the numbers is even so can be written as $2m$.
One of the other numbers is a multiple of 4 so can be written as $4n$.
If the other two numbers are p and $p + 2$, their product is $2m \times 4n \times p \times (p + 2) = 8mnp(p + 2)$ so is divisible by 8.

17 a Either the first number is even, so it and the next integer can be written as $2m$ and $2m + 1$, or the second number is even so it and the previous integer can be written as $2n$ and $2n - 1$.

b $2m + (2m + 1) = 4m + 1$ or $2n + 2n - 1 = 4n - 1$
$4m$ are multiples of 2 so are even, so $4m + 1$ and $4n - 1$ are odd.

2.3 Equations

1 a 6 **b** 24 **c** 12

2 a $8x + 6$ **b** $21x - 4$ **c** $-8x + 17$

3 a $x = 7$ **b** $x = 1$ **c** $x = 21$

4 a $3x + 1 = 5x - 9$
$1 = 2x - 9$
$10 = 2x$
b $x = 5$

5 a $x = 5$ **b** $x = 4$ **c** $x = 10$ **d** $x = -2$

6 $3x + 7 = 5x - 3$
$7 = 2x - 3$
$10 = 2x$
$x = 5$
Width of rectangle $= 3x + 7 = 15 + 7 = 22\,\text{cm}$
Length $= 88 \div 22 = 4\,\text{cm}$, so $y = 4$

7 a i $12x - 16$ **ii** $7x - 21$
b $x = -1$

8 a $3x + 16$ **b** $x = 3$

9 a $x = 1$ **b** $x = -1$

10 $x = -\frac{13}{2}$

11 a $x = -\frac{3}{11}$ **b** $x = \frac{22}{7}$ **c** $x = \frac{29}{2}$
d $x = -\frac{4}{3}$ **e** $x = \frac{21}{25}$ **f** $x = \frac{33}{37}$

12 $\frac{7x - 1}{4} = 5$
$7x - 1 = 20$
$x = 3$

13 a $x = 5$ **b** $x = \frac{11}{2}$ **c** $x = -17$ **d** $x = -\frac{22}{5}$
e $x = -\frac{1}{3}$ **f** $x = -\frac{1}{6}$ **g** $x = -9$ **h** $x = \frac{47}{15}$

14 $\frac{10}{x - 4} = 3$
$10 = 3(x - 4)$
$x = \frac{22}{3}$

15 a $x = 7$ **b** $x = -2$ **c** $x = -\frac{9}{7}$ **d** $x = \frac{15}{8}$

16 $\frac{2x + 1}{3} = \frac{x - 5}{9}$
$\frac{9(2x + 1)}{3} = x - 5$
$3(2x + 1) = x - 5$
$x = -\frac{8}{5}$

17 a $x = \frac{7}{2}$
b Multiply by the LCM of the denominators.

18 a $b = 9$ **b** $n = 1$ **c** $c = \frac{13}{3}$
d $x = -\frac{1}{5}$ **e** $x = \frac{41}{6}$

19 $30°$

2.4 Formulae

1 $6\,\text{m}^2$

2 a 7.5×10^7 **b** $300\,000\,000$

3 1.22

4 a Formula **b** Equation **c** Expression
d Identity **e** Expression **f** Formula
g Expression **h** Equation **i** Identity
j Equation
k Students' own answers

5 b $x(x - 1)$

6 a 2000 **b** -2

7 a 350 **b** 8

8 a 130 minutes **b** $T = 30 + 40m$

9 a $A = \frac{bh}{2}$
b i 9 **ii** 10

10 £12 521.56

11 a 320 m **b** $22.4\,\text{m/s}^2$

12 a $a = \frac{v - u}{t}$ **b** $n = \frac{m - E}{2}$
c $G = \frac{WH}{3}$ **d** $Q = 7(R - C)$
e $V = 3T + W, W = V - 3T$
f $a = \frac{2}{t^2}(s - ut), u = \frac{s}{t} - \frac{1}{2}at$

13 a $v = 1$, or $v = -1$ **b** $a = \frac{v^2 - u^2}{2s}$

14 a $82.4\,°\text{F}$ **b** $C = \frac{5F - 160}{9}$ **c** $40\,°\text{C}$

15 a $T = \frac{D}{S}$ **b** 192 seconds

16 a 4659 **b** 183 747
Answers to parts **a** and **b** are based on assumption that the distance from the top of a person's head to their eye level is 8 cm.

17 a 5.35×10^{-1}
b New value of P is 4.75×10^{-1}; the denominator increases more than the numerator, so the value of $\frac{x}{l^3}$ decreases.

2.5 Linear sequences

1 5.7

2 a 6 **b** 16 **c** 26

3 4, 25

4 a 2, 4, 6, 8, 10 **b** 4, 7, 10, 13, 16
c $-4, -8, -12, -16, -20$ **d** $1, -1, -3, -5, -7$

5 a 2, 7, 12, 47, 497 **b** 10, 13, 16, 37, 307
c 98, 96, 94, 80, -100 **d** $2\frac{1}{2}, 3, 3\frac{1}{2}, 7, 52$

6 a 0.02 and 0.67 **b** $\frac{1}{2}$ and $\frac{5}{4}$
c -5 and -8 **d** 1 and 2.569

7 a $2, 3, -4, -2, 5, 3, -2, \frac{1}{2}$
b In front of n
c i 5 **ii** -3
d i 3, 8, 13 **ii** 1, -2, -5

8 a $2n + 1$ **b** $4n + 10$ **c** $10n - 8$
d $-3n + 16$ **e** $-3n + 59$ **f** $1.3n + 1.9$

9 a nth term $= 3n + 2$. The solution to the equation
$3n + 2 = 596$ is $n = 198$, which is a whole number.
Therefore 596 is a term in the arithmetic sequence.

b The solution to the equation $7n - 3 = 139$ is $n = \frac{142}{7}$,
which is not a whole number.
Therefore 139 is not a term in the arithmetic sequence.

c Students' own answers

10 a $6n - 3$

b No, Ben is not right. The solution to the equation
$6n - 3 = 150$ is $n = 25.5$, which is not a whole number.
Therefore 150 is not a term in the arithmetic sequence.

11 4.01

12 a $n = 125.375$

b From part **a** it is the 126th term; this is $8 \times 126 - 3 = 1005$

13 a 4007 **b** 49

14 28 weeks

15 27 weeks

16 a 10, 17, 24, 31 **b** 7 **c** 3

d 7 is the number in front of n, and 3 is the zero term.

e -3, 7, 100, 2

17 a -3 **b** $u_n = 4n - 3$

18 a $2n - 1$ **b** $2n$ **c** $\frac{2n-1}{2n}$ or $1 - \frac{1}{2n}$

19 a $\frac{5n+2}{4n}$ or $\frac{5}{4} + \frac{1}{2n}$ **b** $\frac{3n-1}{2n+3}$

20 a i 9, 21, 33, 45, 57
ii 41, 81, 121, 161, 201

b i Input difference 3, output difference 12
ii Input difference 10, output difference 40
The differences are scaled by 4, which is the multiplier in the function machine.

21 a 4 **b** 8 **c** $p = 2$ **d** $q = 4$

22 a $p = 7, q = 6$

2.6 Non-linear sequences

1 a 29 **b** 64

2 a 48, 96. Multiply by 2.

b 27, $\frac{1}{3}$. Divide by 3.

c 18. Multiply by -3.

3 a £1248 **b** £153

4 a i 5, 8, 13 **ii** 5, 9, 14 **iii** -1, 0, -1

b No; there is not a constant difference between the terms.

5 a i 1, $\frac{1}{2}$, $\frac{1}{3}$, $\frac{1}{4}$ **ii** 2, 4, 8, 16

iii 0.3, 0.09, 0.027, 0.0081

b Sequences **ii** and **iii** are geometric.

6 a $\sqrt{2}$, 2, $2\sqrt{2}$, 4, $4\sqrt{2}$ **b** 3, $6\sqrt{3}$, 36, $72\sqrt{3}$, 432

7 $u_4 = 1 \times 3^3$, $u_5 = 1 \times 3^4$, $u_6 = 1 \times 3^5$, $u_7 = 1 \times 3^6$, $u_8 = 1 \times 3^7$,
$u_9 = 1 \times 3^8$, $u_{10} = 1 \times 3^9$

8 a $u_{10} = 2^9$ **b** $u_{10} = 10^{10}$ **c** $u_{10} = 5000 \times \left(\frac{1}{2}\right)^9$

d $u_{10} = 5 \times \left(\sqrt{5}\right)^9$

9 a £10, £20, £40, £80, ... **b** 8 months

10 $u_5 \times u_8 = 10^5 \times 10^8 = 10^{5+8} = 10^{13} = u_{13}$

11 a 2, 4, 8, 16

b $u_m \times u_n = 2^m \times 2^n = 2^{m+n} = u_{m+n}$

12 a 1, 4, 9, 16, 25, 36

b i $n^2 + 1$ **ii** $n^2 - 1$ **iii** $(n+1)^2$

13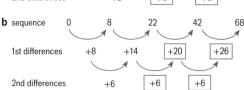

14 a 126 **b** 46 **c** 10

15 a sequence 8, 11, 16, 23, 32; 1st differences $+3$, $+5$, $+7$, $+9$; 2nd differences $+2$, $+2$, $+2$

b sequence 0, 8, 22, 42, 68; 1st differences $+8$, $+14$, $+20$, $+26$; 2nd differences $+6$, $+6$, $+6$

c Constant; 2 times the number in front of n^2

16 a $2n^2 + 1$ **b** $3n^2 - 5$ **c** $n^2 + 3$
d $6n^2 - 5$ **e** $10 - n^2$ **f** $\frac{1}{2}n^2 + 4$

17 a 1, 5, 10, 10, 5, 1 **b** 4, 8, 16, 32
c 2^n

18 $2n^2 - 5$

19 a 2. Halve the second difference to find the coefficient of n^2.
Therefore $a = 1$.

b 3, 5, 7 **c** $2n - 1$ **d** $n^2 + 2n - 1$

20 a $n^2 + 3n$ or $n(n+3)$ **b** $n^2 - 2n + 1$ or $(n-1)^2$
c $2n^2 + n + 2$ **d** $3n^2 - n + 1$

2.7 More expanding and factorising

1 a 8 and -8

b i 1 and 12, 2 and 6, 3 and 4
ii -1 and 6, 1 and -6, -2 and 3, 2 and -3

2 a $4x^2$ **b** $25y^2$ **c** $4t$ **d** $10n$

3 a $(x+2)(x+1)$
b $x^2 + x + 2x + 2$; $x^2 + 3x + 2$

4 a $x^2 + 16x + 60$ **b** $x^2 + 3x - 18$
c $x^2 + 6x - 40$ **d** $x^2 - 7x + 12$

5 a $x^2 + 4x + 4$ **b** $x^2 - 6x + 9$
c $x^2 + 10x + 25$ **d** $x^2 - 8x + 16$

6 a $2x^2 + 13x + 15$ **b** $6x^2 + 7x + 2$
c $9x^2 + 6x + 1$ **d** $4x^2 - 4x + 1$

7 a $(51+49)(51-49) = 2 \times 100 = 200$
b i 400 **ii** 0.12

8 a $x^2 - 16$ **b** $x^2 - 4$ **c** $m^2 - 64$

d Students' own answers, for example, When the brackets
are expanded, the answer is of the form
$a^2 - b^2$, which is a difference of two squares.

9 a $(x-5)(x+5)$ **b** $(y+7)(y-7)$
c $(t-9)(t+9)$ **d** $(10-n)(10+n)$

10 a $(x+2)(x+3) = x^2 + 5x + 6$
b $(x-3)(x+8) = x^2 + 5x - 24$

11 a $(x+1)(x+7)$ **b** $(x+3)(x+4)$
c $(x+3)(x+5)$ **d** $(x+1)^2$

12 a $(x+3)(x-1)$ **b** $(x-3)(x+1)$
c $(x-7)(x+1)$ **d** $(x-8)(x+2)$

13 a $(x-2)(x-4)$ **b** $(x-3)(x-4)$
c $(x-2)^2$ **d** $(x-12)(x-2)$

14 a $(x+5)(x+2) = x^2+7x+10$
   b $7x+10$ **c** $x=3$
15 $x=1.5$
16 a $4x^2-9 = (2x)^2-3^2 = (2x+3)(2x-3)$
   b $16y^2-1 = (4y)^2-1^2 = (4y+1)(4y-1)$
17 a $(3m-5)(3m+5)$ **b** $(9-5c)(9+5c)$
   c $(x-7y)(x+7y)$
18 a $3(x^2-4) = 3(x-2)(x+2)$
19 $4(x-2)(x+2)$

2 Check up

1 a $20p^4$ **b** $5x^2$ **c** $64d^6$ **d** n
2 a $5q$ **b** $2x^2+2x$
3 a $2y(x-3)$ **b** $3a(b-2a)$
4 a $x^2-2x-24$ **b** $x^2+10x+25$
5 a $\dfrac{2}{x^2}$ **b** 4 **c** $\dfrac{1}{b^6}$
   d y^2 **e** $3c$ **f** $\dfrac{4}{p^5}$
6 a $x^2-2x-15$ **b** x^2+6x+9
7 a $(x-9)(x+9)$ **b** $(x-2)(x-7)$
8 a Formula   **b** Identity
   c Expression   **d** Equation
9 $x = \dfrac{9}{2}$
10 $x = -17$
11 94
12 $C = 25+36n$
13 a $y = \dfrac{4-x}{3}$ **b** $b = \dfrac{S-4a^2}{6a}$
14 $x = 10$
15 18, 29
16 11, 15, 19, 23, 87
17 a $9n-7$
   b The equation $9n-7 = 167$ has solution $n = \dfrac{174}{9}$,
      which is not a whole number.
      Therefore 167 is not a term in the sequence.
   c 173
18 $3n^2+7$
20 a Clockwise from top left:
      x^2+x-6, $3x^2-7x+2$, $6x^2+10x-4$, $2x^2+10x+12$.
   b $12x^2+14x+4$. Any order would give the same result,
      multiplication is commutative.
   c $2(2x+1)(3x+2)$

2 Strengthen

Simplifying, expanding and factorising

1 a t^5 **b** t^7 **c** t^4
2 a t^2 **b** t^{-7} **c** t^2 **d** t^{-1}
3 a $18p^5$ **b** $72z^5$ **c** $14b^8$ **d** $8r^3$
   e $10s^{-6}$ **f** $6x$ **g** $6m^{\frac{2}{3}}$
4 a t^4 **b** t^3 **c** $t^0 = 1$
   d x^2 **e** x^{-3} **f** y^3
5 a $5p^4$ **b** $3a^5$ **c** $3y^{-3}$ **d** $2p^3$
6 a $(x^2)^2 = x^2 \times x^2 = x^4$
   b $(x^2)^3 = x^2 \times x^2 \times x^2 = x^6$
   c $(x^2)^4 = x^2 \times x^2 \times x^2 \times x^2 = x^8$
   d When you find the power of a power you multiply the
      powers together.
7 a x^{12} **b** a^2 **c** r^{-2} **d** g

8 a $6x+3y$ **b** $6x-8y$ **c** $12x-5y$
9 a $11c+d$ **b** $14m+10n$
10 a $ab(3b-2)$ **b** $pq(5p-2)$
   c $2x(4y+3)$ **d** $2p(2r+3)$
   e $3st(t-2)$ **f** $7b(2ab+3)$
11 a

×	x	$+5$
x	x^2	$5x$
$+4$	$4x$	$+20$

   b $(x+4)(x+5) = x^2+5x+4x+20$
                      $= x^2+9x+20$
12 $x^2-12x+36$

×	x	-6
x	x^2	$-6x$
-6	$-6x$	$+36$

13 a x^2-16
   b x^2-2x-3
   c $x^2-11x+28$
14 a 3 and 4, 2 and 6   **b** 2 and 6
   c $(x+2)(x+6)$
15 a $(x+12)(x+1)$ **b** $(x+3)(x+4)$
16 a 2 and −5, 1 and −10, −1 and 10
   b i $(x-10)(x+1)$ **ii** $(x+10)(x-1)$
      iii $(x+5)(x-2)$ **iv** $(x-5)(x+2)$

Equations and formulae

1 a When there is no = sign it is **an expression**.
   b When the two sides are always equal it is **an identity**.
   c When you can solve it to find the value of the letter it is **an
      equation**.
2 a Expression   **b** Identity
   c Formula   **d** Equation
3 a 9   **b** 36   **c** 41   **d** 31
4 19
5 $x = \dfrac{y+4}{2}$ or $\dfrac{1}{2}(y+4)$ or $\dfrac{1}{2}y+2$
6 $x = \dfrac{5-y}{3}$
7 a $Q = aP-ab$ or $a(P-b)$
   b $b = \dfrac{4c}{3}$ **c** $s = \dfrac{x-y}{2}$
8 a $3x+6 = 5x$
        $6 = 2x$
        $3 = x$
   b $7x-4 = 5x+2$
        $2x-4 = 2$
        $2x = 6$
        $x = 3$
9 $x = 4$
10 a i $14x-28$ **ii** $6x+10$
   b $14x-28 = 6x+10$ **c** $x = \dfrac{19}{4}$
11 a $2x-2$ **b** $x = \dfrac{7}{2}$
12 a $x = 20$ **b** $x = \dfrac{5}{3}$
   c $x = 11$ **d** $x = 7$
13 a $x = 18$ **b** $x = \dfrac{7}{4}$
   c $x = 11$ **d** $x = 7$
   e The denominator

14 a 20

b $\frac{20x}{4} - \frac{20x}{5} = 3 \times 20$

c $\frac{\overset{5}{\cancel{20}}x}{\underset{1}{\cancel{4}}} - \frac{\overset{4}{\cancel{20}}x}{\underset{1}{\cancel{5}}} = 3 \times 20$

$5x - 4x = 60$

d $x = 60$

Sequences

1 a 13, 21 **b** 50, 81 **c** 42, 68

2 a 5, 7, 9 **b** 48, 46, 44

c 2, 5, 10 **d** 10, 40, 90

3 a 3 **b** 36 **c** The general term is $3n$

4 a $10n$ **b** $7n$ **c** $12n$

5 a $4n$ **b** 3 **c** $4n + 3$

6 a i 30, 36 **ii** 9, 11

iii 16, 19 **iv** 5, 0

b i $6n$ **ii** $2n - 1$

iii $3n + 1$ **iv** $-5n + 30$

7 a 14, 18, 22, 26, 30

b No, 10 is even and $4n$ will be even; even + even is always even.

c No, the numbers in the sequence are even but 351 is odd.

d 23rd

8 a 53; 14, 18; 4, 4 **b** $a = 2$

c $b = 3$ **d** $2n^2 + 3$

9 a $4n^2 + 5$ **b** $n^2 - 10$

2 Extend

1 a i 6, 7, 8 **ii** 20, 10, 5

iii 3, -1, -5 **iv** -3, 9, -27

b Sequences **i** and **iii** are arithmetic, **ii** and **iv** are geometric.

2 a 0.473 **b** 11.5

3 43

4 a $2n$, $3n$, $5n$, $8n$ **b** m, $2m$, $3m$, $5m$

b Students' own answers, e.g. 6, 6, 12, 18, 30, ...

0, 10, 10, 20, 30, ...

5 $100^x \times 10\,000^y = (10^2)^x \times (10^4)^y = 10^{2x} \times 10^{4y} = 10^{2x + 4y}$

$10^{2x + 4y} = 10^t$ so $2x + 4y = t$

6 a In-store: 12 800, 10 240; Online: 3240, 4860

b 2021

7 $x + 2$

8 £1478.18

9 13

10 $(x + 2)^2 - x^2 = (x^2 + 4x + 4) - x^2 = 4x + 4$

11 a $a = \frac{2A - bh}{h}$ or $\frac{2A}{h} - b$

b $h = \frac{3V}{\pi r^2}$ **c** $a = \frac{(r - 1)S}{r^n - 1}$ **d** $y = \frac{a^2 x - c}{b^2}$

12 a $12x^2 y$ **b** $16m^{-1}n^3$

c $2p^{-1}q^4$ **d** $3x^3 y^{\frac{5}{2}}$

13 a It is not lower as the temperature in the classroom is $25\,°C$.

b $F = \frac{9C + 160}{5}$

14 a The odd numbers are 1 greater than the even numbers which are multiples of 2.

b $(2m + 1)(2n + 1) = 4mn + 2m + 2n + 1 = 2(2mn + m + n) + 1$, which is odd

15 a $(x - 4)(x - 8)$ **b** $(x - 6)^2$

c $(x - 2)(x + 1)$ **d** $\left(\frac{x}{5} - \frac{y}{7}\right)\left(\frac{x}{5} + \frac{y}{7}\right)$

16 a $x = -\frac{5}{6}$ **b** $x = 26$

c $x = -\frac{24}{5}$ **d** $x = -1$

17 If the consecutive numbers are n and $n + 1$ then the difference between their squares is
$(n + 1)^2 - n^2 = n^2 + 2n + 1 - n^2 = 2n + 1$, which is an odd number.

18 a $-2n^2 + 3$ **b** $-n^2 + 2n - 1$ or $-(n - 1)^2$

2 Test ready

Sample student answers

1 You can factorise $x^2 - 9$ to $(x - 3)(x + 3)$ so the student's answer is not fully factorised.

Full answer is $5(x - 3)(x + 3)$

2 First the student should have added x^2 to both sides, then divided by $3a$.

The correct answer is $b = \frac{y^2 + x^2}{3a}$

2 Unit test

1 47, 76

2 a equation **b** expression

c identity **d** formula

3 $x = -3$

4 $m = 0.5$

5 $x = \frac{29}{5}$

6 a $63q^5$ **b** $5y^3$

c c^8 **d** $5d^3$

7 $10x + 21$

8 a $12x^2 + 3xy$ **b** $x^2 + x - 12$

c $x^2 - 14x + 49$ **d** $2x^2 + 5x - 7$

9 27, 9, 3

10 a $6n - 2$

b The terms in the sequence are all even but 231 is odd.

c 238, when $n = 40$

11 a 1 **b** $4x^2$ **c** $2x^{-1}y^{-2}$

12 $\frac{-4n + 29}{3n + 4}$

13 $x^2 + 20x + 19$

14 $\frac{y + 5}{5t} = x$

15 Odd number $= 2k + 1$

$2a + 1$ is an odd number.

$2b + 1$ is an odd number.

$(2a + 1) - (2b + 1) = 2a + 1 - 2b - 1$

$= 2a - 2b = 2(a - b)$

Any $2k$ is an even number. Hence $2(a - b)$ is an even number.

16 nth term $= 3n^2 - 1$

17 a $\frac{4x - 3}{15} = \frac{x + 3}{5}$

b $x = 12$

c 2 cm

18 a 2.7×10^4 **b** $m = \frac{2E}{v^2}$

19 a $(x - 4)(x + 4)$

b $3y(2y - 3x)$

c $(x + 5)(x - 2)$

d $(2x + 10)(2x - 10)$ or $4(x + 5)(x - 5)$

20 a i 3   **ii** 6   **iii** 10   **iv** 15

b $\frac{1}{2}(2)(2+1) = (1)(3) = 3$

$\frac{1}{2}(3)(3+1) = (1.5)(4) = 6$

$\frac{1}{2}(4)(4+1) = (2)(5) = 10$

$\frac{1}{2}(5)(5+1) = (2.5)(6) = 15$

c $\frac{1}{2}(100)(100+1) = (50)(101) = 5050$

d i 9   **ii** 36   **iii** 100   **iv** 225

e $\left(\frac{1}{2}(n)(n+1)\right)^2$

21 Students' own answers

UNIT 3 Interpreting and representing data

3.1 Statistical diagrams 1

1 Mode 2, median 3, range 5

2 a 10   **b** 89 kg

    c Yes; the number of people is 10 < 12 and total mass is 716 kg < 800 kg.

3 a 750   **b** Theatre

    c $20\,000 \times (45 \div 360) = 2500$ at festival but only $1500 \times (90 \div 360) = 375$ at theatre

4 a 35 cm   **b** 108 cm   **c** 13   **d** 7

    e 110 cm

5 a 3.7 s   **b** 32.7 s

    c No; although 6 of the leaves in the diagram are 3, they do not have the same stem; the mode is 32.7 cm.

6 On average Sophie has a better score than Celia because her median is lower. She is also more consistent because her range is lower.

7 a Maths: median 60, range 54
English: median 58, range 37

    b The maths marks are more spread out since the range for maths is far greater than the range for English. The average marks are very similar since the median mark for maths is only 2 marks higher than the median English mark.

    c Maths scores are more spread out, implying a greater range.

8 a

	A		B	
		1	3 6	
9 9 6 4		2	3	
7 6 0		3	1 4 7 7 7 8 9	
8 7 6		4	2 2 3	
9 5 2		5	2 3	
		6	4	

Key: (A) 4 | 2 represents 24 cm
(B) 1 | 3 represents 13 cm

    b For type A there is an even spread of tulips in the range 20 to 59 cm because the numbers on the left-hand side appear as a block. For type B most tulips are between 30 and 39 cm, with a few shorter and a few taller, because the numbers show a distribution that is peaked at the centre and diminishes on either side of the centre.

9 a, b

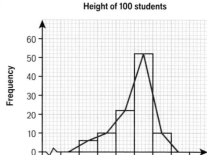

Height of 100 students

c Plot the frequency for each group against the midpoint of the group.

10 a

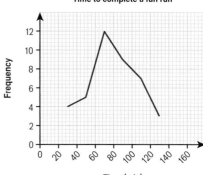

Time to complete a fun run

    b 20 min   **c** 120 min

    d The times are grouped so we do not know the actual longest and shortest times taken.

11

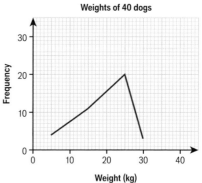

Weights of 40 dogs

12 a *B*   **b** About the same   **c** *A*

3.2 Time series

1 a 12   **b** 3

2 a B   **b** D   **c** A   **d** C

    e E

3 a 37.3 °C   **b** 38.3 °C, 10 am

c

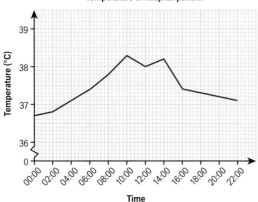

Temperature of hospital patient

d 37.6 °C; the patient's temperature was not recorded at 7 am and may not have increase steadily over the 2-hour period.

e The temperature increased steadily between midnight and 10 am, then fluctuated around 38 °C for four hours. Between 14:00 and 16:00 it decreased sharply, then continued to decrease slowly until 22:00.

4 a

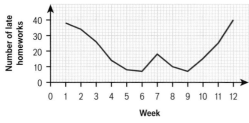

Late homeworks

b The number of late homeworks starts off very high, decreases mid-term but then gets steadily higher during the last three weeks of term. There is small blip near half-term.

5 a

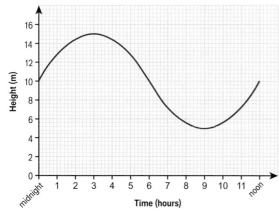

Height of sea water in a harbour

b 3 am

c The water depth increases from midnight to 3 am, then falls to a minimum at 9 am. Between 9 am and noon, the depth increases.

d Between 7 am and 11 am

6 a £4.90

b Yes; magazine A has gone up by £3.40 whereas magazine B has only risen by 90p.

c Yes; the graph is bending downwards, or the slope of the graph is going down.

d Students' own answers, e.g. both magazines are likely to be the same price of about £7.00; likely to be inaccurate as people may not be willing to pay £7.00 for a print magazine by 2022.

7 a 66 000

b

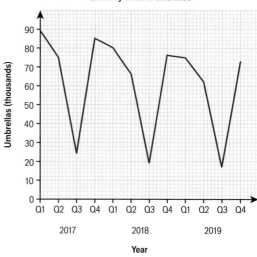

Quarterly sales of umbrellas

c Q1 of 2017

d Due to seasonal variations, sales fluctuate wildly. The overall trend is a decrease in sales.

e 2017: 68 250
2018: 60 250
2019: 56 750

8 a

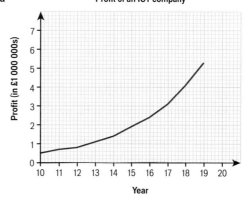

Profit of an ICT company

b Profit increases at an increasing rate.

c About £1.9 million   **d** About £6.9 million

e Students' own answers, e.g. **c** is likely to be reliable as the graph is rising steadily around 2015; **d** is less reliable as the trend might not continue.

9 Students' own answers, e.g. points joined with curve, not straight lines; should not start at vertical axis as this is not labelled with a 'time'; scale on vertical axis does not go up in equal-sized steps (not linear) or 10.5 and 11.5 are missing; it is not clear what the numbers 1, 2, 3, 4 along the horizontal axis mean; 2018 and 2019 do not show (or leave space for) values for all the quarters.

3.3 Scatter graphs

1 **A** Negative **B** Zero **C** Positive

2 Point A

3 a

Maths and science test results

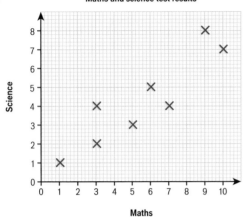

b In general, students with higher maths scores got **higher** science scores and students with lower maths scores got **lower** science scores.

4 a A No correlation **B** Negative correlation
C Positive correlation

b As price increases, sales **decrease**.

c As temperature increases, **sales increase**.

5 a

Engine size and distance

b Negative correlation

c The larger the engine, the shorter the distance travelled on a litre of petrol.

6 a

Score and values of paintings

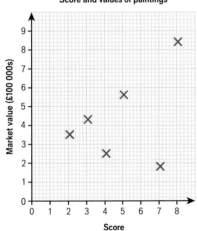

b No correlation: there is no relationship between the value of painting and the score awarded.

7 a

Road accidents and restaurants in towns

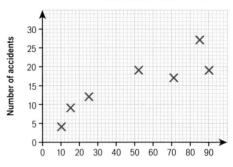

Positive correlation: towns with a larger number of takeaway restaurants tend to have a larger number of road accidents.

b The data provides no support for the councillor's views. Although there is positive correlation it may not be one of cause and effect: large, busy towns are likely to have both more takeaway restaurants and more accidents than small, quiet towns.

8 a Negative correlation **b** Positive correlation
c No correlation

9 a

Mass of product at different temperatures

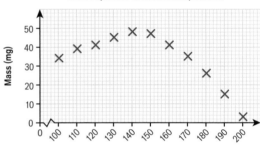

b Positive correlation at temperatures up to about 145 °C, negative correlation at temperatures over 145 °C.

c The mass increases to a maximum and then steadily decreases.

10 a Negative correlation

b As money spent on quality control goes up, the proportion of faulty mp3 players goes down.

c 4.2% **d** £73 000

3.4 Line of best fit

1 When the correlation between x and y is negative, as values of x increase, values of y **decrease**.

2 a 4 **b** 3

3 C

4 a, b

Height and weight of athletes

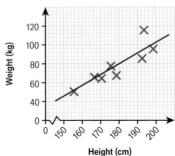

b About 85 kg **c** About 163 cm

5 **a** (3, 1600) **b** Negative correlation
c About 3 years
d Yes; the trend is a general decrease in price as the age increases.

6 **a, c**

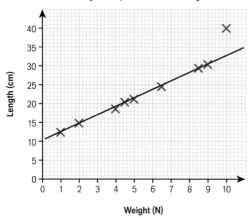

Length of rope with different weights

b The last point does not fit into the pattern of the other points. This might be due to an experimental misreading or even a change in behaviour of the elastic when it is subject to a larger weight.
d About 26 cm

7 **a**

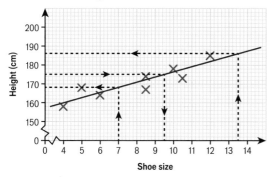

Height and shoe size of male students

b **i** About 9.5   **ii** About 168 cm   **iii** About 186 cm
c **iii** is the least reliable because it lies outside the range of the data points.

8

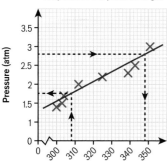

Temperature and pressure of gas

a About 348 K   **b** About 1.75 atm

9 **a** Jack 2.9, Joe 2.3
b Jack's estimate is more reliable. He uses more points, and the points on his diagram are much closer to the line of best fit.

10 **a** Negative correlation
b The point (2.5, 750) lies well away from the overall pattern on the scatter graph.
c About £240

11 **a**

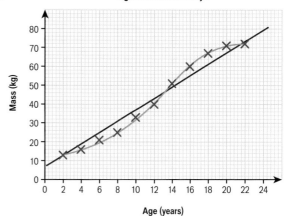

Age and mass of 11 boys

b **i** About 52 kg   **ii** About 79 kg
c **i** is more reliable because the age of 15 is inside the range of the data points whereas 24 is outside.
d **i** About 56 kg   **ii** About 72 kg
e **d** is more reliable. The points nearly lie exactly on a smooth curve. This is a better fit of the data points. People have a growth spurt during their teenage years, which slows down until it stops at the age of about 24 for boys so the graph should flatten off.

12 Students' own answer, e.g. use given data to make predictions about unknown values using interpolation or extrapolation.

3.5 Averages and range

1 **a** 15.5   **b** 30
2 **a** 14   **b** 1
3 14
4 $7.68 \approx 8$
5 **a** Mean £19 400, median £15 000, mode £12 000
b Median; mean is distorted by one high salary and mode is lowest salary so neither of these gives a typical salary.
6 **a** Mean 8.375, median 7.75, mode 7
b Mode; this is the most popular shoe size so it makes sense to order what customers are likely to want to buy. The values of the mean and median aren't proper shoe sizes.
7 **a** Median; the low value of 6 s distorts the mean, making it too low, and the mode gives the longest time so neither of these is typical.
b Mode; the data is qualitative so you cannot work out the mean or median.
8 **a** Mean £212, median £190, mode £180
b Mean, as it takes into account all five values and could be used to work out the total bill.
9 Students' own answers, e.g.
Mean: takes all the values into account but is affected by outliers, e.g. for car fuel consumption.
Median: gives a good idea of a typical value, not affected by outliers, e.g. for quoting a typical salary.
Mode: the most common value, the only average that can be used with qualitative data, e.g. for the most popular car colour.
10 **a** Outlier 7 kg, range 25 kg
b Outlier £38 000, range £24 000

11 a 2.9 and 500 are outliers, which are probably misreadings so should be ignored; 18 °C

b −£250 000 is an outlier; without any information to the contrary it is probably correct and just a bad year so should be included; £400 000.

12 a

Time, T (min)	Frequency, f	Midpoint, x	xf
$0 \leqslant T < 4$	27	2	$2 \times 27 = 54$
$4 \leqslant T < 10$	34	7	$7 \times 34 = 238$
$10 \leqslant T < 20$	15	15	$15 \times 15 = 225$
$20 \leqslant T < 60$	4	40	$40 \times 4 = 160$
Total	**80**		**677**

Mean = 8.4625 minutes

b 60 minutes; the times are grouped so we do not know the actual longest and shortest call lengths.

13 a 3   **b** 8   **c** 16

d $20 \leqslant t < 30$

e There are 21 data values, so the median is in position $\frac{21+2}{2} = 11$

f $20 \leqslant t < 30$

14 a 36   **b** $7.5 \leqslant d < 8.0$

c $7.0 \leqslant d < 7.5$

d Ben: mean = 7.58 m (3 s.f.); Jamie: mean = 7.47 m (3 s.f.)

e Ben: modal class $7.5 \leqslant d < 8.0$, range 2 m
Jamie: modal class $7.5 \leqslant d < 8.0$, range 2.5 m

f Jamie, because he has done more jumps in training over 8.0 m.

15 The annual mean of coarse particles is 34.1 mg/m^3 and the mean for fine particles is 23.4 mg/m^3. Both annual means are below the legal limit for that type of particulate.

16 a 6

b Mean = $(1 \times 1 + 3 \times 3 + 5 \times 4 + 7 \times 2 + 9 \times 3 +$
$\qquad 11 \times 2 + 13 \times 1 + 15 \times 2 + 17 \times 4 + 19 \times 0) \div 22$
$= (1 + 9 + 20 + 14 + 27 + 22 + 13 + 30 + 68 + 0) \div 22$
$= 204 \div 22 = 9.27 \ldots$
so no compensation.

3.6 Statistical diagrams 2

1 530

2 a Pie chart with Tea 72°, Coffee 180°, Cola 45°, Water 63°

b

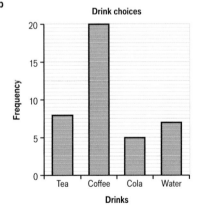

Drink choices

3

	Yes	No	Total
Boys	50	30	80
Girls	25	75	100
Total	75	105	180

4 a

	No change	Improved	Much improved	Total
Drug A	10	45	5	60
Drug B	7	20	13	40
Total	17	65	18	100

b $\frac{2}{5}$

c Students' own answer, e.g. drug B had a greater proportion much improved but drug A had a greater proportion improved.

5 a Any suitable two-way table

b No, as only 56% want the extra lockers.

6 a The vertical scale does not start from zero. This makes a small difference look like a big difference.

b The number who want the rail link is very similar to the number who don't want it.

7 The bar for 'Nutty Oats' is wider than the rest.
The vertical axis has no scale or units.

8 a £4   **b** £300

c Bought in April and sold in September.

9 a The data is not quantitative.

b i Pie chart   **ii** Dual bar chart

c 198

10 a It is possible to see the actual marks in a stem and leaf diagram.

b

Boys		Girls
7 7 6 5 3	0	1 6
5 0 0	1	1 5 6 7
3 1	2	0 4 5 8
9 4 1	3	9 9

Key: (Boys) 0 | 1 represents 10 marks
(Girls) 1 | 5 represents 15 marks

c Boys' median = 10, girls' median = 18.5
Boys' range = 36, girls' range = 38
So the girls had higher test marks than the boys, on average, and their marks were slightly more spread out.

11 Frequency polygon. Students' reasons, for example:
Stem and leaf diagrams cannot be used with grouped data.
Scatter diagrams are for data pairs so cannot be used.
The researcher wants to compare the performance of several hospitals so could plot two or three frequency polygons on the same diagram. Not easy to compare waiting times across several hospitals by drawing several pie charts.

3 Check up

1

	Party A	Party B	Total
Men	120	80	200
Women	130	50	180
Total	250	130	380

a 180   **b** 130

2 a 24

b No; the proportions are the same but the numbers are different. 12 adults and 8 children chose maths.

3 a 15

b Range for cod is 39 and range for plaice is 28.

c 28.5 cm

d The cod lengths are uniformly spread out whereas the plaice lengths are concentrated between 17 and 19 cm and 42 and 45 cm.

4

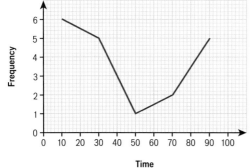

5 a Outlier £4800; range £4350

   b Outliers 22 cm, 24 cm; range 29 cm

6 a 9.625 **b** $5 \leqslant x < 10$

   c 25 **d** $5 \leqslant x < 10$

7 a 5000 **b** Seasonal variations in weather

   c Sales of sun cream are generally increasing.

8 a Positive correlation

   b i 42 **ii** 96

   c i, because **ii** is outside the range of the data points.

9 Students' own answers

10 a, b Students' own answers

   c The new mean is 3 more than the old mean.

   d Old mean $= \dfrac{w+x+y+z}{4}$

    New mean $= \dfrac{(w+3)+(x+3)+(y+3)+(z+3)}{4}$

    $= \dfrac{w+x+y+z+12}{4}$

    $= \dfrac{w+x+y+z}{4}+3$

    $=$ old mean $+3$

   e Mean is multiplied by c.

    New mean $= \dfrac{cw+cx+cy+cz}{4}$

    $= \dfrac{c(w+x+y+z)}{4}$

    $= c \times$ old mean

3 Strengthen

Statistical diagrams

1 a $\dfrac{1}{2}$ **b** 36 **c** 10

   d No; the proportions are the same but the numbers are different. 5 boys and 9 girls chose archery.

2 a 2 **b** 6 **c** 14

   d

	Yes	No	Total
Boys	**2**	4	**6**
Girls	3	**11**	**14**
Total	5	**15**	20

3 a 10 **b** 14 minutes

   c In the last row of the chart. **d** 2

4 a

```
    Set A      |   | Set B
        7 0    | 2 | 6 8 8
    8 2 0 0    | 3 | 2 3
          9    | 4 | 0
```

| Key: (Set A) 0 | 2 represents 20 |
| (Set B) 2 | 6 represents 26 |

   b Both sets have a median of 30.

   c Set A 29, set B 14

   d Set A has a much higher range than set B, but the medians are the same.

5 a

Time, t (hours)	$4 \leqslant t < 6$	$6 \leqslant t < 8$	$8 \leqslant t < 10$
Frequency	9	5	2
Time midpoint	5	7	9

   b

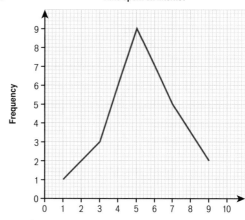

6 a

Midpoint	2.5	3.5	4.5
Interval	$2 \leqslant t < 3$	$3 \leqslant t < 4$	$4 \leqslant t < 5$
Frequency	4	5	3

   b $1+2+4+5+3 = 15$

Averages and range

1 a 46 cm

   b He has probably misread the length during the experiment or has forgotten to put in the decimal point.

   c 2.9 cm

2 a, b

Length, L (cm)	Frequency	Midpoint	Frequency × midpoint
$0 \leqslant L < 10$	7	5	$7 \times 5 = 35$
$10 \leqslant L < 20$	12	15	$12 \times 15 = 180$
$20 \leqslant L < 30$	20	**25**	**$20 \times 25 = 500$**
$30 \leqslant L < 40$	8	**35**	**$8 \times 35 = 280$**
$40 \leqslant L < 50$	3	**45**	**$3 \times 45 = 135$**
Total	50		1130

   c 22.6 cm

   d $20 \leqslant L < 30$

   e Third group, $20 \leqslant L < 30$

Scatter graphs and time series

1 a No correlation **b** Negative correlation

   c Positive correlation

2 a, d

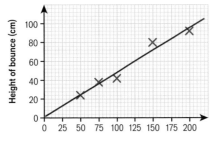

Drop height and bounce

b As the height of the drop increases, the height of the bounce **increases**.

c Positive correlation

e About 60 cm

3 **a** Sales increased in Q1 and Q2, reaching a maximum in Q3, and then decreased in Q4.

b

Year	Q1	Q2	Q3	Q4
2018	400	**800**	1700	**500**
2019	**600**	1300	**2500**	1000

c Higher   **d** Increasing

3 Extend

1 **a** C and D; both points have the same y-coordinate.

b B; D is a lot more expensive than B but only a little heavier.

c A and B; they lie on a straight line from the origin so they are in direct proportion.

d E; it is the most expensive but almost the smallest bag.

e No correlation

2 **a** Negative   **b** Positive   **c** Positive

3 **a** 4, 4, 6, 7, 14; no

b 4, 4, 4, 8, 8, 14 or 4, 4, 5, 7, 8, 14
or 3, 4, 4, 8, 10, 13

4 **a** 8 kg   **b** 4

c Yes, greenhouse mean amount of fruit is 6.5 kg and the mean amount outdoors is 3 kg.

5 **a** 28.46; the actual marks are unknown.

b $\frac{50+1}{2} = 25.5$ so the median is halfway between the 25th and 26th items. The first two groups contain 16 and the next one has 22 so the median is in the third group, 26–30.

c 20

d **i** Decrease **ii** Increase

6 **a** 36

b There might be more students in Year 11.

7 **a** 40

b

Women		Men
9	0	8
6	1	2 8
3 3	2	1 6 7
1	3	1 4 7 9
8 5	4	0 0 0 2 5
8 3	5	0 7 7 8
4 2	6	2 3 4
7	7	0
2 1	8	3

Key: (Women) 9 | 0 represents 9 years
(Men) 0 | 8 represents 8 years

c The women's ages are uniformly spread out whereas the men's ages are concentrated in the 30–59 age range.

8 a, b, d

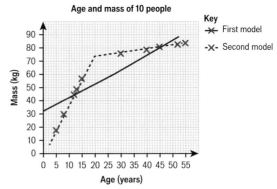

Key
✱ First model
-✗- Second model

c About 56 kg   **d** About 75 kg

9 **a**

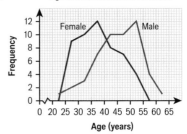

Age of male and female teachers

b The mean age of male teachers is 45.2 and the mean age of female teachers is 38.1, showing that the male teachers are, on average, 7 years older than the female teachers.

c The male frequency polygon is to the right of the female frequency polygon.

10 **a**

	Under £30 000	At least £30 000	Total
Men	60	**30**	90
Women	**60**	50	**110**
Total	120	80	200

b 55%   **c** 66.7% (1 d.p.)   **d** 62.5%

11 $x = 15$

12 **a** 47.2, 50.3, 18, 23.4, 25.9, 11.7, 46, 39.5

b 32.75

c 3275

13 $x = 16$
$y = 12$

3 Test ready

Sample student answer

Points are not plotted at the midpoints of the classes.
The first and last points should not be joined to each other.

3 Unit test

1 He needs a total mark of 279 over three papers.
He already has a total of 176 over the first two papers.
So, he would need 103% on the last paper which is impossible.

2 **a** 7.1%   **b** Q4 2012

c The percentage of people unemployed is decreasing.

3 **a** 38   **b** 39

4 **a** 4.4 minutes (1 d.p.)   **b** $2 \leqslant t < 4$

c The mean waiting time will be slightly shorter.
The median waiting time is unchanged.

5 a

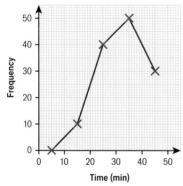

Time taken to clean cars

b $30 \leqslant t < 40$ **c** 40 minutes

6 a

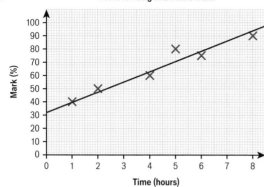

Hours revising and maths mark

b There is a positive correlation. In this context it means that studying more hours is associated with getting higher marks on the maths test.

c 55%

d The scatter graph only shows correlation not causation. There is no guarantee that studying for 10 hours will allow him to get 100%.

7 a Frequency polygons can only be drawn when the data is numerical.

b Pie chart drawn with the correct angles.

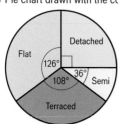

c It depends on how many properties are sold in total: it is impossible to tell without this information.

8 a

	16 GB	32 GB	64 GB	Total
Men	12	15	20	47
Women	12	21	20	53
Total	24	36	40	100

b $\frac{9}{25}$ or equivalent

9 Scatter graph: it will show if there is a correlation between the favourite colours of the men and women in the survey.

10 a Students' own answers
  b Students' own answers
  c Students' own answers

UNIT 4 Fractions, ratio and percentages

4.1 Fractions

1 $\frac{7}{6}$

2 a 10   **b** 9   **c** $3\frac{1}{3}$ **d** $3\frac{2}{3}$

3 a 54   **b** 40   **c** 27

4 $1\frac{17}{24}$

5 a $\frac{1}{8}$ **b** $\frac{3}{2}$ **c** $\frac{3}{4}$ **d** 7

  e The numerator and denominator are swapped.

6 a 2   **b** $\frac{1}{0.27}$ or $\frac{100}{27}$

  c $\frac{1}{0.145}$ or $\frac{200}{29}$ **d** $\frac{1}{0.003}$ or $\frac{1000}{3}$

  e Students' own answers, for example, Write the decimal as a fraction and swap numerator and denominator.

7 a $\frac{4}{5}$ **b** $\frac{3}{17}$ **c** $\frac{2}{5}$ **d** $\frac{5}{24}$

8 No, because $\frac{1}{0}$ is undefined.

9 a $\frac{5}{24}$ **b** $\frac{14}{15}$ **c** $4\frac{1}{8}$ **d** 6

10 a 5   **b** $\frac{1}{5}$

  c $\frac{1}{2} \times 5 = 2\frac{1}{2}, \frac{1}{2} \div \frac{1}{5} = 2\frac{1}{2}$

11 a $2\frac{5}{14}$ **b** $7\frac{1}{2}$ **c** $1\frac{1}{2}$ **d** $1\frac{1}{7}$

12 Yes. Students' own answer, e.g. compare the answers of $3 \div \frac{1}{2}$ and 3×2.

13 a $4\frac{7}{10} + 3\frac{1}{2} = 7\frac{7}{10} + \frac{1}{2} = 7\frac{7}{10} + \frac{5}{10} = 7\frac{12}{10} = 8\frac{2}{10} = 8\frac{1}{5}$

  b $4\frac{1}{2}$ **c** $6\frac{1}{8}$ **d** $11\frac{19}{30}$ **e** $9\frac{7}{36}$

14 a $4\frac{1}{2} - 1\frac{4}{5} = \frac{9}{2} - \frac{9}{5} = \frac{45}{10} - \frac{18}{10} = \frac{27}{10} = 2\frac{7}{10}$

  b $-1\frac{1}{8}$ **c** $3\frac{29}{40}$ **d** $-\frac{17}{18}$

15 a No. If the second fraction is smaller than the first, you can subtract the whole numbers and fractions separately.

  b Yes, adding the whole numbers and fractions separately always works, as in Q14.

16 Yes, the part will fit the machine because it is $7\frac{1}{9}$ cm, which is within the acceptable range.

17 25 minutes

4.2 Ratios

1 a 5   **b** $\frac{3}{2}$ **c** $\frac{9}{5}$

2 a 2   **b** $\frac{15}{14}$ or $1\frac{1}{14}$ **c** $\frac{1}{18}$

3 a 1 : 2   **b** 3 : 5   **c** 4 : 7

4 a 2 : 1   **b** 1 : 4   **c** 15 : 2

5 a 1 : 5   **b** 1 : 7   **c** 1 : 0.5

  d 1 : 6   **e** 1 : 0.45   **f** $1 : \frac{7}{12}$

6 a 3 : 1   **b** 5 : 1   **c** $\frac{2}{3} : 1$

  d $\frac{1}{14} : 1$ **e** 15 : 1   **f** $\frac{5}{6} : 1$

7 a 1 : 0.2   **b** 1 : 0.016   **c** $1 : \frac{3}{8}$ **d** 1 : 36.5

8 a 11.5 : 1   **b** The first school

9 Julie (Julie uses 5 parts of water to 1 part squash, Hammad uses 5.7 parts water).

10 No, because the ratio red : yellow = 4 : 5 is the same as yellow : red = 5 : 4, which is not the same as 16 : 20.

11 £84

12 a 5 : 2   **b** 22.5 g   **c** 4.8 g

13 a 300 : 1 **b** 81 cm

14 44 g

15 16

16 Benji gets 217 bricks and Freddie gets 248.

17 8.16 m

18 320 cm^2

19 a £68 : £136 : £170
  b £5.85 : £17.55 : £23.40
  c 26.1 m : 8.7 m : 52.2 m
  d 129 kg : 451.5 kg : 129 kg : 64.5 kg
  e Often sensible to round money answers to 2 decimal places (nearest penny) and kg answers to 3 decimal places (nearest gram).

20 a

R	R	R	R	R	W	W	B	B	B	B

  b 36

21 £66

22 a $3 + 1 = 4$ so the total number of flowers must be divisible by 4.
  b Yes, it is still correct as the numbers of tulips and roses are unchanged.
  c The total number must be a multiple of 4 *and* of $1 + 5 = 6$, so it must be a multiple of 12 (the LCM of 4 and 6).

23 a 40 : 73   **b** 142 : 241   **c** 3 : 7   **d** 15 : 1

24

Size	Blue	Green	Yellow
1 litre	0.6	0.375	0.025
2.5 litres	1.5	0.9375	0.0625
5.5 litres	3.3	2.0625	0.1375

4.3 Ratio and proportion

1 $\frac{2}{9}$

2 a $\frac{3}{4} \times 4 = 3$ **b** $\frac{4}{3} \times 3 = 4$

3 2 : 5 and 6 : 15

4 a 360 AUD   **b** 420 GBP

5 Cheaper in HK by £2 or HK$24.80.

6 a 1 : 1.6   **b** Adrian, by 3.4 km or 2.1 miles (to 1 d.p.).

7 a $\frac{1}{4}$ **b** 5.7 m

8 Alex is correct; the musicians make up $\frac{3}{8}$ of the company (not $\frac{3}{5}$) and the actors make up $\frac{5}{8}$.

9 a i $s = \frac{4}{3}b$ **ii** $b = \frac{3}{4}s$
  b 156 g

10 a $c = \frac{n}{250}$ **b** 11 chillies   **c** $c = \frac{n}{125}$

11 a 1 : 12   **b** All five ratios simplify to 1 : 12.
  c Yes, because multiplying e by any number multiplies w by the same number.

12 a 2 : 3
  b Yes, because Q is always $1.5 \times$ the value of P.
  c $Q = 1.5 \times P$

13 $P = 48$, $Q = 56$, $R = 12.5$, $S = 45$

14 No, the number of bread rolls and cost are not in direct proportion. If they were in direct proportion, then 15 bread rolls would cost £2.40 $(1.6 \div 10 \times 15)$, not £2.24.

15 2.4 m

16 The 2-litre size is cheaper. (100 ml costs 23.75p, compared with 30p for the 600 ml bottle.)

17 England is better value for money. (In Italy the pasta would cost £15.09 per kg.)

4.4 Percentages

1 a 25   **b** 75   **c** 50 : 200   **d** 1 : 2.5

2 a 1.3   **b** 1.05   **c** 0.88   **d** 0.94

3 a $60 \div 1.2 = \square$, 50   **b** $96 \div 0.8 = \square$, 120

4 84

5 a 1 : 3.2   **b** 1 : 4

6 Yes. Crista gets $\frac{15}{54} \times$ £540 = £150 if the money is shared in the ratio of their ages and £540 $\div$ 3 = £180 if it is shared equally. 20% of £150 is £30, and £180 is £30 more than £150.

7 a £6695   **b** £6895.85

8 £6144

9 a i £30   **ii** £12.60
  b £17 436.25

10 a £2800   **b** £3252   **c** £6900   **d** £14 540

11 £379.26

12 £43.80

13 £900.00

14 1.0506, £1.0506x, so a 5.06% increase

15 a 2.9%   **b** £170 000

16 1.9%

17 a £128   **b** 4%

18 23%

19 95%

20 50%

4.5 Fractions, decimals and percentages

1 a B, C and D   **b** C

2 a $m = \frac{1}{3}$ **b** $n = \frac{2}{3}$

3

Fraction	Decimal	Percentage
$\frac{3}{5}$	0.6	60%
$\frac{1}{8}$	0.125	12.5%
$\frac{9}{20}$	0.45	45%
$\frac{2}{3}$	$0.\dot{6}$	$66.\dot{6}\%$
$\frac{4}{5}$	0.8	80%
$\frac{3}{2}$	1.5	150%

4 a 3.75   **b** 10   **c** $\frac{1}{8}$
  d £28.50   **e** 0.143

5 a $\frac{4}{15}$ **b** 5%

6 a £17.10   **b** 158.3%

7 15

8 30%

9 $\frac{2}{7}$

10 Students' own answers, for example:
The percentage of absences in Term 2 for both years was approximately the same (52.1% in 2017/2018 and 50% in 2018/2019).
The percentage of absences in Term 1 fell from 31.5% in 2017/2018 to 21.9% in 2018/2019.
The percentage of absences in Term 3 rose from 16.4% in 2017/2018 to 28.1% in 2018/2019.
The ratio of absences in 2017/2018 : 2018/2019 were 23 : 14 for Term 1, 19 : 16 in Term 2 and 2 : 3 in Term 3.

11 £38.25

12 $0.6 + 0.06 + 0.006 + \ldots = 0.\dot{6} = \frac{2}{3}$

13 $x = \frac{37.5}{99} = \frac{12.5}{33} = \frac{25}{66}$

14 a $\frac{2}{3}$ **b** $\frac{1}{9}$ **c** $\frac{52}{99}$
   d $\frac{2}{11}$ **e** $\frac{743}{999}$ **f** $\frac{29}{111}$

15 $100n - n = 12.72727\ldots - 0.12727\ldots = 12.6$
$99n = 12.6$
$n = \frac{12.6}{99} = \frac{1.4}{11} = \frac{7}{55}$

16 $0.3\dot{6} = \frac{11}{30}$ and $0.5\dot{4} = \frac{6}{11}, \frac{11}{30} \times \frac{6}{11} = \frac{6}{30} = \frac{1}{5}$

4 Check up

1 a $4\frac{9}{40}$ **b** $\frac{7}{18}$ **c** $2\frac{11}{12}$ **d** 4

2 7 : 40

3 $1 : \frac{18}{5}$

4 a €57.15   **b** £385

5 £66, £44, £22

6 a 200 : 75 = 8 : 3   **b** $f = \frac{8b}{3}$ **c** 80

7 a £481.50   **b** 849.1 kg

8 20%

9 £720

10 a 9.3%   **b** £15 300.43

11 $100x - x = 21.2121\ldots - 0.2121\ldots = 21$
$99x = 21$
$x = \frac{21}{99} = \frac{7}{33}$

13 2; Students' own problem and answer

4 Strengthen

Fractions

1 a i $\frac{2}{15}$ **ii** $\frac{3}{28}$
   b i $\frac{8}{15}$ **ii** $\frac{8}{27}$
   c i $3\frac{1}{8}$ **ii** $4\frac{19}{20}$

2 a i $\frac{4}{5}$ **ii** $1\frac{1}{5}$
   b i $4\frac{4}{5}$ **ii** $7\frac{1}{5}$
   c i $\frac{18}{25}$ **ii** $\frac{24}{35}$

3 a $6\frac{1}{12}$ **b** $6\frac{19}{24}$ **c** $4\frac{1}{45}$ **d** $10\frac{59}{70}$
   e $2\frac{7}{8}$ **f** $1\frac{24}{35}$ **g** $\frac{9}{40}$

Ratio and proportion

1 a £27, £45   **b** £56, £16
   c £6, £12, £54   **d** £36, £24, £12

2 a D only   **b** A and C

3 a i 1 : 5   **ii** 0.2 : 1
   b i 1 : 0.25   **ii** 4 : 1
   c i 1 : 8   **ii** 0.125 : 1
   d i 1 : 0.57   **ii** 1.75 : 1

4 a 150 ml : 4000 ml   **b** 100 g : 2000 g
   c 3000 cm : 80 cm

5 a 3 : 80   **b** 1 : 20   **c** 75 : 2

6 a 13 : 8   **b** 10 : 17   **c** 7 : 10   **d** 7 : 11

7 a i $8   **ii** $10
   b i £3   **ii** £5

8 a 4 : 9   **b** 18   **c** 20

9 a

A	B	B	C	C	C	C

   b £40, £80, £160

10 a 2 : 6 = 1 : 3   **b** oil = vinegar × 3
   c $o = 3v$ **d** 15 tablespoons   **e** 60 ml

Fractions, decimals and percentages

1 a 1.04   **b** 1.265   **c** 0.95   **d** 0.883

2 a i £416   **ii** £506
   b i £380   **ii** £353.20

3 a 4.5%   **b** Students' own answers

4 a 2.25, 8, 28.125%   **b** 25, 145, 17.2%
   c 115, 615, 18.7%

5 a 1.28
   b
$$x \longrightarrow \boxed{\times 1.28} \longrightarrow £13.44$$
   c £10.50

6 a £780   **b** £185 000

7 a 5000 × 1.025 = £5125   **b** £5283.88

8 a $n = 0.\dot{6}\dot{3} = 0.636363\ldots$
   b $100n = 100 \times 0.\dot{6}\dot{3} = 63.6363\ldots$
   c

1	0	0	n		6	3	.	6	3	6	3	…
−			n	−			0	.	6	3	6	3 …
	9	9	n	=	6	3	.	0	0	0	0	…

   d $99n = 63$, $n = \frac{63}{99} = \frac{7}{11}$

4 Extend

1 a Students' own answer, e.g. Let original value $= n$;
20% increase → 1.2n; 20% of 1.2n = 0.24n;
1.2n − 0.24n = 0.96n, which is a decrease of 4%.
   b The final amount will be the same.

2 $\frac{279}{560}$

3 50%

4 $\frac{17}{42}$

5 43%

6 £1.92

7 87 : 113

8 a 1   **b** 1   **c** $\frac{10}{81}$

9 14 : 12 : 21 : 6

10 25%

11 $\frac{3}{10}$

4 Test ready

Sample student answers

1 The student has not stated the value of the percentage increase in the workforce, which is 17%.

2 a Student 2 made the mistake. They worked out $BC = 3.5 \times AB$ when they should have worked out $AC = 3.5 \times AB$.

   b $AB = 4$
   $AC = 3.5 \times 4 = 14$
   $BC = 14 - 4 = 10$
   $CD = BC = 10$
   $AB : BC : CD = 4 : 10 : 10 = 2 : 5 : 5$

4 Unit test

1 a $\frac{4}{11}$ **b** $\frac{40}{51}$

2 a $1\frac{24}{25}$ or equivalent   **b** $2\frac{19}{24}$ or equivalent

3 £19.38

4 $3\frac{5}{12}$ acres

5 £3055.50

6 a $1 : 6.75$

   b The second nursing home as the ratio is $1 : 6.67$ (there are fewer patients per nurse).

7 €680

8 a $a = 27$ **b** $b = 32.5$ **c** $J = \frac{13K}{9}$

9 350%

10 £1250

11 8.6% increase

12 Original area $= LW$
New area $= 0.6L \times 1.3W = 0.78LW$
This is a 22% decrease

13 $0.9\dot{6} = \frac{96}{99} = \frac{32}{33}$

   $1.\dot{4}\dot{5} = \frac{144}{99} = \frac{16}{11}$

   $\frac{32}{33} \div \frac{16}{11} = \frac{32}{33} \times \frac{11}{16} = \frac{2}{3}$

14 a 50%

   b Students' own sensible answers

15 Students' own answers in the form of provided statement template

Mixed exercise 1

1 23.4 cm   → **3.5**

2 a 273   **b** $2n - 1$ → **2.5**

3 a → **3.1, 4.4**

15	6 8 9
16	2 3 6 7 8 8 9
17	0 1 2 2 3 5 6 7
18	0 1

Key: 15 | 6 means 156 cm

   b 45%

4 3   → **4.2**

5 525   → **2.5**

6 Yes. Total number of children $= 1590$
Total number of adults $= 11\,660$
Total number of people $= 13\,250$
$11\,660 \div 15\,800 \times 100 = 83.9\%$ → **4.2, 4.4**

7 $3 : 4 : 8$ → **2.3, 4.2**

8 $(x+4)^2 = 30$, $x^2 + 8x + 16 = 30$, so $x^2 + 8x = 14$ → **2.7**

9 $3n^2 = 2^6 \times 3^5 \times p^8$ → **1.3, 1.4, 2.1**

10 a, e, f

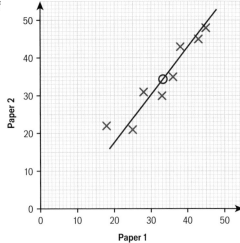

→ **3.3, 3.4**

   b Yes, the graph shows positive correlation so students who get higher marks on one paper tend to get higher marks on the other paper.

   c 33.25   **d** 34.375   **g** 39

11 a $p = 5, q = 6$ → **1.5, 2.1**

   b $p = 2, q = 4$

   c $p = 27, q = 3$

12 $p = -6, q = 30$ → **2.2, 2.4**

13 Yes, as the first term in sequence S is 1 and the second term in sequence T is 1 but sequence S is increasing and sequence T is decreasing so there are no more numbers that are in both sequences.   → **2.5, 2.3**

14 8   → **2.4**

15 a mean $= 5.01 \times 10^7$, median $= 3.12 \times 10^7$, no mode   → **1.6, 3.5**

   b The mean, because there are no outliers and the mean takes into account all of the values.

   c Venus and Saturn

16 13   → **4.3**

17 $1\frac{7}{10}$ → **4.1**

18 347   → **2.6**

19 $15 : 11$ → **3.2, 4.4**

20 $\frac{1}{4}$ → **1.1, 4.1, 4.2**

21 $1 : 6.25 \times 10^9$ → **1.6, 4.2**

22 $\frac{15 + 2\sqrt{5}}{41}$ → **1.7**

UNIT 5 Angles and trigonometry

5.1 Angle properties of triangles and quadrilaterals

1 a i Isosceles trapezium

   ii Rhombus

   iii Equilateral triangle

   iv Isosceles right-angled triangle

   v Kite

   b i   **ii** 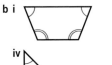   **iii**

   iv   **v**

2 a $60°, 60°, 60°$ **b** $130°, 25°, 25°$

   c $60°, 60°$, and two angles that add to $240°$

3 $a = 105°$ (corresponding angles are equal)
$b = 75°$ (angles on a straight line add up to $180°$)
$c = 105°$ (vertically opposite angles are equal)

4 **a** b, g, i, k, m, o, q, with student's own valid reasons
b $o = 74°$ (corresponding angles are equal)
$p = 180 - 74 = 106°$ (angles on a straight line add up to $180°$)
$q = 74°$ (corresponding angles are equal)
So $o + p + q = 74 + 106 + 74 = 254°$

5 $a + b = 180°$ (angles on a straight line add up to $180°$)
$c = b$ (corresponding angles are equal)
So $a + c = 180°$

6 **a** $75°$ (co-interior angles add up to $180°$)
b $68°$ (angles on a straight line add up to $180°$)
c $68°$ (co-interior angles add up to $180°$)
d $7°$ (angles in a triangle add up to $180°$)

7 **a i** BA **ii** DA
b $\angle BAD = 80°$ (co-interior angles add up to $180°$)
$\angle ADC = 100°$ (co-interior angles add up to $180°$)
$\angle DCB = 80°$ (co-interior angles add up to $180°$)
c Opposite angles are equal.
d Yes
e Opposite angles of a parallelogram are equal.

8 **a** $180°$ (angles on a straight line add up to $180°$)
b i $\angle CAB = x$ (alternate angles are equal)
ii $\angle ABC = z$ (alternate angles are equal)
c $x + y + z = 180°$ (angles on a straight line add up to $180°$)
so the angle sum of a triangle is $180°$

9 $x = 60°$, with students' own valid reasoning

10 $a + b + c = 180°$ and $e + d + f = 180°$
$a + b + c + d + e + f = 360°$
Therefore the angle sum of a quadrilateral $= 360°$

11 Students' own answer, e.g.
$\angle DEF = 102°$ (corresponding angles are equal)
$\angle DFE = 180 - 29 - 102 = 49°$ (angles in a triangle add up to $180°$)
$\angle CBD = \angle DFE = 49°$ (alternate angles are equal)

12 **a** $\angle ABC = 180 - 35 - 68 = 77°$ (angles in a triangle add up to $180°$)
$y = 180 - 77 = 103°$ (angles on a straight line add up to $180°$)
b $\angle LMN = \frac{180 - 42}{2} = 69°$ (angles in a triangle sum to $180°$, and base angles of an isosceles triangle are equal)
$y = 180 - 69 = 111°$ (angles on a straight line add up to $180°$)
c $\angle RQT = \angle TRQ = 180° \div 3 = 60°$ (angles in a triangle add up to $180°$, and angles in an equilateral triangle are equal)
$y = z = 180 - 60 = 120°$ (angles on a straight line add up to $180°$)
d Exterior angle is equal to the sum of the two interior angles at the other two vertices.

13 $\angle BCE + \angle CBE = 132°$ (exterior angle of a triangle is equal to the sum of the two interior angles at the other two vertices)
$\angle BCE = \angle CBE$ (base angles of isosceles triangle BEC are equal)
So $\angle BCE = \angle CBE = 132 \div 2 = 66°$
$\angle CBA = 66°$ (alternate angles are equal)
$\angle DAB = \angle CBA$ ($ABCD$ is an isosceles trapezium)
$\angle DAB = 66°$

14 $\angle CBE = 110°$ (corresponding angles are equal)
$\angle CBA = 70°$ (angles on a straight line add up to $180°$)
$\angle ACB = 180 - (74 + 70) = 36°$ (angles in a triangle add up to $180°$)

15 $4x + 6x = 180°$ (co-interior angles add up to $180°$)
so $x = 18°$, and $6x = 108°$
$\angle ACB + \angle BAC = 108°$ (exterior angle of a triangle is equal to the sum of the two interior angles at the other two vertices)
$\angle ACB = \angle BAC$ (base angles of isosceles triangle ABC are equal)
$\angle ACB = 108 \div 2 = 54°$

16 $\angle ADC = \angle ABC = a - 10°$ ($ABCD$ is a kite)
$2a + 30 + a - 10 + a + a - 10 = 360°$ (angles in a quadrilateral add up to $360°$)
$5a + 10 = 360$, so $a = 70°$
$\angle ADC = a - 10 = 70 - 10 = 60°$

5.2 Interior angles of a polygon

1 **a** **A** Regular octagon **B** Regular pentagon
C Regular hexagon **D** Regular decagon
b All the sides are the same length, and all the angles are the same size.

2 **a** 180 **b** 540 **c** 900 **d** 1080

3 **a** $x = 180 - 73 - 62 = 45°$ (angles in a triangle add up to $180°$)
b $x = (180 - 52) \div 2 = 64°$ (angles in a triangle add up to $180°$, and isosceles triangles have two equal sides and two equal angles)
c $y = 360 - 93 - 105 - 81 = 81°$ (angles in a quadrilateral add up to $360°$)
d $z = 360 \div 6 = 60°$ (angles around a point add up to $360°$)

4 $30°, 60°, 90°$

5 **a, b** Students' own drawing, e.g.

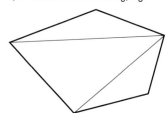

c 3 **d** Yes
e Angles in a triangle add up to **$180°$**
So angles in a pentagon add up to $\mathbf{3 \times 180 = 540°}$

6 **a** $720°$ **b** $1080°$

7 **a**

Polygon	Number of sides (n)	Number of triangles formed	Sum of interior angles
triangle	3	1	180°
quadrilateral	4	**2**	**360°**
pentagon	5	3	540°
hexagon	6	**4**	**720°**
heptagon	7	**5**	**900°**

b Number of triangles formed = number of sides $- 2$

8 **a** $3240°$ **b** $162°$
c No, because an irregular polygon has angles of different sizes.

9 **a** $108°$ **b** $128.6°$ **c** $156°$

10 $105°$

11 Students' own answer, e.g. all the angles of any triangle are at a point where the other angles are $120°$ (regular hexagon) and $180°$ (straight line); angles around a point add up to $360°$ so the triangle's angle is $60°$; this is true for all the angles of all the triangles so they are equilateral triangles.

12 a $a = 130°$
  b $x = 60°$: angles are $60°, 180°, 60°, 120°, 120°$
  c $x = 15°$: angles are $135°, 120°, 105°, 150°, 90°, 120°$

13 $18°$

14 $(n-2) \times 180° = 1620°$; $n - 2 = \frac{1620}{180}$; $n - 2 = 9$; $n = 11$

15 19 sides

16 a $72°$ **b** $54°$ **c** $54°$

17 a Rhombus, hexagon
  b Square, hexagon; $360°$ must contain a whole number of the equal angles, and the only factors of 360 that make regular polygons are 60, 90, 120.

18 a, b

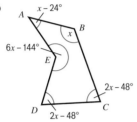

  c $12x - 264° = 540°$
  d $x = 67°$; angle $AED = 6x - 144° = 258°$

19 $150°$

20 $105°$

5.3 Exterior angles of a polygon

1 $a = 108°, b = 53°, c = 135°, d = 93°$

2 a $900°$ **b** $540°$ **c** $1440°$ **d** $720°$

3 a i $a = 96°, b = 156°, c = 108°$
   ii $a = 140°, b = 140°, c = 80°$
   iii $a = 120°, b = 120°, c = 120°$
  b i–iii $a + b + c = 360°$

4 a i $a = 95°, b = 85°, c = 85°, d = 95°$
   ii $a = 103°, b = 77°, c = 103°, d = 77°$
  b i–ii $a + b + c + d = 360°$

5 a Pentagon: $a = 60°, b = 60°, c = 90°, d = 100°, e = 50°$
   Hexagon: $a = 50°, b = 70°, c = 70°, d = 70°,$
   $e = 60°, f = 40°$
  b Sum of exterior angles is $360°$.
  c Both sets of exterior angles sum to $360°$.

6 a $80°$ **b** $66°$
  c $x = 50°, 2x = 100°, 2x - 50 = 50°, x + 40 = 90°$

7 a Angle GAB is outside the hexagon so it is not an interior angle; AD is not a side of the hexagon so it is not an exterior angle.
  b $120°$

8 a 36 sides   **b** 5 sides   **c** 18 sides

9 a 6 sides   **b** 15 sides   **c** 20 sides

10 6 sides

11 a $150°$ **b** 12 sides

12 $n = 8$

5.4 Pythagoras' theorem 1

1 $\sqrt{6}$ and $\sqrt{14}$; all the others can be simplified to a whole number or a fraction.

2 a $\sqrt{8} = \sqrt{4} \times \sqrt{2} = 2\sqrt{2}$ **b** $\sqrt{45} = \sqrt{9} \times \sqrt{5} = 3\sqrt{5}$

3 a 58.7 **b** 7.7

4 14.4

5 a Eleri's; she does not round the value before she finds the square root.
  b Yes

6 No; the hypotenuse is BC.

7 No; $x^2 = 4^2 + 5^2 = 16 + 25 = 41$, and the rest of the working is as before.

8 a 6.32 cm   **b** 4.47 cm   **c** 12.6 cm

9 a $2\sqrt{10}$ cm, $2\sqrt{5}$ cm, $4\sqrt{10}$ cm
  b Answers to Q9a are more accurate because, being surds, they are not rounded.

10 a 6.1 cm (1 d.p. or 2 s.f.)
  b The same accuracy as the values given

11 22.6 miles (3 s.f.)

12 £532 (3 s.f., nearest pound)

13 No; $4^2 + 5^2 \neq 8^2$

14 33.2 cm

15 $BF^2 = 1^2 + 2^2 = 5$, $CF^2 = 1^2 + BF^2 = 6$
  $DF^2 = 1^2 + CF^2 = 7$, $EF^2 = 1^2 + DF^2 = 8$
  $EF = \sqrt{8} = \sqrt{4} \times \sqrt{2} = 2\sqrt{2}$

5.5 Pythagoras' theorem 2

1 Length a

2 8.1 cm

3 a $a = 3$ **b** $b = 8$
  c $c = 12$ **d** $d = 5$

4 a 39.9 cm   **b** 6.26 cm   **c** 7.35 cm

5 a $\sqrt{12} = 2\sqrt{3}$ cm   **b** $\sqrt{27} = 3\sqrt{3}$ cm
  c $\sqrt{125} = 5\sqrt{5}$ cm

6 Students' own answer, e.g. he should subtract 8^2 from 15^2 as XZ is the hypotenuse.

7 2.7 m (1 d.p.)

8 2.98 m

9 4.5 cm

10 31.0 cm

11 $\sqrt{3}$ cm

12 $10\sqrt{2}$ cm

13 8.49 cm (3 s.f.)

14 29.1 cm

5.6 Trigonometry 1

1 a AC **b** AC **c** BC

2 a $55°$ **b** $45°, 45°$ **c** $36°, 54°$

3 a $x = 20$ **b** $x = 2$ **c** $x = 7.35$ **d** $x = 1.05$

4 a Accurate drawing of triangle ABC with sides correctly labelled
  b Opposite $(AC) = 2.9$ cm, hypotenuse $(BC) = 5.8$ cm
  c i $\frac{2.9}{5.8} = 0.5$ **ii** $\frac{5}{5.8} = 0.9$ **iii** $\frac{2.9}{5} = 0.6$
  d i Opposite $= 4.0$ cm, hypotenuse $= 8.1$ cm
   $\frac{\text{opp}}{\text{hyp}} = 0.5$, $\frac{\text{adj}}{\text{hyp}} = 0.9$, $\frac{\text{opp}}{\text{adj}} = 0.6$
   ii Opposite $= 4.6$ cm, hypotenuse $= 9.2$ cm
   $\frac{\text{opp}}{\text{hyp}} = 0.5$, $\frac{\text{adj}}{\text{hyp}} = 0.9$, $\frac{\text{opp}}{\text{adj}} = 0.6$
  e The ratio of corresponding sides stays the same.

5 a 0.6 **b** 1.0 **c** 7.1

6 a 4.17 cm   **b** 9.66 cm   **c** 1.88 cm

7 Students' own answers

8 a 8.5 cm   **b** 9.1 m   **c** 5.6 cm

9 Students' own answers, e.g. in **Q6** you multiply a number by the trigonometric ratio and in **Q8** you divide by the ratio.

10 15.7 cm

11 2.6 m

12 123 m

13 1.96 m

5.7 Trigonometry 2

1 Opposite sides are BC, QR; adjacent sides are AB, PQ.

2 2.83 cm

3 $\frac{1}{\sqrt{3}} = \frac{1}{\sqrt{3}} \times \frac{\sqrt{3}}{\sqrt{3}} = \frac{\sqrt{3}}{3}$

4 a 34.2° **b** 36.4° **c** 13.8°
d 53.1° **e** 85.9° **f** 36.5°

5 a 53.1° **b** 64.6° **c** 32.0°

6 a 48.2° **b** Decrease; the denominator has increased.

7 a 26.6°
b Angle of depression = angle of elevation (alternate angles are equal)

8 31.0°

9 43.6°

10 31.8°

11 a 1 **b** $\sqrt{2}$ cm
c i $\frac{1}{\sqrt{2}}$ **ii** $\frac{1}{\sqrt{2}}$
d i $\frac{\sqrt{2}}{2}$ **ii** $\frac{\sqrt{2}}{2}$

12 a i $\frac{1}{2}$ **ii** $\frac{1}{2}$ **b** $\sqrt{3}$ cm
c i $\frac{\sqrt{3}}{2}$ **ii** $\sqrt{3}$ **iii** $\frac{\sqrt{3}}{2}$ **iv** $\frac{1}{\sqrt{3}}$

13 a

	0°	30°	45°	60°	90°
sin	0	$\frac{1}{2}$	$\frac{\sqrt{2}}{2}$	$\frac{\sqrt{3}}{2}$	1
cos	1	$\frac{\sqrt{3}}{2}$	$\frac{\sqrt{2}}{2}$	$\frac{1}{2}$	0
tan	0	$\frac{\sqrt{3}}{3}$	1	$\sqrt{3}$	

b i 45° **ii** 2 **iii** $\sqrt{3}$

5 Check up

1 a 144° **b** 72°

2 8 sides

3 140°

4 $14x + 22x = 180$ (angles on a straight line add up to 180°)
$x = 5°$
$\angle ABE = \angle BED = 70°$ (alternate angles are equal)

5 Any quadrilateral can be split into two triangles by joining one vertex to all the other vertices. The sum of angles in a triangle is 180°. Therefore the sum of the angles in a quadrilateral is 360°.

6 $\angle ABE = \angle ACD = 90°$ (corresponding angles are equal)
$\angle AFE = \angle ABE = 90°$ ($ABEF$ is a kite)
$\angle FAB + \angle FEB = 360 - 90 - 90 = 180°$ (angles in a quadrilateral add up to 360°)
$\angle FEB = 120°$ and $\angle FAB = 60°$ (from ratio given)

7 $\angle DBC = 62°$ (corresponding angles are equal)
$x = 180 - (2 \times 62) = 56°$ (angles in a triangle add up to 180°, and base angles of isosceles triangle BCD are equal)

8 a 2.2 m **b** $3\sqrt{5}$ cm

9 No; $6^2 + 3^2 \neq 7^2$ and for a triangle to be right angled the square of the longest side must equal the sum of the squares of the two shorter sides.

10 217 cm^2

11 a 8.63 cm **b** 8.43 m **c** 21.8°

12 56.7°

13 a 1 **b** $\frac{1}{2}$ **c** $\frac{1}{2}$

15 a 90°, 45°, 45°
b i 108°, 36°, 36° **ii** 120°, 30°, 30°
iii 150°, 15°, 15° **iv** 174°, 3°, 3°
c The width (the side opposite the unique angle) increases and the height decreases – the triangle is becoming 'flatter'.

5 Strengthen

Angles and polygons

1 a

Polygon	Quadrilateral	Pentagon	Hexagon	Heptagon
Number of sides (n)	4	5	6	7
Number of triangles	2	3	4	5
Sum of interior angles	$2 \times 180° = 360°$	$3 \times 180° = 540°$	$4 \times 180° = 720°$	$5 \times 180° = 900°$

b Number of triangles = $n - 2$
Sum of interior angles = $(n - 2) \times 180°$
c 1440°

2 a 140° **b** 150° **c** 162°

3 a 90° **b** 36° **c** 20°

4 a $n = \frac{360°}{\text{exterior angle}}$
b i 4 **ii** 6 **iii** 12 **iv** 30

5 a Interior angle $DCB = 162°$
Exterior angle = x or DCE
b 18° **c** 20

6 a $x + 110° + 80° + 130° + 115° + 120° = 720°$
b 165°

7 a, b

c $2x + 75 + x + 75 = 360$, $3x = 210$, $x = 70$
$\angle ABC = 2x = 140°$

8 174°

9 $x = 56°$ (alternate angles are equal)
$y = (180 - 56) \div 2 = 62°$ (angles in a triangle add up to 180°, and base angles of an isosceles triangle are equal)
$z = 180 - 62 = 118°$ ($\angle ABC = y = 62°$, and angles on a straight line add up to 180°)

10 a False. Angles on a straight line add up to 180°.
b False. Angles in a triangle add up to 180°.
c True. Angles in a triangle add up to 180°, as do angles on a straight line.
d True. Angles on a straight line add up to 180°.
e True. Angles in a triangle add up to 180°.

11 a, b i

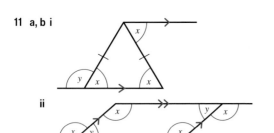

ii

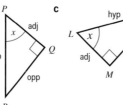

c Opposite angles of a parallelogram are equal.

Pythagoras' theorem

1 **a** AB **b** PR **c** LN
2 $c^2 = 8^2 + 6^2$; $c^2 = 100$; $c = \sqrt{100}$; $c = 10\,\text{cm}$
3 **a** $17\,\text{cm}$ **b** $25.5\,\text{m}$
4 $10^2 = 6^2 + b^2$; $100 = 36 + b^2$; $b^2 = 100 - 36$
$b = \sqrt{64}$; $b = 8\,\text{cm}$
5 **a** $12\,\text{cm}$ **b** $5.5\,\text{m}$
6 **a**

25 cm

20 cm

b $300\,\text{cm}^2$
7 No; $18^2 \neq 7^2 + 16^2$
8 **a** $x^2 = 2^2 + 6^2 = 4 + 36 = 40$
$x = \sqrt{40} = \sqrt{4} \times \sqrt{10} = 2\sqrt{10}$
b $x = 3\sqrt{3}$ **c** $x = 4\sqrt{2}$

Trigonometry

1 **a** **b** **c**

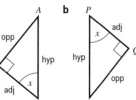 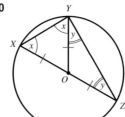

2 **a** $\sin x = \dfrac{\text{opposite}}{\text{hypotenuse}} = \dfrac{8}{10}$ or $\dfrac{4}{5}$

b $\cos x = \dfrac{\text{adjacent}}{\text{hypotenuse}} = \dfrac{6}{10}$ or $\dfrac{3}{5}$

c $\tan x = \dfrac{\text{opposite}}{\text{adjacent}} = \dfrac{8}{6}$ or $\dfrac{4}{3}$

3 **a** 0.37 **b** 0.73 **c** 0.34 **d** 1.60
4 **a** 19.0° **b** 53.7° **c** 40.3° **d** 41.8°
e 19.7°
5 $x = 5 \times \tan 36°$; $x = 3.6\,\text{cm}$
6 **a** $10.5\,\text{cm}$ **b** $1.7\,\text{cm}$
7 $\cos = \dfrac{\text{adj}}{\text{hyp}}$; $\cos x = \dfrac{12}{15}$; $x = \cos^{-1}\left(\dfrac{12}{15}\right)$; $x = 36.9°$
8 68.0°
9 b is angle of elevation; a is angle of depression.
10 **a** **b** ABC **c** 39.3°

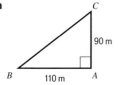

C

90 m

B   110 m   A

11 **a** $\dfrac{1}{2}$ **b** $\dfrac{\sqrt{2}}{2}$ **c** $\dfrac{\sqrt{3}}{2}$

d $\dfrac{\sqrt{3}}{2}$ **e** $\dfrac{\sqrt{2}}{2}$ **f** $\dfrac{1}{2}$

g $\dfrac{\sqrt{3}}{3}$ **h** 1 **i** $\sqrt{3}$

12 **a** 0 **b** 1 **c** 0
d 1 **e** 0

5 Extend

1 48 700 feet
2 7.1 cm
3 0.199
4 Angles in a pentagon add up to 540°
Each angle in a regular pentagon $= 540 \div 5 = 108°$
$\angle CBF = 108°$
$\angle ABF = 180 - 108 = 72°$ (angles on a straight line add up to 180°)
5 $\dfrac{x}{2} + 90°$
6 10 sides
7 32.5°
8 $\cos 60° = \dfrac{\text{adj}}{\text{hyp}} = \dfrac{20}{x}$; $x = 20 \div \cos 60° = 20 \div \dfrac{1}{2} = 40$ mm
9 $\dfrac{9}{2} + \dfrac{3\sqrt{3}}{2}$ or $\dfrac{3}{2}(3 + \sqrt{3})$
10

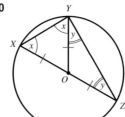

$\angle XOY = 180 - 2x$ (angles in a triangle add up to 180°, and base angles of isosceles triangle OXY are equal)
$\angle YOZ = 180 - 2y$ (angles in a triangle add up to 180°, and base angles of isosceles triangle OZY are equal)
$\angle XOY + \angle YOZ = 180°$ (angles on a straight line add up to 180°)
$180 - 2x + 180 - 2y = 180$
$180 - 2(x + y) = 0$
$x + y = \angle XYZ = 90°$
11 197 mm
12 $h = 43.1\,\text{m}$

5 Test ready

Sample student answers

a Alternate angles are equal.
b The student wrongly identified BE as opposite to the 32° angle rather than adjacent, and so used sine rather than cosine.
The student did not give their answer to the correct degree of accuracy (3 s.f.).

5 Unit test

1 **a** 1260° **b** 40°
2 Angle $EBC = 180° - 132° = 48°$ (angles on a straight line add up to 180°)
Angle $ECB =$ angle $EBC = 48°$ (base angles of an isosceles triangle are equal)
$x = 48°$ (alternate angles are equal)
3 $p + y + q = 180°$ (angles on a straight line add up to 180°)
$p = x$ (alternate angles are equal)
$q = z$ (alternate angles are equal)
$p + y + q = x + y + z = 180°$

4 **a** 1   **b** 1   **c** $\frac{\sqrt{2}}{2}$ **d** $\frac{\sqrt{3}}{2}$

5 **a** 8.32 cm   **b** 72.0 mm

6 38.31 cm

7 63°

8 45.3°

9 30°

10 2.83 miles

11 $5\sqrt{13}$ m

12 $4 \times 2 = 8\,\text{cm} = OP = OQ = QP$
OPQ is equilateral
$8^2 - 4^2 = 64 - 16 = 48$
$\sqrt{48}$ = height of OPQ
$8 \times \sqrt{48} \times 0.5 = 4\sqrt{48} = 4 \times \sqrt{4}\sqrt{12}$
$\qquad\qquad = 8\sqrt{12} = 8\sqrt{4}\sqrt{3} = 16\sqrt{3}$ cm

13 4

14 Students' own answer

UNIT 6 Graphs

6.1 Linear graphs

1 **a** Positive B, negative A

   b A: x-intercept $(7, 0)$, y-intercept $(0, 5)$
     B: x-intercept $(-3, 0)$, y-intercept $(0, 4)$

2 $y = 2x - 5$

3 **a** $y = 6$ **b** $x = -2$

4 A: 2, B: 1, C: $\frac{1}{2}$, D: -1

5 **a**

Equation of line	Gradient	y-intercept
A: $y = 2x + 4$	2	$(0, 4)$
B: $y = 2x$	2	$(0, 0)$
C: $y = 2x - 3$	2	$(0, -3)$
D: $y = -2x + 4$	-2	$(0, 4)$

   b **i** B **ii** A and D **iii** A, B, C

   c **i** The number term is the same.

     ii The coefficient of x is the same.

     iii The gradient is the coefficient of x, and the
       y-intercept is the number term.

6 **a** A: $y = 2x - 2$, B: $y = 3x + 1$, C: $y = 2x + 1$, D: $y = -x$

   b B

   c The steepest graph has the greatest x-coefficient.

7 A: $y = 2x$, B: $y = 2x + 2$, C: $y = -x - 1$,
D: $y = 6x - 8$, E: $y = x + 4$, F: $y = 2x - 2$

8 **a** B and D   **b** A and D

9 **a** **i**

x	0	-3
y	$1\frac{1}{2}$	0

     ii

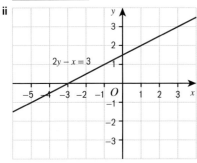

b **i**

x	0	4
y	4	0

   ii

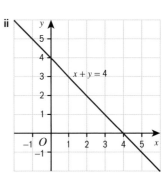

c **i**

x	0	7
y	7	0

   ii

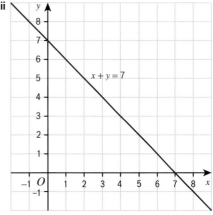

d **i** $(3, 0)$ and $(0, 3)$ **ii** $(-1, 0)$ and $(0, -1)$

10 **a** $y = \frac{3+x}{2}$ or $y = \frac{1}{2}x + \frac{3}{2}$; $y = 4 - x$; $y = 7 - x$

   b Gradient $\frac{1}{2}$, y-intercept $\left(0, \frac{3}{2}\right)$
     Gradient -1, y-intercept $(0, 4)$
     Gradient -1, y-intercept $(0, 7)$

   c Students' own check.

11 C

12 L_1: $y = 2x - \frac{7}{2}$, L_2: $y = 2x - \frac{2}{3}$
$m = 2$ in both rearranged equations.

13 B and E

14 C and D

6.2 More linear graphs

1 Parallel: B and D
Same y-intercept: A and B

2 **a** Any line with gradient = 5

   b Any line with gradient = 0.5

   c Any line with gradient = -3

3 A: $y = 2x + 2$, B: $y = -\frac{1}{3}x - 1$, C: $y = -2x + 1$

4 A: $(-1, 0)$, B: $(-3, 0)$, C: $\left(\frac{1}{2}, 0\right)$

5 $c = 3$

6 a

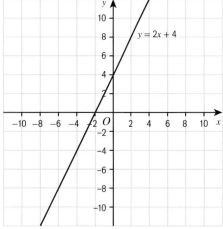

b

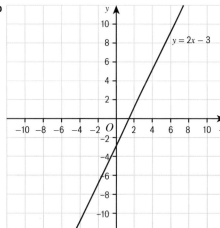

c

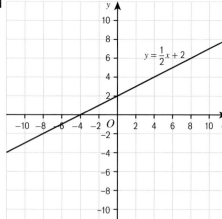

d

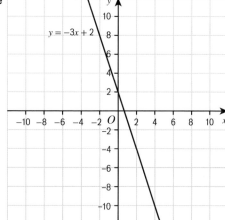

e

7 a D   **b** C   **c** B
  d E   **e** A

8 Students' own answers, e.g. where the graph crosses the axes; you do not need to work out and plot y-values for a range of x-values.

9 a i x-intercept $= (0, 0)$, y-intercept $= (0, 0)$

    ii x-intercept $= \left(-\frac{1}{3}, 0\right)$, y-intercept $= (0, 1)$

    iii x-intercept $= (5, 0)$, y-intercept $= (0, 5)$

    iv x-intercept $= (-5, 0)$, y-intercept $= (0, -6)$

    v x-intercept $= (-2, 0)$, y-intercept $= (0, 2)$

    vi x-intercept $= (-2, 0)$, y-intercept $= (0, 4)$

  b Students' sketches of the graphs.

10 A, B, C, D

11 Straight line

12 a No   **b** Yes   **c** No

13 a $-1 = 4 \times \frac{1}{2} + c$ **b** $c = -3$ **c** $y = 4x - 3$

14 a $y = 3x + 5$ **b** $y = -x + 3$ **c** $y = 2x - 3$

  d $y = \frac{1}{2}x - 2$ **e** $y = -2x + 6$

15 a, b $\frac{3}{4}$ **c** Students' own answers.

16 a $-\frac{1}{2}$ **b** $y = -\frac{1}{2}x + c$; $c = 5$

  c $y = -\frac{1}{2}x + 5$

17 $y = \frac{1}{2}x - 1$

18 a $x = 3$ **b** $y = 9$ **c** $(3, 9)$

19 $(1, 1)$

20 $(-1, -1)$

6.3 Graphing rates of change

1 34 km/h

2 a 10 mm²   **b** 10.5 cm²

3 a 6 km   **b** 5.42 pm   **c** 30 minutes

   d 2 hours 30 minutes

4 a i 12 km/h   **ii** 20 km/h

   b 12, −20; the gradients are the same as the speeds (the negative gradient of the cycle from the cinema simply shows she was returning home).

5 a The distance stays the same: the object is not moving.

   b The gradient represents the speed of the object.

6 a

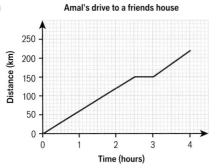

Amal's drive to a friends house

   b 60 km/h

7 a

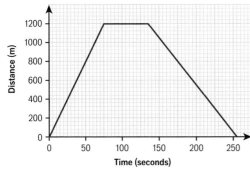

Kirsty's speed skating

   b 16 m/s

8 a

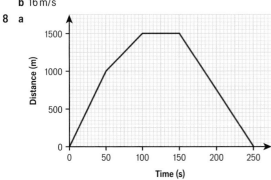

   b In between 0 and 50 seconds; the steepest section

   c 20 m/s

9 a

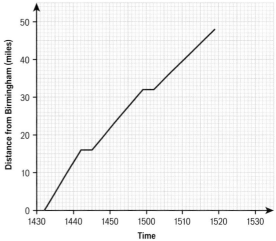

Train journey from Birmingham to Shrewsbury

   b 96 mph   **c** 56.5 mph   **d** 61.3 mph

   e The average speed is usually slower than the speed over each part of the journey; it is the same if the speed is constant.

10 55 km/h

11 a About 80 miles   **b** Train A

   c Students' own answers, e.g. They give a good overall impression but do not show the trains braking and accelerating. Assumptions include: The trains travel at a constant speed between stations, and do not take any time to accelerate or slow down to a standstill at stations.

12 a C   **b** iv

   c i B   **ii** A   **iii** D   **iv** C

   d The containers' widths are not constant, and the water depth increases more quickly where they are narrow.

13 a i B   **ii** A

   b Students' own sketches of straight-line graphs, with B the steepest and A the least steep.

14 a A   **b** D   **c** C   **d** B

15

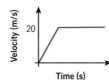

16 a 1.6 m/s   **b** In the stages QR and ST

   c 5 minutes   **d** 0.0092 m/s²   **e** 96 m

   f Gavin accelerated at 0.0092 m/s² for the first 2 minutes, then ran at a constant velocity of 1.1 m/s for 5 minutes. Next, he accelerated at 0.0083 m/s² for 1 minute, then ran at a constant velocity of 1.6 m/s for 8 minutes. Then he decelerated at 0.013 m/s² for the last 2 minutes.

17 Constant speed is shown by a horizontal line, constant acceleration by an upward-sloping straight line (positive gradient) and constant deceleration by a downward-sloping straight line (negative gradient).

6.4 Real-life graphs

1 **a** Scatter graph **b** Positive **c** Line of best fit

2 $y = 24x + 40$

3 **a**

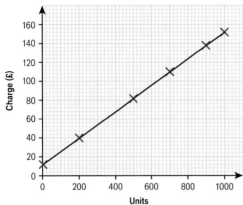
Charge for electricity

b i £124 **ii** 340 units

4 **a** £1.00 **b** £25.00 **c** £54 **d** 149

5 **a** C$14 **b** €7 **c** 1.4
d The gradient of the graph represents the number of **dollars** per **euro**.

6 **a** 25
b The hire charge increases by £25 for each additional day.
c The minimum charge for hiring the van is £40.

7 B and C

8 The conversion graph (**Q5**); it is the only graph that goes through the origin, as C$0 = €0.

9 **a**

Chilli powder (grams)	1	4	10
Cumin (grams)	2.5	10	25

b

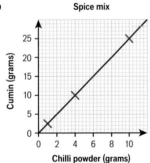
Spice mix

c $y = 2.5x$ **d** 34 g
e x and y are in direct proportion.

10 **a i** The y-intercept tells you the initial temperature of the freezer.
ii The x-intercept tells you at what time the temperature reaches 0 °C.
b 10 °C **c** 20 °C
d Yes; it is a straight line.

11 **a**

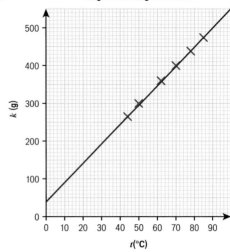
Sugar dissolving into coffee

b i 16 °C **ii** 455 g
c $a = 5, b = 50$
d Yes. 4 teaspoons is much less than 500 g.

12 **a i** This is the minimum monthly charge – you have to pay this even if you don't use the phone that month.
ii The point of intersection is where the two plans charge the same amount for the same number of minutes.
b About £1.75 **c** Molly: Plan C; Theo: Plan B

13 **a, c**

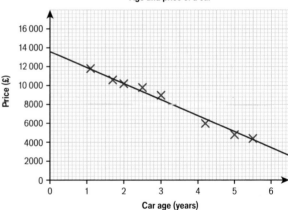
Age and price of a car

b Negative
d $y = -1700x + 13\,600$
e £7650 or about £8000
f The y-intercept, i.e. about £14 000

14 **a i** about 84 **ii** about 87
b 2022, because 2022 is closer to the years covered by the data.

6.5 Line segments

1 **a** Parallel: lines that always stay the same distance apart
Perpendicular: lines that meet at a right angle (90°)

2 3

3 13 cm

4 $y = 2x - 3$; gradient 2, y-intercept $(0, -3)$

5 a

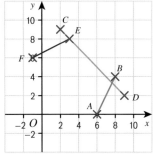

b i (7, 2)　　**ii** (5.5, 5.5)　　**iii** (1, 7)

c i The *x*-coordinate of the midpoint is the mean of the *x*-coordinates.

  ii The *y*-coordinate of the midpoint is the mean of the *y*-coordinates.

6 a (1.5, 5.5)　　**b** (4, −1)　　**c** (2, 0.5)　　**d** (−1, −2)

7 a 3　　**b** −2　　**c** $-\frac{1}{2}$　　**d** $\frac{1}{3}$

8 a 3.6 (1 d.p.)　**b** 10　　**c** 13.6 (1 d.p.)

9 a $y = 2x + c$　**b** $y = 2x - 9$

10 $y = \frac{1}{3}x - 5$

11 a A_1: 2, A_2: $-\frac{1}{2}$; B_1: 3, B_2: $-\frac{1}{3}$; C_1: $\frac{1}{4}$, C_2: −4

  b The products are all −1.

12 a $-\frac{1}{3}$　　**b** 4　　**c** $-\frac{3}{2}$

13 a $y = x - 4$　**b** $y = -\frac{3}{2}x - 5$

14 $y = -\frac{1}{2}x + 5$

6.6 Quadratic graphs

1 Same: they are both straight lines.

Different: the graph of $x = 2$ is a vertical line whereas the graph of $y = 2$ is a horizontal line.

2

x	−4	−3	−2	−1	0	1	2	3	4
y	16	9	4	1	0	1	4	9	16

3

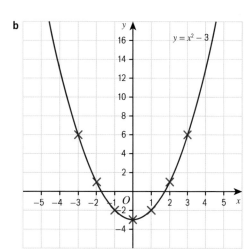

4 a

x	−3	−2	−1	0	1	2	3
y	6	1	−2	−3	−2	1	6

b

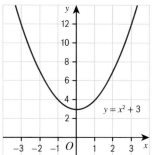

5 The points are joined with straight lines not a smooth curve.

6 a i

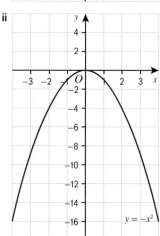

ii

iii

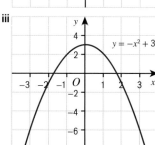

b Students' own answers, e.g.

  i Same parabola shape as **Q6a i** but passing through (0, 5)

  ii Same parabola shape as **Q6a i** but passing through (0, −5)

  iii Same 'upside down' parabola shape as **Q6a ii** and **iii** but passing through (0, −5)

7 a

x	−2	−1	0	1	2
y	12	3	0	3	12

b

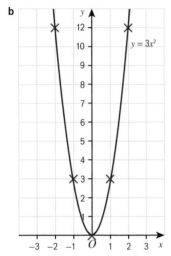

8 a Same parabola shape

b **Q3**, **Q4**, **Q6a i** and **Q7** have minimum, **Q6a ii** and **iii** have maximum.

c **Q3**: (0, 0), **Q4**: (0, −3), **Q6a i**: (0, 3), **Q6a ii**: (0, 0), **Q6a iii**: (0, 3), **Q7**: (0, 0)

d $x = 0$ for all six graphs

9 a Quadratic

b Just after take-off and just before landing

c 2.6 seconds   **d** 32 m   **e** 5.2 seconds

10 a

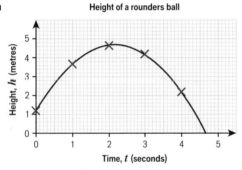

b About 4.7 seconds

11 a $x = 1$ or −1 **b** $x = 2$ or −2

12 a $x = -0.7$ or 2.7

b $x = -2.6$ or 0.6

c $x = -3.3$ or 0.3

d The curve does not meet or cross the x-axis (or $y = 0$).

13 $x^2 - 2x + 5 = x + 3$

Straight line graph: $y = x + 3$

14 a

x	−4	−3	−2	−1	0	1	2	3	4
y	35	20	9	2	−1	0	5	14	27

b

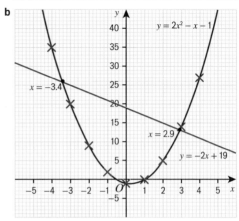

c $x = -3.7$ or 2.3

6.7 Cubic and reciprocal graphs

1 a Straight line **b** Parabola

2

x	−3	−2	−1	0	1	2	3
y	−27	−8	−1	0	1	8	27

3

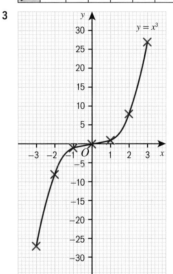

4 a Method 2   **b** Method 1

5 a Students' own estimates

b i 4.91 (2 d.p.)

ii −2.22 (2 d.p.)

c Calculator answers are more accurate.

6 a i, ii, iii

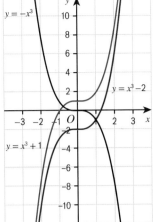

b Students' own answers, e.g. The graph in part **a i** is a reflection (in the x-axis or y-axis) of the graph in **Q3**. The graphs in part **a ii** and **iii** have the same shape as the graph in **Q3** but are moved up or down (translated).

7 Students' own answers e.g.

a Same shape as **Q3** but passing through $(0, 5)$

b Same shape as **Q3** but passing through $\left(0, -\frac{1}{2}\right)$

8 a $x = -1$ **b** $x = -1$

9 a

x	-3	-2	-1	0	1	2	3
y	-9	4	5	0	-5	-4	9

b

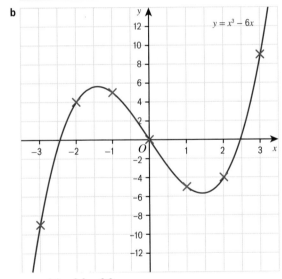

c $x = -2.3, -0.3$ or 2.6

10 a $x = -1.3$ or 0 or 1.7 **b** $x = -1.6$ or 1

11 a

x	-3	-2	-1	$-\frac{1}{2}$	$-\frac{1}{4}$	$\frac{1}{4}$	$\frac{1}{2}$	1	2	3
y	$-\frac{1}{3}$	$-\frac{1}{2}$	-1	-2	-4	4	2	1	$\frac{1}{2}$	$\frac{1}{3}$

b

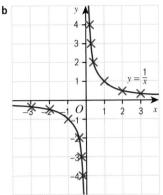

12 a

x	-3	-2	-1	$-\frac{1}{2}$	$-\frac{1}{4}$	$\frac{1}{4}$	$\frac{1}{2}$	1	2	3
y	$\frac{1}{3}$	$\frac{1}{2}$	1	2	4	-4	-2	-1	$-\frac{1}{2}$	$-\frac{1}{3}$

b

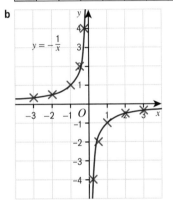

c Students' own answers, e.g. The two graphs have the same shape but are in different quadrants.

13 a

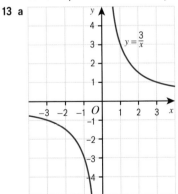

b i -3 **ii** -1.2

c $x = 1.2$

6.8 More graphs

1 a $x = 2$ **b** $y = 2$

2 Student's circle with radius $5\,\text{cm}$

3 $2\sqrt{2}$

4 a 17 counts per second   **b** 12.5 minutes
  c 9 minutes   **d** No

5 a C   **b** A   **c** B

6 a £1000　　**b** £1126　　**c** £24
d 2.4%

7 a 70 mph　　**b** 21:30　　**c** 36 mph
d The bus's speed is increasing.

8 a

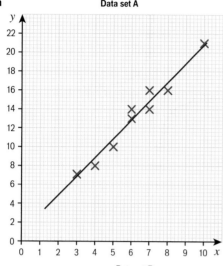

Data set A

Data set B

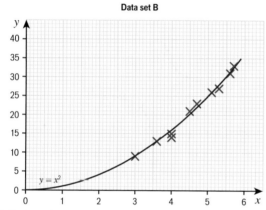

b Both graphs show strong positive correlation.
c x is proportional to y.
d

x	3.0	3.2	3.5	3.7	4.0
y	9.00	10.24	12.25	13.69	16.00

x	4.5	4.8	5.0	5.5	6.0
y	20.25	23.04	25.00	30.25	36.00

e All the plotted points lie very close to $y = x^2$, so y is proportional to x^2.

9 a

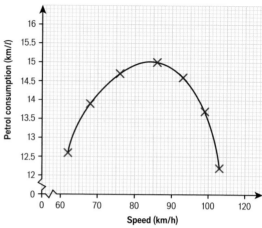

Petrol consumption of a car

b i 14.6 km/l　　**ii** 65 km/h and 100 km/h

10 a–d

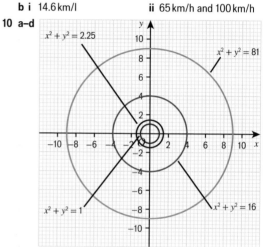

11 $2\sqrt{5}$

6 Check up

1 Gradient $-\frac{2}{3}$, y-intercept $\left(0, \frac{7}{3}\right)$

2 A: $y = 3x + 2$, B: $y = -2x + 3$, C: $y = \frac{1}{2}x + 5$,
D: $y = \frac{1}{2}x$, E: $y = -\frac{1}{4}x - 1$

3

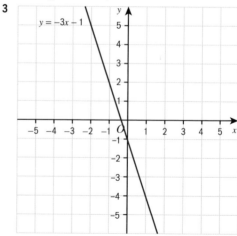

4 a $y = -\frac{1}{2}x + 3$　　　　**b** $y = 3x - 7$

5

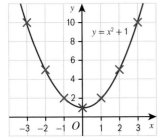

$y = x^2 + 1$

6 a 15.3 (3 s.f.); Hamzah is cycling at 15.3 km/h.
   b 14.7 km/h
   c 2.75 to 3 hours (or final 15 minutes)
   d 40 km/h

7 a There is a minimum cost of £6, for up to 3 cupcakes.
   b Price per cupcake   **c** No

8 a $(-0.5, -3)$ **b** 6.4 (1 d.p.)

9 a $y = 3x - 13$
   b Any equation with $y = -\frac{1}{3}x$ plus a constant other than 1,
   e.g. $y = -\frac{1}{3}x + 8$

10 a A   **b** E   **c** B   **d** G
   e C   **f** F   **g** D

11 $x = -1.9, 0.3, 1.5$

12 7

13 a $(0.75, 2)$ **b** 2 m   **c** 2.1 seconds
   d The height that the water comes out of the hosepipe

14 a D   **b** A   **c** C   **d** B

16 Students' own games

6 Strengthen

Linear graphs

1 a B and C **b** $(0, -3)$ **c** C and D **d** A and B

2 a D **b** B **c** C **d** A

3 a 20   **b** $\frac{\text{Distance}}{\text{Time}}$ **c** Speed
   d 20 miles   **e** 2 hours   **f** 10 mph
   g AB **h** 20 mph

4 a e.g   **b** e.g

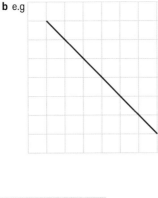

   c e.g.

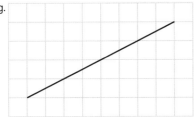

5 a Gradient 4, y-intercept $(0, -3)$
   b, c, d

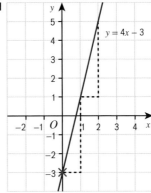

$y = 4x - 3$

6 a, b, c

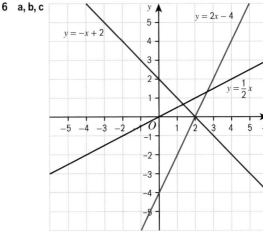

$y = -x + 2$ $y = 2x - 4$ $y = \frac{1}{2}x$

7 a 5   **b** 5   **c** 1
   d $1 = 1 \times (-3) + c$ **e** $c = 4$
   f $y = x + 4$ **g** Students' own checks

8 a i 3   **ii** 6
   b $y = 2x + 3$

9 $(-0.5, 4)$

10 a A and F, B and D
   b Any equation with $y = 2x$ plus a constant other than -3 or
   1, e.g. $y = 2x - 8$
   Any equation with $y = -x$ plus a constant other than -1 or
   4, e.g. $y = -x + 5$

11 a 3   **b** $y = 3x + 10$

12 a i $-\frac{1}{2}$ **ii** -2 **iii** $\frac{1}{2}$
   iv -4 **v** 1
   b A and G, B and H, C and F, D and E

Non-linear graphs

1 a F   **b** E   **c** D
   d A reciprocal graph approaches the axes but never
   touches them.

2 a i Linear   **ii** Quadratic
   iii Cubic   **iv** Reciprocal
   v Quadratic **vi** Cubic
   b i D   **ii** F   **iii** E
   iv C   **v** A   **vi** B

3 a $x^2 + y^2 = 3^2$
   $x^2 + y^2 = 9$
   b 10

Real-life graphs

1 a Quadratic   **b** (0, 5)   **c** 4.6 m
   d 3.5 m and −3.5 m
   e Distance in front of the posts
   f 5 m   **g** Yes

2 a The water level in vase 1 rises faster first, then more slowly. The water level in vase 2 rises slowly at first, then faster.
   b Vase 1: graph B, vase 2: graph A

3 a i £1.25   **ii** £8.75   **iii** 95 (or 96)
   b 0.05
   c The gradient represents the profit made per **light bulb**.
   d Yes

6 Extend

1 a C and D   **b** A and C
2 (11, −2), (13, −4), (11, −6), (9, −4)
3 a $x^2 - 3x - 2x - 1 + 1 = x^2 - 5x = 0$
   b $y = 2x - 1$ **c** $x = 0$ or 5
4 a

x	−3	−2	−1	−0.5	−0.1
y	1.7	2	3	5	21

x	0.1	0.5	1	2	3
y	−19	−3	−1	0	0.3

   b

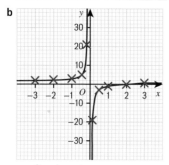

   c $x = 0$ and $y = 1$
5 $k = 7$; $D = (4, 7)$; $x = 4$ and $y = 7$ satisfy the equation $y = 2x - 1$.
6 a Graph plotted with points at (0, 0), (1, 0.6), (2, 2.4), (3, 5.4), (4, 9.6), (5, 15), (6, 21.6), (7, 29.4), (8, 38.4), (9, 48.6), (10, 60)
   b 12.2 m   **c** 8.2 seconds
7 2
8 a i C   **ii** D   **iii** A   **iv** B
   b A: $x = 0$, B: no line symmetry, C: $x = 0$, D: $y = x$ and $y = -x$
9 $y = 4x + 20$
10 $P(\frac{8}{3}, 0)$; $21x + 9y - 56 = 0$

6 Test ready

Sample student answers

The student wrote that line PQ has gradient $-\frac{2}{5}$ but the gradient is $\frac{2}{5}$
So $3 = \frac{2}{5} \times 5 + c$
   $c = 1$
and the equation is $y = \frac{2}{5}x + 1$

The correct expression is $b = \frac{2}{5}a + 1$

6 Unit test

1 Graph of $y = 2x - 1$ correctly drawn: y-intercept of −1 seen, gradient = 2, line drawn, graph and axes labelled

2 a Gradient = −3
   b Midpoint = (0.5, 2.5)
   c Length = 9.5 (1 d.p.)

3 Positive correlation; x and y are directly proportional.

4 a

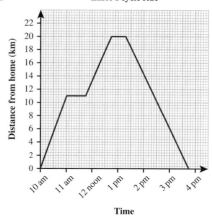

Elliot's cycle ride

   b 9 km/h

5 a Acceleration $= \frac{1}{5} = 0.2$ m/s^2
   b Distance = area under the graph for first 5 seconds = 2.5 m

6 a $y = 0.4x + 3$
   b The extra number of grams of salt that dissolves for each 1 °C rise in temperature.

7 a Table copied correctly. y values from left to right: 0.5, 1, 2, −2, −1, −0.5.
   b

   c −1.33 (to 3 s.f.)

8 a 6.75 J
   b Graph correctly plotted and labelled
   c 3.5 m/s (3 s.f.)

9 a $y = 3x + c$ where $c \neq -2$
   b $2y + 5x = c$ where $c \neq 1$
   c $y = \frac{1}{2}x - 5$

10 a (1, −2)   **b** $x = 1$
   c $x = -0.20$, $x = 2.20$
   d It sits above the x-axis and so doesn't cross it at any point.

11 $\sqrt{1.21} = 1.1$

12 a Students' own answers
   b Students' own answers

13 Students' own answers with sketches.

UNIT 7 Area and volume

7.1 Perimeter and area

1 Areas: 3 cm^2, 7 m^2, 46 mm^2
Perimeters: 5 km, 32 mm, 10 cm

2 a 12 cm^2, 16 cm   **b** 30 cm^2, 30 cm
   c 96 cm^2, 44 cm

3 a $x = 20$ mm, $y = 34$ mm   **b** 194 mm
   c 1548 mm^2

4 48 cm^2

5 $46.5\,\text{m}^2$, $29\,\text{m}$

6 $2976\,\text{mm}^2$

7 **a** $60\,\text{cm}^2$ **b** $30\,\text{cm}^2$ **c** $26.6\,\text{m}^2$
    d $373.5\,\text{cm}^2$

8 Any triangle with area $40\,\text{cm}^2$, e.g. with height 10, base 8

9 $276\,\text{cm}^2$, $72\,\text{cm}$

10 No; she needs to buy 7 boxes but does not have £62.93.

11 $4\,\text{cm}$

12 **a** $a = 6\,\text{cm}$ **b** $b = 2.8\,\text{m}$ (1 d.p.)

13 $100\,\text{cm}^2$

14 Students' own answers.

7.2 Units and accuracy

1 **a** 3.6 **b** 320 **c** 8.50 **d** 15.7

2 **a i** $2.5\,\text{kg}$ **ii** $22.5\,\text{kg}$ **iii** $27.5\,\text{kg}$
    b i $2\,\text{m}$ **ii** $38\,\text{m}$ **iii** $42\,\text{m}$

3 **a** $1\,\text{cm} = 10\,\text{mm}$, so they have same side length.
    b $1\,\text{cm}^2$ and $100\,\text{mm}^2$
    c $1\,\text{cm}^2 = 100\,\text{mm}^2$

4 **a** Suitable sketch of the squares.
    b $1\,\text{m}^2 = 10\,000\,\text{cm}^2$ **c** Divide by $10\,000$

5 **a** $2.5\,\text{cm}^2$ **b** $340\,\text{mm}^2$ **c** $2\,\text{m}^2$
    d $80\,000\,\text{cm}^2$ **e** $8000\,\text{cm}^2$ **f** $0.7\,\text{m}^2$
    g $0.75\,\text{m}^2$ **h** $88\,500\,\text{cm}^2$ **i** $4000\,\text{cm}^2$
    j $400\,000\,\text{mm}^2$ **k** $600\,000\,\text{mm}^2$
    l $2.8\,\text{m}^2$

6 **a** $0.6\,\text{m}^2$ **b** $544\,\text{mm}^2$ **c** $468\,\text{mm}^2$
    d $21\,600\,\text{cm}^2$ **e, f** Students' own answers.

7 $24.2\,\text{ha}$

8 $1\,600\,000$

9 **a, b** Suitable sketch of the squares.
    c $1\,\text{km}^2 = 100\,\text{ha}$ **d** $2\,073\,500\,\text{ha}$

10 **a** $33\,\text{mm}$, $27\,\text{mm}$
    b $27\,\text{mm} \leqslant \text{length} \leqslant 33\,\text{mm}$

11 $19\,\text{g} \leqslant \text{mass} \leqslant 21\,\text{g}$

12 **a i** $35.5\,\text{cm}$ **ii** $111.5\,\text{cm}$
    b i $2.45\,\text{cm}$ **ii** $6.65\,\text{kg}$

13 **a i** $7.5\,\text{cm}$ **ii** $8.5\,\text{cm}$
    b i $5.25\,\text{kg}$ **ii** $5.35\,\text{kg}$
    c i $11.35\,\text{m}$ **ii** $11.45\,\text{m}$
    d i 2.245 litres   **ii** 2.255 litres
    e i $4500\,\text{m}$ **ii** $5500\,\text{m}$
    f i $31.5\,\text{mm}$ **ii** $32.5\,\text{mm}$
    g i $1.525\,\text{kg}$ **ii** $1.535\,\text{kg}$
    h i $12.45\,\text{cm}$ **ii** $12.55\,\text{cm}$

14 **a** $17.5\,\text{m} \leqslant x < 18.5\,\text{m}$
    b $24.45\,\text{kg} \leqslant y < 24.55\,\text{kg}$
    c $1.35\,\text{m} \leqslant z < 1.45\,\text{m}$
    d $5.255\,\text{km} \leqslant n < 5.265\,\text{km}$

15 $3.65 \leqslant n < 3.75$

16 $4.275 \leqslant x < 4.285$

17 Students' own answers, e.g. Maisie's interval includes 12.5, but 12.5 rounds to 13 so should be excluded.

18 **a i** 2 **ii** 2.4
    b i 8 **ii** 8.9
    c i 6 **ii** 6.2
    d i 4 **ii** 4.5

19 **a** 5 **b** $5.999\ldots$

20 $9 \leqslant N < 10$

21 $4.2 \leqslant n < 4.3$

22 **a** $16.5\,\text{cm}$, $17.5\,\text{cm}$, $27.5\,\text{cm}$, $28.5\,\text{cm}$
    b Lower bound $88\,\text{cm}$, upper bound $92\,\text{cm}$
    c $90\,\text{cm}$ to the nearest $10\,\text{cm}$

23 Upper bound $80.798\,\text{m}^2$, lower bound $79.008\,\text{m}^2$

24 **a** Area $23.5\,\text{cm}^2$, $24.5\,\text{cm}^2$; height $6.15\,\text{cm}$, $6.25\,\text{cm}$
    b i 3.92 **ii** 3.98 (2 d.p.)
    c $\dfrac{\text{upper bound for area}}{\text{lower bound for height}}$, $3.98\,\text{cm}$ (2 d.p.)
    d $3.76\,\text{cm}$
    e $4\,\text{cm}$ to the nearest cm

25 **a** Upper bound of $y = 31.808$ (5 s.f.)
    b Lower bound of $y = 29.095$ (5 s.f.)
      Upper bound of $y = 31.808$ (5 s.f.)
      Bounds agree when rounded to nearest 10 (or to 1 s.f.), so $y = 30$.

7.3 Prisms

1 **a** $1000\,\text{ml}$ **b** $100\,\text{cm}$

2 $72\,\text{cm}^3$

3 **a** $b = 8$ **b** $h = 4$

4 **a** Students' own sketches.
    b, c Areas are $20\,\text{cm}^2$, $28\,\text{cm}^2$ and $35\,\text{cm}^2$.
      The identical pairs are (top, bottom), (front, back) and (left side, right side).
    d $166\,\text{cm}^2$
    e Twice the sum of the areas of the three different faces.

5 $72\,\text{cm}^2$

6 **a** Yes, because it has the same cross-section all through its length.
    b $12\,\text{cm}^2$
    c $72\,\text{cm}^3$; same value as for volume calculated in **Q2**.
    d The cuboid is a prism; area of cross-section is the product of any two dimensions, and the length is the third dimension.

7 **a** $80\,\text{cm}^3$ **b** $370\,\text{cm}^3$ **c** $204\,\text{cm}^3$ **d** $81\,\text{cm}^3$

8 Students' own answers. The boxes will fit exactly into a cuboid box with dimensions $9\,\text{cm} \times 12\,\text{cm} \times 12\,\text{cm}$ (some are rotated by $90°$, to fill the gaps at the sides).

9 **a** $48 = \frac{1}{2} \times 3 \times h \times 8$, $4\,\text{cm}$
    b Students' own nets, $108\,\text{cm}^2$

10 $1.5\,\text{cm}$ or $15\,\text{mm}$

11 **a** Suitable sketch of the cubes
    b $1\,\text{cm}^3 = 1000\,\text{mm}^3$ **c** Divide by 1000

12 **a** $1\,\text{m}^3$ and $1\,000\,000\,\text{cm}^3$ **b** Multiply by $1\,000\,000$

13 **a** $5000\,\text{mm}^3$ **b** $52\,000\,\text{mm}^3$ **c** $4\,\text{cm}^3$
    d $0.4\,\text{cm}^3$ **e** $3.421\,\text{cm}^3$ **f** $3\,000\,000\,\text{cm}^3$
    g $4\,500\,000\,\text{cm}^3$ **h** $0.006\,\text{m}^3$ **i** $9.5\,\text{m}^3$

14 **a** $5200\,\text{ml} = 5.2$ litres   **b** $700\,\text{ml} = 700\,\text{cm}^3$
    c $175\,\text{cm}^3$ **d** $1750\,\text{cm}^3$
    e $2\,000\,000\,\text{cm}^3 = 2\,000\,000\,\text{ml} = 2000$ litres
    f 3000 litres

15 **a** $9.44\,\text{m}^2$ **b** 3

16 $9.2\,\text{cm}$

17 **a** $0.05\,\text{m}^3$
    b Estimated volume of leaf mould in wood is
      $20\,000 \times 0.2 = 4000\,\text{m}^3$, $4000 \div 0.05 = 80\,000$,
      $12 \times 80\,000 = 960\,000$ worms

18 16

7.4 Circles

1 **a** 5 cm, 31 mm **b** 10 cm, 62 mm

2 **a** $r = 5$ **b** $r = \pm 8$ **c** $r = \pm 5$

3 **a** $x = \frac{y}{m}$ **b** $x = \pm t$ **c** $x = \pm\sqrt{p}$

4 **a** All ratios are 3.14 to 2 d.p. **b** 3.141 592 65
  c Multiply circumference by π; multiply radius by $2 \times \pi$

5 **a** 28.3 cm **b** 14.8 m **c** 75.4 mm **d** 21.4 cm
  e You can work out the diameter from the radius (or vice versa) so you only need to remember one formula.

6 37.70 m

7 **a** 50.3 cm^2 **b** 4.5 m^2 **c** 38.5 m^2 **d** 21.2 cm^2

8 Students' own answers.

9 **a** 25π cm^2, 10π cm **b** 49π cm^2, 14π cm
  c 100π cm^2, 20π cm **d** 144π cm^2, 24π cm

10 **a i** 36π cm^2, 12π cm **ii** 110 cm^2, 38 cm
  b The answers in terms of π, because they have not been rounded.

11 66 cm^2

12 Yes; total area = 225π cm^2, shaded area = 75π cm^2,
  $\frac{75\pi}{225\pi} = \frac{1}{3}$

13 No; area is about 51 m^2.

14 Circumference = 201 cm, $1000 \div 2.01 = 497$

15 **a** $104 = \pi d$ **b** $d = 33.1$ cm

16 3.8 cm (1 d.p.)

17 **a** 12.87 m **b** 28.3 cm

18 **a** $\frac{A}{\pi} = r^2$, $\sqrt{\frac{A}{\pi}} = r$
  b X 3.6 cm, Y 2.8 cm, Z 4.7 cm

7.5 Sectors of circles

1 **a** $\frac{1}{8}$ **b** $\frac{1}{6}$

2 **a** 16π cm, 64π cm^2 **b** 50.3 cm, 201 cm^2

3 **a** $4x$ **b** 4π
  c $2\pi + 10.2$ **d** $3\pi + 7$

4 **a** 18π cm^2 **b** 25π cm^2
  c 56.5 cm^2, 78.5 cm^2

5 **a** $(3\pi + 6)$ cm **b** $(5\pi + 10)$ cm
  c 15.4 cm, 25.7 cm

6 **a** $(4\pi + 16)$ cm **b** 28.6 cm

7 4.41 m^2, 8.80 m

8 21.5 cm^2

9 Area of square = 64
  Area of semicircle = 8π
  Area of quarter circle = 16π
  Unshaded area = $16\pi - 8\pi = 8\pi$
  $\frac{8\pi}{64} = \frac{\pi}{8}$

10 **a** 3.090 193 616 cm **b** 3.1 cm (1 d.p.)

11 25.1 cm^2

12 4.19 cm, 28.2 cm

13 **a** 24.4 cm, 85.5 cm^2
  b 73.7 cm$^2 \leqslant$ area < 98.2 cm^2

14 **a** $10 = \frac{x}{360} \times \pi \times 3^2$ **b** 127°

15 74°

16 8.6 m (2 s.f.)

17 111°, 23.7 cm

18 4.97 cm (3.s.f.)

7.6 Cylinders and spheres

1 49π cm^2, 14π cm

2 Students' own nets.

3 **a** ± 6 **b** ± 9 **c** ± 1.6 **d** 2.2

4 **a** πr^2 **b** $V = \pi r^2 \times h$

5 **a** 197.9 cm^3 **b** 167 283.5 mm^3 **c** 2.6 m^3

6 0.267 m^3

7 **a** $125 = \pi \times 3.5^2 \times h$ **b** 3.2 cm

8 **a** 188.5 cm^2 **b** 16 889.2 mm^2 **c** 41.3 m^2

9 Yes; surface area is $4 \times 1.4608... = 5.843...$ m^2 and 2 tins cover $2 \times 3 = 6$ m^2, so 2 tins is enough.

10 26 mm

11 **a** 2.19 cm (2 d.p.) **b** 300 ml

12 **a** 324π mm^2, 972π mm^3 **b** 100π cm^2, $\frac{500}{3}\pi$ cm^3

13 **a** 1072.33 cm^3 **b** 402.12 cm^2 **c** 603.19 cm^2

14 **a** $\frac{1000}{3}\pi = 1050$ mm^3 **b** $175\pi = 550$ mm^2

15 17 mm

16 6.31 m (2 d.p.)

17 509 cm^2

18 You can work out the volume and surface area of a cylinder from the formulae for the area and circumference of a circle (its cross-section), and its length.

7.7 Pyramids and cones

1 **a** 125 mm^3 **b** 4 cm

2 **a** 20 cm^2 **b** 21 cm^2

3 9.4 cm

4 **a** Net of square-based pyramid, square 4 cm side, height of each triangle 6 cm
  b Triangular face 12 cm^2, square face 16 cm^2
  c 64 cm^2
  d No; surface area = area of base + area of each triangular face

5 90 cm^2

6 213 cm^3

7 **a** 8.7 cm (1 d.p.) **b** 950 cm^3 (2 s.f.)

8 **a** 96π cm^3 **b** 302 cm^3 (3 s.f.)

9 **a** 25π cm^2 **b** 65π cm^2 **c** 90π cm^2

10 **a** $l^2 = 4^2 + 9^2 = 16 + 81 = 97$ so $l = \sqrt{97}$
  b 123.8 cm^2
  c Max's, because it has not been rounded.

11 9694 mm^2 (to nearest mm^2), 63 363 mm^3 (to nearest mm^3)

12 10.6 cm (3 s.f.)

13 **a** Step 4: Find the radius of the large cone.
    Step 5: Find the diameter of the large cone.
  b Radius of large cone: $73.5\pi = 6\pi r^2$
    $12.25 = r^2$
    3.5 cm $= r$
    Diameter of large cone: $d = 2 \times 3.5 = 7$ cm

14 Radius of sphere = 5.2322... cm
  Height of cone = 20.9 cm (3 s.f.)

15 Volume of whole cone = 144π cm^3
  Volume of smaller cone = $\frac{128}{3}\pi$ cm^3
  Volume of frustum = $\frac{304}{3}\pi$ cm^3

16 51π cm^3

7 Check up

1 375 mm^2

2 7 cm

3 **a** 50.3 cm **b** 64π cm^2

4 25.7 cm

5 **a** 15.7 cm^2 **b** 5.2 cm

6 **a** 40 000 cm^2 **b** 0.56 m^2
c 9.5 m^3 **d** 4000 ml = 4000 cm^3

7 **a** 35.5 m ⩽ 36 m < 36.5 m
b 23.55 km ⩽ 23.6 km < 23.65 km
c 9.15 cm ⩽ 9.2 cm < 9.25 cm

8 36 cm^3

9 492.9 cm^2 (1 d.p.)

10 36π cm^3

11 400 cm^3, 360 cm^2

12 301.6 cm^3 (1 d.p.)

14 Students' own answers.

7 Strengthen

2D shapes

1 **a** 2 cm **b** 10.3 cm
c

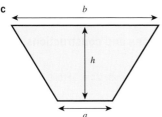

d 5.5 cm^2

2 **a**

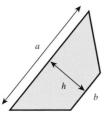

b $55 = \frac{1}{2}(7 + b) \times 10$

c $55 = 35 + 5b$ **d** $b = 4$ cm

3 **a** $C = 2\pi r$
b i 4π cm, 12π cm **ii** 12.6 cm, 37.7 cm

4 **a** $2\pi r = 19.5$ cm, $\pi r^2 = 34$ cm^2
b $A = \pi r^2$ **c** $C = 2\pi r$

5 **a** 4π cm^2, 36π cm^2 **b** 12.6 cm^2, 113.1 cm^2

6 **a** $\frac{1}{2}$
b i 153.9 cm^2 **ii** 77.0 cm^2 **iii** 44.0 cm **iv** 22.0 cm
v 14.0 cm **vi** 36.0 cm

7 **a** $\frac{90}{360} = \frac{1}{4}$ **b** $\frac{45}{360} = \frac{1}{8}$ **c** $\frac{100}{360} = \frac{5}{18}$

8 **a** $\frac{1}{8}$
b i 201.1 cm^2 **ii** 25.1 cm^2 **iii** 50.3 cm **iv** 6.3 cm
v 16 cm **vi** 22.3 cm

Accuracy and measures

1 **a i** 10 000 cm^2 **ii** 20 000 cm^2
b

2 **a i** 1 000 000 cm^3 **ii** 2 000 000 cm^3
b

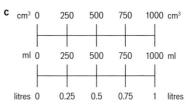

c

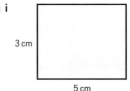

3 **a** 22.5 cm ⩽ l < 23.5 cm **b** 31.5 mm ⩽ l < 32.5 mm

3D solids

1 **a i**

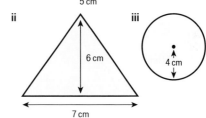

b i 60 cm^3 **ii** 63 cm^3 **iii** $240\pi = 754$ cm^3

2 **a** Students' own nets.
b i 113.1 cm^2 **ii** 37.7 cm **iii** 301.6 cm^2 **iv** 527.8 cm^2

3 **a** Surface area = $4\pi r^2$ **b** 452.39 cm^2
c Volume = $\frac{4}{3}\pi r^3$ **d** 904.78 cm^3

4 **a** 36 cm^2 **b** 4 cm **c** 48 cm^3
d

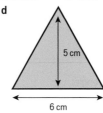

e i 15 cm^2 **ii** 60 cm^2 **f** 96 cm^2

5 **a** 4 cm **b** 5 cm **c** 37.7 cm^3 **d** 75.4 cm^2

7 Extend

1 **a** $50xy$ **b** $500xyz$

2 **a** Draw a line parallel to the wall to form a rectangle and a right-angled triangle. The hypotenuse of the triangle is 5 m and the right-hand side is $11 - 8 = 3$ m. These are two sides of a Pythagorean triple, so the third side is 4 m. This side is the same length as the wall, so the wall is 4 m long.
b Area of lawn = 38 m^2; 2 bottles

3 210 m

4 Capacity of tank = 942 477.8 cm^3 = 942 477.8 ml
Time to fill = 3142 seconds = 52 minutes

5 32%

6 Area of trapezium $= \frac{1}{2}(a+b)h$

So $144 = \frac{1}{2}((x-6)+(x+2)) \times 3x$

$144 = \frac{1}{2}(2x-4) \times 3x$

$144 = (x-2) \times 3x$

Therefore $3x^2 - 6x = 144$

7 7.14 cm

8 6 litres

9 $n = 72$

10 a 19.9   **b** 24.8625

     c 389.098125   **d** 3.7710...

11 a 7000 (to 2 s.f.)   **b** 20 000 (to 2 s.f.)

12 $3.85 \times 10^{13} \, \text{m}^2$

13 $h = 3\sqrt{14}$ cm

7 Test ready

Sample student answer

No, the student has not given their answer to 3 s.f. as required by the question.

7 Unit test

1 9.5 cm

2 $90\pi = 283 \, \text{cm}$

3 a $210 \, \text{cm}^2$ **b** 60 cm

4 6 cm

5 156 cubes

6 $9.20 \leqslant V < 9.30$

7 16.1 cm (3 s. f.)

8 a $64\pi \, \text{cm}^2$ **b** 11.3 cm (nearest mm)

9 15.16 cm (2 d.p.)

10 $368 \, \text{cm}^3$

11 $144\pi \, \text{cm}^2$

12 $15 \, \text{cm}^2$

13 $159.2 \, \text{cm}^3$ (lower bound); $165.4 \, \text{cm}^3$ (upper bound)

14 $k = 22$

15 a Correct section shaded (top rectangle)
     b Correct section shaded (top and middle rectangles shaded)
     c Correct section shaded (either triangle)

16 Students' own answers in given sentence format.

Mixed exercise 2

1 $x = 50°$. For example, $62 + 68 = 130$ as the exterior angle of a triangle is equal to the sum of the interior angles at the other two vertices. $x = 180 - 130 = 50$ as supplementary angles total $180°$.   **→ 5.1**

2 Graph A **iv**   Graph B **i**   Graph C **v**   **→ 6.4, 6.6, 6.7**

3 No, Ali is not correct.
     SA $= 384 \, \text{cm}^2$
     Area of each face of cube $= 384 \div 6 = 64 \, \text{cm}^2$
     Side length of cube $= \sqrt{64} = 8$ cm
     Volume of cube $= 8^3 = 512 \, \text{cm}^3$
     Volume of cuboid $= 432 \, \text{cm}^3$ **→ 7.3**

4 $a = 36°$ **→ 5.1, 5.2**

5 $V = \frac{1}{2} \times 10(x+3)(x+12) = 5(x^2+15x+36) = 5x^2+75x+180$ **→ 7.3, 2.7**

6 $x = 108°$ **→ 5.2**

7 No, as the gradients are different. The gradient of line L is 2 and the gradient of $2y = 6x - 3$ is 3.   **→ 6.1, 6.2, 6.5**

8 $1 : 1.78$ **→ 7.6, 4.2**

9 $y = -\frac{3}{2}x + 15$ **→ 6.2, 6.5**

10 75.3%   **→ 7.5, 4.4**

11 a $3\sqrt{5}$ **b** 7.5 units   **→ 1.7, 5.4, 6.5**

12 a $(-9, 0)$ **b** $(0, 9)$ **c** $y = -x$ **→ 6.2, 6.5, 6.8**

13 $16.0°$ **→ 4.2, 5.5, 5.7**

14 a Total distance $= 4505 \, \text{m}$
     $40 + (4505 \div 2 - 340) \div 17 = 152.5$ seconds
     b For example, the acceleration during first part is positive (0.425) but the acceleration/deceleration during last part is negative (-0.567).   **→ 6.3**

15 $120 \, \text{cm}^2$ (2 s.f.)   **→ 7.2, 7.6**

16 $114 \, \text{cm}^2$ **→ 5.4, 7.4**

17 $220°$
     Radius of the cone $= 3.694257...$, $l = 6.057...$
     Surface area of cone $= 70.29...$
     Angle $AOB = 220°$ **→ 5.4, 7.5, 7.7**

18 $L_1: y = -2x + 3$, $L_2: y = \frac{1}{2}x - 2$
     $A(0, -2)$, $B(0, 3)$, $C(2, -1)$
     Area $= 5$ units^2 **→ 6.1, 6.2, 6.5**

UNIT 8 Transformations and constructions

8.1 3D solids

1 Top: 3 cm by 4 cm   Side: 4 cm by 2 cm   Front: 3 cm by 2 cm

2 5 cm

3 a e.g.   **b** e.g.

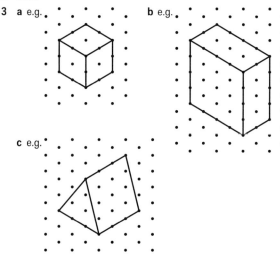

     c e.g.

4 3 planes of symmetry

5 a

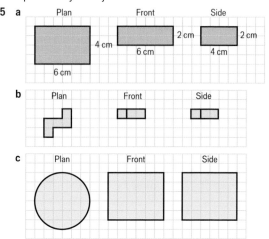

6 a 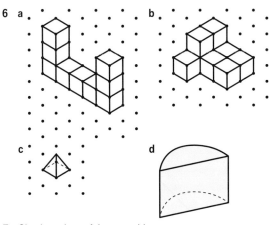 **b**

c **d**

7 Slanting edges of the pyramid

8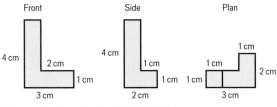

9 C

10
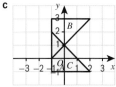

Front
4 cm
2 cm
1 cm
3 cm

Side
4 cm
1 cm
1 cm
2 cm

Plan
1 cm
1 cm 1 cm
2 cm
3 cm

11

side   front

12 a 96 cm²

b

Plan
4 cm
4 cm

Side
2 cm
4 cm

Front
2 cm
4 cm

c 64 cm²

d

Plan
4 cm
4 cm

Side
4 cm
√32 cm

Front
4 cm
4 cm

70.6 cm²

e The total surface area of the two half-cubes includes the areas of the two new faces creating by cutting, as well as the faces of the original cube.

8.2 Reflection and rotation

1 a Yes   **b** Yes

2
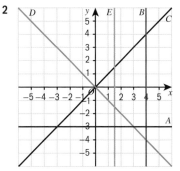

3 a, b, c, d
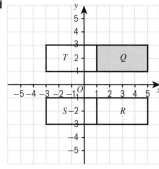

e Reflection in the line $x = 1$

4 a, b, c

d The line $y = x$ is a line of symmetry in triangle A.

5 a, c
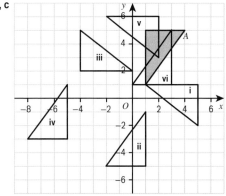

c A 180° rotation is a half turn, so the image is the same for a rotation in either direction.

6 a Q, R, T, U **b** S, V, W

7 a Reflection in the y-axis (or the line $x = 0$)
  b Reflection in the line $y = -1$
  c Rotation 90° clockwise about (2, 0)
  d Reflection in the line $y = -x$
  e Reflection in the line $x = 3.5$
  f Rotation 90° anticlockwise about (−1, −2)
  g Rotation 180° about (−1, −1)

8 a Reflection in the line $x = 3$
  b Reflection in the line $y = -x$
  c Rotation 180° about (0, −3)
  d Reflection in the line $x = 2.5$
  e Rotation 90° clockwise about (−3, 2)
  f Reflection in the line $y = x$

9 Reflection in the line $y = 0.5$ or rotation 180° about (0, 0.5)

10 Rotation 90° anticlockwise about (0, 0)

11 Always true. The image of point (a, b) reflected in the x- then the y-axis is $(-a, -b)$, which is equivalent to a rotation of 180° about the origin.

8.3 Enlargement

1 **a** Scale factor 1.5   **b** K

2

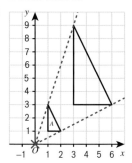

3 **a, b, c**

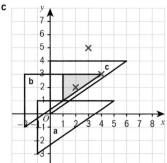

4 **a** Scale factor 3

b

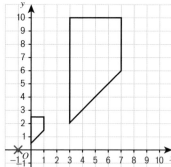

c $(-5, -2)$

d Enlargement by scale factor 3, centre $(-5, -2)$.

5 **a** $6\,\text{cm}^2$ **b** $24\,\text{cm}^2$ **c** $54\,\text{cm}^2$ **d** $96\,\text{cm}^2$

e

Shape	Scale factor	Area of enlarged shape / Area of shape A
B	2	4
C	3	9
D	4	16

f The area is enlarged by scale factor k^2.

6 **a** e.g.

b e.g.

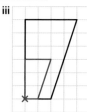

7 **a** The image is smaller than the object.

b The image is larger than the object.

c The image is the same size as the object.

8 **a i**

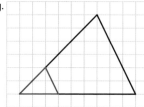

   ii   **iii**

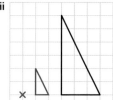

b Scale factor $\left(\frac{1}{2}\right)^2 = \frac{1}{4}$

9

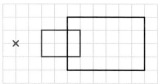

10 **a** Enlargement by scale factor $\frac{1}{3}$, centre $(-5, -2)$

b Enlargement by scale factor $\frac{1}{3}$, centre $(2, -5)$

c The image is smaller than the object.

11

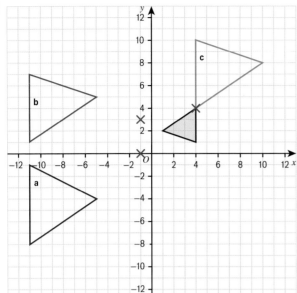

12 a

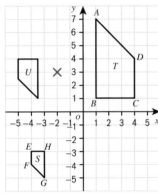

b i G **ii** H **iii** E **iv** F

c The image is on the opposite side of the centre of enlargement.

d Enlargement, scale factor -3, centre $(-2, -2)$

13 Enlargement, scale factor $-\frac{1}{3}$, centre $(-2, -2)$

8.4 Translations and combinations of different transformations

1 Reflection in the y-axis (or the line $x = 0$)
Rotation $90°$ clockwise about $(0, 0)$

2 A 2 squares right, 2 squares up
B 2 squares left, 2 squares up
C 2 squares left, 2 squares up
D 1 square left, 2 squares up
E 2 squares left, 5 squares down

3

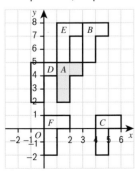

4 a $\begin{pmatrix} 4 \\ 2 \end{pmatrix}$ **b** $\begin{pmatrix} 0 \\ -4 \end{pmatrix}$ **c** $\begin{pmatrix} 4 \\ -6 \end{pmatrix}$

d $\begin{pmatrix} 5 \\ 1 \end{pmatrix}$ **e** $\begin{pmatrix} -5 \\ -1 \end{pmatrix}$

f Multiply the movements parallel to the x- and y-axes by -1.

5 $\begin{pmatrix} -a \\ -b \end{pmatrix}$; the movements parallel to the x- and y-axes are in the opposite directions, so multiply by -1.

6 a, b

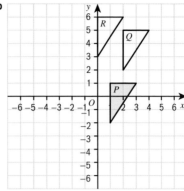

c $\begin{pmatrix} -1 \\ 5 \end{pmatrix}$ **d** $1 + (-2) = -1$, and $4 + 1 = 5$

7 a $\begin{pmatrix} 4 \\ 1 \end{pmatrix}$

b $\begin{pmatrix} a+c \\ b+d \end{pmatrix}$; this is the total horizontal movement and the total vertical movement.

8 $c = 3, d = 0$

9 a, b, c, d

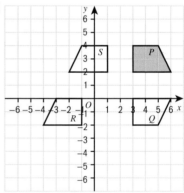

e Reflection in the line $x = 2$

10 a Yes, with explanation, e.g.

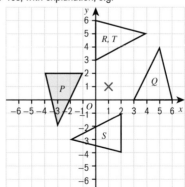

11 a, b, c

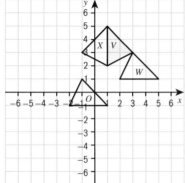

d Reflection in the line $x = 1$

12 (3, 3)

13 a, b, c

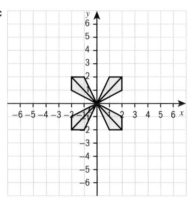

d Enlargement, scale factor 3, centre (0, 0)

14 Adam's statement is not always true. When a shape is enlarged, the image and the original are similar but not congruent.

8.5 Scale drawings and bearings

1 **a** $x = 100°$ **b** $y = 120°$ **c** $z = 120°$ **d** $w = 310°$

2 **a** 20 m   **b** 2.5 cm

3 **a** Accurate scale drawing of right-angled triangle with base 6 cm, hypotenuse 10 cm
    b 36 m

4 **a** 5 km   **b** 2.5 km   **c** 1.25 km   **d** 0.25 km

5 **a** 1 cm : 200 000 cm = 2000 m = 2 km
    b i 10 cm   **ii** 5 cm   **iii** 4 cm

6 **a** 2.5 km   **b** 16 cm

7 **a** 1 cm : 120 m
    b i 360 m   **ii** 600 m
    c Answer between 4 and 4.24 minutes

8 **a** Accurate scale drawing, with $AB = 5$ cm
    b $AC = 67$ km, $CB = 78$ km

9 **a** 072°   **b** 255°

10 Bearing of 285° accurately drawn

11

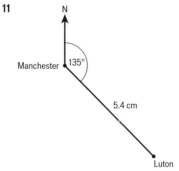

12 a

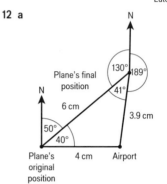

b 189°
c About 78 km

13 a

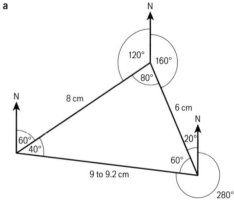

b 27 km   **c** 280°

14

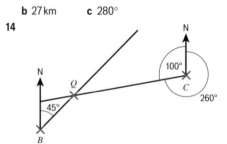

15 a 37°   **b** 323°   **c** 323°
16 a 260°   **b** 050°
17 311°

18 a 220°

b

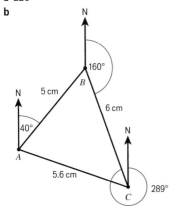

    i About 11.1 km
    ii 289°   **iii** 109°

8.6 Constructions 1

1 a At right angles
  b Part of the circumference of a circle

2 Accurate drawing of the triangle

3 a Accurate drawing of the triangle
  b Yes; there are infinitely many similar triangles with these angles.

4 Accurate drawing of the triangle

5 a, b, c Accurate drawings of the triangles

6 Accurate drawing of equilateral triangle with side 6.5 cm. All angles should be 60°.

7 The sum of the two shorter sides is less than the longest side so the triangle will not be possible.

8 Accurate drawing of triangle with sides of length 5.5 cm, 5.5 cm and 10 cm (for real-life sides of 11 m, 11 m and 20 m respectively).

9 Accurate net with sides of length 6 cm

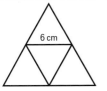

10 a, b Perpendicular bisector of line segment AB of length 7 cm drawn accurately
    c AP is the same distance as BP.
    d Construct the perpendicular bisector of the line AB.

11 a, b

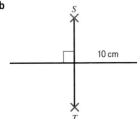

The perpendicular bisector of ST shows possible positions of the lifeboat.

12 a, b, c Perpendicular bisector from point P to the line AB accurately constructed
     d The length of the perpendicular line from P to AB

13 a, b, c Perpendicular bisector of XY accurately constructed.

14 a Shortest distances to sides accurately drawn
   b 2.5 m   **c** 10 seconds

8.7 Constructions 2

1 45° angle accurately constructed

2 a Accurate drawing of triangle with sides 10 cm, 8 cm, 6 cm
  b Right-angled triangle

3 a Accurate construction of equilateral triangle with sides 5 cm
  b 60°

4 a, b Angles accurately drawn and bisected

5 a 90°
  b i Accurate construction of 90° angle
    ii Accurate construction of 45° angle
  c The two methods are the same.

6 a Equilateral triangle
  b i Accurate construction of 60° angle
    ii Accurate construction of 30° angle

7 Accurate construction of 120° angle

8 a, b, c, d Accurate construction of right-angled triangle PQR with 60° angle at Q

9 a Accurate scale drawing with sides 3 cm and 5 cm
  b 115 m²

10 a Accurate scale drawing
   b 2.4 m   **c** 27.7 m

11 a Accurate construction of triangle
   b Accurate construction of line perpendicular to AB that passes through C
   c 16 cm²

12 a Accurate construction of triangle with sides 5 cm, 8 cm and 10 cm
   b, c, d, e

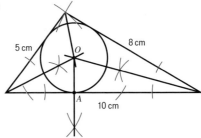

   e The circle fits exactly inside the triangle.

13 a, b, c Construction of regular hexagon in a circle
   d Hexagon
   e Angle AOB is 60° because a hexagon has 6 sides and $360 \div 6 = 60$.

14 Construction of regular octagon in circle with radius 5 cm

8.8 Loci

1 No; the points at the corners of the dashed rectangle are furthest from the solid line.

2 Circle with radius 4 cm

3 Sketch of circle with radius marked 5 m

4 a, b

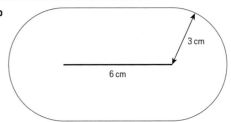

5 a, b

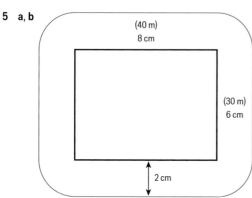

(40 m)
8 cm

(30 m)
6 cm

2 cm

6 a, b, c

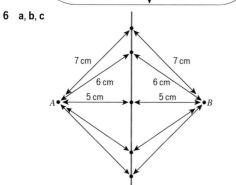

7 cm   7 cm
6 cm   6 cm
5 cm   5 cm
A   B

d Yes (if the perpendicular bisector is extended)

7

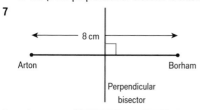

8 cm

Arton   Borham

Perpendicular
bisector

8 a, b

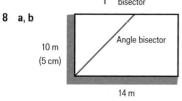

10 m
(5 cm)

Angle bisector

14 m
(7 cm)

9 a, b, c

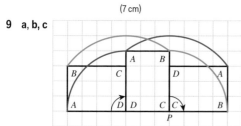

B   C   A B   D   A
A   D D   C C   B
                P

10

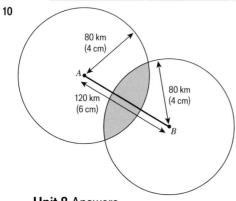

80 km
(4 cm)

A

120 km
(6 cm)

80 km
(4 cm)

B

11 a, b

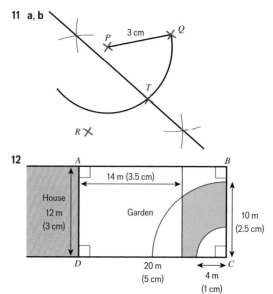

3 cm
P   Q
T
R

12

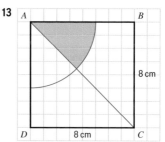

A   14 m (3.5 cm)   B

House
12 m   Garden   10 m
(3 cm)   (2.5 cm)

D   20 m   C
               (5 cm)   4 m
                              (1 cm)

13

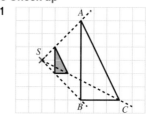

A   B

8 cm

D   8 cm   C

14 a Square with quarter circles radius 3.5 cm drawn at each
vertex. Region between the quarter circles shaded.
  b $10.52 \, \text{cm}^2$ (2 d.p.)
15 $50.3 \, \text{km}^2$ (3 s.f.)

8 Check up

1

A
S
B   C

2 a Reflection in the line $y = x$
  b Rotation 90° anticlockwise about (4, −1)
  c Translation $\begin{pmatrix} -4 \\ 4 \end{pmatrix}$

3 a Enlargement by scale factor 2, centre (−3, 5)
  b Enlargement by scale factor $\frac{1}{2}$, centre (−3, 3)
  c Enlargement by scale factor −1, centre (0, −2.5)

4 a, b, c

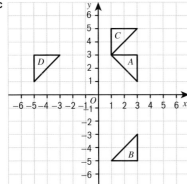

d Reflection in the line $x = -1$

5

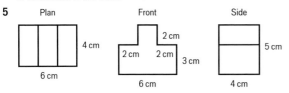

Plan   Front   Side

4 cm

2 cm

2 cm   2 cm   3 cm

6 cm

6 cm   4 cm

5 cm

6 4 cm

7 290°

8 a

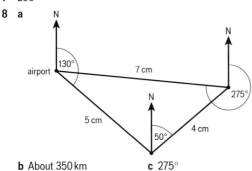

N

airport   130°   7 cm

N

275°

N

5 cm   50°   4 cm

b About 350 km   **c** 275°

9 Perpendicular bisector accurately constructed on a line AB of length 10 cm

10 Angle accurately bisected

11 a, b

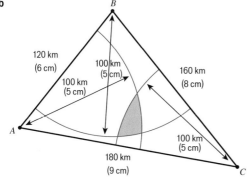

B

120 km
(6 cm)   100 km
(5 cm)   160 km
(8 cm)

100 km
(5 cm)

A   100 km
(5 cm)

180 km
(9 cm)   C

13 a Square correctly constructed.

  b Circle correctly drawn through all 4 vertices of square.

  c Construct the square and draw the circle as described in part **b**. Construct perpendicular bisectors of the sides of the square, then join the intersection of each perpendicular bisector and circle to the square's vertices.

8 Strengthen

Transformations

1 a, b

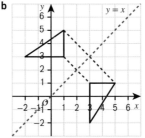

$y = x$

c When folded on the line of reflection, the triangle on the tracing paper becomes the image.

2 a, b, c

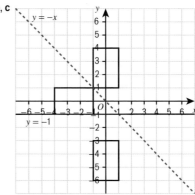

$y = -x$

$y = -1$

3 a

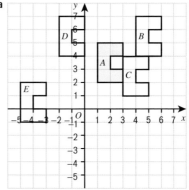

A

B

b Shape A is reflected in the line $y = x$ to give image B.

4 a $\begin{pmatrix} 3 \\ 2 \end{pmatrix}$ **b** $\begin{pmatrix} 5 \\ 1 \end{pmatrix}$ **c** $\begin{pmatrix} 2 \\ -1 \end{pmatrix}$

  d $\begin{pmatrix} -3 \\ 2 \end{pmatrix}$ **e** $\begin{pmatrix} -6 \\ -2 \end{pmatrix}$ **f** $\begin{pmatrix} 3 \\ -4 \end{pmatrix}$

5 a

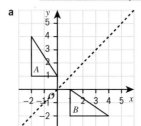

D

B

A

C

E

b 3 right, 1 up or $\begin{pmatrix} 3 \\ 1 \end{pmatrix}$

c i 5 left or $\begin{pmatrix} -5 \\ 0 \end{pmatrix}$ **ii** 2 left, 3 down or $\begin{pmatrix} -2 \\ -3 \end{pmatrix}$

  iii 6 left, 6 down or $\begin{pmatrix} -6 \\ -6 \end{pmatrix}$

6 a, b, c

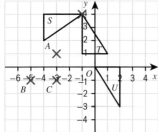

d C

7 a Rotation of 90° clockwise about (0, 0)
   b Rotation of 180° about (0, 2)
   c Rotation of 90° anticlockwise about (4, −1)

8 a, b, d

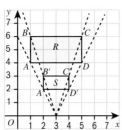

c $\frac{1}{2}$

e Enlargement by scale factor $\frac{1}{2}$ with centre of enlargement (3, 0).

9 a A 2 right, 2 up; B 2 right, 4 up; C 6 right, 4 up
   b i A 1 right, 1 up; B 1 right, 2 up;
        C 3 right, 2 up
      ii A 2 left, 2 down; B 2 left, 4 down;
        C 6 left, 4 down
      iii A 4 left, 4 down; B 4 left, 8 down;
        C 12 left, 8 down

c

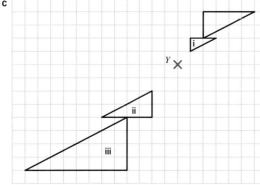

10

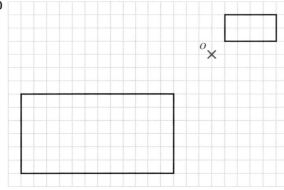

11 Students' own answers, e.g.
   a i There is no mirror line that you can fold along to place one triangle on top of the other.
      ii The two triangles are not 'the same way round'.
   b Trace triangle A, and rotate the tracing around a pencil tip; if the pencil tip is placed at (0, 0), the rotated triangle fits on top of triangle B after a rotation of 180°.

12 Rotation: angle, direction and centre of rotation
Translation: horizontal movement and vertical movement (or translation vector)
Enlargement: scale factor and centre of enlargement

Drawings and bearings

1

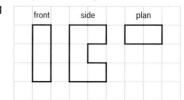

2 a 2 cm   **b** 2 cm

c

d Top edge of the front face of the solid

e

3 a 50 000 cm = 500 m = 0.5 km
   b
       Map (cm)

       1   2   3   4   5   6
       | | | | | |
      0.5   1   1.5   2   2.5   3

       Real life (km)

   c i 1 km   **ii** 2.5 km   **iii** 6 km   **iv** 4.25 km

4 $x = 65°$ (co-interior angles add up to 180°)
   $y = 360 − x$ (angles around a point add up to 360°)
   $= 360 − 65 = 295°$
   Bearing of A from B is 295°

5 a, b, c

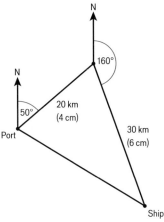

d i 30 km   **ii** 301°

Constructions and loci

1 Accurate construction of triangle with sides of length 10 cm, 7 cm, 6 cm

2 Accurate construction of triangle with sides of length 7 cm, 8 cm, 9 cm

3 Accurate construction of the perpendicular bisector of line of length 12 cm

4 Accurate construction of the perpendicular bisector of line of length 7 cm

5 Accurate construction of angle bisector of 70° angle

6 Accurate construction of angle bisector of 100° angle

7 a

b Circle

c Points that are equidistant from a centre make a circle.

8 a, b, c

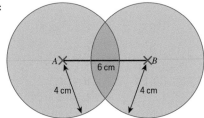

8 Extend

1 Enlargement by scale factor −2, centre of enlargement (−1, 0)

2 a, b, d

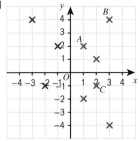

c When points are reflected in the x-axis, the y-coordinate is multiplied by −1.

d When points are reflected in the y-axis, the x-coordinate is multiplied by −1.

e i $(p, -q)$ **ii** $(-p, q)$ **iii** $(-p, -q)$

3 a, b, c

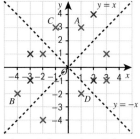

d i (q, p) **ii** $(-q, -p)$ **iii** $(-p, -q)$

e Both combined transformations produce the same image, $(-p, -q)$.

4 $(-2, -1), (-4, -1), (-3, -5), (-5, -5)$

5 Reflection in $y = x$ followed by reflection in the y-axis
   Reflection in $y = -x$ followed by reflection in the x-axis

6 a, d

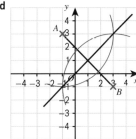

b $y = -x + 2$ **c** 1

7 a

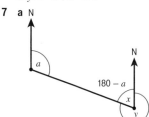

$x = 180 - a$ (co-interior angles add up to 180°)
$y = 360 - (180 - a)$ (angles around a point add up to 360°)
$\quad = 180 + a$

b $(a - 180)°$

8 a 60°

b, c Accurate construction of hexagon

9 Accurate construction of triangle with area 30 cm²

10 a Sphere, radius 20 m   **b** Circle

11

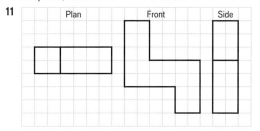

12 a, b

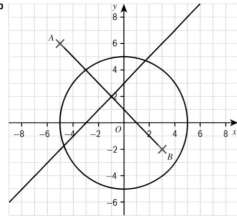

b (1.7, 4.7) and (−4.7, −1.7)

13 52 minutes

8 Test ready

Sample student answers

Student B gives the best answer.
Student A has not given the direction or centre of rotation.
Student C has given two transformations. The question asks for a single transformation.

8 Unit test

1

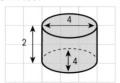

2 Correct triangle and arcs

3 a i Reflection in the line $y = x$

　　ii Rotation 90° anticlockwise, centre of rotation (2,1)

　　iii Translation by vector $\begin{pmatrix} -3 \\ 1 \end{pmatrix}$

　b $n = 2$

4 a

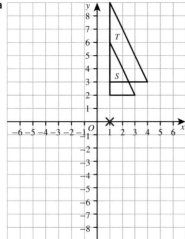

---

b

5 Enlargement, scale factor 2 about (1, 3)

6 a Completely correct diagram: 3 perpendicular bisectors and an angle bisector constructed, sides the correct lengths (marked dimensions are 5 cm and 8 cm)

　b Answer in the range 45–47 m

7 21.7 cm^2

8 8 km

9 a Correct scale drawing　　**b** 258–262°

10 075°

11 (−3, 2)

12 a Correctly enlarged triangle drawn and labelled.

　b Rotation, 180° about (0, 0)

　c Yes

13 Students' own answers

UNIT 9 Equations and inequalities

9.1 Solving linear inequalities

1 A

2 a $x \geqslant 2$　　**b** $x < 2$　　**c** $1 < x \leqslant 5$

3 a $x = \frac{1}{2}$　　**b** $x = 2$　　**c** $x = \frac{2}{3}$　　**d** $x = -2$

4 a −4, −3, −2, −1, 0, 1, 2, 3　**b** 1, 2, 3, 4
　c −3, −2, −1, 0, 1, 2　　**d** −1, 0, 1

5 a −2, −1, 0, 1　　　　　　**b** $-4 \leqslant n < 2$

6 a $x > 1$　　**b** $x < 1$　　**c** $x > 1$　　**d** $x < 1$

7 a The set of all x values such that x is less than 2

　b The set of all x values such that x is less than or equal to −2

　c The set of all x values such that x is greater than or equal to 0

　d The set of all x values such that x is greater than −1

8 a $\{x : x > 3\}$　　　　　**b** $\{x : x \geqslant 2\}$

　c $\{x : x > 3\}$　　　　　**d** $\{x : x \leqslant 2\}$

9 3

10 a $\{x : x > 4\}$　　**b** $\{x : x \leqslant 7\}$　　**c** $\{x : x > -3\}$
　d $\{x : x > -5.5\}$　　**e** $\{x : x \geqslant 1.8\}$　　**f** $\{x : x \leqslant \frac{1}{3}\}$

11 $-4 < x \leqslant 2$

12 a $-3 < x \leqslant 4$ **b** $-3 \leqslant x \leqslant 9$
   c $-1 < x \leqslant 3$

13 a $x < 3$
   b

14 $1.25 \leqslant t \leqslant 3.75$ seconds

15 a No   **b** No
   c The inequality sign is reversed.

16 a $x \leqslant 4$ **b** $x > -3$ **c** $x \geqslant \frac{4}{5}$
   d $2 < x < 8$ **e** $-5 < x < 2$ **f** $-2 \leqslant x < 4$

17 a $\{x : x \geqslant -3\}$ **b** $\{x : -2 < x \leqslant 4\}$
   c $\{x : 1\frac{1}{2} < x \leqslant 3\}$

18 0, 1, 2, 3

9.2 Solving quadratic equations 1

1 a 10, −10   **b** 12, −12   **c** 7, −7

2 −2 and 6

3 a $x(x-5)$ **b** $(y-2)(y+2)$ **c** $(x+5)(x-2)$

4 a $z = \pm 6$ **b** $z = \pm 4$ **c** $z = \pm 5$

5 a $x = \pm 4$ **b** $x = \pm 7$ **c** $x = \pm 5$

6 $2 \times (-3)^2 - 3 = 2 \times 9 - 3 = 18 - 3 = 15$

7 a $x = 4$ or $x = 6$ **b** $x = 4$ or $x = -6$
   c $x = -4$ or $x = -6$ **d** $x = 5$ or $x = -6$
   e $x = -5$ or $x = 6$ **f** $y = 1$ or $y = -2$
   g $y = -2$ or $y = -1$ **h** $y = -1$ or $y = 2$
   i $y = -2$ or $y = 5$

8 a $x = -3$ or $x = 2$ **b** $(x+3)(x-2)$

9 a $x^2 + 5x = x(x+5)$
   b If the product of two numbers is 0, one of them must be 0.
   c For $x = 0$, $x^2 + 5x = 0^2 + 5 \times 0 = 0$
     For $x = -5$, $x^2 + 5x = (-5)^2 + 5 \times (-5) = 25 - 25 = 0$

10 a $x = 0$ or $x = -7$ **b** $y = 0$ or $y = 4$
   c $y = 0$ or $y = 4$ **d** $y = 0$ or $y = -4$

11 a The solutions are where $y = x^2 - 4x + 4 = 0$, and the curve only touches the x-axis in one place, at $x = 2$
   b $(x-2)^2$

12 a $x = 3$ **b** $x = -3$ **c** $x = 5$
   d $x = -7$ **e** $x = -11$ **f** $x = 9$

13 a $(x+4)(x-4)$; $x = -4$ and $x = 4$
   b $(2+y)(2-y)$; $y = -2$ and $y = 2$
   c $x(x-1)$; $x = 0$ and $x = 1$
   d $x(x-2)$; $x = 0$ and $x = 2$
   e $(t+2)(t+3)$; $t = -2$ and $t = -3$
   f $(r+4)(r-2)$; $r = -4$ and $r = 2$
   g $(s-3)(s-4)$; $s = 3$ and $s = 4$
   h $(m+5)(m-2)$; $m = -5$ and $m = 2$

14 a $x = -1$ or $x = -6$ **b** $x = -4$ or $x = 3$
   c $x = 2$ or $x = 4$ **d** $x = 0$ or $x = 7$

15 $(x-4)(x+6)$ or any multiple, e.g. $(2x-8)(x+6)$, $(x-4)(2x+12)$

9.3 Solving quadratic equations 2

1 a 5, −5   **b** 8, −8   **c** 15, −15

2 a $x = -1$ or $x = -3$ **b** $x = -1$ or $x = -4$
   c $x = 3$ or $x = -2$

3 a $2x^2 + 7x + 3$ **b** $3x^2 + 5x - 2$
   c $2x^2 - 6x - 8$ **d** $4x^2 + 13x - 12$

4 a 0.38   **b** 0.15

5 a $2\sqrt{6}$ **b** $2\sqrt{7}$ **c** $2\sqrt{10}$
   d $-1 + \sqrt{2} = \sqrt{2} - 1$ **e** $\frac{\sqrt{3}}{2} - 1$

6 a $x(x+1) = 30$; $x = 5$ m
   b The height of the rectangle cannot be negative.

7 $2a(a+1) = 12$
   $2a^2 + 2a = 12$
   $2a^2 + 2a - 12 = 0$
   $(2a+6)(a-2) = 0$
   Therefore $a = -3$ or $a = 2$
   Since a cannot be −3, small rug is 2 m × 2 m

8 a $x = \sqrt{5}$ and $x = -\sqrt{5}$
   b $x = \sqrt{5} - 1$ and $x = -\sqrt{5} - 1$
   c $x = \sqrt{5} + 1$ and $x = -\sqrt{5} + 1$
   d $x = \sqrt{\frac{5}{2}} + 1$ and $x = -\sqrt{\frac{5}{2}} + 1$

9 $x = 3 + \sqrt{7} = 5.65$ and $x = 3 - \sqrt{7} = 0.354$

10 a $ac = -10$ **b** $5 \times (-2) = -10$; $5 + (-2) = 3$
   d $x(2x+5) - (2x+5)$ **e** $(2x+5)(x-1)$

11 $2x^2 - 2x + 5x - 5 = 2x(x-1) + 5(x-1) = (2x+5)(x-1)$

12 a $(2x+3)(x-1)$ **b** $(2x-1)(x+3)$
   c $(5x+2)(x+1)$ **d** $(5x+1)(x+2)$
   e $(3x-2)(x-5)$ **f** $(3x-5)(x-2)$

13 a $x^2 + x - 42 = x^2 + 7x - 6x - 42 = x(x+7) - 6(x+7)$
     $= (x-6)(x+7)$
   b Students' own answers

14 a $a = -2.5$ or $a = 8$ **b** $x = 4.5$ or $x = -4$
   c $y = \frac{4}{3}$ or $y = -2.5$ **d** $b = \frac{3}{4}$ or $b = 2\frac{2}{3}$

15 a $5(x^2 + 3x + 2) = 0$
     $x^2 + 3x + 2 = 0$
     $(x+2)(x+1) = 0$
     $x = -2$ or $x = -1$
   b i $(4x+6)(x-3) = 0$ so either $x = -1.5$ or $x = 3$
     ii $(2x+5)(3x-3) = 0$ so either $x = -2.5$ or $x = 1$
     iii $2(2x+1)(x-2)$ so either $x = -\frac{1}{2}$ or $x = 2$

16 a $4x^2 + 18x = 10$
   b $2x^2 + 9x - 5 = 0$
     So $(2x-1)(x+5) = 0$
     Therefore $x = 0.5$ or $x = -5$; since −5 is not a realistic solution, border should be 0.5 m wide.

17 $(4x-7)(2x+3)$, giving $x = 1.75$ or $x = -1.5$

18 a $x = -2.5 + \frac{\sqrt{5}}{2}$ or $x = -2.5 - \frac{\sqrt{5}}{2}$
   b $x = -3.5 + \frac{\sqrt{41}}{2}$ or $x = -3.5 - \frac{\sqrt{41}}{2}$
   c $x = -1 + \sqrt{3}$ or $x = -1 - \sqrt{3}$
   d $x = 1 + \sqrt{7}$ or $x = 1 - \sqrt{7}$
   e $x = -1.5 + \frac{\sqrt{21}}{6}$ or $x = -1.5 - \frac{\sqrt{21}}{6}$
   f $x = -1.5 + \frac{\sqrt{141}}{6}$ or $x = -1.5 - \frac{\sqrt{141}}{6}$
   g $x = 1.5 + \frac{\sqrt{141}}{6}$ or $x = 1.5 - \frac{\sqrt{141}}{6}$
   h $x = 0.8 + \frac{\sqrt{6}}{5}$ or $x = 0.8 - \frac{\sqrt{6}}{5}$

19 a $x = 1.36$ or $x = -7.36$ **b** $x = 3.39$ or $x = -0.89$
   c $x = 0.55$ or $x = -1.22$ **d** $x = 1.39$ or $x = -2.89$
   e $x = 1.65$ or $x = 0.23$ **f** $x = 0.13$ or $x = -1.30$

20 a $2x^2 - 7x - 15 = 0$
   b i, ii $x = -1.5$ or $x = 5$
   c No; better to use the formula when factors are not obvious (or when the quadratic cannot be factorised).

21 $x = 0.477$ and $x = -1.68$

9.4 Completing the square

1 A positive or negative whole number or zero

2 a $x^2+8x+16$ **b** x^2-6x+9
   c $4x^2+12x+9$ **d** x^2+4x+8
   e x^2+2x+8

3 $(x+1)^2$

4 a $3\sqrt{5}$ **b** $4\sqrt{2}$ **c** $4\sqrt{3}$
   d $3\sqrt{10}$ **e** $5\sqrt{3}$

5 a $x=\sqrt{7}-1$ or $x=-\sqrt{7}-1$
   b $x=\sqrt{7}+3$ or $x=-\sqrt{7}+3$
   c $x=\sqrt{\frac{7}{2}}+3$ or $x=-\sqrt{\frac{7}{2}}+3$

6 $x^2+10x+25$

7 a $(x+3)^2$ **b** $(x+4)^2$ **c** $(x+5)^2$ **d** $(x-6)^2$

8 a x^2+4x+4
   b i $(x+2)^2+1$ **ii** $(x+2)^2+2$
     iii $(x+2)^2-5$

9 a $(x+1)^2-2$ **b** $(x+4)^2-16$ **c** $(x+6)^2-36$
   d $(x+3)^2+2$ **e** $(x-3)^2+2$

10 $(x+7)^2-50$

11 $(x+2)^2-4+1=0$
    $(x+2)^2=3$
    $x=-2-\sqrt{3}$ or $x=-2+\sqrt{3}$

12 a $x=-1-\sqrt{6}$ or $x=-1+\sqrt{6}$
   b $x=1+\sqrt{6}$ or $x=1-\sqrt{6}$
   c $x=-3-\sqrt{2}$ or $x=-3+\sqrt{2}$
   d $x=7$ or $x=-1$
   e $x=-4-\sqrt{7}$ or $x=-4+\sqrt{7}$
   f $x=9$ or $x=-1$

13 $3x^2-12x-1=3(x^2-4x)-1$
            $=3[(x-2)^2-4]-1$
            $=3(x-2)^2-12-1$
            $=3(x-2)^2-13$

14 a $2(x+3)^2-17$ **b** $2(x-3)^2-17$
   c $3(x-1)^2+2$ **d** $3(x-1)^2-8$
   e $5(x+1)^2+20$ **f** $4\left(x+\frac{3}{2}\right)^2-16$

15 a $x=3+\sqrt{\frac{11}{2}}$ or $x=3-\sqrt{\frac{11}{2}}$
   b $x=-2+\sqrt{\frac{13}{3}}$ or $x=-2-\sqrt{\frac{13}{3}}$
   c $x=-1+\sqrt{\frac{2}{5}}$ or $x=-1-\sqrt{\frac{2}{5}}$

16 a x^2-2x-4
   b $(x-1)^2-1-4=0$
      $(x-1)^2=5$
      $x-1=\pm\sqrt{5}$
      $x=1\pm\sqrt{5}$
      $x=-1.24$ or $x=3.24$
   c Giving answers as surds is more accurate.

17 a $x=1.24$ or $x=-3.24$ **b** $x=1.08$ or $x=-3.08$
   c $x=0.60$ or $x=-2.10$

18 $6\left[x^2+\frac{1}{2}x\right]-1=0$
   $6\left[\left(x+\frac{1}{4}\right)^2-\frac{1}{16}\right]-1=0$
   $6\left(x+\frac{1}{4}\right)^2-\frac{6}{16}-1=0$
   $6\left(x+\frac{1}{4}\right)^2-\frac{3}{8}-1=0$
   $6\left(x+\frac{1}{4}\right)^2=\frac{11}{8}$
   $\left(x+\frac{1}{4}\right)^2=\frac{11}{48}$
   $x+\frac{1}{4}=\pm\sqrt{\frac{11}{48}}$
   $x=\sqrt{\frac{11}{48}}-\frac{1}{4}$ or $x=-\sqrt{\frac{11}{48}}-\frac{1}{4}$
   $x=0.23$ or $x=-0.73$ (to 2 d.p.)

19 $x=-1.74$ or $x=1.24$

9.5 Solving simple simultaneous equations

1 C and D

2 a $b=2a+12$ **b** $b=\frac{10-6c}{2}=5-3c$ **c** $b=\frac{5a-5}{3}$

3 a $x+y=12$ **b** $x-y=4$ or $y-x=4$

4 $x=5,\ y=2$

5 a $x=5,\ y=2$ **b** Yes

6 a $x=3,\ y=2$ **b** $x=1,\ y=4$
   c $x=6,\ y=2$ **d** $x=-3,\ y=2$

7 a $x=4,\ y=-5$ **b** $x=3,\ y=4$
   c $x=4,\ y=-1$ **d** $x=-2,\ y=-9$
   e $x=4,\ y=2$ **f** $x=\frac{1}{2},\ y=2$
   g $x=5,\ y=\frac{1}{3}$ **h** $x=\frac{3}{4},\ y=-\frac{1}{3}$

8 $x+y=23;\ x-y=5;\ x=14,\ y=9$

9 a $x=14,\ y=-6$ **b** $x=8.5,\ y=11.5$
   c $x=3,\ y=9$ **d** $x=2,\ y=4$

10 a $2x+y=29$ **b** $x=y+10$
   c £13   **d** £3

11 a $6x+2y=36$ **b** $10x+0=50;\ x=5$
   c $y=3$

12 a $x=7,\ y=4$ **b** $x=-2,\ y=10$
   c $x=\frac{1}{2},\ y=\frac{1}{2}$ **d** $x=-\frac{1}{3},\ y=2$

13 $x=2,\ y=-1$

14 a, b $x=0,\ y=0$ **c** No

15 a $x=-2,\ y=3$ **b** $x=-1,\ y=-4$
   c $x=\frac{1}{2},\ y=3$ **d** $x=1,\ y=-\frac{3}{4}$

16 50p

17 a £12   **b** £24

18 Tea £1.70, biscuit 90p

9.6 More simultaneous equations

1 $y=mx+c$

2 a $8x+12y=24$ **b** $4x-24y=28$

3 a $x=2,\ y=4$ **b** $x=4,\ y=2$

4 a $5=2m+c$ **b** $8=3m+c$
   c $m=3,\ c=-1$ **d** $y=3x-1$

5 $y=3-x$

6 $d=5$

7 a $x=2,\ y=1$ **b** $x=3,\ y=2$
   c $x=-5,\ y=-3$ **d** $x=2,\ y=4$
   e $x=4,\ y=-6$ **f** $x=5,\ y=2$
   g $x=2.3,\ y=3$ **h** $x=-1.8,\ y=0.75$

8 $x = £15$ and $y = £0.50 = 50p$
So a 50-mile hire would cost $£15 + 50 \times £0.50 = £40$

9 Adult £1.80, child £1.00

10 Pear 25p, banana 60p

11 $x = 1.2$, $y = -0.45$

12 Sand 20 kg, cement 40 kg

13 a $4a - 4b = -2$ and $2a + b = 8$
b $a = 2.5$, $b = 3$
c Rectangle is 6 m by 10 m

9.7 Solving linear and quadratic simultaneous equations

1 a $y = 4 - 3x$ and $y + x = 4$
b $x^2 - 4x + 2 = 0$
c $x^2 + y^2 = 16$

2 a $x = 1$ or $x = -4$ **b** $x = 1.5$ or $x = -1$
c $x = \frac{1}{3}$ or $x = -2$

3 a $x = 1.19$ or $x = -4.19$ **b** $x = 1.18$ or $x = -0.85$
c $x = 0.50$ or $x = -3.00$

4 a $x = -4$, $y = -4$ and $x = 3$, $y = 3$
b $x = -2$, $y = -11$ and $x = 4$, $y = 1$
c $x = -0.5$, $y = 4$ and $x = 1$, $y = 10$
d $x = -1.33$, $y = -9.67$ and $x = 1$, $y = 2$
e $x = 0.70$, $y = 5.90$ and $x = -5.70$, $y = 25.10$
f $x = 3.37$, $y = 9.74$ and $x = -2.37$, $y = -1.74$

5 $(1, 0)$ and $(-1, 8)$

6 a $x = 1$, $y = 1$ and $x = -2$, $y = 4$
b $x = 1.41$, $y = 0.59$ and $x = -1.41$, $y = 3.41$
c $x = -5$, $y = 0$ and $x = 0$, $y = 5$
d $x = 1.82$, $y = 0.63$ and $x = 0.18$, $y = -2.63$
e $x = -1$, $y = -3$ and $x = 3$, $y = 5$
f $x = -3$, $y = 1$ and $x = 9$, $y = 5$

7 a $y = 2x + 3$ **b** $2x^2 + x - 3 = 0$
c $x = 1$, $y = 5$; width = 5 m

8 $(0, -1)$ and $(6, 11)$

9 $2\sqrt{5}$ or equivalent

10 a $x^2 + y^2 = 4$ **b** $(1.27, 1.54)$ and $(-0.47, -1.94)$

11 a $x = -4.93$, $y = -1.93$ and $x = 1.93$, $y = 4.93$
b $x = -1.54$, $y = -5.71$ and $x = 0.773$, $y = 5.87$
c $x = -4.30$, $y = -5.61$ and $x = 1.90$, $y = 6.81$

12 a

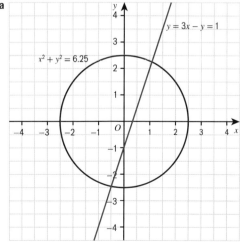

b $x \approx 1.1$, $y \approx 2.3$ and $x \approx -0.5$, $y \approx -2.5$

13 $x = 3$, $y = -1$ and $x = -\frac{51}{13}$, $y = \frac{23}{13}$ or equivalent

9 Check up

1 1, 0, −1, −2, −3, −4 and −5

2 a $0 < x \leqslant 4.5$ **b** $\{x : 0 < x \leqslant 4.5\}$

3 $(x - 2)(x - 4) = 3$
$x^2 - 6x + 5 = 0$
$x = 1$ and $x = 5$, but $x = 5$ is the only realistic answer.

4 a $x = 0$ or $x = -3$ **b** $x = 2$ or $x = -3$

5 $(3x + 2)(x - 2)$

6 $x = 1 + \sqrt{7}$ or $x = 1 - \sqrt{7}$

7 $(x + 3)^2 - 6$

8 $x = -3 + 2\sqrt{3}$ or $x = -3 - 2\sqrt{3}$

9 a $x = 7$, $y = -2$ **b** $x = 0.5$, $y = -3$

10 $y = 2x - 3$

11 $x = -5$, $y = 15$ or $x = 1$, $y = 3$

13 a 6 years old   **b** Students' own answers.

9 Strengthen

Inequalities

1 a $-2 < x \leqslant 1$
b i $2 \geqslant x > -3$ **ii** $-3 < x \leqslant 2$
c i $-5 \leqslant x < -2$ **ii** $-2 < x \leqslant 3$
iii $1 \leqslant x < 5$

2 a $x > 1$ **b** $x < 4$ **c** $1 < x < 4$; 2, 3

3 0, 1, 2

4 a $\{x : x > 4\}$ **b** $\{x : x < \frac{7}{8}\}$
c $\{x : 0 \leqslant x < 3.5\}$ **d** $\{x : -2 < x \leqslant 5\}$

Quadratic equations

1 $x = 0$, $x = -7$

2 a $x(x + 5)$
b Either $x = 0$ or $x + 5 = 0$; $x = 0$, $x = -5$

3 a −4 and 3   **b** $(x + 3)(x - 4)$
c $x = -3$ or $x = 4$

4 a $x = -6$ or $x = 3$ **b** $x = 4$ or $x = 3$
c $x = -5$ or $x = 3$

5 a $x(x - 2) = x^2 - 2x$ **b** $(x + 4)^2 = x^2 + 8x + 16$

6 a $(x + 1)(x - 2) = x^2 - x - 2$
b $x^2 - x - 2 = 4$ **c** $x^2 - x - 6 = 0$
d $x = 3$ or $x = -2$; $x = 3$ m is the only realistic answer.

7 a −1, 6; 1, −6; −2, 3; 2, −3
b $(2x - 3)(x + 2)$ **c** $x = 1.5$ or $x = -2$

8 a $x = \frac{4}{3}$ or $x = -3$ **b** $x = -\frac{4}{3}$ or $x = 2$
c $x = 1.5$, $x = 2$ **d** $x = 4$ or $x = \frac{3}{4}$

9 a $a = 2$, $b = 3$, $c = 1$ **b** $a = 2$, $b = -4$, $c = -6$
c $a = 3$, $b = 4$, $c = -1$

10 a $9 - 8 = 1$ **b** $16 + 48 = 64$ **c** $16 + 12 = 28$

11 a $x = -1$ or $x = -\frac{1}{2}$ **b** $x = 3$ or $x = -1$
c $x = -\frac{2}{3} - \frac{\sqrt{7}}{3}$ or $x = -\frac{2}{3} + \frac{\sqrt{7}}{3}$

12 a i $x^2 + 6x + 9$ **ii** $x^2 - 10x + 25$
b $12x$ **c** $x^2 + 12x + 36$

13 a $(x + 2)^2 = x^2 + 4x + 4$
$(x + 2)^2 - 4 = x^2 + 4x$
b $(x + 2)^2 - 4 = 8$; $(x + 2)^2 = 12$
c $x = -2 - 2\sqrt{3}$ or $x = -2 + 2\sqrt{3}$

14 a $(x - 3)^2 = x^2 - 6x + 9$
$(x - 3)^2 - 9 = x^2 - 6x$
b $x = 3 + 3\sqrt{2}$ or $x = 3 - 3\sqrt{2}$

Simultaneous equations

1 $y = 4$

2 **a** $x = 2, y = 1$ **b** $x = 4, y = 3$
  c $x = 3, y = 1$ **d** $x = 4, y = 5$

3 **a i** 2   **ii** $4x + 2y = 22$ **iii** $x = 5, y = 1$
  b i 3   **ii** $6x - 3y = 18$ **iii** $x = 4, y = 2$
  c i 5   **ii** $15x + 5y = 35$ **iii** $x = 2, y = 1$
  d i 4   **ii** $20x - 8y = 164$ **iii** $x = 9, y = 2$

4 **a** 6   **b** $15x + 6y = 51$
  c $8x + 6y = 30$ **d** $x = 3, y = 1$

5 **a** $y = 4 - 5x$ **b** $x^2 - 2x - (4 - 5x) = 6$
  c $x^2 + 3x - 4 = 6$ **d** $x^2 + 3x - 10 = 0$
  e $x = 2$ or $x = -5$
  f When $x = 2, y = -6$; when $x = -5, y = 29$

6 $x = 1, y = 1$ and $x = -6, y = 8$

9 Extend

1 **a** $x(x + 1) = 30$ **b** 5 and 6

2 $23.32 \,\text{m}$

3 $3(x + 0.4)^2 - 0.48$; $a = 3, p = 0.4, q = -0.48$

4 $68 \,\text{m} \times 105 \,\text{m}$

5 **a** Area $= x(x + 4) + x(x + 1) = x^2 + 4x + x^2 + x$
    $2x^2 + 5x = 75$
    So $2x^2 + 5x - 75 = 0$
  b $x = 5$ or $x = -7.5$; the dimensions of a shape cannot be negative, so $x = 5$.

6 $x = 26$ and $y = 12$. Perimeter $= 76 \,\text{cm}$.

7 $L_1: y = 3x - 4$
  $L_2: y = -2x$
  $P\left(\frac{4}{5}, -\frac{8}{5}\right)$ or equivalent

8 $a = 3, b = -2$; 6th term is 96

9 $x = -5$ or $x = \frac{8}{3}$
  Since -5 is not a valid solution in this case, $x = 2\frac{2}{3}$ m

10 $1.52 \,\text{m}$

11 $x = -5, y = -2$

12 $\{x : -5 < x \leqslant 1\}$

13 **a** $(x + p)^2 + q = (x + p)(x + p) + q = x^2 + 2px + p^2 + q$
  b i $(x + 3)^2 + 6$ **ii** $(x + 4)^2 - 19$
    iii $(x - 2)^2 - 2$ **iv** $\left(x + \frac{3}{2}\right)^2 + \frac{19}{4}$

14 $a = 2, b = 3$; $y = \sqrt{2} + 3$ or equivalent

15 $a = 1, b = 4$ and $a = \frac{5}{4}, b = 5$

16 **a** $(y - 4)(y - 9)$
  b $\dfrac{x^2(x^2 + x - 6)}{(x^2 - 4)(x^2 - 9)} = \dfrac{x^2(x + 3)(x - 2)}{(x + 2)(x - 2)(x + 3)(x - 3)}$
    $= \dfrac{x^2}{(x + 2)(x - 3)}$

9 Test ready

a Student A has square rooted incorrectly: $\sqrt{x^2 + y^2} \neq x + y$
  Student B has squared incorrectly: $(2x + 14)^2 \neq 4x^2 + 196$

b Student C has only found the x values. For a full answer you need to find the y value for each x value.

9 Unit test

1 $(3x + 1)(3x - 2)$

2 $x = 5, x = -1.5$

3 **a** $x^2 + 2x$ or $x(x + 2)$
  b $x = 3$ (x cannot be negative in this context so $x = -5$ is not a possible solution)

4 $x = 1.22, x = -0.549$

5 Border is 1 cm wide

6 **a** $x = 3, y = -1.5$ **b** $x = -44, y = 31$

7 One apple costs 35p, one pear costs 40p.

8 $x > 1, x < 3, x = 2$

9 **a** $y > -\frac{1}{2}$ **b** $\{x : 1 \leqslant x < 5.5\}$

10 $x = 3, y = -4$ and $x = 5$ and $y = 0$

11 $x = 0.378$ (3 s.f.)

12 $2(x + 3)^2 - 5$

13 $(1.1, 4.9)$ and $(-3.6, 9.6)$

14 $x^2 + y^2 = 12$
  $y = 7 - x$
  $x^2 + (7 - x)^2 = 12$
  $x^2 + (49 - 14x + x^2) = 12$
  $2x^2 - 14x + 37 = 0$
  $x = \dfrac{14 \pm \sqrt{14^2 - 4 \times 2 \times 37}}{4}$
  $= \dfrac{14 \pm \sqrt{196 - 296}}{4}$

This has no solutions because you cannot take a square root of a negative number. Therefore there is no point of intersection of the circle and the line.

15 Students' own answers in the sentence form given.

UNIT 10 Probability

10.1 Combined events

1 $\frac{1}{2}$

2 **a** 6   **b** 8   **c** 10   **d** 18
  e mn

3 **a**

	Glasses	No glasses	Total
Boys	4	10	14
Girls	6	12	18
Total	10	22	32

  b $\frac{5}{16}$ **c** $\frac{9}{16}$

4 **a** $\frac{1}{25}$ **b** $\frac{1}{5}$ **c** $\frac{11}{25}$ **d** $\frac{19}{25}$

5 **a** BA, BP, BS, LA, LP, LS, CA, CP, CS, HA, HP, HS, MA, MP, MS
  b 15   **c** $\frac{1}{15}$ **d** $\frac{2}{15}$

6 **a** $\frac{1}{4}$ **b** $\frac{1}{2}$

7 $\frac{21}{80}$

8 **a i** $\frac{1}{18}$ **ii** $\frac{1}{2}$ **iii** $\frac{5}{18}$
  b 7

9 **a**

	A	B	C	D	E
A	—	A, B	A, C	A, D	A, E
B	B, A	—	B, C	B, D	B, E
C	C, A	C, B	—	C, D	C, E
D	D, A	D, B	D, C	—	D, E
E	E, A	E, B	E, C	E, D	—

  b 20   **c** $\frac{2}{5}$ **d** $\frac{1}{10}$

10 **a** $\frac{1}{12}$ **b** $\frac{1}{4}$ **c** $\frac{3}{4}$

11 $\frac{1}{8}$

12 $\frac{3}{5}$

10.2 Mutually exclusive events

1 $\frac{1}{3}$

2 a $\frac{1}{3}$ **b** $\frac{1}{2}$ **c** $\frac{1}{3}$

3 A square number (**a**) and a multiple of 3 (**c**)

4 a $\frac{1}{5}$

     b The number of cubes of each colour must be a whole number, and $\frac{1}{5} \times 22$ is not a whole number.

5 a $\frac{4}{5}$

     b No, because the outcomes 8 and 10 are not included in the set of events.

6 0.35

7 a 0.4   **b** 0.9

8 $\frac{1}{9}$

9 0.12

10 a $\frac{7}{20}$ **b** $\frac{13}{20}$

11 0.62

12 a i $\frac{3}{4}$ **ii** $\frac{5}{8}$ **iii** $\frac{3}{8}$

     b 8

13 a White 0.3, blue 0.3   **b** 50

14 a 0.05

     b 20, because P(yellow) $= 0.05 = \frac{1}{20}$; for the smallest number of counters, we need 1 yellow so there are 20 counters in total.

15 a $\frac{2}{9}$ **b** $\frac{7}{9}$

16 8

17 $\frac{3}{50}$

10.3 Experimental probability

1 a 15   **b** 140   **c** 70   **d** 120

2 a $\frac{1}{3}$ **b** 100

3 a 50

     b i $\frac{43}{50}$ **ii** $\frac{7}{50}$

     c 86

     d No, the frequencies will probably not be exactly the same in repeat experiments; increase the number of trials.

4 P(1) $= 0.26$; P(1 or 4) $= 0.39$; $0.39 \times 200 = 78$

5 a $\frac{5}{12}$ **b** 75

6 18

7 $\frac{7}{30}$

8 Yes, because the experimental probabilities of 0.23, 0.195, 0.185, 0.2, 0.19 are all close to the theoretical probability of 0.2.

9 No. A fair dice has a theoretical probability of 0.17 for each outcome. For this dice, the experimental probability of rolling a 1 is more than three times that of rolling a 6.

10 No. Assuming there are more than 200 tickets in the draw, there will be more than 200 tickets that do not win, so buying 200 tickets will not guarantee a prize.

11 a 5   **b** 30   **c** 75

10.4 Independent events and tree diagrams

1 a $\frac{3}{5}$ **b** $\frac{7}{9}$ **c** $\frac{3}{4}$ **d** $\frac{5}{8}$

2 a $\frac{7}{45}$ **b** $\frac{5}{12}$ **c** 0.08   **d** 0.42

3

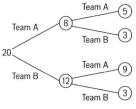

4 a

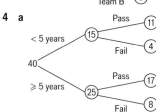

     b $\frac{3}{10}$

5 a

Positive results (19) — Developed virus (11), No virus (8)

(80) — Negative results (61) — Developed virus (2), No virus (59)

     b $\frac{13}{80}$

     c

	Virus	No virus	Total
Positive	11	8	19
Negative	2	59	61
Total	13	67	80

     d Students' own answers.

6 0.24

7 a 0.55   **b** 0.65   **c** 0.3575

     d The two traffic lights are independent of each other.

8 $\frac{1}{64}$

9 a

1st game   2nd game

$\frac{1}{5}$ Win — $\frac{1}{5}$ Win, $\frac{4}{5}$ Lose

$\frac{4}{5}$ Lose — $\frac{1}{5}$ Win, $\frac{4}{5}$ Lose

     b i $\frac{1}{25}$ **ii** $\frac{16}{25}$ **iii** $\frac{8}{25}$ **iv** $\frac{9}{25}$

10 a

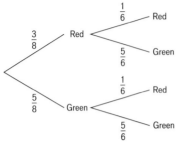

|Bag A|Bag B|

b i $\frac{7}{12}$ **ii** $\frac{5}{12}$ **iii** $\frac{25}{48}$ **iv** $\frac{23}{48}$

c P(red, red) + P(red, green) + P(green, red)

$= \frac{3}{48} + \frac{15}{48} + \frac{5}{48} = \frac{23}{48}$

$1 - \text{P(no red)} = 1 - \frac{25}{48} = \frac{23}{48}$

11 $\frac{15}{32}$

12 a 0.41 **b** 0.07 **c** 35

13 42

10.5 Conditional probability

1 a $\frac{2}{5}$ **b** $\frac{3}{5}$

2 a $\frac{47}{130}$ **b** $\frac{87}{130}$

3 a Dependent **b** Independent **c** Independent
d Independent **e** Dependent

4 a 0.043 **b** 0.031 **c** 0.915

5 a

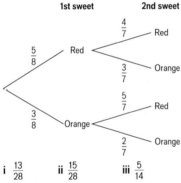

1st sweet 2nd sweet

b i $\frac{13}{28}$ **ii** $\frac{15}{28}$ **iii** $\frac{5}{14}$

6 e.g. Denominator for 2nd student is incorrect, or denominator for 2nd student should be 27, or probabilities for 2nd student do not add up to 1.

7 a

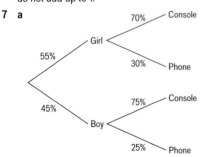

b 11.25%

8 0.7875

9 a

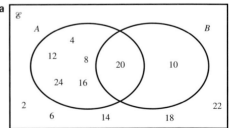

Emily Zoe

b $\frac{14}{45}$

c You only need to find P(C, C), P(S, S) and P(G, G) so you don't need P(C, S), for example.

10 $\frac{5}{18}$

11 a $\frac{1}{84}$

b More likely

e.g. For 12 balls, $P(G, G, G) = \frac{4}{12} \times \frac{3}{11} \times \frac{2}{10} = \frac{24}{1320} = \frac{1}{55}$

and $\frac{1}{55} > \frac{1}{84}$.

10.6 Venn diagrams and set notation

1 a 1, 2, 3, 4, 5 **b** −2, −1, 0, 1

2 a 2 **b** 32 **c** 100 **d** $\frac{17}{100}$

3 a $A = \{2, 4, 6, 8\}$; $B = \{2, 3, 5, 7\}$
b i True **ii** False **iii** True

4 a i $\{1, 3, 5, 7, 9, 11, 13, 15\}$ **ii** $\{1, 4, 9\}$
iii $\{1, 2, 3, 4, 5, 6, 7, 8, 9, 10, 11, 12, 13, 14, 15\}$
b Q
c $P = \{\text{odd numbers} < 16\}$; $\mathscr{E} = \{\text{positive numbers} < 16\}$

5 a $\{1, 3, 4, 5, 7, 9, 11, 13, 15\}$
b $\{1, 9\}$
c $\{2, 4, 6, 8, 10, 12, 14\}$
d $\{2, 3, 5, 6, 7, 8, 10, 11, 12, 13, 14, 15\}$
e $\{4\}$
f $\{3, 5, 7, 11, 13, 15\}$

6 a

b $\frac{7}{12}$

7 **a** $\frac{5}{12}$ **b** $\frac{1}{2}$ **c** $\frac{1}{12}$ **d** $\frac{5}{6}$
  e $\frac{7}{12}$ **f** $\frac{1}{2}$ **g** $\frac{1}{3}$ **h** $\frac{2}{3}$

8 $\frac{1}{10}$

9 **a** $\frac{7}{25}$ **b** $\frac{3}{7}$

10 **a** $\frac{73}{120}$ **b** $\frac{1}{6}$

11 **a**

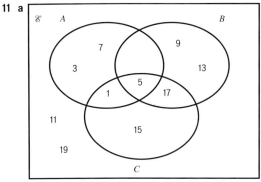

  b $\frac{1}{5}$

12 **a** $\frac{7}{40}$ **b** $\frac{11}{40}$ **c** $\frac{11}{13}$

13 **a** $\frac{13}{40}$

  b P(1st learns only Italian) $= \frac{13}{80}$

  P(2nd learns only Italian) $= \frac{12}{79}$

  $\frac{13}{80} \times \frac{12}{79} = \frac{156}{6320} = \frac{39}{1580}$ or 0.025 (3 d.p.)

10 Check up

1 **a**

		Dice					
		1	2	3	4	5	6
Spinner	2	3	4	5	6	7	8
	4	5	6	7	8	9	10
	6	7	8	9	10	11	12
	8	9	10	11	12	13	14

  b i $\frac{1}{8}$ **ii** $\frac{1}{3}$ **iii** $\frac{3}{8}$

2 **a** $\frac{4}{5}$ **b** $\frac{7}{10}$

3 **a** 0.75 **b** 0.075

4 0.15

5 $\frac{2}{17}$

6 **a**

Number	1	2	3	4	5	6
Probability	0.2	0.3	**0.1**	0.15	**0.1**	0.15

  b 45

  c No, because the probabilities are different. If the spinner were fair the probabilities would all be the same.

7

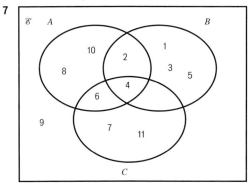

8 **a**

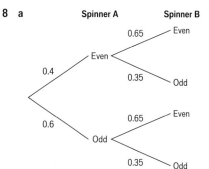

Spinner A   Spinner B

Even — 0.65 — Even
Even — 0.35 — Odd
(0.4)

Odd — 0.65 — Even
Odd — 0.35 — Odd
(0.6)

  b i 0.21 **ii** 0.53

9 **a**

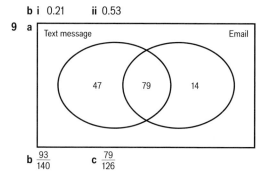

Text message   Email
47   79   14

  b $\frac{93}{140}$ **c** $\frac{79}{126}$

11 **a, b** Students' own answers

10 Strengthen

Calculating probability

1 **a** $\frac{1}{5}$ **b** $\frac{4}{5}$ **c** $\frac{4}{5}$

  d The answers are the same.

  e i $\frac{3}{10}$ **ii** $\frac{7}{10}$

2 **a** $\frac{1}{10}$ **b** $\frac{3}{10}$ **c** $\frac{2}{5}$

  d A tile cannot be both A and S.

  e The answer to part **c** is the sum of the answers to parts **a** and **b**.

  f $\frac{1}{2}$

3 0.15

4 **a**

		Spinner B				
		0	2	4	6	8
Spinner A	1	1, 0	1, 2	1, 4	1, 6	1, 8
	2	2, 0	2, 2	2, 4	2, 6	2, 8
	3	3, 0	3, 2	3, 4	3, 6	3, 8

  b 15 **c i** $\frac{1}{3}$ **ii** $\frac{1}{5}$

  d

		Spinner B				
		0	2	4	6	8
Spinner A	1	1	3	5	7	9
	2	2	4	6	8	10
	3	3	5	7	9	11

  e 3, 5, 7 or 9 **f** $\frac{8}{15}$

5 **a** 77 **b** $\frac{41}{77}$ **c** $\frac{41}{77}$

6 **a** 0.8 **b** 0.07

  c You add to find P(A or B) when A and B are mutually exclusive events. You multiply to find P(A and B) when A and B are independent events.

Experimental probability

1 a 30

   b No, because the actual number of threes was only half the expected number.

2 a

Number	Frequency	Experimental probability
1	16	$\frac{1}{5}$
2	12	$\frac{3}{20}$
3	14	$\frac{7}{40}$
4	17	$\frac{17}{80}$
5	21	$\frac{21}{80}$

   b 30

Tree diagrams and Venn diagrams

1 a

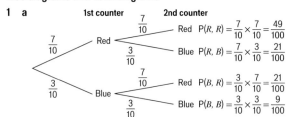

   b R, B and B, R **c** $\frac{21}{50}$

2 a–f

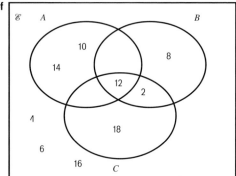

3 a i, ii and iii

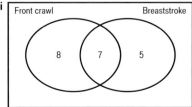

   b 20

   c i $\frac{7}{20}$ **ii** $\frac{2}{5}$

   d $\frac{7}{15}$

10 Extend

1 Any multiple of: 2 red, 2 green, 5 blue and 1 yellow.

2 No; the correct probability is $0.7 \times 0.2 = 0.14$.

3 $\frac{5}{12}$

4 $\frac{8}{25}$

5 a $\frac{5}{14}$ **b** $\frac{1}{28}$ **c** $\frac{1}{7}$

6 a 90   **b** $\frac{3}{8}$

7 51

8 $\frac{3}{5}$

9 a $A \cup B$ **b** $B' \cup A$ **c** $B \cap C \cap A'$

10 8 blue, 14 yellow

11 a

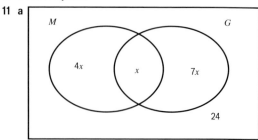

   b $4x + x + 7x = 72 - 24$

     $12x = 48$

     $x = 4$

     P(maths and geography) $= \frac{4}{72} = \frac{1}{18}$

10 Test ready

Sample student answers

a No; the student has found the probability of exactly one sweet. They should have included $P(O, O)$ in the calculation.

b $\frac{5}{12}$

10 Unit test

1 a 15 combinations   **b** $\frac{1}{15}$

2 a 4 green counters

   b Half of the cubes are blue. Half of an odd number does not equal a whole number. Therefore, the number of cubes in the bag must be even.

3 No, the coins are not fair. The probability of two tails for fair coins is 0.25. This would equate to 40 out of the 160 flips. These coins gave two tails almost half the time rather than a quarter.

4 $\frac{3}{5}$ (BE is the same as EB, for example)

5 $\frac{6}{10}$

6 P(not B) = 0.55

7 a 0.495   **b** 44

8 a 12

   b $\frac{27}{70}$ (15 had tomato and lettuce, 12 had all 3 fillings)

   c $\frac{35}{51}$ (23 had cheese and lettuce, 12 had all 3 fillings)

9 $P(W, W) = \frac{4}{10} \times \frac{3}{9} = \frac{12}{90}$

   P(at least 1 red) $= 1 - \frac{12}{90} = \frac{78}{90}$ or $\frac{13}{15}$

10 $\frac{35}{117}$

11 Students' own answers justified with probability

12 Students' own answers

Mixed exercise 3

1 Accurate construction of an isosceles triangle with base 90 mm and height 28 mm.   → **8.1**

2 Ahmed is correct as the first inequality does not include 1 but the second one does. Also, the first inequality includes 5 but the second one doesn't.   → **9.1**

3 For example, Zach has used a scale factor of 2.5   → **8.3**

4

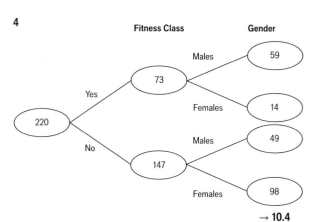

Fitness Class — Gender

Yes: 73 — Males: 59, Females: 14
No: 147 — Males: 49, Females: 98
(220)

→ **10.4**

5 **a** For example, Nadia shouldn't have divided by x as this results in working out only one value of x. → **9.2**

  b $x = 0$ or $x = -\frac{4}{5}$ → **9.2**

6 $120(0.6 - x)$ or equivalent expression → **10.2**

7 Mobile phone case £7.50, charging lead £3.50 → **9.6**

8 Rotation 90° clockwise about the point $(-1, -1)$ → **8.4**

9 3 cm → **9.2**

10 **a** → **10.6**

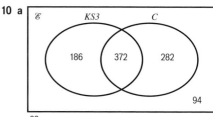

$\mathscr{E}$, KS3, C: 186, 372, 282, 94

  b $\frac{62}{109}$ → **10.6**

11

A — B (top)
5 cm
3 cm
4 cm
D — 6 cm — C

→ **8.7, 8.8**

12 $y = 7$ → **10.6**

13 **a** The LCM of 9 and 11 is 99. → **4.2**

  b 26 → **10.1**

14 **a** $\frac{1}{2} \times 4x(x - 2 + x + 7) = 266$

        $2x(2x + 5) = 266$

         $x(2x + 5) = 133$

      $2x^2 + 5x - 133 = 0$ → **7.1**

  b $x = 7$ → **9.3**

15 $\frac{1}{125}$ → **10.4**

16 $3x^2 + 9x + 4 = 0$ → **9.3**

17 180° rotation about $(-3, -1)$ or 180° rotation about $(-6, -1)$ → **8.4**

18 $\frac{8}{15}$ → **10.5**

19 $x + 1 = 4x^2 + 13x + 10$

    $4x^2 + 12x + 9 = 0$

    $(2x + 3)(2x + 3) = 0$

There is only one solution, $x = -\frac{3}{2}$, so the curve and the line have only one point of intersection. → **9.7**

20 **a** $x^2 + (2x + k)^2 = 97$

    $x^2 + 4x^2 + 4kx + k^2 = 97$

    $5x^2 + 4kx + k^2 - 97 = 0$ → **9.7**

  b $(4, 9)$ and $\left(-\frac{24}{5}, -\frac{43}{5}\right)$ → **9.3**

Index

2D shapes
    area 200–3, 210–17, 224, 226
    perimeters 200–2, 224, 226
3D solids
    elevations 240–2, 268, 273, 277, 278
    plans 240–2, 268, 273, 277, 278
    surface area 207, 225, 229, 232
    volume 225, 228–9

acceleration 171, 196
accuracy
    measurement 203–6, 217, 224, 227–8, 231, 232
    upper and lower bounds 204–6, 228, 231, 232
addition, indices 9, 28
adjacent side 142, 143, 145–6, 154, 158
algebra 32–61
    arithmetic sequences 42–4, 53, 57, 58, 60–1
    equations 35, 37–8, 39, 52–3, 55–6, 59, 60
    expanding brackets 35–6, 49–51, 52, 54–5, 61
    expressions 39, 49–51, 52, 55–6, 60
    factorising 35–6, 49–51, 52, 53, 54–5, 59
    Fibonacci sequences 45, 53, 56, 57, 61
    formulae 39–41, 52–3, 55–6, 60
    geometric sequences 45–6, 58, 61
    identities 35, 39, 52, 55, 60
    indices 32–4, 54, 60
    linear sequences 42–4
    non-linear sequences 45–8
    quadratic sequences 46–8, 57, 61
    sequences 42–8, 53, 56–8
    simplifying expressions 32–4, 52, 53, 54–5, 59
angle bisectors 261–3, 265, 269, 275, 279
angles 125–59
    alternate 125, 151
    co-interior 125, 158
    corresponding 125
    depression 144, 146, 155, 157, 159
    elevation 144, 146, 155, 156, 159
    exterior *see* exterior angles
    interior *see* interior angles
    parallelograms 126
    quadrilaterals 125–8, 148, 150, 151
    on straight line 125, 151
    triangles 125–8, 151, 158
    vertically opposite 125
appreciation 105, 117
approximation 3–4
    see also estimation
arcs, circles 214–17, 233
area 200–33
    2D shapes 200–3, 210–17, 224, 226
    circle sectors 215–17, 224, 230, 233
    circles 211–13, 224, 226, 231, 233
    parallelograms 206
    rectangles 227, 304
    trapezia 201–2, 224, 226, 231, 232, 307
    unit conversions 203–6, 232
arithmetic sequences 42–4, 53, 57, 58, 60–1
asymptotes 182, 194
averages 64–7, 78–81, 85, 89, 94
    see also mean; median; mode

back-to-back stem and leaf diagrams 65–6, 84, 85, 87–8, 94
bar charts 83, 84, 95
bar models 102, 113, 116, 118
bearings 256–7, 268, 274, 279
bisectors
    angle 261–3, 265, 269, 275, 279
    perpendicular 259–60, 262, 265, 269, 275, 278–9
bivariate data 71, 94
brackets
    expanding 35–6, 49–51, 52, 54–5, 61
    squaring 49, 61

capacity 209, 231, 232
centres of enlargement 246–9, 267, 272, 278
centres of rotation 244, 271, 278
circles 157
    arcs 214–17, 223
    area 211–13, 224, 226, 231, 233
    circumferences 210–13, 214, 215, 224, 226–7, 233
    equations 185, 187, 192, 197
    graphs 185, 187, 192, 197
    as loci 264, 279
    sectors 214–17, 224, 227, 230, 233
circumferences 210–13, 214, 215, 224, 226–7, 233
column vectors 250–3, 270, 278
combinations 1–2, 20, 26, 28, 268
combined events 312–14, 331, 333
common differences 42–4, 57, 60–1
completing the square 291–3, 304, 308
conditional probability 324–6, 336–7, 338, 339
cones
    surface area 222–3, 229, 231, 233
    volume 222–3, 225, 229, 233
congruence 253, 278
consecutive integers 36, 60
constant multipliers 45
constructions 258–66, 269, 274–5, 279
    angle bisectors 261–3, 265, 269, 275, 279
    loci 264–6, 269, 279
    perpendicular bisectors 259–60, 262, 265, 269, 275, 278–9
    triangles 258–9, 263, 274–5, 277
correlation 73–4, 77, 86, 89–90, 91, 94
    graphs 175, 184, 197
$\cos^{-1}$ 145, 159
cosines 143, 147, 155, 159
cube roots 8, 12, 28
cubes
    surface area 209, 242
    volume 209
cubic equations 181–2, 191–2
cubic functions 181–2, 197
cuboids
    surface area 207
    volume 208, 228
currency conversions 103, 104, 110, 112, 173
cylinders
    surface area 218–20, 225, 228–9, 231, 233
    volume 218–20, 230, 231, 233

data
    bivariate 71, 94

    see also statistics
data representation 64–95
    averages 64–7, 78–81, 85, 89, 94
    frequency polygons 66–7, 81, 85, 88, 91, 93, 94
    pie charts 64, 84, 85, 87, 95
    range 65–7, 73, 78–81, 85, 88–9, 92
    scatter graphs 71–7, 86, 89–90, 91, 92, 94, 175
    statistical diagrams 64–7, 82–5, 87–8
    stem and leaf diagrams 65–6, 84, 85, 87–8, 92, 94
    time series graphs 68–70, 86, 90, 94
deceleration 171
decimals
    fractions and 108–9, 110, 113–14, 117
    percentages and 108–9, 110, 113–14
    recurring 109, 118
decomposition, prime factors 5–7, 28
denominators, rationalising 19, 21, 25, 27, 29
dependent events 324–6, 336–7, 338
depreciation 105, 117
depression, angle of 144, 146, 155, 157, 159
diagrams, statistical 64–7, 82–5, 87–8
dimensions 207, 232
direct proportion 104, 112, 117
    graphs 173, 196
discontinuity symbol 172, 196
distance–time graphs 168–70, 184, 195, 196
distance travelled, velocity–time graphs 171, 196, 230
division, inequalities 285, 308
double brackets, expansion 49–51, 55, 61

elements, sets 327, 338–9
elevation, angle of 144, 146, 155, 156, 159
elimination 295, 297, 308
enlargement 246–9, 267, 272–3, 278
equations
    algebra 35, 37–8, 39, 52–3, 55–6, 59, 60
    circles 185, 187, 192, 197
    linear 163–7, 196
    quadratic *see* quadratic equations
    simultaneous 294–301, 302, 305, 306–7, 308–9
equidistant points 260, 279
equilateral triangles 141, 147
error intervals 204, 217, 224, 232
estimation 3–4
    place value 3–4
events
    combined 312–14, 331, 333
    dependent 324–6, 336–7, 338
    exhaustive sets of 315, 318, 338
    independent 320–3, 331, 334, 336, 338
    mutually exclusive 315–17, 331, 333, 334, 338
exchange rates 103, 110, 112
exhaustive sets of events 315, 318, 338
expanding, brackets 35–6, 49–51, 52, 54–5, 61
experimental probability 318–19, 332, 334, 338
expressions, algebra 39, 49–51, 52, 55–6, 60
exterior angles
    polygons 133–5, 148, 150–1, 156, 158
    quadrilaterals 133
    triangles 127–8, 158
extrapolation 76, 94

factorials 2
factorisation
    algebraic expressions 35–6, 49–51, 52, 53, 54–5, 59
    in solving equations 286–7, 299, 303, 308
factors, decomposition 5–7, 28
fair games 318–19, 332, 333, 334
Fibonacci sequences 45, 53, 56, 57, 61
FOIL (firsts, outers, inners, lasts) 49
formulae
    algebra 39–41, 52–3, 55–6, 60
    subjects 40–1, 53, 56, 59, 60
fractional indices 11–13, 28
fractional scale factors 247–8, 272, 278
fractions 98–9, 108–11, 113–16, 117, 118
    decimals and 108–9, 110, 113–14, 117
    improper 98–9, 111, 117
    percentages and 108–9, 110, 113–14
    reciprocals 98–9, 111, 117
frequency polygons 66–7, 81, 85, 88, 91, 93, 94
frequency trees 320, 338
front elevations 240–2, 268, 273, 277, 278
frustrums 223
function machines 44
functions, linear 166, 196

geometric sequences 45–6, 58, 61
gradients
    linear graphs 162–7, 186, 189–91, 193, 194, 196
    perpendicular lines 177, 191, 197, 276
graphs 162–97
    circles 185, 187, 192, 197
    correlation 175, 184, 197
    cubic 181–2, 191–2
    direct proportion 173, 196
    distance–time 168–70, 184, 195, 196
    intersections of 300, 301, 306, 309
    line 83–4, 95
    line segments 176–7, 187, 196–7
    linear 162–7, 186–7, 189–91, 196
    non-linear 183–5, 187, 191–2
    quadratic 178–80, 191–2, 194, 195, 197
    rate of change 168–71, 196
    real-life 172–5, 183–5, 187–8, 192–3
    reciprocal 182, 191–2, 197
    scatter 71–7, 86, 89–90, 91, 92, 94, 175
    time series 68–70, 86, 90, 94
    velocity–time 170–1, 196, 230
grouped frequency tables 80, 85, 89, 93, 94–5

half-life 183
HCF (highest common factor) 5–7, 20, 23, 26, 28, 36
hectares 204, 232
hemispheres 220
heptagons 130, 132, 150
hexagons 130, 132, 134, 135, 138, 150–1, 277
highest common factor (HCF) 5–7, 20, 23, 26, 28, 36
hypotenuse 136–8, 142–3, 146, 152, 154, 158

identities 35, 39, 52, 55, 60
images 243–5, 278
improper fractions 98–9, 111, 117
inclusive 2
income 106, 117
independent events 320–3, 331, 334, 336, 338
index form 6, 20, 28
indices 8–16, 20–1, 23–5, 28
    addition 9, 28

algebraic 32–3, 54, 60
    fractional 11–13, 28
    multiplication 10, 28
    negative 11–13, 28
    powers of 10 14–16, 28
    prefixes 14, 28
    subtraction 9, 28
    zero 11–13, 28, 33
inequalities
    with lower limit and upper limit 285, 308
    solving 283–5, 302, 303, 308
integers, consecutive 36, 60
interest, simple 106, 117
interior angles
    polygons 129–32, 148, 150–2, 156, 158
    quadrilaterals 125–8, 148, 150, 151
    triangles 125–8, 151, 158
interpolation 76, 94
intersections
    of graphs 300, 301, 306, 309
    set notation 328–30, 339
invariant points 252, 279
inverse operations, percentage changes 106–7, 118
inverse trigonometric functions 145, 159
irrational numbers 18
isosceles trapezia 128, 201, 232
isosceles triangles 128, 131, 147, 149

kites 151

LCM (lowest common multiple) 5–7, 20, 23, 26, 28, 37–8, 56
line of best fit 74–7, 86, 92, 94
line graphs 83–4, 95
line segments, graphs 176–7, 187, 196–7
linear equations 163–7, 196
linear functions 166, 196
linear graphs 162–7, 186–7, 189–91, 196
    gradients 162–7, 186, 189–91, 193, 194, 196
linear inequalities, solving 283–5, 302, 303, 308
linear sequences 42–4
lists, in problem-solving 1–2
loci (locus) 264–6, 269, 279
lower bounds 204–6, 228, 232
lowest common multiple (LCM) 5–7, 20, 23, 26, 28, 37–8, 56

maps see scale drawings
maximum points 179, 192, 197
mean 78–81, 85, 86, 92, 93, 94
measurement, accuracy 203–6, 217, 224, 227–8, 231, 232
median 64–5, 78–80, 85, 88–9, 92, 94–5
midpoints, line segments 176, 187, 190, 196–7
minimum points 179, 197
mirror lines 244, 270
mixed numbers 98–9, 111, 117
modal class 80, 85, 95
mode 78–9, 94
multiplication
    indices 10, 28
    inequalities 285, 308
mutually exclusive events 315–17, 331, 333, 334, 338

negative indices 11–13, 28
negative scale factors 248–9, 272, 278
non-linear graphs 183–5, 187, 191–2
non-linear sequences 45–8
not equal to 15, 28
nth terms, arithmetic sequences 42–4, 53, 57, 60

number 1–29
    estimation 3–4
    indices see indices
    place value 3–4
    powers of 10 14–16, 28
    prime factors 5–7, 20, 23, 26, 28
    problems 1–2
    reasoning 1–2
    rounding 3–4, 22
    standard form 15–16, 21, 25, 27, 28
    surds 17–19, 20–1, 23–5, 27, 29
number lines 4, 283–5

objects 243–5, 278
octagons 130, 263
operations, priority of 4, 23, 28
opposite side 142, 143, 145–6, 154, 158
outliers 75–7, 79, 85, 89, 94

parabolas 178, 197
parallel lines 162–3, 165, 176–7, 187, 191, 196
parallelograms 126, 158
    angles 126
    area 206
Pascal's triangle 48
pentagons 129–30, 134, 148, 150, 156
percentages 105–7, 108–9, 110, 113–16
    changes in 106–7, 110, 113–14, 117–18
    decimals and 108–9, 110, 113–14
    fractions and 108–9, 110, 113–14
    inverse operations 106–7, 118
    loss (or profit) 107, 114, 117
perfect squares 291–2, 308
perimeters
    2D shapes 200–2, 224, 226
    circle sectors 215–17, 227
    rectangles 206
    trapezia 138, 201, 226
    triangles 141, 157
    see also circumferences
perpendicular bisectors 259–60, 262, 265, 269, 275, 278–9
perpendicular lines, graphs 177, 187, 191, 195, 197
pictures, in problem-solving 1–2
pie charts 64, 84, 85, 87, 94, 95
place value 3–4
plans, 3D solids 240–2, 268, 273, 277, 278
plus or minus 288
polygons
    exterior angles 133–5, 148, 150–1, 156, 158
    interior angles 129–32, 148, 150–2, 156, 158
powers see indices
prefixes, indices 14, 28
prime factors 5–7, 20, 23, 26, 28
    trees 5, 23, 28
prisms
    surface area 208
    volume 207–9, 230, 232
probability 312–39
    combined events 312–14, 331, 333
    conditional 324–6, 336–7, 338, 339
    dependent events 324–6, 336–7, 338
    experimental 318–19, 332, 334, 338
    fair games 318–19, 332, 333, 334
    frequency trees 320, 338
    independent events 320–3, 331, 334, 336, 338
    mutually exclusive events 315–17, 331, 333, 334, 338
    product rule 312

sample space diagrams 312–13, 331, 333, 338
set notation 327–30, 337
theoretical 318–19, 338
two-way tables 320, 324, 331, 334
Venn diagrams 327–30, 332, 335, 337
probability tree diagrams 321–3, 325–6, 332, 334, 338
product rule 312
proportion 103–4, 110, 112–13, 117
direct 104, 112, 117, 173, 196
pyramids
surface area 221–2, 225, 229
volume 222, 225, 229, 233
Pythagoras' theorem 136–41, 149, 152–3, 158

quadratic equations
graphs 178–80, 191–2, 194, 195, 197
solutions 180, 197, 286–92, 299–304, 306, 308
quadratic expressions 50, 61, 289, 306, 307, 308
completing the square 291–3, 304, 308
quadratic formula 290, 299, 304, 308
quadratic functions, roots 287, 308
quadratic graphs 178–80, 191–2, 194, 195, 197
quadratic sequences 46–8, 57, 61
quadrilaterals
exterior angles 133
interior angles 125–8, 148, 150, 151

range 65–7, 73, 78–81, 85, 88–9, 92
rates of change, graphs 168–71, 196
rational numbers 18, 29
rationalising the denominator 19, 21, 25, 27, 29
ratios 100–4, 110, 111–13, 116, 117, 118
unit 100, 110, 112, 117
real-life graphs 172–5, 183–5, 187–8, 192–3
reasoning, number 1–2
reciprocal functions 182, 191–2, 197
reciprocals 98–9, 111, 117
rectangles 137–8, 149, 153, 157
area 227, 304
perimeters 206
recurring decimals 109, 118
reflections 243–5, 268, 270, 273, 276, 278
representation of data see data representation
resultant vectors 252, 278
right-angled triangles
adjacent side 142, 143, 145–6, 154, 158
hypotenuse 136–8, 142–3, 146, 152, 154, 158
opposite side 142, 143, 145–6, 154, 158
Pythagoras' theorem 136–41, 149, 152–3, 158
roots, quadratic functions 287, 308
rotations 243–5, 268, 271, 273, 278
rounding 3–4, 22

sample space diagrams 312–13, 331, 333, 338
scale drawings 254–6, 263, 268, 274
scale factors 246–9, 267, 272, 278
fractional 247–8, 272, 278
negative 248–9, 272, 278
scatter graphs 71–7, 86, 89–90, 91, 92, 94, 175
extrapolation 76, 94
interpolation 76, 94
line of best fit 74–7, 86, 92, 94
outliers 75–7, 79, 94
scientific notation see standard form
sectors, circles 214–17, 224, 227, 230, 233
semicircles 214–16, 224, 227
sequences

algebra 42–8, 53, 56–8
arithmetic 42–4, 53, 57, 58, 60–1
Fibonacci 45, 53, 56, 57, 61
general term 42, 60
geometric 45–6, 58, 61
linear 42–4
non-linear 45–8
nth terms 42–4, 53, 57, 60
quadratic 46–8, 57, 61
set notation 284–5, 303, 307, 308, 327–30, 337
side elevations 240–2, 268, 273, 277, 278
similarity 278
simple interest 106, 117
simplifying, algebraic expressions 32–4, 52, 53, 54–5, 59
simultaneous equations 294–301, 302, 305, 306–7, 308–9
linear and quadratic 299–301, 309
$\sin^{-1}$ 145, 159
sines 143, 147, 155, 159
SOH CAH TOA 143, 154–5
speed
average 169–70
on distance–time graphs 168–70, 184, 196
spheres
surface area 219–20, 229, 231, 233
volume 219–20, 225, 229, 233
square roots 4, 8, 12, 22, 28
squares (of numbers)
difference of two 50–1
perfect 291–2, 308
squares (trigonometry) 141, 156
squaring, brackets 49, 61
standard form 15–16, 21, 25, 27, 28
statistics
bar charts 83, 84, 95
correlation 73–4, 77, 86, 89–90, 91, 94
diagrams 64–7, 82–5, 87–8
frequency polygons 66–7, 81, 85, 88, 91, 93, 94
line graphs 83–4, 95
mean 78–81, 85, 86, 92, 93, 94
median 64–5, 78–80, 85, 88–9, 92, 94–5
mode 78–9, 94
outliers 75–7, 79, 85, 89, 94
pie charts 64, 84, 85, 87, 94, 95
range 65–7, 73, 78–81, 85, 88–9, 92
scatter graphs 71–7, 86, 89–90, 91, 92, 94, 175
stem and leaf diagrams 65–6, 84, 85, 87–8, 92, 94
time series graphs 68–70, 86, 90, 94
stem and leaf diagrams 65–6, 84, 85, 87–8, 92, 94
straight lines, equations 297
subjects, formulae 40–1, 53, 56, 59, 60
substitution 295, 297, 305, 308
subtraction, indices 9, 28
surds 17–19, 20–1, 23–5, 27, 29, 136–7
surface area 207
cones 222–3, 229, 231, 233
cubes 209, 242
cuboids 207
cylinders 218–20, 225, 228–9, 231, 233
prisms 208
pyramids 221–2, 225, 229
spheres 219–20, 229, 231, 233

$\tan^{-1}$ 145, 159
tangents 143, 147, 155, 159

tessellation 130, 135, 158
theoretical probability 318–19, 338
time series graphs 68–70, 86, 90, 94
transformations 240–57, 267–8, 270–4, 276–9
bearings 256–7, 268, 274, 279
combinations 252–3, 268
enlargement 246–9, 267, 272–3, 278
reflections 243–5, 268, 270, 273, 276, 278
rotations 243–5, 268, 271, 273, 278
scale drawings 254–6, 263, 268, 274
translations 250–3, 268, 271, 273, 278
translations 250–3, 268, 271, 273, 278
trapezia 138, 141, 147
area 201–2, 224, 226, 231, 232, 307
isosceles 128, 201, 232
perimeters 138, 201, 226
tree diagrams, probability 321–3, 325–6, 332, 334, 338
trees, prime factors 5, 23, 28
trends 69–70, 86, 90, 94
triangles
constructions 258–9, 263, 274–5, 277
equilateral 141, 147
exterior angles 127–8, 158
interior angles 125–8, 151, 158
isosceles 128, 131, 147, 149
perimeters 141, 157
right-angled see right-angled triangles
trigonometric ratios 143, 147, 155, 159
trigonometry 142–7, 149, 154–5
truncation 205, 232
two-way tables 82, 85, 87, 95
probability 320, 324, 331, 334

unions, set notation 328–9, 339
unit ratios 100, 110, 112, 117
units
area 203–6, 232
volume 207–9, 232
universal set 327, 338
upper bounds 204–6, 228, 231, 232

Value Added Tax (VAT) 106, 117
variables 39, 60
vectors
column 250–3, 270, 278
resultant 252, 278
velocity 170–1, 196
velocity–time graphs 170–1, 196, 230
Venn diagrams 327–30, 332, 335, 337
prime factors 5, 7, 23, 26, 28
volume 207–9, 222–3, 232
cones 222–3, 225, 229, 233
cubes 209
cuboids 208, 228
cylinders 218–20, 230, 231, 233
prisms 207–9, 230, 232
pyramids 222, 225, 229, 233
spheres 219–20, 225, 229, 233
unit conversions 207–9, 232

x-intercepts, linear graphs 162, 164–6, 174, 196

y-intercepts
linear graphs 162–6, 174, 186, 189–90, 194, 196
non-linear graphs 187

zero indices 11–13, 28, 33